W9-CTX-235

Elements of Discrete Mathematics

A Computer Oriented Approach

Fourth Edition

ABOUT THE AUTHORS

C L Liu received his BSc degree (1956) at the National Cheng Kung University in Taiwan, and his Science Master and Electrical Engineering degrees (1960) and his Science Doctor degree (1962) at the Massachusetts Institute of Technology. He was on the faculty of the Massachusetts Institute of Technology (1962–1972) and the University of Illinois at Urbana-Champaign (1972–1998), where he was Associate Provost from 1995 to 1998. Professor Liu has also worked as Visiting Professor at City University of Hong Kong, and Waseda University, Tokyo, Japan; Li K T Honorary Chair Professor at National Central University, Hsinchu, Taiwan; and Mei Yi Chi Honorary Chair Professor at National Tsing Hua University, Hsinchu, Taiwan. He is the author and co-author of eight books and monographs, and over 200 technical papers.

He is a member of Academia Sinica, a Fellow of the Institute of Electrical and Electronics Engineers, and a Fellow of the Association for Computing Machinery.

D P Mohapatra received his PhD from Indian Institute of Technology (IIT), Kharagpur and ME from Regional Engineering College (now NIT), Rourkela. He joined the faculty of the Department of Computer Science and Engineering at the National Institute of Technology, Rourkela, in 1996, where he is now Associate Professor. His research interests include software engineering, real-time systems, discrete mathematics and distributed computing. He has published many research papers in these fields in various international journals and conferences.

Dr Mohapatra has been teaching discrete mathematics to undergraduate and postgraduate students at NIT Rourkela for the past fifteen years, besides being a member of the IEEE. He has received the Young Scientist Award for the year 2006 by Orissa Bigyan Academy. He has also received the Prof. K Arumugam National Award and Maharashtra State National Award for outstanding research work in Software Engineering for the years 2009 and 2010 respectively by the Indian Society for Technical Education (ISTE), New Delhi. He has also received Bharat Sikshya Ratan Award for his significant contribution in academics by the Global Society for Health and Educational Growth, New Delhi. He is currently involved in three research projects from DST and UGC, Govt. of India.

Elements of Discrete Mathematics

A Computer Oriented Approach

Fourth Edition

C L Liu
Department of Computer Science
University of Illinois
Urbana-Champaign, US

D P Mohapatra
Assosiate Professor
CSE Department
National Institute of Technology
Rourkela, Odisha

McGraw Hill Education (India) Private Limited
CHENNAI

McGraw Hill Education Offices
Chennai New York St Louis San Francisco Auckland Bogotá Caracas
Kuala Lumpur Lisbon London Madrid Mexico City Milan Montreal
San Juan Santiago Singapore Sydney Tokyo Toronto

McGraw Hill Education (India) Private Limited

Published by McGraw Hill Education (India) Private Limited,
444/1, Sri Ekambara Naicker Industrial Estate, Alapakkam, Porur, Chennai 600116,
Tamil Nadu, India.

Special Indian Edition 2013, 2008.

Indian Adaptation done by arrangement with McGraw-Hill Global Education Holdings, LLC, New York.

Sales Territories: Worldwide except North America

Elements of Discrete Mathematics, 4e

Copyright © 1985, by McGraw Hill Education (India) Private Limited.

Fourteenth reprint 2018
RXCBCDDERYBQ

All rights reserved. No part of this publication may be reproduced or distributed in any form or by any means, electronic, mechanical, photocopying, recording, or otherwise or stored in a database or retrieval system without the prior written permission of the publishers. The program listings (if any) may be entered, stored and executed in a computer system, but they may not be reproduced for publication.

This edition can be exported from India only by the publishers,
McGraw Hill Education (India) Private Limited.

ISBN (13 digits): 978-1-25-900639-5
ISBN (10 digits): 1-25-900639-5

15 16 17 18 19 SAI 22 21 20 19 18

Head—Higher Education (Publishing and Marketing): *Vibha Mahajan*
Senior Publishing Manager: *Shalini Jha*
Senior Production Manager: *Satinder S Baveja*
General Manager—Production: *Rajender P Ghansela*
Manager—Production: *Reji Kumar*

Information contained in this work has been obtained by McGraw Hill Education (India), from sources believed to be reliable. However, neither McGraw Hill Education (India) nor its authors guarantee the accuracy or completeness of any information published herein, and neither McGraw Hill Education (India) nor its authors shall be responsible for any errors, omissions, or damages arising out of use of this information. This work is published with the understanding that McGraw Hill Education (India) and its authors are supplying information but are not attempting to render engineering or other professional services. If such services are required, the assistance of an appropriate professional should be sought.

Typeset at Print-O-World, 2579, Mandir Lane, Shadipur, New Delhi 110008, and
Printed and Bound in India at Sai Printo Pack Pvt. Ltd., A 102/4, Okhla Industrial Area,
Phase – II, New Delhi 110020.

Visit us at: www.mheducation.co.in ; (Toll free in India): 1800 103 5875
Write to us at: info.india@mheducation.com

CIN: U22200TN1970PTC111531

To my parents,
beloved wife, **Mami**, *and*
daughters, **Harapriya** *and* **Bishnupriya**

Your love, encouragement and support are my greatest
inspiration

— **D P Mohapatra**

CONTENTS

4. Graphs and Planar Graphs 208

5. Trees and Cut-Sets 292

PREFACE TO THE FOURTH EDITION

The fourth edition of this book was necessary to include some important topics and more illustrative examples in the field of discrete mathematics. The third edition of this book has been used successfully in many universities in India and abroad. Although the third edition had an extremely effective text, many readers requested some changes/ additions in order to make this book more effective. I have devoted some time and energy to incorporate these requests in the fourth edition, working hard to find my own ways to make the book better!

The outcome is the fourth edition that offers both students and teachers much more than the third edition. In the fourth edition, an improved topic organization has been implemented which makes the book a more effective teaching tool. In addition, changes have been made making this edition more effective for students. Additional examples and explanations have been added to make students understand the difficult portions easily. Many computer programs have been included which will enable students to better understand the concepts by executing the programs with different input data.

The following are the major additions/improvements in the fourth edition of this book:

- A new section on Binomial Theorem has been added in Chapter 2 with Binomial Theorem for Negative Integral Index and Pascal's Triangle. Probability Distribution Function, its properties and some relevant examples are discussed in Chapter 2.
- Concepts of Connected and Disconnected Graphs and Bipartite Graphs are included in Chapter 4 along with some relevant examples.
- The concepts of Sub-algebra and Direct Product of algebras have been introduced in Chapter 10, with new sections and sub-sections on Subrings and Dihedral Groups.
- Definition of Boolean Algebra has been added in Chapter 11 with a new section for Identity of Boolean Algebra

Besides these, the major highlights of the fourth edition are as follows:

- Almost total syllabi coverage of major universities
- Increased C program codes to illustrate algorithm implementation
- Demonstrates utility of subject-related concepts through various real-world applications

- Simple and to-the-point language
- Refreshed Pedagogy:
  - 310 Solved Examples
  - 760 Unsolved Problems for practice
  - 36 Programming Exercises
  - 21 Algorithms with C Program codes
  - 480 Illustrations

The revised Online Learning Center can now be accessed at http://www.mhhe.com/liu/dm4 and contains the following material:

- *For Instructors*—Solution Manual
- *For Students*—New article on Sequence Series and Matrices, Sample chapter on Analysis of Algorithms, List of important formulae and symbols

Many people have contributed to the fourth edition of this book. I would like to thank all the teachers and students of NIT Rourkela, and other institutes who have used this book and provided me their valuable feedback and meaningful suggestions. Their input has made this a much better book than it would have been otherwise.

I would especially like to express my appreciation to Prof. Sunil Kumar Sarangi, Hon. Director, NIT Rourkela, for being a constant source of inspiration and encouragement. I am grateful to Prof. G K Panda of NIT Rourkela, and Prof. Abhishek Ray of KIIT University, Bhubaneswar, for helping me prepare the manuscript.

At this stage, let me also thank the numerous reviewers of the fourth edition who reviewed the manuscript and gave me useful suggestions. Selected names are given below:

Natthan Singh	*Institute of Enggineering and Technology, Gautam Buddha Technical University (GBTU) Lucknow, Uttar Pradesh*
B K Sharma	*Ajay Kumar Garg College of Engineering Ghaziabad, Uttar Pradesh*
Prabhakar Gupta	*Shri Ram Murti Smarak College of Engineering and Technology (SRMSCET) Bareilly, Uttar Pradesh*
Kuntla Patra	*Gauhati University, Guwahati, Assam*
Anjali Pendse	*Kashibhai Navale College of Engineering, Pune University, Pune*
G Sethuraman	*Anna University, Tamil Nadu*
B Prabha	*Sri Sivasubramaniya Nadar (SSN) College of Engineering, Kalpakkam, Tamil Nadu*
A N S Srinivas	*Annamacharya Institute of Technology and Science, Andhra Pradesh*
B R Shankar	*National Institute of Technology(NIT) Surathkal, Karnataka*

I would also like to thank the editorial and production team members of Tata McGraw-Hill Education, India, for their strong support to this project. Particularly, I am very much thankful to Ms Shalini Jha, Ms Smruti Snigdha, Mr Sourabh Maheshwari, Ms Sohini Mukherjee, Mr Satinder Baveja, Ms Yukti Sharma and others for their painstaking and meticulous effort during the developmental, editing and proofreading stages of the manuscript.

Several students have contributed directly and indirectly to the contents of the fourth edition. In particular, the UG and PG students of the CSE department of NIT Rourkela have given me numerous ideas. The questions they posed in the classroom gave me the much-required hints about areas that required elaboration and the examples that should be included. I would particularly like to thank Subhrakanta, Anup, Vikas, Apurva, Manish, Sai, Gaurav, Susnata and Krupasindhu for their help in preparing the manuscript.

I also take this opportunity to thank my family members for their constant support. I thank my parents, my parents-in-law, my uncles and aunts, my brothers and sister-in-law for their moral support. I also thank Pinki, Shiva and Bapi for their help. I must thank my daughters, Harapriya and Bishnupriya, for their patient wait when I was working on this revision. I sincerely express my gratitude to my wife, Mami, for her love and support and help in keying in the manuscript. Without their constant encouragement and permission to spend extra hours at work, this revision would never have been complete.

I would welcome messages regarding typographical and other errors, comments and constructive suggestions to improve this edition, which can be sent to me at durga@nitrkl.ac.in or durgapm2004@yahoo.com

D P Mohapatra

Publisher's Note

Do you have any feedback? We look forward to receive your views and suggestions for improvement. The same can be sent to tmh.csefeedback@gmail.com, mentioning the title and author's name in the subject line.

PREFACE TO THE FIRST EDITION

This book presents a selection of topics from set theory, combinatorics, graph theory, and algebra which I consider basic and useful to students in Applied Mathematics, Computer Science, and Engineering. It is intended to be a textbook for a course in Discrete Mathematics at the sophomore-junior level, although it can also be used in a freshman-level course since the presentation does not assume any background beyond high-school mathematics. The material in this book can be covered, in a one-semester course at a rather brisk pace. On the other hand, it is quite possible to omit some of the topics for a slower course. A section marked with an asterisk can be omitted without disrupting the continuity.

This book is an outgrowth of a set of lecture notes I wrote for a course I taught in the Department of Computer Science at the University of Illinois at Urbana-Champaign. I hope it is not only a record of what I covered in the course but also a reflection of how I lectured the material in the classroom. I have tried to be rigorous and precise in presenting the mathematical concepts and, in the meantime, to avoid complicated formalisms and notations.

As a rule I would not state a definition or a fact if I could not illustrate the utilization of the definition or the fact in some meaningful way later on. Consequently, it is quite possible that I have omitted some "important" definitions or facts in this book. I trust, however, that the students will be quite capable of looking them up somewhere else when such definitions and facts are needed. I have attempted to teach my students some useful mathematics in an interesting and exciting way.

I hope that I have demonstrated to them how mathematics can be applied to solve nontrivial real-life problems. Furthermore, I hope that my students not only learned in the course some powerful mathematical tools but also developed their ability to perceive, to formulate and to solve mathematical problems. I have tried to bring in an algorithmic point of view in the treatment of several topics, although I decided not to include explicit computer programs, mainly because of time consideration. I hope that some of these personal views and tastes can be shared to some extent by the instructor using this book.

I would like to thank James N Snyder, my department head, for his encouragement and support; Murray Edelberg, Jane W S Liu, and Andrew H Sherman for their careful review of the manuscript; Donald K Friesen for his contribution to the preparation of the Instructor's Manual; and Edward M Reingold and F Frances Yao for their many helpful suggestions. Several years ago, I had an opportunity to serve on a panel on the impact of computing on mathematics sponsored by the Committee on the Undergraduate Program in Mathematics of the Mathematical Association of America. I benefited greatly from the panel's discussion on the teaching of discrete mathematics, and I am much indebted to the members of the panel. I also thank Glenna Gochenour, Connie Nosbisch, Judy Watkins, and June Wingler for their typing and editorial assistance. Finally, thanks to Kathleen D Liu for her assistance in the preparation of the index.

There is a certain amount of overlap between this book and the book *Introduction to Combinatorial Mathematics* I wrote a few years ago. In a number of instances, I follow quite closely the presentation in *Introduction to Combinatorial Mathematics*.

C L Liu

LIST OF SYMBOLS

Notations and Symbols used in this book

$\vee$ – or (disjunction/alternation)

$\wedge$ – and (conjuction)

$\oplus$ – Exclusive or, ring sum

$\in$ – belongs to

$\notin$ – does not belong to

$\subseteq$ – subset

$\subset$ – proper subset

$\cup$ – union (disjunction)

$\cap$ – intersection (conjunction)

$P(A)$ – power set of A

$p \rightarrow q$ – p implies q (conditional).

$p \leftrightarrow q$ – p if and only if q (biconditional)

$\bar{p}, \sim p, p', \neg p$ – negation of p

$\forall$ – for all (Universal quantifier)

$\exists$ – there exists (Existential quantifier)

Σ – summation

$\prod_{i_1 i_2}$ – projection

$\equiv$ – congruent modulo, equivalent

π – partition

∇ – backward difference

Δ – forward difference

ψ – number of elements those are invariant

N – set of all natural numbers

I – set of all integers

I^+ – set of all positive integers

I^- – set of all negative integers

R – set of all real numbers

R^+ – set of all positive real numbers

R^- – set of all negative real numbers

$A \times B$ – cartesian product of the sets A and B

$A R b$ – a is related to b under the relation R

f^{-1} – inverse of the function f

gof – composition of the functions f and g

Objective

To discuss the concepts associated with set theory, propositions, predicate calculus and their applications.

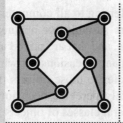

CHAPTER

ONE

SETS AND PROPOSITIONS

1.1 INTRODUCTION

A major theme of this book is to study discrete objects and relationships among them. The term *discrete objects* is a rather general one. It includes a large variety of items such as people, books, computers, transistors, computer programs, and so on. In our daily lives as well as in our technical work we frequently deal with these items, making statements such as, "The people in this room are Computer Science majors in their second year of study," "All the books I bought are detective stories written by A. B. Charles," and "We want to select and buy a computer among those that are suitable for both scientific and business applications at a price not exceeding $200,000." We would like to abstract some of the basic concepts dealing with the many different kinds of discrete objects and establish certain common terminology for dealing with them.

A hint of the possibility of such an abstraction is quite evident when we observe that all the three statements have "something" in common. To be specific, in the first statement, we are referring to people who possess the two attributes of being a Computer Science major and of being a sophomore; in the second statement, we are referring to books that possess the two attributes of being a detective story and of being written by A. B. Charles; and in the third statement, we are referring to computers that possess the three attributes of being suitable for scientific applications, of being suitable for business applications, and of being priced at no more than $200,000. To put it in another way, consider the group of all the Computer Science majors and the group of all the sophomores in the university. In our first statement, we are then referring to those students who belong to both of these groups. Also, consider the collection of all detective stories and the collection of all books written by A. B. Charles. In our second statement we are then referring to those books that belong to both these collections. Finally, in our third statement, we are referring to all computers that belong to the three categories of computers that are suitable for business applications, that are suitable for scientific applications, and that are priced at no more than $200,000.

Our example illustrates the many occasions on which we deal with several classes of objects and wish to refer to those objects that belong to all classes. Similarly, one would immediately perceive occasions on which we refer to objects that belong to one of several classes of objects, such as in the statement, "I want to interview all the students who speak either German or French," where we refer to those who belong either to the group of German-speaking students or to the group of French-speaking students.

We begin with the introduction of some basic terminology and concepts in elementary set theory. A *set* is a collection of *distinct* and well defined objects. Thus, the group of all sophomores in the university is a set. So is the group of all Computer Science majors in the university, and so is the group of all second-year Computer Science majors. We use the notation $\{a, b, c\}$ to denote the set which is the collection of the objects a, b, and c. The objects in a set are also called the *elements* or the *members* of the set. We usually also give names to sets. For example, we write $S = \{a, b, c\}$ to mean that the set named S is the collection of the objects a, b, and c. Consequently, we can refer to the set S as well as to the set $\{a, b, c\}$. As another example, we may have

Second-year-Computer-Science-majors
$$= \{\text{Smith, Jones, Wong, Yamamoto, Vögeli}\}$$

(The name of the set {Smith, Jones, Wong, Yamamoto, Vögeli] is Second-year-Computer-Science-majors, which is rather long. The reader probably would want to suggest alternative names such as S or CS. However, there is nothing wrong conceptually with having a "long" name.) We use the notation $a \in S$ to mean that a is an element in the set S. In that case, we also say that S *contains* the element a. We use the notation $d \notin S$ to mean that d is not an element in the set S. In that case, we also say that S does not contain the element d. Thus, in the example above, Jones $\in$ Second-year-Computer-Science-majors, while Kinkaid $\notin$ Second-year-Computer-Science-majors.

Note that a set contains only distinct elements. Thus, $\{a, a, b, c\}$ is a redundant representation of the set $\{a, b, c\}$. Similarly, {*The-Midnight-Visitor, The-Midnight-Visitor, The-Missing-Witness, 114-Main-Street*} is a redundant representation of the detective stories written by A. B. Charles. One might ask the question: "What should we do if our collection of detective stories by A. B. Charles in the library indeed contains two copies of the book *The-Midnight Visitor*?" In that case, the set {*The-Midnight-Visitor, The-Missing-Witness, 114-Main-Street*} is a set of distinct titles of detective stories by A. B. Charles in our library, while the set [*The-Midnight-Visitor-1, The-Midnight-Visitor-2, The-Missing-Witness, 114-Main-Street*} is the set of detective stories by A. B. Charles in our library; where *The-Midnight-Visitor-1* is copy 1 of the book *The-Midnight-Visitor*, and *The-Midnight-Visitor-2* is copy 2 of the book. Note that *The-Midnight-Visitor-1* and *The-Midnight-Visitor-2* are two distinct elements in the latter set.

Note also that the elements in a set are not ordered in any fashion. Thus, $\{a, b, c\}$ and $\{b, a, c\}$ represent the same collection of elements.

As was introduced above, one way to describe the membership of a set is to list exhaustively all the elements in that set. In many cases, when the elements in a set share some common properties, we can describe the membership of the set by stating the properties that uniquely characterize the elements in the set. For example, let $S = \{2, 4, 6, 8, 10\}$. We can also specify the elements of S by saying that S is the set of all even positive integers that are not larger than 10. Indeed, we can use the notation

$$S = \{x \mid x \text{ is an even positive integer not larger than } 10\}$$

for the set $\{2, 4, 6, 8, 10\}$. In general, we use the notation

$$\{x \mid x \text{ possesses certain properties}\}$$

for a set of objects that share some common properties. Thus,

$$S = \{\text{Smith, Jones, Wong, Yamamoto, Vögeli}\}$$

and

$$S = \{x \mid x \text{ is a second-year Computer Science major}\}$$

are two different ways to describe the same set of elements.

It should be pointed out that our concept of a set does not preclude the possibility of having a set containing *no* elements. The set that contains no element is known as the *empty set*, and is denoted by $\{\ \}$. We are consistent with the notation of using a pair of braces to enclose all the elements in the set. In this case, it just happens that there is no element in the enclosure. In literature, the empty set is also denoted by ϕ. So that the reader will be familiar with both notations, we shall use them interchangeably. For example, let S denote the set of all detective stories by A. B. Charles that were published in 1924. Clearly, S is the empty set if A. B. Charles was born in 1925. As another example, let S denote the set of all students who failed in the course of Discrete Mathematics. S might turn out to be the empty set if all students in the course studied hard for the final examination.

Let us note that we did not place any restriction on the elements in a set. Thus, $S = \{\text{Smith}, \textit{The-Midnight-Visitor}, \text{CDC-6600}\}$ is a well-defined set. That the elements, Smith (a person), *The-Midnight-Visitor* (the title of a book), and CDC-6600 (a computer) do not seem to share anything in common does not prohibit them from being elements of the same set. Indeed, we should point out that it is perfectly all right to have sets as members of a set. Thus, for example, the set $\{\{a, b, c\}, d\}$ contains the two elements $\{a, b, c\}$ and d, and the set $\{\{a, b, c\}, a, b, c\}$ contains the four elements $\{a, b, c\}$, a, b, and c. The set of all committees in the U.S. Senate could be represented by $\{\{a, b, c], \{a, d, e, f\}, \{b, e, g\}\}$, where each element of the set is a committee which, in turn, is a set with the senators in the committee as elements. Similarly, $\{a, \{a\}, \{\{a\}\}\}$ is a set with three *distinct* elements a, $\{a\}$, $\{\{a\}\}$. Also, the set $\{\{\ \}\}$, which can also be written as $\{\phi\}$, contains one element—the empty set. The set

{{ }, {{ }}}, which can also be written as $\{\phi, \{\phi\}\}$, contains two elements (–) the empty set and a set that contains the empty set as its only element. Perhaps an analogy will be helpful here. We can imagine that $\{a, b, c\}$ corresponds to a box in which there are three objects a, b, and c. Thus, $\{a, b, c, \{a, b\}\}$ corresponds to a box in which there are four objects a, b, c, and a box, in which there are two objects, a and b. Also, { } corresponds to an empty box; {{ }} corresponds to a box in which there is an object that happens to be an empty box; and {{ }, {{ }}} corresponds to a box in which there are two boxes—one empty and the other not. As another example, let

$$S_1 = \{\text{John, Mary}\}$$
$$S_2 = \{\{\text{John, Mary}\}\}$$
$$S_3 = \{\{\{\text{John, Mary}\}\}\}$$

We note that

$$\text{John} \in S_1$$
$$\text{John} \notin S_2$$
$$\text{John} \notin S_3$$
$$S_1 \in S_2$$
$$S_1 \notin S_3$$
$$S_2 \in S_3$$

Given two sets P and Q, we say that P is a *subset* of Q if every element in P is also an element in Q. We shall use the notation $P \subseteq Q$ to denote that P is a subset of Q, For example, the set $\{a, b\}$ is a subset of the set $\{y, x, b, c, a\}$, but it is not a subset of the set $\{a, c, d, e\}$. The set of all second-year Computer Science majors is a subset of the set of all sophomores. It is also a subset of the set of all Computer Science majors. On the other hand, the set of all Computer Science majors is not a subset of the set of all sophomores, nor is the set of all sophomores a subset of the set of all Computer Science majors. Let $A = \{a, b, c\}$ and $B = \{\{a, b, c\}, a, b, c\}$. We note that it is indeed possible to have both $A \in B$ and $A \subseteq B$. As further examples, we ask the reader to check the following statements:

1. For any set P, P is a subset of P.
2. The empty set is a subset of any set. However, the empty set is not always an element of any set.
3. The set $\{\phi\}$ is not a subset of the set $\{\{\phi\}\}$, although it is an element of the set $\{\{\phi\}\}$.

Two sets P and Q are said to be *equal* if they contain the same collection of elements. For example, the two sets

$$P = \{x \mid x \text{ is an even positive integer not larger than } 10\}$$
$$Q = \{x \mid x = y + z \text{ where } y \in \{1, 3, 5\}, z \in \{1, 3, 5\}\}$$

are equal. In a seemingly roundabout way, we can also say that two sets P and Q are equal if P is a subset of Q, and Q is a subset of P. We shall see later that on some occasions this is a convenient way to define the equality of two sets.

Let P be a subset of Q. We say that P is a *proper subset* of Q if P is not equal to Q, that is, there is at least one element in Q that is not in P. For example, the set $\{a, b\}$ is a proper subset of the set $\{y, x, b, c, a\}$. We use the notation $P \subset Q$ to denote that P is a proper subset of Q.

1.2 COMBINATIONS OF SETS

Now we shall show how sets can be *combined* in various ways to yield new sets. For example, let P be the set of students taking the course. Theory of Computation and Q be the set of students taking the course Music Appreciation. If a certain announcement was made in both the Theory of Computation and the Music Appreciation classes, what is the set of students who know about the news announced? Clearly, it is the set of students who are taking either Theory of Computation or Music Appreciation, or both. If both these courses have their final examinations scheduled in the same hours, what is the set of students who will have conflicting final examinations? Clearly, it is the set of students who are taking both Theory of Computation and Music Appreciation. To formalize these notions, we define the union and the intersection of sets. The *union* of two sets P and Q, denoted $P \cup Q$, is the set whose elements are exactly the elements in either P or Q (or both).* For example,

$$\{a, b\} \cup \{c, d\} = \{a, b, c, d\}$$
$$\{a, b\} \cup \{a, c\} = \{a, b, c\}$$
$$\{a, b\} \cup \phi = \{a, b\}$$
$$\{a, b\} \cup \{(a, h)\} = \{a, b, \{a, b\}\}$$

The *intersection* of two sets P and Q, denoted $P \cap Q$, is the set whose elements are exactly those elements that are in both P and Q. For example,

$$\{a, b\} \cap \{a, c\} = \{a\}$$
$$\{a, b\} \cap \{c, d\} = \phi^{\dagger}$$
$$\{a, b\} \cap \phi = \phi$$

If the elements in P are characterized by a common property and the elements in Q are characterized by another common property, then the union of P and Q is the set of elements possessing at least one of these properties, and the intersection of P and Q is the set of elements possessing both of these properties. According to the definitions, $P \cup Q$ and $Q \cup P$ denote the same set, as do $P \cap Q$ and $Q \cap P$.

It follows that the union of the set $P \cup Q$ and the set R, denoted $(P \cup Q) \cup R$ where the parentheses are used as delimiters to avoid confusion, contains exactly the elements in P, the elements in Q, and the elements in R. We shall use the notation $P \cup Q \cup R$ for $(P \cup Q) \cup R$, and shall refer to the set $P \cup Q \cup R$ as the union of the three sets P, Q, R. In general, the union of the set $(...((P_1 \cup P_2) \cup P_3)...) \cup P_{k-1}$ and the set P_k, denoted $(...((P_1 \cup P_2) \cup P_3)... \cup P_{k-1}) \cup$

---

* We do not wish to introduce the notion of algebraic operations until Chapter 10. Thus. at this, moment. $P \cup Q$ is simply a name we have chosen for a set.

$\dagger$ Two sets are said to be *disjoint* if their intersection is the empty set.

P_k, contains exactly the elements in P_1 the elements in P_2, ..., the elements in P_{k-1}, and the elements in P_k. We shall use the notation $P_1 \cup P_2 \cup P_3 \ldots \cup P_{k-1} \cup P_k$ for $(\ldots((P_1 \cup P_2) \cup P_3) \ldots \cup P_{k-1}) \cup P_k$ and shall refer to the set $P_1 \cup P_2 \cup P_3 \ldots \cup P_{k-1} \cup P_k$ as the union of the k sets $P_1, P_2, P_3, \ldots, P_{k-1}, P_k$. Similarly, the intersection of the set $P \cap Q$ and the set R, denoted $(P \cap Q) \cap R$, contains exactly the elements that are in P, Q, and R. Also, the intersection of the set $(\ldots((P_1 \cap P_2) \cap P_3) \ldots) \cap P_{k-1}$ and the set P_k, denoted $(\ldots((P_1 \cap P_2) \cap P_3) \ldots \cap P_{k-1}) \cap P_k$, contains exactly the elements that are in P_1 and P_2, ..., and P_{k-1}, and P_k. We shall use the notation $P_1 \cap P_2 \cap P_3 \ldots \cap P_{k-1} \cap P_k$ for $(\ldots((P_1 \cap P_2) \cap P_3) \ldots \cap P_{k-1}) \cap P_k$ and shall refer to the set $P_1 \cap P_2 \cap P_3 \ldots \cap P_{k-1} \cap P_k$ as the intersection of the k sets $P_1, P_2, P_3, \ldots, P_{k-1}, P_k$. For example, the set of all undergraduate students in a university is the union of the sets of freshmen, sophomores, juniors, and seniors, and the set of graduating seniors is the intersection of the set of seniors, the set of students who have accumulated 144 or more credit hours, and the set of students who have a C or better grade-point average.

Let P denote the set of students taking Theory of Computation, Q denote the set of students taking Music Appreciation, and R denote the set of students having type AB blood. Suppose an emergency announcement was made in the classes of Theory of Computation and Music Appreciation calling for type AB blood donors. We want to determine the members of the set of potential donors who heard about the emergency call. Since $S = P \cup Q$ is the set of students who heard about the emergency call, $R \cap S$ is the set of potential donors who heard about the emergency call. Instead of using a new name S for the set $P \cup Q$, we can simply write $R \cap (P \cup Q)$. Note that the set of potential donors who heard about the emergency call is also the set of students with type AB blood in the Theory of Computation class together with the set of students with type AB blood in the Music Appreciation class—that is, the set $(R \cap P) \cup (R \cap Q)$. This example suggests very strongly that for any sets P, Q, R, the two sets $R \cap (P \cup Q)$ and $(R \cap P) \cup (R \cap Q)$ are equal. Indeed, this is the case, as we now show.

We show first that $R \cap (P \cup Q)$ is a subset of $(R \cap P) \cup (R \cap Q)$ by showing that every element in $R \cap (P \cup Q)$ is also in $(R \cap P) \cup (R \cap Q)$. Let x be an element in $R \cap (P \cup Q)$. The element x must be in R and must be either in P or Q. If x is in P, x is in $R \cap P$. If x is in Q, x is in $R \cap Q$. Consequently, x is in $(R \cap P) \cup (R \cap Q)$, and we conclude that $R \cap (P \cup Q)$ is a subset of $(R \cap P) \cup (R \cap Q)$. Second, we show that $(R \cap P) \cup (R \cap Q)$ is a subset of $R \cap (P \cup Q)$. Let x be an element in $(R \cap P) \cup (R \cap Q)$. Thus, x must either be in $R \cap P$ or be in $R \cap Q$. That is, x must either be in both R and P or be in both R and Q. In other words, x must be in R and must be either in P or in Q. Consequently, x is in $R \cap (P \cup Q)$, and we can conclude that $(R \cap P) \cup (P \cap Q)$ is a subset of $R \cap (P \cup Q)$. It follows that the two sets $R \cap (P \cup Q)$ and $(R \cap P) \cup (R \cap Q)$ are equal.

In a similar manner, we can show that for any sets P, Q, R, the two sets $R \cup (P \cap Q)$ and $(R \cup P) \cap (R \cup Q)$ are equal. Furthermore, we have

$$R \cap (P_1 \cup P_2 \cup \ldots \cup P_k) = (R \cap P_1) \cup (R \cap P_2) \cup \ldots \cup (R \cap P_k)$$
$$R \cup (P_1 \cap P_2 \cap \ldots \cap P_k) = (R \cup P_1) \cap (R \cup P_2) \cap \ldots \cap (R \cup P_k)$$

We leave the details to the reader.*

The *difference* of two sets P and Q, denoted $P - Q$, is the set containing exactly those elements in P that are not in Q. For example,

$$\{a, b, c\} - \{a\} = \{b, c\}$$
$$\{a, b, c\} - \{a, d\} = \{b, c\}$$
$$\{a, b, c\} - \{d, e\} = \{a, b, c\}$$

If P is the set of people who have tickets to a ball game and Q is the set of people who are ill on the day of the game, then $P - Q$ is the set of people who will go to the game. Note that Q might contain some or none of the elements of the set P. However, these elements will not appear in $P - Q$ in any case, just as in the example, those people who are ill but do not have tickets to the ball game will not go to the game anyway. Indeed, if the elements in Q are characterized by some common property, then $P - Q$ is the set of elements in P that do not possess this property. If Q is a subset of P, the set $P - Q$ is also called the *complement of Q with respect to P*. For example, let P be the set of all students in the course Theory of Computation and Q be the set of those students who have passed the course. Then $P - Q$ is the set of students who failed the course. On many occasions, when the set P is clear from the context, we shall abbreviate the *complement of Q with respect to P as the complement of Q*, which will be denoted $\overline{Q}$. For example, let P be the set of all students in the course Theory of Computation. Let Q be the set of Computer Science majors in the course, and R be the set of sophomores in the course. Then the complement of Q refers to the set of students in the course who are not Computer Science majors, and the complement of R refers to the set of those students who are not sophomores, if it is understood that in our discussion we always restrict ourselves to students in the course Theory of Computation. Indeed, when our discussion is always restricted to the subsets of a set P, P is referred to as the *universe*.

The *symmetric difference* of two sets P and Q, denoted $P \oplus Q$, is the set containing exactly all the elements that are in P or in Q but not in both. In other words, $P \oplus Q$ is the set $(P \cup Q) - (P \cap Q)$. For example,

$$\{a, b\} \oplus \{a, c\} = \{b, c\}$$
$$\{a, b\} \oplus \phi = \{a, b\}$$
$$\{a, b\} \oplus \{a, b\} = \phi$$

If we let P denote the set of cars that have defective steering mechanisms and Q denote the set of cars that have defective transmission systems, then $P \oplus Q$ is the set of cars that have one but not both of these defects. Suppose that a student will get an A in a course if she did well in both quizzes, will get a B if she did well in one of the two quizzes, and will get a C if she did poorly in both quizzes.

---

* Again, we do not wish to introduce the notions of algebraic operations, associativity, and distributivity until Chap. 10. Note, however, these notions are not needed here because $P \cap Q$, $P_1 \cap P_2 \cap \ldots \cap P_k$, $P \cup Q$, $P_1 \cup P_2 \cup \ldots \cup P_k$ are simply names for sets obtained according to our definitions.

Let P be the set of students who did well in the first quiz and Q be the set of students who did well in the second quiz. Then $P \cap Q$ is the set of students who will get A's, $P \oplus Q$ is the set of students who will get B's, and $S - (P \cup Q)$ is the set of students who will get C's, where S is the set of all students in the course. We define $P_1 \oplus P_2 \oplus \ldots \oplus P_k$ to be the set of elements that are in an odd number of the sets $P_1 P_2, \ldots, P_k$.

The *power set* of a set A, denoted $\mathscr{P}(A)$, is the set that contains exactly all the subsets of A. Thus $\mathscr{P}(\{a, b\}) = \{\{ \}, \{a\}, \{b\}, \{a, b\}\}$, and $\mathscr{P}(\{ \}) = \{\{ \}\}$. Note that for any set A, $\{ \} \in \mathscr{P}(A)$ as well as $\{ \} \subseteq \mathscr{P}(A)$. For example, let $A = \{$novel, published-in-1975, paperback$\}$ be the three attributes concerning the books in the library in which we are interested. Then $\mathscr{P}(A)$ is the set of all possible combinations of these attributes the books might possess, ranging from books that have none of these attributes [the empty set in $\mathscr{P}(A)$] to books that have all three of these attributes [the set A in $\mathscr{P}(A)$].

Sets obtained from combinations of given sets can be represented pictorially. If we let P and Q be the sets represented by the cross-hatched areas in Fig. 1.1a, then the cross-hatched areas in Fig. 1.1b represent the sets $P \cup Q, P \cap Q, P - Q$, and $P \oplus Q$, respectively. These diagrams are known as *Venn diagrams*.

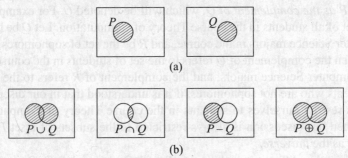

(a)

(b)

Fig. 1.1

1.3 FINITE AND INFINITE SETS

Intuitively, it is quite clear that by the size of a set we mean the number of distinct elements in the set. Thus, there is little doubt when we say the size of the set $\{a, b, c\}$ is 3, the size of the set $\{a, \phi, d\}$ is also 3, the size of the set $\{\{a, b\}\}$ is 1, and the size of the set ϕ is 0. Indeed, we could stop our discussion on the size of sets at this point if we were only interested in the size of "finite" sets. However, a much more intriguing topic is the size of "infinite" sets. At this point, a perceptive reader will probably ask the question, "What is an infinite set in the first place?" An evasive answer such as, "An infinite set is not a finite set," is no answer at all, because if we start to think about it, we should also ask the question, "What is a finite set anyway?"

Let us begin by declaring that we have not yet committed ourselves to the precise definitions of finite sets and infinite sets. As the basis of our discussion, we want to construct an example of an infinite set. For a given set A, we define the *successor* of A, denoted A^+, to be the set $A \cup \{A\}$. Note that $\{A\}$ is a set that contains A as the only element. In other words, A^+ is a set that consists of all the elements of A together with an additional element which is the set A. For example, if $A = \{a, b\}$ then $A^+ = \{a, b\} \cup \{\{a, b\}\} = \{a, b, \{a, b\}\}$; and if $A = \{\{a\}, b\}$ then $A^+ = \{\{a\}, b, \{\{a\}, b\}\}$. Let us now construct a sequence of sets starting with the empty set ϕ. The successor of the empty set is $\{\phi\}$, whose successor is $\{\phi, \{\phi\}\}$, and whose successor, in turn, is $\{\phi, \{\phi\}, \{\phi, \{\phi\}\}\}$. It is clear that we can go on constructing more and more successors. Let us also assign names to these sets. In particular, we use 0, 1, 2, 3, ... as the names of the sets.*

Let
$$0 = \phi$$
$$1 = \{\phi\}$$
$$2 = \{\phi, \{\phi\}\}$$
$$3 = \{\phi, \{\phi\}, \{\phi, \{\phi\}\}\}$$

We have, clearly, $1 = 0^+$, $2 = 1^+$, $3 = 2^+$, and so on. Let us now define a set N such that

1. N contains the set 0.
2. If the set n is an element in N, so is the set n^+.
3. N contains no other sets.

Since for every set in N, its successor is also in N, the reader probably would agree that N is indeed an "infinite set." However, let us proceed in a more precise way.

We shall talk about the sizes of sets in a comparative manner. To this end, let us introduce a definition: Given two sets P and Q, we say that there is a *one-to-one correspondence* between the elements in P and the elements in Q if it is possible to pair off the elements in P and Q such that every element in P is paired off with a distinct element in Q.[†] Thus, there is a one-to-one correspondence between the elements in the set $\{a, b\}$ and the elements in the set $\{c, d\}$, because we can pair a with c and b with d, or we can pair a with d and b with c. There is also a one-to-one correspondence between the elements in the set $\{a, b, c\}$ and the elements in the set $\{\phi, a, d\}$. On the other hand, there is no one-to-one correspondence between the elements in the sets $\{a, b, c\}$ and $\{a, d\}$. The intention of introducing the notion of one-to-one correspondence between the elements of two sets is quite obvious, because we can now compare two sets and say that they are of the same size or that they are of different sizes. The basis of our comparison is indeed the sets we constructed above, namely, 0, 1, 2, 3, ..., and N. We are now ready to introduce some formal definitions. A set is said to be *finite* if there is a one-to-one correspondence between the elements in the set and the elements in some set

---

* Using 0, 1, 2, 3, ... as names of sets is just as good as using A, B, C, D, ... As will be seen, it is intentional that we choose 0, 1, 2, 3, ... as names.

[†] Such an intuitive definition will be made more formal in Chap. 3.

n, where $n \in N$; n is said to be the *cardinality* of the set. Thus, for example, the cardinalities of the sets $\{a, b, c\}$, $\{a, \phi, d\}$, $\{\phi, \{\phi\}, \{\phi, \{\phi\}\}\}$ are all equal to 3. Note that it is now precise for us to say that a set is an infinite set if it is not a finite one. We can, however, be more precise about the "size" of infinite sets: A set is said to be *countably infinite* (or the cardinality of the set is countably infinite)* if there is a one-to-one correspondence between the elements in the set and the elements in N. We observe first of all that the set of all natural numbers $\{0, 1, 2, 3, \ldots\}^\dagger$ is a countably infinite set. It follows that the set of all non-negative even integers $\{0, 2, 4, 6, 8, \ldots\}$ is a countably infinite set because there is an obvious one-to-one correspondence between all non-negative even integers and all natural numbers, namely, the even integer $2i$ corresponds to the natural number i for $i = 0, 1, 2, \ldots$. Similarly, the set of all non-negative multiples of 7 $\{0, 7, 14, 21, \ldots\}$ is also a countably infinite set. So is the set of all positive integers $\{1, 2, 3, \ldots\}$. We note that a set is a countably infinite set if starting from a certain element we can sequentially list all the elements in the set one after another, because such a listing will yield a one-to-one correspondence between the elements in the set and the natural numbers. For example, the set of all integers $\{\ldots, -2, -1, 0, 1, 2, \ldots\}$ is a countably infinite set, since its elements can be listed sequentially as $\{0, 1, -1, 2, -2, 3, -3, \ldots\}$. This example suggests that the union of two countably infinite sets is also a countably infinite set. It indeed is the case. As a matter of fact, the union of a finite number of countably infinite sets is a countably infinite set and, furthermore, so is the union of a countably infinite number of countably infinite sets (see Prob. 1.26).

1.4 UNCOUNTABLY INFINITE SETS

We show in this section that there are infinite sets with cardinalities that are not countably infinite. We now introduce a "proof technique" that probably is new to the reader.[‡]

Three boys—James, Joe, and John—were asked to taste ice cream of three different flavours—chocolate, vanilla and strawberry. The following table summarises the flavors they each like and dislike:

---

* In the literature, the cardinality of a countably infinite set is also referred to as $\aleph_0$. ($\aleph$ is the first letter in the Hebrew alphabet.)

† The notation is perhaps confusing. However. it is intentional, because the set N is *indeed* a precise definition of the set of natural numbers.

‡ Indeed, throughout this book, we will need to show on many occasions that something cannot possibly exist, or some task can never be done. We are all familiar with how to demonstrate the existence of something or how to describe a procedure for performing a certain task. But, how does one demonstrate something that cannot possibly exist under any circumstances? How does one prove that some task cannot be done by anybody however intelligent, or any machine however powerful?

	Chocolate	Vanilla	Strawberry
James	Yes	No	Yes
Joe	No	No	Yes
John	Yes	Yes	Yes

We make a trivial observation: Suppose we were told that there is a boy who disagrees with James on whether chocolate ice cream is delicious (that is, James likes chocolate ice cream, but the boy dislikes it), who disagrees with Joe on whether vanilla ice cream is delicious (that is, Joe dislikes vanilla ice cream, but the boy likes it), and who also disagrees with John on whether strawberry ice cream is delicious (that is, John likes strawberry ice cream, but the boy dislikes it). Clearly, this boy cannot be James, Joe, or John, but must be a *different* boy, since he disagrees with each of their tastes on at least one of the flavors as illustrated in the following table:

	Chocolate	Vanilla	Strawberry
James	(Yes)	No	Yes
Joe	No	(No)	Yes
John	Yes	Yes	(Yes)
New boy	No	Yes	No

We may have a more general situation. Suppose that there are n boys and ice cream of n different flavors. If we were told that there is a boy who disagrees with the first boy on whether the first flavor is delicious, who disagrees with the second boy on whether the second flavor is delicious, and who disagrees with the nth boy on whether the nth flavor is delicious then we can be certain that this boy is not one of the n boys, because he disagrees with each of them in at least one way. This seemingly frivolous example illustrates a *diagonal argument* in which we assert that a certain object (a new boy) is not one of the given objects (the n boys we know), using the fact that this object is different from each of the given objects in at least one way.

As an example of infinite sets with cardinalities that are not countably infinite, we now show that the set of real numbers between 0 and 1 is not a countably infinite set. Our proof procedure is to assume that the set is countably infinite and then show the existence of a contradiction. If the cardinality of the set of real numbers between 0 and 1 is countably infinite, there is a one-to-one correspondence between these real numbers and the natural numbers. Consequently, we can exhaustively list them one after another in decimal form as in the following:*

$$0 \cdot a_{11} a_{12} a_{13} a_{14} \ldots$$
$$0 \cdot a_{21} a_{22} a_{23} a_{24} \ldots$$
$$0 \cdot a_{31} a_{32} a_{33} a_{34} \ldots$$
$$0 \cdot a_{i1} a_{i2} a_{i3} a_{i4} \ldots$$

---

*A number such as 0.34 can be written in two different forms, namely, 0.34000... or 0.339999 .... We follow an arbitrarily chosen convention of writing it in the latter form.

where a_{ij} denotes the jth digit of the ith number in the list. Consider the number

$$0 \cdot b_1 b_2 b_3 b_4 \ldots$$

where

$$b_i = \begin{cases} 1 & \text{if} \quad a_{ii} = 9 \\ 9 - a_{ii} & \text{if} \quad a_{ii} = 0, 1, 2, \ldots, 8 \end{cases}$$

for all i. Clearly, the number $0 \cdot b_1 b_2 b_3 b_4 \ldots$ is a real number between 0 and 1 that does not have an infinite string of trailing 0s (for example, 0.34000 ...). Moreover, it is different from each of the numbers in the list above because it differs from the first number in the first digit, the second number in the second digit, the ith number in the ith digit, and so on. Consequently, we conclude that the list above is not an exhaustive listing of the set of all real numbers between 0 and 1, contradicting the assumption that this set is countably infinite.

It is possible to continue in this direction to classify infinite sets so that notions such as some infinite sets are "more infinite" than other infinite sets can be made precise. This, however, will be beyond our scope of discussion.

1.5 PRINCIPLE OF INCLUSION AND EXCLUSION

We present in this section some results related to the cardinality of finite sets. We shall use the notation $|P|$ to denote the cardinality of the set P. Some simple results, the derivation of which is left to the reader, are:

$$|P \cup Q| \leq |P| + |Q|$$
$$|P \cap Q| \leq \min \left(|P|, |Q| \right)$$
$$|P \oplus Q| = |P| + |Q| - 2|P \cap Q|$$
$$|P - Q| \geq |P| - |Q|$$

We show in the following a less obvious result. Let A_1 and A_2 be two sets. We want to show that

$$|A_1 \cup A_2| = |A_1| + |A_2| - |A_1 \cap A_2| \tag{1.1}$$

i.e. the number of elements in the union of two sets (say, A_1 and A_2) is the sum of the numbers of elements in the two sets A_1 and A_2 minus the number of elements in the intersection of A_1 and A_2. This is known as the *Principle of Inclusion and Exclusion*. Equation 1.1 can be represented by a Venn diagram as given in Fig. 1.2.

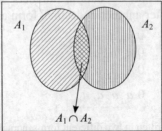

$$A_1 \cap A_2$$

Fig.1.2

Note that the sets A_1 and A_2 might have some common elements. To be specific, the number of common elements between A_1 and A_2 is $|A_1 \cap A_2|$. Each of these elements is counted twice in $|A_1| + |A_2|$ (once in $|A_1|$ and once in $|A_2|$), although it should be counted as one element in $|A_1 \cup A_2|$. Therefore, the *double count* of these elements in $|A_1| + |A_2|$ should be adjusted by the subtraction of the term $|A_1 \cap A_2|$ in the right-hand side of (1.1). As an example, suppose that among a set of 12 books, 6 are novels, 7 were published in the year 1984, and 3 are novels published in 1984. Let A_1 denote the set of books that are novels, and A_2 denote the set of books published in 1984. We have

$$|A_1| = 6 \quad |A_2| = 7 \quad |A_1 \cap A_2| = 3$$

Consequently, according to (1.1),

$$|A_1 \cup A_2| = 6 + 7 - 3 = 10$$

That is, there are 10 books which are either novels or 1984 publications, or both. Consequently, among the 12 books there are 2 non-novels that were not published in 1984.

Extending the result in (1.1), for three sets A_1, A_2 and A_3,

$$|A_1 \cup A_2 \cup A_3| = |A_1| + |A_2| + |A_3| - |A_1 \cap A_2| - |A_1 \cap A_3| \\ - |A_2 \cap A_3| + |A_1 \cap A_2 \cap A_3| \tag{1.2}$$

As we shall prove a more general result in the following, we shall not prove the result in (1.2) here. On the other hand, we suggest that a reader check the result in (1.2) by examining the Venn diagram in Fig. 1.3.

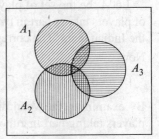

Fig. 1.3

Let us consider some illustrative examples.

Example 1.1 In a class, 18 boys have Dell laptops, 10 boys have HP laptops and 6 boys have both Dell laptops and HP laptops. We want to know how many boys are there in the class. Let A_1 be the set of boys having Dell laptops and A_2 be the set of boys having HP laptops. Then, $A_1 \cap A_2$ is the set of boys who have Dell laptops and HP laptops. The corresponding Venn diagram is given in Fig. 1.4.

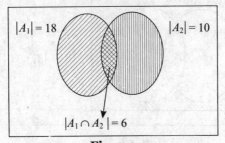

Fig. 1.4

Now, $|A_1| = 18 \; |A_2| = 10$ and $|A_1 \cap A_2| = 6$

By examining the Venn diagram given in Fig. 1.4, we note that the total number of boys in the class will be given by

$$|A_1 \cup A_2| = |A_1| + |A_2| - |A_1 \cap A_2|$$
$$= 18 + 10 - 6 = 22 \quad \blacksquare$$

Example 1.2 Suppose, there are 21 cricket players in the Indian team. Out of these, 6 players are taking part in a one-day match, 7 players are taking part in twenty-20 match and 5 players are taking part in both one-day and twenty-20 matches. We want to know how many players are not taking part either in a one-day or in twenty-20 match.

To find the number of players who are not taking part in either one-day or twenty-20, we have to subtract the number of players that are taking part in either of these matches from the total number of players.

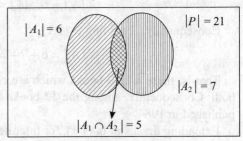

Fig. 1.5

Let A_1 be the set of players taking part in the one-day match, let A_2 be the set of players taking part in twenty-20 match and P be the total number of players in the Indian team. The corresponding Venn diagram is given in Fig. 1.5

Now,

$$|A_1| = 6, \qquad |A_2| = 7 \qquad \text{and} \quad |A_1 \cap A_2| = 5$$

By examining the Venn diagram given in Fig.1.5, we note that the number of players taking part in either one-day or twenty-20 match will be given by

$$|A_1 \cup A_2| = |A_1| + |A_2| - |A_1 \cap A_2|$$
$$= 6 + 7 - 5 = 8$$

Consequently, there are $21 - 8 = 13$ players who are not taking part either in a one-day or in a 20-20 match. This is shown in the Venn diagram of Fig. 1.6. $\blacksquare$

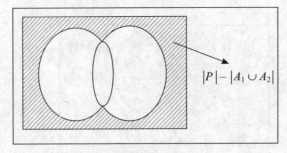

Fig. 1.6

Example 1.3 Suppose 100 out of 120 Computer Science students study at least one of the following languages: French, German and Russian. It is given that 65 students study French, 45 students study German, 42 students study Russian, 20 students study French and German, 25 students study French and Russian and 15 students study German and Russian. We want to find the number of students who study

(i) Only French and German, but not Russian

(ii) Only French and Russian, but not German

(iii) Only German and Russian, but not French

(iv) Only French

(v) Only German

(vi) Only Russian

(vii) None of the three languages

Let A_1, A_2 and A_3 denote the set of students who study French, German, and Russian respectively. Let P be the set of students who study at least one of the above three languages. The corresponding Venn diagram is given in Fig. 1.7.

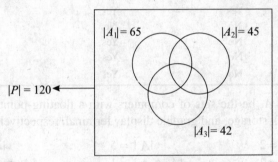

Fig. 1.7

Now,

$$|A_1| = 65, |A_2| = 45$$

$$|A_3| = 42$$

$$|A_1 \cap A_2| = 20, |A_1 \cap A_2| = 25,$$

$$|A_2 \cap A_3| = 15, \text{ and } |A_1 \cup A_2 \cup A_3| = 100$$

By examining the Venn diagram given in Fig. 1.7, we obtain

$$|A_1 \cup A_2 \cup A_3| = |A_1| + |A_2| + |A_3| - |A_1 \cap A_2| - |A_1 \cap A_3| - |A_2 \cap A_3| + |A_1 \cap A_2 \cap A_3|$$

$$\Rightarrow \quad 100 = 65 + 45 + 42 - 20 - 25 - 15 + |A_1 \cap A_2 \cap A_3|$$

$$\Rightarrow \quad |A_1 \cap A_2 \cap A_3| = 8$$

Now, let us find the number of students who study

(i) Only French and German, but not Russian $= |A_1 \cap A_2| - |A_1 \cap A_2 \cap A_3|$

$$= 20 - 8 = 12$$

(ii) Only French and Russian, but not German = $|A_1 \cap A_2| - |A_1 \cap A_2 \cap A_3|$
$$= 25 - 8 = 17$$

(iii) Only German and Russian, but not French = $|A_2 \cap A_3| - |A_1 \cap A_2 \cap A_3|$
$$= 15 - 8 = 7$$

(iv) Only French = $|A_1| - |A_1 \cap A_2| - |A_1 \cap A_3| + |A_1 \cap A_2 \cap A_3|$
$$= 65 - 20 - 25 + 8 = 28$$

(v) Only German = $|A_2| - |A_1 \cap A_2| - |A_2 \cap A_3| + |A_1 \cap A_2 \cap A_3|$
$$= 45 - 20 - 15 + 8 = 18$$

(vi) Only Russian = $|A_2| - |A_1 \cap A_2| - |A_2 \cap A_3| + |A_1 \cap A_2 \cap A_3|$
$$= 42 - 25 - 15 + 8 = 10$$

(v) None of the three languages = $|A_1 \cap A_2 \cap A_3| = 8$ ∎

Example 1.4 Suppose we have six computers with the following specifications:

Computer	Floating-point arithmetic unit	Magnetic disk memory	Graphic display terminal
I	Yes	Yes	No
II	Yes	Yes	Yes
III	No	No	No
IV	No	Yes	Yes
V	No	Yes	No
VI	No	Yes	Yes

Let A_1, A_2, and A_3 be the sets of computers with a floating-point arithmetic unit, magnetic-disk storage, and graphic display terminal, respectively. We have

$$|A_1| = 2 \qquad\qquad |A_2| = 5 \qquad\qquad |A_3| = 3$$
$$|A_1 \cap A_2| = 2 \qquad |A_1 \cap A_3| = 1 \qquad |A_2 \cap A_3| = 3$$
$$|A_1 \cap A_2 \cap A_3| = 1$$

Consequently,

$$|A_1 \cup A_2 \cup A_3| = 2 + 5 + 3 - 2 - 1 - 3 + 1 = 5$$

That is, five of the six computers have one or more of the three kinds of hardware considered. ∎

Example 1.5 Out of 200 students, 50 of them take the course Discrete Mathematics, 140 of them take the course Economics, and 24 of them take both the courses. Since both courses have scheduled examinations for the following day, only students who are not in either one of these courses will be able to go to the party, the night before. We want to know how many students will be at the party. Examining the Venn diagram in Fig. 1.8a, where A_1 is the set of students in the course Discrete Mathematics and A_2 is the set of students in the course Economics, we note that the number of students who take either one or both courses is equal to

$$50 + 140 - 24 = 166$$

Consequently, the number of students who will be at the party is

$$200 - 166 = 34$$

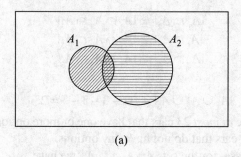

(a)

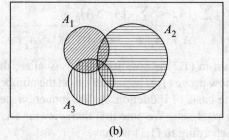

(b)

Fig. 1.8

Suppose that 60 of the 200 are underclass students. Among the underclass students, 20 of them take Discrete Mathematics, 45 of them take Economics, and 16 of them take both. We want to know how many upperclass students will be at the party. According to the Venn diagram in Fig. 1.8b, where A_3 is the set of underclass students, we have

$$|A_1 \cup A_2 \cup A_3| = 50 + 140 + 60 - 24 - 20 - 45 + 16 = 177$$

Thus, the number of upperclass students who will go to the party is

$$200 - 177 = 23 \qquad\blacksquare$$

Example 1.6 Thirty cars were assembled in a factory. The options available were a radio an air conditioner and white-wall tires. It is known that 15 of the cars have radios, 8 of them have air conditioners and 6 of them have white-wall tires. Moreover, 3 of them have all three options. We want to know at *least* how many cars do not have any options at all. Let A_1, A_2 and A_3 be the sets of cars with a radio, an air conditioner and white-wall tires, respectively. Since

$$|A_1| = 15 \qquad |A_2| = 8 \qquad |A_3| = 6$$

and

$$|A_1 \cap A_2 \cap A_3| = 3$$

according to (1.2)

$$|A_1 \cup A_2 \cup A_3| = 15 + 8 + 6 - |A_1 \cap A_2| - |A_1 \cap A_3| - |A_2 \cap A_3| + 3$$
$$= 32 - |A_1 \cap A_2| - |A_1 \cap A_3| - |A_2 \cap A_3|$$

Since,

$$|A_1 \cap A_2| \geqq |A_1 \cap A_2 \cap A_3|$$
$$|A_1 \cap A_3| \geqq |A_1 \cap A_2 \cap A_3|$$
$$|A_2 \cap A_3| \geqq |A_1 \cap A_2 \cap A_3|$$

we have,

$$|A_1 \cup A_2 \cup A_3| \leqq 32 - 3 - 3 - 3 = 23$$

That is, there are *at most* 23 cars that have one or more options. Consequently, there are *at least* 7 cars that do not have any options. ∎

In the general case, for the sets $A_1, A_2, ..., A_r$, we have

$$|A_1 \cup A_2 \cup ... \cup A_r| = \sum_i |A_i| - \sum_{1 \leqq i < j \leqq r} |A_i \cap A_j|$$
$$+ \sum_{1 \leqq i < j < k \leqq r} |A_i \cap A_j \cap A_k| + ... + (-1)^{r-1}|A_1 \cap A_2 \cap ... \cap A_r| \qquad (1.3)$$

Although the result in (1.2) is not difficult to visualize, the result in (1.3) is not as obvious. We now prove (1.3) by induction on the number of sets r. Clearly, (1.1) can serve as the basis of induction. As the induction step, we assume that (1.3) is valid for any $r - 1$ sets. We note first that, viewing $(A_1 \cup A_2 \cup ... \cup A_{r-1})$ and A_r as two sets, according to (1.1) we have

$$|A_1 \cup A_2 \cup ... \cup A_r| = |A_1 \cup A_2 \cup ... \cup A_{r-1}| + |A_r|$$
$$- |A_r \cap (A_1 \cup A_2 \cup ... \cup A_{r-1})| \qquad (1.4)$$

Now,

$$|A_r \cap (A_1 \cup A_2 \cup ... \cup A_{r-1}| = |(A_r \cap A_1) \cup (A_r \cap A_2) \cup ...$$
$$\cup (A_r \cap A_{r-1})|$$

According to the induction hypothesis, for the $r - 1$ sets $A_r \cap A_1, A_r \cap A_2, ..., A_r \cap A_{r-1}$, we have

$$|(A_r \cap A_1) \cup (A_r \cap A_2) \cup ... \cup (A_r \cap A_{r-1})|$$
$$= |A_r \cap A_1| + |A_r \cap A_2| + ... + |A_r \cap A_{r-1}|$$
$$- |(A_r \cap A_1) \cap (A_r \cap A_2)| - |(A_r \cap A_1) \cap (A_r \cap A_3)|$$
$$- ...$$
$$- |(A_r \cap A_1) \cap (A_r \cap A_2) \cap (A_r \cap A_3)| + ...$$
$$- ...$$
$$+ (-1)^{r-2}|(A_r \cap A_1) \cap (A_r \cap A_2) \cap ... \cap (A_r \cap A_{r-1})|$$
$$= |A_r \cap A_1| + |A_r \cap A_2| + ... + |A_r \cap A_{r-1}|$$
$$- |A_r \cap A_1 \cap A_2| - |A_r \cap A_1 \cap A_3| - ...$$
$$+ |A_r \cap A_1 \cap A_2 \cap A_3| + ...$$
$$- ...$$
$$+ (-1)^{r-2}|A_r \cap A_1 \cap A_2 \cap ... \cap A_{r-1}| \qquad (1.5)$$

Also, according to the induction hypothesis, for the $r-1$ sets $A_1, A_2, ..., A_{r-1}$, we have,

$$|A_1 \cup A_2 \cup ... \cup A_{r-1}| = |A_1| + |A_2| + ...$$
$$- |A_1 \cap A_2| - |A_1 \cap A_3| - ...$$
$$+ ...$$
$$+ (-1)^{r-2}|A_1 \cap A_2 \cap ... \cap A_{r-1}| \qquad (1.6)$$

Substituting (1.5) and (1.6) into (1.4), we obtain (1.3).

Example 1.7 Let us determine the number of integers between 1 and 250 that are divisible by any of the integers 2, 3, 5 and 7. Let A_1 denote the set of integers between 1 and 250 that are divisible by 2, A_2 denote the set of integers that are divisible by 3, A_3 denote the set of integers that are divisible by 5, and A_4 denote the set of integers that are divisible by 7. Since,

$$|A_1| = \left\lfloor \frac{250}{2} \right\rfloor^* = 125 \qquad\qquad |A_2| = \left\lfloor \frac{250}{3} \right\rfloor = 83$$

$$|A_3| = \left\lfloor \frac{250}{5} \right\rfloor = 50 \qquad\qquad |A_4| = \left\lfloor \frac{250}{7} \right\rfloor = 35$$

$$|A_1 \cap A_2| = \left\lfloor \frac{250}{2 \times 3} \right\rfloor = 41 \qquad\qquad |A_1 \cap A_3| = \left\lfloor \frac{250}{2 \times 5} \right\rfloor = 25$$

$$|A_1 \cap A_4| = \left\lfloor \frac{250}{2 \times 7} \right\rfloor = 17 \qquad\qquad |A_2 \cap A_3| = \left\lfloor \frac{250}{3 \times 5} \right\rfloor = 16$$

$$|A_2 \cap A_4| = \left\lfloor \frac{250}{3 \times 7} \right\rfloor = 11 \qquad\qquad |A_3 \cap A_4| = \left\lfloor \frac{250}{5 \times 7} \right\rfloor = 7$$

$$|A_1 \cap A_2 \cap A_3| = \left\lfloor \frac{250}{2 \times 3 \times 5} \right\rfloor = 8 \qquad |A_1 \cap A_2 \cap A_4| = \left\lfloor \frac{250}{2 \times 3 \times 7} \right\rfloor = 5$$

$$|A_1 \cap A_3 \cap A_4| = \left\lfloor \frac{250}{2 \times 5 \times 7} \right\rfloor = 3 \qquad |A_1 \cap A_3 \cap A_4| = \left\lfloor \frac{250}{3 \times 5 \times 7} \right\rfloor = 2$$

$$|A_1 \cap A_2 \cap A_3 \cap A_4| = \left\lfloor \frac{250}{2 \times 3 \times 5 \times 7} \right\rfloor = 1$$

we have,

$$|A_1 \cup A_2 \cup A_3 \cup A_4| = 125 + 83 + 50 + 35 - 41 - 25 - 17 - 16 - 11 - 7$$
$$+ 8 + 5 + 3 + 2 - 1 = 193 \qquad \blacksquare$$

We shall present more examples on the application of the formula (1.3), which is called the *principle of inclusion and exclusion*, in later chapters.

Example 1.8 The number of positive divisors of a natural number is given by the following rule:

Let $n \geq 2$ be a natural number. If $n = p_1^{m1} p_2^{m2} .... p_k^{mk}$, where $p_1, p_2, ... p_k$ are distinct primes, then the number of positive divisors of n is $(m_1 + 1)(m_2 + 1) .... (m_k + 1)$.

---

* We use $\lfloor x \rfloor$ to denote the largest integer that is smaller than or equal to x.

Now, let us find the number of positive divisors which divide either of the following two numbers: 5400 and 18000.

Let $A_1 = \{x \in N \mid x$ is a divisor of 5400$\}$ and $A_2 = \{x \in N \mid x$ is a divisor of 18000$\}$.
We have to find $|A_1 \cup A_2|$.

By Principle of Inclusion and Exclusion, $|A_1 \cup A_2| = |A_1| + |A_2| - |A_1 \cap A_2|$.

First, we have to find $|A_1|, |A_2|$ and $|A_1 \cap A_2|$.

It may be observed that,

$$5400 = 2^3 \times 3^3 \times 5^2 \text{ and } 18000 = 2^4 \times 3^2 \times 5^3.$$

Thus, by applying the rule stated above, we have

$$|A_1| = (3 + 1)(3 + 1)(2 + 1) = 48 \text{ and}$$
$$|A_2| = (4 + 1)(2 + 1)(3 + 1) = 60.$$

By definition, $|A_1 \cap A_2|$ is the set of common positive divisors of 5400 and 18000, and so it is the set of positive divisors of the Greatest Common Divisor (GCD) of 5400 and 18000.

Since GCD $\{5400, 18000\}$ = GCD $[2^3 \times 3^3 \times 5^2, 2^4 \times 3^2 \times 5^3]$ = $2^3 \times 3^2 \times 5^2$, it follows that,

$$|A_1 \cap A_2| = (3 + 1)(2 + 1)(2 + 1) = 36 \text{ and}$$

Hence,

$$|A_1 \cup A_2| = |A_1| + |A_2| - |A_1 \cap A_2| = 48 + 60 - 36 = 72.$$

So, there are 72 positive divisors which divide either of the two numbers 5400 and 18000. ■

1.6 MULTISETS

We recall that a set is a collection of distinct objects. There are many occasions, however, when we encounter collections of nondistinct objects. For example, consider the names of the students in a class. We might have two or more students who have the same name, and we might wish to talk about the collection of the names of the students. We define a *multiset* to be a collection of objects that are not necessarily distinct. Thus, $\{a, a, a, b, b, c\}$, $\{a, a, a, a\}$, $\{a, b, c\}$, and $\{ \ \}$ are all examples of multisets. The *multiplicity* of an element in a multiset is defined to be the number of times the element appears in the multiset. Thus, the multiplicity of the element a in the multiset $\{a, a, a, c, d, d\}$ is 3. The multiplicity of the element b is 0, the multiplicity of the element c is 1, and the multiplicity of the element d is 2. Note that sets are merely special instances of multisets in which the multiplicity of an element is either 0 or 1. The cardinality of a multiset is defined to be the cardinality of the set it corresponds to, *assuming* that the elements in the multiset are all distinct.

Let P and Q be two multisets. The union of P and Q, denoted $P \cup Q$, is a multiset such that the multiplicity of an element in $P \cup Q$ is equal to the maximum of the multiplicities of the element in P and in Q. Thus, for $P = \{a, a, a, c, d, d\}$ and $Q = \{a, a, b, c, c\}$

$$P \cup Q = \{a, a, a, b, c, c, d, d\}$$

For example, let the multiset $R = \{$electrical engineer, electrical engineer, electrical engineer, mechanical engineer, mathematician, mathematician, physicist$\}$ be the personnel needed in the first phase of an engineering project, and the multiset $S = \{$electrical engineer, mechanical engineer, mechanical engineer, mathematician, computer scientist, computer scientist$\}$ be the personnel needed in the second phase of the project. The multiset $R \cup S$ is the personnel we should hire for the project.

The intersection of P and Q, denoted $P \cap Q$, is a multiset such that the multiplicity of an element in $P \cap Q$ is equal to the minimum of the multiplicities of the element in P and in Q. Thus, for $P = \{a, a, a, c, d, d\}$ and $Q = \{a, a, b, c, c\}$

$$P \cap Q = \{a, a, c\}$$

For the example above on the engineering project, the multiset $R \cap S$ is the personnel that will be involved in both phases of the project.

The difference of P and Q, denoted $P - Q$, is a multiset such that the multiplicity of an element in $P - Q$ is equal to the multiplicity of the element in P minus the multiplicity of the element in Q if the difference is positive, and is equal to 0 if the difference is 0 or is negative. For example, let $P = \{a, a, a, b, b, c, d, d. e\}$ and $Q = \{a, a, b, b, b, c, c, d, d, f\}$. We have

$$P - Q = \{a, e\}$$

For the engineering project example, the multiset $R - S$ is the personnel to be reassigned after the first phase of the project.

Note that the definitions of union, intersection, and difference of multisets are so chosen that they are consistent with that of sets. We did not define the symmetric difference of two multisets here; the interested reader might want to see Prob. 1.64.

Finally, we define the sum of two multisets P and Q, denoted $P + Q$, to be a multiset such that the multiplicity of an element in $P + Q$ is equal to the sum of the multiplicities of the element in P and in Q. Note that there is no corresponding definition of the sum of two sets. For example, let $P = \{a, a, b, c, c\}$ and $Q = \{a, b, b, d\}$. We have $P + Q = \{a, a, a, b, b, b, c, c, d\}$. As another example, let R be a multiset containing the account numbers of all the transactions in a bank on a certain day, and S be a multiset containing the account numbers of all the transactions on the next day. R and S are multisets because an account might have more than one transaction in a day. Thus, $R + S$ is a combined record of the account numbers of the transactions in these two days.

1.7 MATHEMATICAL INDUCTION

Let us consider some illustrative examples:

Example 1.9 Suppose we have stamps of two different denominations, 3 cents and 5 cents. We want to show that it is possible to make up exactly any postage of 8 cents or more using stamps of these two denominations. Clearly, the approach of showing case by case for how to make up postage of 8 cents, 9 cents, 10 cents, and so on, using 3-cent and 5-cent stamps will not be a fruitful one, because there is an infinite number of cases to be examined*. Let us consider an alternative approach. We want to show that if it is possible to make up exactly a postage of k cents using 3-cent and 5-cent stamps, then it is also possible to make up exactly a postage of $k + 1$ cents using 3-cent and 5-cent stamps. We examine two cases: Suppose we make up a postage of k cents using at least one 5-cent stamp. Replacing a 5-cent stamp by two 3-cent stamps will yield a way to make up a postage of $k + 1$ cents. On the other hand, suppose we make up a postage of k cents using 3-cent stamps only. Since $k \geq 8$, there must be at least three 3-cent stamps. Replacing three 3-cent stamps by two 5-cent stamps will yield a way to make up a postage of $k + 1$ cents. Since it is obvious how we can make up a postage of 8 cents, we conclude that we can make up a postage of 9 cents, which in turn, leads us to conclude that we can make up a postage of 10 cents, which in turn, leads us to conclude that we can make up a postage of 11 cents, and so on. ∎

Example 1.10 Suppose we remove a square from a standard 8×8 chessboard as shown in Fig. 1.9a. Given 21 L-shaped triominoes*, as shown in Fig. 1.9b, we want to know whether it is possible to *tile* the 63 remaining squares of the chessboard with the triominoes. (By tiling the remaining squares of the chessboard, we mean to cover each of them exactly once without parts of the triominoes extending over the removed square or the edges of the board.) The answer to our question is affirmative, as Fig. 1.10 shows. We can actually prove a more general result, which we shall proceed to do.

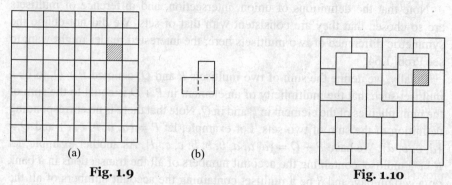

(a)   (b)

Fig. 1.9   **Fig. 1.10**

---

* See. however, Prob. 1.30

* The word *trio*mino is derived from the word domino. Also, there are *tetr*ominoes, *pent*ominoes, *hex*ominoes and, in general, *poly*ominoes.

A chessboard with one of its squares removed will be referred to as a *defective* chessboard. We want to show that any defective $2^n \times 2^n$ chessboard can be tiled with L-shaped triominoes.[†] It is trivially obvious that a defective 2×2 chessboard can be tiled with an L-shaped triomino. Let us now assume that any defective $2^k \times 2^k$ chessboard can be tiled with L-shaped triominoes and proceed to show that any defective $2^{k+1} \times 2^{k+1}$ chessboard can also be tiled with L-shaped triominoes. Consider a defective $2^{k+1} \times 2^{k+1}$ chessboard as shown in Fig. 1.11a. Let us divide the chessboard into four quadrants, each of which is a $2^k \times 2^k$ chessboard, as shown in Fig. 1.11b. One of these $2^k \times 2^k$ chessboards is a defective one. Furthermore, by placing an L-shaped triomino at the center of the $2^{k+1} \times 2^{k+1}$ chessboard, as shown in Fig. 1.11c, we can imagine that the other three quadrants are also defective $2^k \times 2^k$ chessboards. Since we assume that any defective $2^k \times 2^k$ chessboard can be tiled with L-shaped triominoes, we can tile each of the quadrants with L-shaped triominoes, and conclude that any defective $2^{k+1} \times 2^{k+1}$ chessboard can be tiled with L-shaped triominoes. Thus, starting with the tiling of any defective 2×2 chessboard, we have proved that we can tile any $2^n \times 2^n$ defective chessboard. ∎

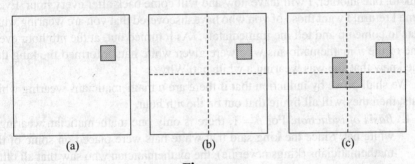

      (a)   (b)   (c)

Fig. 1.11

These two examples illustrate a very powerful proof technique in mathematics, known as the principle of *mathematical induction*.

For a given statement involving a natural number n, if we can show that:

1. The statement is true for $n = n_0$; and
2. The statement is true for $n = k + 1$, assuming that the statement is true for $n = k$, $(k \geq n_0)$,

then we can conclude that the statement is true for all natural numbers $n \geq n_0$. (1) is usually referred to as the *basis of induction*, and (2) is usually referred to as the *induction step*. Also, the assumption that the statement is true for $n = k$ in (2) is usually referred to as the *induction hypothesis*. For example, in the postage-stamp problem, we want to prove the statement, "It is possible to make up exactly any postage of n cents using 3-cent stamps and 5-cent stamps for $n \geq 8$." In order to prove the statement we show that:

1. *Basis of induction.* It is possible to make up exactly a postage of 8 cents.

[†] One would immediately question whether $2^n \times 2^n - 1$ is always divisible by 3. The answer is affirmative. (See Prob. 1.36.)

2. *Induction step*. It is possible to make up exactly a postage of $k + 1$ cents, assuming it is possible to make up exactly a postage of k cents, ($k \geq 8$).

We note that the principle of mathematical induction is a direct consequence of the definition of natural numbers. Consider a set S such that

1. The natural number n_0 is in S.
2. If the natural number k is in S then the natural number $k + 1$ is also in S, ($k \geq n_0$).

According to the definition of the set of natural numbers, we can conclude that S contains all the natural numbers larger than or equal to n_0. However, this is exactly the statement of the principle of mathematical induction when we consider S to be the set of natural numbers for which a given statement is true.

We consider now more examples:

Example 1.11 The king summoned the best mathematicians in the kingdom to the palace to find out how smart they were. The king told them: "I have placed white hats on some of you and black hats on the others. You may look at, but not talk to, one another. I will leave now and will come back after every hour. Every time I return, I want those of you who have discovered that you are wearing white hats to come up and tell me immediately." As it turned out, at the nth hour every one of the n mathematicians who were given white hats informed the king that she knew that she was wearing a white hat. Why?

We shall prove by induction that if there are n mathematicians wearing white hats, then they will all figure that out on the nth hour.

1. *Basis of induction*. For $n = 1$, there is only one mathematician wearing a white hat. Since the king said that white hats were placed on some of the mathematicians (kings never lie), the mathematician who saw that all other mathematicians had on black hats would realize immediately that she was wearing a white hat. Consequently, she would inform the king on the first hour (when the king returned for the first time) that she was wearing a white hat.

2. *Induction step*.* Assume that if there were k mathematicians wearing white hats, then they would have figured out that they were wearing white hats and informed the king so on the kth hour. Now, suppose that there were $k + 1$ mathematicians wearing white hats. Every mathematician wearing a white hat saw that k of her colleagues were wearing white hats. However, that her k colleagues did not inform the king of their findings on the kth hour can only imply that there were more than k people wearing white hats.

---

* To help you understand the argument better, we will explore the reasoning for the case that there were two mathematicians wearing white hats. Consider one of these two mathematicians. She saw that one of her colleagues was wearing a white hat. She reasoned that if she were wearing a black hat, her colleague would be the only one wearing a white hat. In that case, her colleague would have figured out the situation and informed the king on the first hour. (All mathematicians are smart.) That this did not happen implies that she was also wearing a white hat. Consequently, she told the king on the second hour (and so did the other mathematician with a white hat, since, again, all mathematicians are smart).

Consequently, she knew that she must be wearing a white hat also. On the $(k + 1)$st hour, she (together with all other mathematicians wearing white hats) would tell the king their conclusion. ■

Example 1.12 Consider the following solitaire game: for every integer i, there is an unlimited supply of balls marked with the number i. Initially, we are given a tray of balls, and we throw away the balls from the tray one at a time. If we throw away a ball that is marked with i, we can replace it by any finite number of balls marked $1, 2, ..., i - 1$. (Thus, no replacement will be made if we throw away a ball marked with 1.) The game ends when the tray is empty. We want to know whether the game always terminates for any tray of balls given initially.

We shall prove that the game always terminates by induction on n, the largest number that appears on the balls in the tray.

1. *Basis of induction.* For $n = 1$, there is a finite number of balls marked with 1 in the tray initially. Since there is no replacement after a ball marked 1 is thrown away, the game terminates after a finite number of moves.

2. *Induction step.* We assume that the game terminates if the largest number that appears on the balls is k. Consider the case when the largest number that appears on the ball is $k + 1$. According to the induction hypothesis, we eventually have to throw away a ball marked $k + 1$. (If we throw away only balls marked $1, 2, ..., k$, they will be exhausted in a finite number of moves.) Repeating this argument, we would have thrown away all balls marked with $k + 1$ in a finite number of moves. Again, by the induction hypothesis, the game terminates after a finite number of moves from then on. ■

Example 1.13 Show that
$$1^2 + 2^2 + ... + n^2 = \frac{n(n+1)(2n+1)}{6} \quad n \geqq 1$$
by mathematical induction.

1. *Basis of induction.* For $n = 1$, we have
$$1^2 = \frac{1(1+1)(2+1)}{6}$$

2. *Induction step.* Assume that
$$1^2 + 2^2 + ... + k^2 = \frac{k(k+1)(2k+1)}{6}$$

   We have
$$1^2 + 2^2 + ... + k^2 + (k+1)^2 = \frac{k(k+1)(2k+1)}{6} + (k+1)^2$$
$$= \frac{(k+1)[k(2k+1) + 6(k+1)]}{6}$$
$$= \frac{(k+1)(2k^2 + 7k + 6)}{6}$$
$$= \frac{(k+1)(k+2)(2k+3)}{6}$$
$$= \frac{(k+1)[(k+1) + 1][2(k+1) + 1]}{6} \quad ■$$

Example 1.14 Show that any integer composed of 3^n identical digits is divisible by 3^n. (For example, 222 and 777 are divisible by 3; 222,222,222 and 555,555,555 are divisible by 9.) We shall prove the result by induction on n.

1. *Basis of induction.* For $n = 1$, we note that any 3-digit integer with three identical digits is divisible by 3.*
2. *Induction step.* Let x be an integer composed of 3^{k+1} identical digits. We note that x can be written as

$$x = y \times z$$

where y is an integer composed of 3^k identical digits and

$$z = 10^{2 \cdot 3k} + 10^{3k} + 1 = \underbrace{1000000 \ldots 01}_{3^k - 1 \, 0s}\underbrace{000000 \ldots 01}_{3^k - 1 \, 0s}$$

Since we assume that y is divisible by 3^k and z is clearly divisible by 3, we conclude that x is divisible by 3^{k+1}. ∎

Example 1.15 Show that $2^n > n^3$ for $n \geq 10$.

1. *Basis of induction.* For $n = 10$, $2^{10} = 1024$ which is larger than 10^3.
2. *Induction step.* Assume that $2^k > k^3$. Note that

$$2^{k+1} = 2 \cdot 2^k > \left(1 + \frac{1}{10}\right)^3 \cdot 2^k \geq \left(1 + \frac{1}{k}\right)^3 \cdot 2^k > \left(1 + \frac{1}{k}\right)^3 \cdot k^3 = (k+1)^3 \quad ∎$$

A more "powerful" form of the principle of mathematical induction, which is referred to as the *principle of strong mathematical induction*, can be stated as follows: For a given statement involving a natural number n, if we can show that

1'. The statement is true for $n = n_0$; and
2'. The statement is true for $n = k + 1$, assuming that the statement is true for $n_0 \leq n \leq k$,

then we can conclude that the statement is true for all natural numbers $n \geq n_0$.

We note that this is indeed a more powerful form of the principle of mathematical induction presented at the beginning of this section. Specifically, in the induction step, in order to prove that the statement is true for $n = k + 1$, we are *allowed* to make a stronger assumption in 2' (namely, the statement is true for $n_0 \leq n \leq k$) than in 2 above (namely, the statement is true for $n = k$.) In other words, the principle of strong mathematical induction enables us to make the same conclusion while assuming more. We leave the proof of the principle of strong mathematical induction to Prob. 1.53. We present now some examples:

Example 1.16 A jigsaw puzzle consists of a number of pieces. Two or more pieces with matched boundaries can be put together to form a "big" piece. To be more precise, we use the term *block* to refer to either a single piece or a number

---

* We remind the reader of the elementary result that an integer is divisible by 3 if the sum of its digits is divisible by 3.

of pieces with matched boundaries that are put together to form a "big" piece. Thus, we can simply say that blocks with matched boundaries can be put together to form another block. Finally, when all pieces are put together as one single block, the jigsaw puzzle is said to be solved. Putting two blocks with matched boundaries together is counted as one move. We shall use the principle of strong mathematical induction to prove that for a jigsaw puzzle with n pieces, it will always take $n - 1$ moves to solve the puzzle.

1. *Basis of induction.* For a jigsaw puzzle with one piece, it does not take any moves to solve the puzzle.

2. *Induction step.* Assume that for any jigsaw puzzle with n pieces, $1 \leq n \leq k$, it takes $n - 1$ moves to solve the puzzle. Now, consider a jigsaw puzzle with $k + 1$ pieces. For the last move that produces the solution of the puzzle, two blocks—one with n_1 pieces and the other with n_2, where $n_1 + n_2 = k + 1$—are put together to form a single block. According to the induction hypothesis, it takes $n_1 - 1$ moves to put together one block, and $n_2 - 1$ moves to put the other block together. Including the last move to unite the two blocks, the total number of moves is equal to

$$(n_1 - 1) + (n_2 - 1) + 1 = k + 1 - 1 = k \qquad \blacksquare$$

Example 1.17 We want to show that any positive integer n greater than or equal to 2 is either a prime or a product of primes.

1. *Basis of induction.* For $n = 2$, since 2 is a prime, the statement is true.

2. *Induction step.* Assume that the statement is true for any integer n, $2 \leqq n \leqq k$. For the integer $k + 1$, if $k + 1$ is a prime then the statement is true. If $k + 1$ is not a prime, then $k + 1$ can be written as pq, where $p \leqq k$ and $q \leqq k$. According to the induction hypothesis, p is either a prime or a product of primes. Also, q is either a prime or a product of primes. Consequently, pq is a product of primes. $\qquad \blacksquare$

Example 1.18 Suppose we wish to trace our family tree to identify our ancestors. Quite often, incomplete family records prohibit us from going back beyond a few generations. Figure 1.12*a* and *b* show two examples of family trees. We make a simple assumption, that for any of our ancestors, either we can trace both of his or her parents or we can trace neither of them. In a family tree, a person is referred as a "leaf" if we have no record to go on to trace his or her parents, and a person is referred to as an "internal node" if his or her parents have been traced.*

We want to show that in any family tree, the number of leaves is always one more than the number of internal nodes. We shall prove the statement by induction on n, the number of people in the family tree, using the principle of strong mathematical induction.

---

* We introduce these terms simply for the convenience of our presentation. They will be presented again formally in Chapter 5 when we study trees as a special class of graphs.

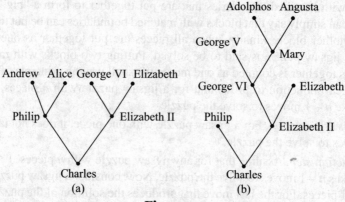

Fig. 1.12

1. *Basis of induction.* We note that the statement is true when $n = 1$. When there is only one person in a family tree, this person is a leaf, and there is no internal node.

2. *Induction step.* We assume that the statement is true for all family trees with n people, for $1 \leq n \leq k$. We want to show the statement is true for any family tree with $k + 1$ people. Consider the family tree of a man that has $k + 1$ people. Let p denote the number of leaves in the tree, and q denote the number of internal nodes in the tree. Since there are at least three people in the tree, both parents of this man are in the tree. Now, consider the family tree of each of his parents, as illustrated in Fig. 1.13. Let n_1 denote the number of people in his father's family tree, with p_1 of them being leaves and q_1 of them being internal nodes. Let n_2 denote the number of people in his mother's family tree, with p_2 of them being leaves and q_2 of them being internal nodes. Since $n_1 \leq k$ and $n_2 \leq k$, according to the induction hypothesis

$$p_1 = q_1 + 1$$
$$p_2 = q_2 + 1$$

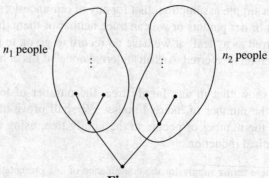

Fig. 1.13

Since

$$p = p_1 + p_2$$
$$q = q_1 + q_2 + 1$$

we have,

$$p = q_1 + q_2 + 2 = q + 1$$ ∎

1.8 PROPOSITIONS

A *proposition* is a declarative sentence that is either true or false. "It rained yesterday," "The pressure inside of the reactor chamber exceeds the safety threshold," and "We shall have chicken for dinner" are all examples of propositions. On the other hand, "What time is it?" and "Please submit your report as soon as possible" are not propositions because they are not declarative sentences, and, consequently, it is not meaningful to speak of them being true or false. Note that we do not rule out the possibility that a proposition is definitely true such as "15 is divisible by 3," and the possibility that a proposition is definitely false such as "Champaign is the state capital of Illinois." A proposition that is true under all circumstances is referred to as a *tautology*, and a proposition that is false under all circumstances is referred to as a *contradiction*.

We shall frequently refer to propositions by symbolic names. For example, if we let p denote the proposition, "Every student in the class passed the final examination," we can conveniently say that p is true or p is false depending on the outcome of the final examination. The two possibilities of a proposition being true or false are also referred to as the two possible values a proposition might assume. It is customary to use T to denote the value *true* and to use F to denote the value *false*. Consequently, instead of saying that the proposition, "Every student in the class passed the final examination" is true, we can simply say that the value of p is T.

The area of logic which deals with propositions is called the *propositional calculus*. It was developed by the great Greek philosopher Aristotle 2300 years ago.

1.9 LOGICAL CONNECTIVES

Two or more existing propositions can be combined to yield new propositions by using logical operators. These logical operators are also known as *logical connectives*. For example, the two propositions, "Water froze this morning" and "Temperature was below 0°C this morning" are equivalent. Also the two propositions, "He was born in 1934" and "He will be 60 years old in 1994" are equivalent. The two propositions, "I will go to the ball game tonight" and "There is no class tomorrow" might or might not be equivalent. On the other hand, the two propositions, "x is a prime number" and "x is not divisible by 2" are not equivalent because that x is not divisible by 2 does not necessarily mean that x is a prime number.

Propositions can be combined to yield new propositions. For example, in connection with the operation of a company, let p denote the proposition that the volume of the monthly sales is less than \$200,000 and let q denote the proposition that the monthly expenditure exceeds \$200,000. We might want to have a proposition to describe the situation where the volume of the monthly sales is less than \$200,000 and the monthly expenditure exceeds \$200,000. We might also want to have a proposition to describe the situation where either the volume of the monthly sales is less than \$200,000 or the monthly expenditure exceeds \$200,000. Clearly, these propositions are examples of "combinations" of the propositions p and q.

Let p and q be two propositions. We define the *disjunction* of p and q, denoted $p \vee q$, to be a proposition which is true when either one or both of p and q are true, and which is false when both p and q are false. In the above example on the operation of a company, the disjunction of the proposition that the monthly volume of sales is less than \$200,000 and the proposition that the monthly expenditure is more than \$200,000 is the proposition that either the monthly volume of sales is less than \$200,000 or the monthly expenditure exceeds \$200,000 or both.

Let us consider another example. Suppose p denotes the proposition, "He must be reading" and q represents the proposition, "He must be writing", then $p \vee q$ represents the proposition, "He must be reading or writing". We can denote disjunction by other symbols such as +, and *or*.

Very often, we use *or* in an exclusive sense. When the exclusive *or* is used to combine the propositions p and q, then the proposition "p or q (but not both)" is resulted. This resulting proposition is true when p is true and q is false, and when p is false and q is true. It is false when both p and q are true and when both p and q are false.

Let p and q be two propositions. We define the *exclusive or* of p and q, denoted by $p \oplus q$, to be a proposition which is true when exactly one of p and q is true and is false otherwise. Suppose p represents the proposition, "I shall complete my homework" and q represents the proposition, "I shall go to the school". Then, $p \oplus q$ represents the proposition, "I shall complete my homework or go to the school (but not both)".

Let p and q be two propositions. We define the *conjunction* of p and q, denoted by $p \wedge q$, to be a proposition which is true when both p and q are true, and is false when either one or both of p and q are false. In the foregoing example concerning the operation of a company, the conjunction of the proposition that the monthly volume of sales is less than \$200,000 and the proposition that the monthly expenditure is more than \$200,000 is the proposition that both the monthly volume of sales is less than \$200,000 and the monthly expenditure exceeds \$200,000.

Let us consider another example. Suppose p represents the proposition, "Ram is a boy" and q represents the proposition, "Sita is a girl". So, the solution for $p \wedge q$ is "Ram is a boy and Sita is a girl". According to the truth table, $p \wedge q$ and $q \wedge p$ have the same truth values. Therefore, the statement which contains a conjunction has different meanings for specific purpose. For example, let us consider the proposition, "Sun is red and sky is blue". We can also write the same proposition as, "Sky is blue and sun is red". But, if the proposition is, "He bought a chair and sat on it" then we cannot write, "He sat on it and bought a chair". Here, the meaning of 'and' is of '*and then*'. So, the conjunction '∧' has different meanings for different situations. We can denote conjunction by other symbols such as '&', a dot (.) or 'AND'.

Let p be a proposition. We define the *negation* of p, denoted $\bar{p}$,* to be a proposition which is true when p is false, and is false when p is true. $\bar{p}$ is read as "not p" and interpreted as "It is not the case that p". Thus, the negation of the proposition that the monthly volume of sales is less than \$200,000 is the proposition that the monthly volume of sales exceeds or equals \$200,000.

Let us consider another example. Suppose p represents, "Hari is a batsman". Then, $\bar{p}$ represents, "Hari is not a batsman".

A proposition obtained from the combination of other propositions is referred to as a *compound* proposition. A proposition that is not a combination of other propositions is referred to as an *atomic* proposition. In other words, a compound proposition is made up of atomic propositions. For example, if p and q are two atomic propositions, then $p \wedge q$, $\bar{p}$, $(p \wedge q) \vee (\bar{p} \wedge q)$, $p \vee (\bar{q})$ are compound propositions. The compound propositions mentioned above are statement formulas derived from the statement variables p and q. So, p and q are called as the components of the statement formulas. It may be noticed that, we have used parentheses in some cases to avoid ambiguity. The use of parenthesis is strongly recommended as $\neg(p \wedge q)$ means negation of the conjunction of p and q whereas $(\neg p) \wedge q$ means negation of p and then conjunction with q. Similarly $\neg(p \vee q)$ $\wedge (p \wedge q)$ means that conjunction of $\neg(p \vee q)$ and $(p \wedge q)$. But for simplicity, we can reduce the number of parenthesis in some cases. For example, we can assume that $\neg p \vee q$ is equivalent to $(\neg p) \vee q$. A convenient and precise way to describe the definition of a compound proposition is a table such as those shown in Fig. 1.14 where the values of a compound proposition are specified for all possible choices of the values of the atomic propositions of the compound proposition. Specifically, the tables in Fig. 1.14 show the definitions of the disjunction, exclusive or and conjunction of two propositions and that of the negation of a proposition. Such tables are called *truth tables* for the compound propositions.

p	q	$p \vee q$		p	q	$p \oplus q$		p	q	$p \wedge q$		p	$\bar{p}$
F	F	F		T	T	F		F	F	F		F	T
F	T	T		T	F	T		F	T	F		T	F
T	F	T		F	T	T		T	F	F			
T	T	T		F	F	F		T	T	T			

Fig. 1.14

* In the literature, the notation $-p$ or $\neg p$ or $\sim p$ is also used.

Truth tables help to determine the truth values of compound propositions. There are various combinations of the components of compound proposition in the truth table. Compound propositions have many components. If there are n distinct components in a compound proposition, then we require 2^n possible combinations of truth values in order to construct the truth table. For example, to construct the truth table for $p \vee q$, we require $2^2 = 4$ combinations of truth values as there are 2 components (p and q) involved in $p \vee q$.

Example 1.19 Construct the truth table for $(p \wedge q) \wedge \overline{p}$.

p	q	$p \wedge q$	$\overline{p}$	$(p \wedge q) \wedge \overline{p}$
T	T	T	F	F
T	F	F	F	F
F	T	F	T	F
F	F	F	T	F

■

1.10 CONDITIONALS AND BICONDITIONALS

There are two other important ways to construct compound propositions that we want to present: Consider the propositions, "The temperature exceeds 70°C" and "The alarm will be sounded," which we shall denote p and q, respectively. Also, consider the proposition, "If the temperature exceeds 70°C then the alarm will be sounded," which we shall denote r. It is easy to see that r is true if the alarm is sounded when the temperature exceeds 70°C (both p and q are true), and r is false if the alarm is not sounded when the temperature exceeds 70°C (p is true and q is false). On the other hand, when the temperature is equal to or less than 70°C (p is false), the proposition r *cannot possibly be false*, no matter whether the alarm is sounded or not. Consequently, we say that r is also true when the temperature is equal to or less than 70°C.

Let us now formalize the notion of combining two propositions p and q to form one that reads "If p then q" introduced in the example above. Let p and q be two propositions. We define a proposition "If p then q," denoted $p \rightarrow q$, which is true if both p and q are true or if p is false, and is false if p is true and q is false, as specified in the truth table in Fig. 1.15. The compound proposition "If p then q" also reads "p implies q and is called a *conditional statement*. A conditional statement is also called as an *implication*. Here, the statement p is known as the antecedent and q the consequent. According to the definition, it is not mandatory that there should be any kind of relation between p and q in order to construct $p \rightarrow q$.

p	q	$p \rightarrow q$
F	F	T
F	T	T
T	F	F
T	T	T

Fig. 1.15

Example 1.20 Write the following statement in symbolic form: The hut will be destroyed if there is a cyclone.

Solution: Let the statements be denoted as follows:

p: The hut will be destroyed.
q: There is a cyclone.

It may be observed that the given statement uses "if" in the sense of "If … then …". So, the given statement may be rewritten as "If there is a cyclone, then the hut will be destroyed. Now, this statement can be symbolized as $q \rightarrow p$.   ■

A reader who sees the compound proposition "If p then q" for the first time would probably feel a bit uncertain about the fact that the compound statement is true whenever p is false, no matter whether q is true or not. Let us examine a few more examples. Consider the statement "If you try then you will succeed." Clearly, if you try and succeed, the statement is true. If you try and fail, the statement is false. However, if you did not try then there is no way for you to argue that the statement is false. Since not being false means being true, we can conclude that if you did not try then the statement is true. As another example, consider the order from the security officer of a company that every visitor must wear a badge. Note that the order can be rephrased as a proposition "If one is a visitor then one wears a badge." To check whether the order has been enforced (whether the proposition is true), we shall stop each person in the plant one by one. If she is a visitor, we can determine whether the order has been enforced by observing whether she is wearing a badge. On the other hand, if she is not a visitor then there is no way we can possibly conclude that the order has not been enforced, and hence the statement is true. As another example, we recall that in Sec. 1.1 we make a statement that the empty set is a subset of any set. According to the definition of a set being a subset of another set, this statement can be rephrased as "If x is an element of the empty set then x is an element of any set". Clearly, the statement is true.

Example 1.21   John made the following statements:

1. I love Lucy.
2. If I love Lucy then I also love Vivian.

Given that John either told the truth or lied in both cases, determine whether John really loves Lucy. Suppose John lied. Then according to statement 1, he does not love Lucy. It follows that statement 2 must be true, which is a contradiction. Consequently, John must have told the truth, and we can confirm that he really loves Lucy.

One can also be a bit more formal by letting p denote the statement, "John loves Lucy," and q denote the statement, "John loves Vivian." The truth table in Fig. 1.15 shows that it is possible for both p and $p \rightarrow q$ to be true but not possible for both of them to be false.   ■

There are some related *implications* which can be constructed from $p \rightarrow q$. For the proposition $p \rightarrow q$, the proposition $q \rightarrow p$ is called its *converse*. The proposition $\overline{q} \rightarrow \overline{p}$ is called the *contrapositive* of $p \rightarrow q$. The proposition $\overline{p} \rightarrow \overline{q}$

▼

is called the *inverse* of $p \to q$. It may be observed that, only the contrapositive, $\bar{q} \to \bar{p}$, of an implication $p \to q$ has the same truth value as $p \to q$. The converse, $q \to p$, and the inverse, $\bar{p} \to \bar{q}$ do not have the same truth value as $p \to q$.

Example 1.22   Give the converse, contrapositive and inverse of the following implication: "If it rains today, I will go to college tomorrow."

Solution: The converse, contrapositive and inverse of the above implication can be written as follows:

Converse: If I will go to college tomorrow, then it would have rained today.

Contrapositive: If I do not go to college tomorrow, then it will not have rained today.

Inverse: If it does not rain today, then I will not go to college tomorrow.   ■

Let p denote the proposition, "A new computer will be acquired" and q denote the proposition, "Additional funding is available." Consider the proposition, "A new computer will be acquired if and only if additional funding is available," which we shall denote r. Clearly, r is true if a new computer is indeed acquired when additional funding is available. (Both p and q are true.) The proposition r is also true if no new computer is acquired when additional funding is not available. (Both p and q are false.) On the other hand, r is false if a new computer is acquired although no additional funding is available (p is true and q is false), or if no new computer is acquired although additional funding is available (p is false and q is true).

Let p and q be two propositions. We define a proposition, "p if and only if q," denoted $p \leftrightarrow q$, which is true if both p and q are true or if both p and q are false, and which is false if p is true while q is false and if p is false while q is true. The compound proposition $p \leftrightarrow q$ is also interpreted as "p is

p	q	$p \leftrightarrow q$
F	F	T
F	T	F
T	F	F
T	T	T

Fig. 1.16

necessary and sufficient for q" and is called a *biconditional statement*. The truth table in Fig. 1.16 shows the definition of $p \leftrightarrow q$.

Example 1.23   An island has two tribes of natives. Any native from the first tribe always tells the truth, while any native from the other tribe always lies. You arrive at the island and ask a native if there is gold on the island. He answers, "There is gold on the island if and only if I always tell the truth." Which tribe is he from? Is there gold on the island? As it turns out, we cannot determine which tribe he is from. However, we can determine if there is gold on the island. Let p denote the proposition that he always tells the truth, and q denote the proposition that there is gold on the island. Thus, his answer is the proposition $p \leftrightarrow q$. Suppose that he always tells the truth; that is, the proposition p is true. Furthermore, his answer to our question must be true; that is, $p \leftrightarrow q$ is true. Consequently, q must be true. Suppose he always lies; that is, the proposition p is false. Also, his answer to our question is a lie, which means that $p \leftrightarrow q$ is false. Consequently, q must be true. Thus, in both cases we can conclude that there is gold on the island, although the native could have been from either tribe.　■

We can combine compound propositions to yield new propositions. For example, let p and q be propositions. We have $p \wedge q$, $\bar{p} \wedge \bar{q}$ and, consequently,

$$((p \wedge q) \vee (\bar{p} \wedge \bar{q})) \to p \tag{1.7}$$

as compound propositions where parentheses are used as delimiters. The value of a compound proposition can always be determined by constructing its truth table in a step-by-step manner. As the table in Fig. 1.17 shows, the entries for the columns corresponding to the compound propositions can be constructed column by column from left to right.

p	q	$p \wedge q$	$\bar{p} \wedge \bar{q}$	$(p \wedge q) \vee (\bar{p} \wedge \bar{q})$	$((p \wedge q) \vee (\bar{p} \wedge \bar{q})) \to p$
F	F	F	T	T	F
F	T	F	F	F	T
T	F	F	F	F	T
T	T	T	F	T	T

Fig. 1.17

1.11　WELL-FORMED FORMULAS

We have already introduced the notion of a statement formula in earlier sections. A statement formula is an expression which consists of variables, parentheses, and connective symbols. All such expressions are not statement formulas. Now, we shall present a formal definition of a statement formula. This is also called as a *well-formed formula (wff)*. A well-formed formula can be produced by using the following rules:

Rule 1　A statement variable itself is a well-formed formula.

Rule 2　If p is a well-formed formula then $\bar{p}$ is also a well-formed formula.

Rule 3　If p and q are two well-formed formulas then $(p \vee q)$, $(p \wedge q)$, $(p \to q)$, and $(p \leftrightarrow q)$ are also well-formed formulas.

Rule 4　A string of symbols consisting of the statement variables, connectives, and parentheses is said to be a well-formed formula, if and only if it can be produced by applying *rules 1, 2 and 3* finitely many times.

Example 1.24　The following, are some well-formed formulas according to this definition:

$$(\overline{p \wedge q}),\ (p \to (q \to r)),\ (p \to (p \wedge q)),\ ((p \to q) \leftrightarrow (\bar{p} \vee q))$$

To reduce the number of parentheses in the well-formed formulas, some conventions may be introduced. For example, we shall omit the outmost parentheses for our convenience. So, we shall write $\overline{p \wedge q}$ instead of $(\overline{p \wedge q})$, $p \to (q \to r)$ instead of $(p \to (q \to r))$, $p \to (p \to q)$ instead of $(p \to (p \wedge q))$ and $(p \to$

$q) \leftrightarrow (\bar{p} \vee q)$ instead of $((p \rightarrow q) \leftrightarrow (\bar{p} \vee q))$. Since, the only formulas we shall discuss in this chapter are well-formed formulas, we shall simply use the term 'formula' for well-formed formulas. ∎

1.12 TAUTOLOGIES

A truth table which is constructed for a given formula represents the truth value which results when the variables are replaced by statement formulas. It is the final column of the truth table which decides the truth value for the whole statement formula. The truth values in the last column of the truth table generally depend upon the truth values of the statement variables rather than on the formulas themselves. But, for the sake of easiness, we use the term "the truth value of a formula" to mean the values of the entries in the last column of the truth table. It is possible to have a case where all the truth values in the last column can be True (T) or can be False (F).

Example 1.25   Let us consider the truth tables for $p \wedge \bar{p}$ and $p \vee \bar{p}$.

Case 1: $p \wedge \bar{p}$, here, all the entries in the last column are false.

p	$\bar{p}$	$p \wedge \bar{p}$
T	F	F
F	T	F

Truth table for $p \wedge \bar{p}$

Case 2: $p \wedge \bar{p}$, here, all the entries in the last column are true.

p	$\bar{p}$	$p \vee \bar{p}$
T	F	T
F	T	T

Truth table for $p \vee \bar{p}$ ∎

Such a statement formula whose truth value is always true regardless of the truth values of the variables concerned is called a *universally valid formula* or a *tautology* and the statement formula whose all truth values are false, is called a *contradiction*.

It may be observed that the conjunction of two tautologies is also a tautology. If p and q be two statement formulas which are tautologies, then $p \wedge q$ is also a tautology.

A formula p is called a *substitution instance* of another formula q, if p can be generated from q by substituting formulas for some variables of q. Here, the condition required is that the same formula is substituted for the same variable each time it occurs.

Example 1.26   Let $(p \wedge q) \to p$ be a formula.

If we replace p by $p \leftrightarrow q$,

Then

$((p \leftrightarrow q) \wedge q \to (p \leftrightarrow q))$ is a substitution instance of the given formula.

It should be remembered that the substitutions are performed only for the atomic formulas, but not for the compound formulas. So, $p \to q$ is not a substitution instance of $p \to \bar{r}$ because, in this case r should be replaced and not $\bar{r}$. It may be observed that, the substitution instance of a tautology is also a tautology.   ■

1.13   LOGICAL EQUIVALENCES

Let p and q be two statement formulas and $a_1, a_2, \ldots a_n$ represent all the variables contained in both p and q. If there exists an assignment of truth values to the statement variables $a_1, a_2, \ldots a_n$ and the resulting truth values of p and q, such that the truth value of p is equal to the truth value of q for each of the 2^n possible sets of truth values, then p and q are said to be *logically equivalent* or simply *equivalent*. In other words, we can say that, the compound propositions which have the same truth values in all possible cases are called *logically equivalent*. Let us assume that the variables and the assignment of truth values to the variables appear in the same order in both the truth tables of p and q. It may be observed that, if p and q are equivalent, then the final columns in both the truth tables of p and q are identical.

For example:

i. $p \vee p$ is equivalent to p.

ii. $p \vee \bar{q}$ is equivalent to $\bar{q} \vee p$.

iii. $\bar{q} \vee q$ is equivalent to $p \vee \bar{p}$.

From the definition of *bi-conditional*, it can be observed that $p \leftrightarrow q$ is true whenever p and q have the same truth values. So, we can say that p and q are *logically equivalent* if $p \leftrightarrow q$ is a *tautology*. Conversely, if $p \leftrightarrow q$ is a *tautology*, then p and q are *equivalent*. We represent the equivalence of two statement formulas, say p and q, by writing $p \equiv q$, which may be read, as "p is equivalent to q". It can be proved that equivalence of two statement formulas is a symmetric relation, i.e. if $p \equiv q$ then $q \equiv p$. Also, this relationship is transitive, i.e. if $p \equiv q$, and $q \equiv r$, then $p \equiv r$.

We can determine whether two propositions are equivalent by examining their truth tables. For example, according to the truth tables in Figs. 1.14 and 1.17, the proposition in (1. 7) is equivalent to the proposition $p \vee q$. As another example, we note that the two propositions $p \leftrightarrow q$ and $(p \to q) \wedge (q \to p)$ are equivalent by comparing the truth tables in Figs. 1.16 and 1.18. Indeed, we realize that the choice of the notation $p \leftrightarrow q$ is not accidental.

p	q	$p \wedge q$	$\bar{p} \wedge \bar{q}$	$(p \wedge q) \vee (\bar{p} \wedge \bar{q})$
F	F	F	T	T
F	T	F	F	F
T	F	F	F	F
T	T	T	F	T

Fig. 1.18

Example 1.27 There are two restaurants next to each other. One has a sign that says, "Good food is not cheap," and the other has a sign that says, "Cheap food is not good." Are the signs saying the same thing? Let g denote the proposition that the food is good, and c denote the proposition that the food is cheap. The first sign

g	c	$\bar{g}$	$\bar{c}$	$g \to \bar{c}$	$c \to \bar{g}$
F	F	T	T	T	T
F	T	T	F	T	T
T	F	F	T	T	T
T	T	F	F	F	F

Fig. 1.19

can then be written as $g \to \bar{c}$, and the second sign be written as $c \to \bar{g}$. The truth table in Fig. 1.19 shows that indeed the two signs say the same thing. ∎

Example 1.28 As a final example, we ask the reader to verify that the two propositions

$$((p \wedge q) \vee (p \wedge r)) \to s$$

and

$$((\bar{p} \vee (\bar{q} \wedge \bar{r})) \vee s$$

are equivalent. ∎

We shall discuss the subject of constructing, manipulating, and simplifying compound propositions in Chapter 11, after we have developed the concept of boolean algebras.

A reader probably will recognize that the combination of propositions to yield new propositions bears a strong similarity to the combination of sets to yield new sets. To be specific, we note the similarity between the notions of the union of two sets and of the disjunction of two propositions, between the notions of the intersection of two sets and of the conjunction of two propositions, and between the notions of the complement of a set and of the negation of a proposition. Such similarities are not accidental, as we shall see in Chapter 11.

1.14 THEORY OF INFERENCE FOR STATEMENT CALCULUS

One of the important functions of logic is to provide principles of reasoning or rules of inference. The theory associated with these rules is known as *inference theory* since it deals with the inferring of a conclusion from some premises or facts or axioms. The process of deriving a conclusion from a set of premises by using the standard rules of inference, is called a *formal proof* or *deduction*. In a formal proof, each rule of inference which is used at any step of the derivation is explicitly mentioned.

Let us see what we mean by the rules and theory of inference. The rules of inference mean the criteria for finding the validity of an argument. The rules are expressed in the forms of statements involved.

In any argument, a conclusion is said to be true if the premises are considered to be true, and the reasoning used in derivation of the conclusion follows some standard rules of inference. This type of argument is called *sound*. In logic, we give importance on the discussion of the rules of inference by using which conclusions are derived. Any conclusion which is derived by using these rules is called a *valid conclusion* and the corresponding argument is called a *valid argument*. In other words, we can say that in logic, our important concern is the *validity* but not necessarily the *soundness* of an argument.

1.14.1 Validity Using Truth Tables

Let p and q be two statement formulas. We define "q is a valid conclusion of the premise p" or "q logically follows from p" if and only if $p \rightarrow q$ is a tautology. We can extend this definition to include a set of formulas. We say that C is a valid conclusion of the set of premises $\{A_1, A_2, ..., A_n\}$ if and only if $A_1 \wedge A_2 \wedge ... \wedge A_n \rightarrow C$ is a tautology. Suppose a set of premises and a conclusion is given to us. Then, we can determine whether the conclusion is a valid conclusion of the given premises by constructing truth tables.

Theoretically, it may be possible to determine in a finite number of steps whether a conclusion is a valid conclusion of the given set of premises by constructing truth tables. But, when the number of variables present in all the statement formulas is large, then this method seems to be very much tedious. This limitation suggests investigating some other possible techniques. We shall discuss some more possible techniques in the next section.

1.14.2 Rules of Inference

Now, we present the derivation process by which one can justify that a particular formula is a valid conclusion of a given set of premises. Before describing the derivation process, we present three rules of inference which we call *Rule P*, *Rule T* and *Rule CP*.

Rule P: A premise can be inserted at any point in the derivation.

Rule T: If the formula q is tautologically implied by any one or more of the previous formulas in a derivation, then q can be inserted in the derivation.

Rule CP: *Rule CP* stands for rule of conditional proof. It is also known as *deduction theorem*. It states that, if we can derive a formula q from p and a set of premises then we can derive $p \rightarrow q$ from the set of premises alone.

Rule CP, is used in the cases, where the conclusion is of the form $p \rightarrow q$. In these cases, p is taken as an extra premise and q is derived from the given premises and from p.

The tautology $(p \wedge (p \rightarrow q)) \rightarrow q$ is the basis for the rule of inference, called *modus ponens* or *law of detachment*.

Before describing the actual process of derivation, we present some important implications and equivalences in Tables 1.1 and 1.2 that will be used very often. The implications and equivalences which will be used more often than the others are given special names.

Now, we present some examples to explain the use of some of the important implications and equivalences in the process of derivation.

Example 1.29 Let the implication, "If it rains today then I shall carry an umbrella" and its hypothesis, "It is raining today", are true. Then, by modus ponens, it is clear that the conclusion of the implication, "I shall carry umbrella" is true. ∎

Example 1.30 Show that q is a valid inference from the premises $p \rightarrow q$, $p \vee q$, and $\overline{q}$.

Solution:

{1}	(1) $p \rightarrow q$	Rule P
{2}	(2) $\overline{q}$	Rule P
{1, 2}	(3) $\overline{p}$	Rule T, (1), (2), and modus tollens
{4}	(4) $p \vee q$	Rule P
{1, 2, 4}	(5) q	Rule T, (3), (4) and disjunctive syllogism.

Table 1.1	Some Important Implications

Rule No.	Tautology
IM_1	$p \wedge q \rightarrow p$ (simplification)
IM_2	$p \wedge q \rightarrow q$ (simplification)
IM_3	$p \rightarrow (p \vee q)$ (addition)
IM_4	$q \rightarrow (p \vee q)$ (addition)
IM_5	$\overline{p} \rightarrow (p \rightarrow q)$
IM_6	$q \rightarrow (p \rightarrow q)$
IM_7	$\overline{(p \rightarrow q)} \rightarrow p$
IM_8	$\overline{(p \rightarrow q)} \rightarrow \overline{q}$
IM_9	$p, q \rightarrow p \wedge q$ (conjunction)
IM_{10}	$[\overline{p}, (p \vee q)] \rightarrow q$ (disjunctive syllogism)
IM_{11}	$[p, (p \rightarrow q)] \rightarrow q$ (modus ponens)
IM_{12}	$[\overline{q}, (p \rightarrow q)] \rightarrow \overline{p}$ (modus tollens)
IM_{13}	$[p \rightarrow q, q \rightarrow r] \rightarrow (p \rightarrow r)$ (hypothetical syllogism)
IM_{14}	$[p \vee q, p \rightarrow r, q \rightarrow r] \rightarrow r$ (dilemma)
IM_{15}	$[p \vee q, \overline{p} \vee r] \rightarrow (q \vee r)$ (resolution)

| **Table 1.2** | Some Important Equivalences |

EQ_1	$\bar{p} \equiv p$ (double negation law)
EQ_2	$p \vee q \equiv q \vee p$ (commutative law)
EQ_3	$p \wedge q \equiv q \wedge p$ (commutative law)
EQ_4	$(p \vee q) \vee r \equiv p \vee (q \vee r)$ (associative law)
EQ_5	$(p \wedge q) \wedge r \equiv p \wedge (q \wedge r)$ (associative law)
EQ_6	$p \vee (q \wedge r) \equiv (p \vee q) \wedge (p \vee r)$ (distributive law)
EQ_7	$p \wedge (q \vee r) \equiv (p \wedge q) \vee (p \wedge r)$ (distributive law)
EQ_8	$\overline{p \vee q} \equiv \bar{p} \wedge \bar{q}$ (De Morgan's law)
EQ_9	$\overline{p \wedge q} \equiv \bar{p} \vee \bar{q}$ (De Morgan's law)
EQ_{10}	$p \vee p \equiv p$ (idempotent law)
EQ_{11}	$p \wedge p \equiv p$ (idempotent law)
EQ_{12}	$r \vee (p \wedge \bar{p}) \equiv r$
EQ_{13}	$r \wedge (p \vee \bar{p}) \equiv r$
EQ_{14}	$r \vee (p \vee \bar{p}) \equiv T$
EQ_{15}	$r \wedge (p \wedge \bar{p}) \equiv F$
EQ_{16}	$p \rightarrow q \equiv \bar{p} \vee q$
EQ_{17}	$\overline{p \rightarrow q} \equiv p \wedge \bar{q}$
EQ_{18}	$p \rightarrow q \equiv \bar{q} \rightarrow \bar{p}$
EQ_{19}	$p \rightarrow (q \rightarrow r) \equiv (p \wedge q) \rightarrow r$
EQ_{20}	$\overline{p \leftrightarrow q} \equiv p \leftrightarrow \bar{q}$
EQ_{21}	$p \leftrightarrow q \equiv (p \rightarrow q) \wedge (q \rightarrow p)$
EQ_{22}	$(p \leftrightarrow q) \equiv (p \wedge q) \vee (\bar{p} \wedge \bar{q})$
EQ_{23}	$p \vee (p \wedge q) \equiv p$ (absorption law)
EQ_{24}	$p \wedge (p \vee q) \equiv p$ (absorption law)
EQ_{25}	$p \vee \bar{p} \equiv T$ (negation law)
EQ_{26}	$p \wedge \bar{p} \equiv F$ (negation law)

Here, the first column of numbers for each row represents the premises on which the formula in the row depends. The second column of numbers shows the formula as well as the row of derivation in which it occurs. In the last column, *P* or *T* represents the rule of inference followed by a comment describing from which formulas and tautology that particular formula has been derived. For example, the fifth row represents that the formula in this row is numbered as (5) and has been derived from the premises in (1), (2) and (4). In this row, the formula *q* has been derived by applying *Rule T* on formulas present in (3) and (4) and by using the implication *disjunctive syllogism*. ∎

Example 1.31 Show that $\bar{p}$ is tautologically implied by $\overline{(p \wedge \bar{q})}, \bar{q} \vee r, \bar{r}$.

Solution:

{1}	(1) $\overline{(p \wedge \bar{q})}$	*Rule P*
{1}	(2) $\bar{p} \vee q$	*Rule T*, (1) and De Morgan's law

{1}	(3) $p \to q$	Rule T, (2) and EQ_{16} $(p \to q \equiv \bar{p} \vee q)$
{4}	(4) $\bar{q} \vee r$	Rule P
{4}	(5) $q \to r$	Rule T, (4) and EQ_{16} $(p \to q \equiv \bar{p} \vee q)$
{1, 4}	(6) $p \to r$	Rule T, (3), (5) and hypothetical syllogism
{7}	(7) $\bar{r}$	Rule P
{1, 4, 7}	(8) $\bar{p}$	Rule T, (6), (7) and modus tollens. ∎

Example 1.32   Derive the following using the *CP* rule:

$$(\bar{p} \vee q, \bar{q} \vee r, r \to s) \to (p \to s)$$

Solution: According to the *CP* rule, here, we will include p as an additional premise and show s first.

{1}	(1) $\bar{p} \vee q$	Rule P
{1}	(2) $p \to q$	Rule T, (1) and EQ_{16} $(p \to q \equiv \bar{p} \vee q)$
{3}	(3) p	P (assumed premise)
{1, 3}	(4) q	Rule T, (2),(3) modus ponens
{5}	(5) $\bar{q} \vee r$	Rule P
{1, 3, 5}	(6) r	Rule T, (4), (5) and disjunctive syllogism
{7}	(7) $r \to s$	Rule P
{1, 3, 5, 7}	(8) s	Rule T, (6), (7) and modus ponens.
{1, 5, 7}	(9) $p \to s$	Rule CP. ∎

1.14.3   Consistency of Premises

A set of formulas $A_1, A_2, \ldots A_m$ is said to be consistent if their conjunction has the truth value T for some assignment of the truth values to the atomic variables appearing in $A_1, A_2, \ldots A_m$.

If for every assignment of the truth values to the atomic variables at least one of the formulas $A_1, A_2, \ldots A_m$ is false, so that their conjunction is identically false, then the formulas $A_1, A_2, \ldots A_m$ are called inconsistent.

Alternatively, a set of formulas $A_1, A_2, \ldots A_m$ is inconsistent if their conjunction implies a contradiction, that is,

$A_1 \wedge A_2 \wedge \ldots \wedge A_m \to B \wedge \bar{B}$, where B is any formula. It may be noted that $B \wedge \bar{B}$ is a contradiction and it is necessary and sufficient for the implication that $A_1 \wedge A_2 \wedge \ldots \wedge A_m$ is a contradiction.

This notion of inconsistency is used in a procedure called *proof by contradiction* or *reduction* and *absurd* or *indirect method of proof*.

Example 1.33   Show that the following system is inconsistent:

$$p \to q, p \to r, q \to \bar{r}, p$$

Solution:

{1}	(1) $p \to q$	Rule P
{2}	(2) p	Rule P

{1, 2}	(3) q	*Rule T*, (1), (2) and modus ponens
{4}	(4) $p \to r$	*Rule P*
{2, 4}	(5) r	*Rule T*, (2), (4) and modus ponnes
{1, 2, 4}	(6) $q \wedge r$	*Rule T*, (3), (5) and conjunction
{7}	(7) $q \to \bar{r}$	*Rule P*
{7}	(8) $\bar{q} \vee \bar{r}$	*Rule T*, (7) and EQ$_{16}$ ($p \to q \equiv \bar{p} \vee q$)
{7}	(9) $\overline{q \wedge r}$	*Rule T*, (8) and De Morgan's law
{1, 2, 4, 7}	(10) $(q \wedge r) \wedge \overline{q \wedge r}$	*Rule T*, (6), (9) and conjunction.

Since, we obtain $(q \wedge r) \wedge \overline{q \wedge r}$, which is a contradiction, so we conclude that the given system is inconsistent. ∎

Example 1.34 Using indirect method, show that

$$(r \to \bar{q}, r \vee s, s \to \bar{q}, p \to q) \to \bar{p}.$$

Solution: Following the indirect method, we introduce p as an additional premise and show that this additional premise leads to a contradiction.

{1}	(1) $p \to q$	*Rule P*
{2}	(2) p	*Rule P* (assumed)
{1, 2}	(3) q	*Rule T*, (1), (2) and modus ponens
{4}	(4) $s \to \bar{q}$	*Rule P*
{1, 2, 4}	(5) $\bar{s}$	*Rule T*, (3), (4) and modus tollens
{6}	(6) $r \vee s$	*Rule P*
{1, 2, 4, 6}	(7) r	*Rule T*, (5), (6) disjunctive syllogism
{8}	(8) $r \to \bar{q}$	*Rule P*
{8}	(9) $\bar{r} \vee \bar{q}$	*Rule T*, (8) and EQ$_{16}$ ($p \to q \equiv \bar{p} \vee q$)
{8}	(10) $\overline{r \wedge q}$	*Rule T*, (8) and De Morgan's law
{1, 2, 4, 6}	(11) $r \wedge q$	*Rule T*, (7), (3) and conjunction
{1, 2, 4, 6, 8}	(12) $r \wedge q \wedge \overline{r \wedge q}$	*Rule T*, (10), (11) and conjunction.

Hence it leads to a contradiction. ∎

1.15 PREDICATE CALCULUS

After getting some idea about statements and statement formulas, now let us pay attention to the concept of a predicate in an atomic statement. The logic associated with the predicates in any statement is called *predicate logic*. In this section, we shall discuss the predicates and predicate calculus. Let us first know what these predicates are?

Consider the two statements:

1. Dog is an animal.
2. Cat is an animal.

Since both the statements are about two individuals which are animals, so expressing these statements by symbols will require two different symbols to denote them.

But, if a new symbol is introduced to denote the phrase, "is an animal" and if by some method we join it with symbols denoting the name of individuals, we are done. The part, "is an animal" is called a *predicate*. Writing the two statements in this form will reveal the common feature also.

We shall use capital letters to represent predicates and lower case letters to represent the names of individuals or objects in general. So, a statement can be written symbolically in terms of the predicate letter followed by the name(s) of the object(s) to which the predicate is applied. Let us again consider the above two statements. Suppose, the predicate, "is an animal" is represented by the predicate letter A, "Dog' by d and "Cat" by c. Then the statements (1) and (2) can be written as $A(d)$ and $A(c)$. In general, any statement of the type "r is S", where S is a predicate and r is the subject, can be written as $S(r)$. A statement which is expressed by using a predicate letter must have at least one name of an object associated with the predicate.

A predicate may require more than one name to express a statement. A predicate that requires $n(n > 0)$ names is known as an n-place predicate. Let us understand it with some examples:

3. The predicate A in (1) and (2) is a one place predicate

4. Consider the statement: x is greater than y.

Suppose predicate G represents "greater than". Then, G is a 2-place predicate since two names are required to express the statement as $G(x, y)$.

In general, if P is an n-place predicate letter and $x_1, x_2, ..., x_n$ are the names of objects, then, $P(x_1, x_2, ..., x_n)$ denotes a statement.

1.16 THE STATEMENT FUNCTION, VARIABLE AND QUANTIFIERS

Consider the phrase, "y is a man". Let this be expressed as $M(y)$. It may be noted that $M(y)$ is not a statement. However, if y is replaced by a name an such as a and a, b, s etc. then it will result in a statement. For example, $M(a)$, $M(b)$, and $M(s)$ represent statements.

We define a *simple statement function* of one variable as an expression which consists of a predicate symbol and an individual variable. Here, $M(y)$ is a simple statement function of one variable. The statement function turns to be a statement when the variable is replaced by the name of an object. The statement which is obtained from the statement function by a replacement is called a *substitution instance* of the statement function.

We can form *compound statement functions* by combining one or more simple statement functions and the logical connectives. Suppose $M(x)$ represents "x is a man" and $V(x)$ represents "x is a vegetarian". Then, we can compose many compound statements functions such as

$$M(x) \wedge V(x), \sim M(x) \vee V(x), \sim V(x) \text{ etc.}$$

It is possible to form statement functions of two variables by using statement function of one variable.

For example, let $M(x)$: x is a man

$V(y)$: y is a vegetarian,

Then, $M(x) \wedge V(y)$: x is a man and y is a vegetarian.

But, always it is not possible to express statement functions of two variables using statement functions of one variable.

So far, we have known that statements can be obtained from statement functions by replacing the variables with names of objects. There is another method to obtain the statements. In order to understand this alternative method, let us first consider the following statements:

5. All dogs are animals.

6. Every rose is red.

Clearly, each one is a statement about all individuals or objects belonging to a particular set.

We can also write the above statements in the following way:

(5′) For all x, if x is a dog, then x is an animal.

(6′) For all x, if x is a rose then x is red.

Now, if a symbol is introduced which denote the phrase "For all x" then the statements (5′) and (6′) can be symbolized.

We use the symbol $(\forall x)$ or (x) to represent the phrase "For all x". Now, using the following:

$D(x)$: x is a dog

$A(x)$: x is an animal

$R(x)$: x is red

$C(x)$: x is rose

(5′) and (6′) can be written as

5″. $\forall x(D(x) \rightarrow A(x))$

6″. $\forall x(C(x) \rightarrow R(x))$.

The symbols (x) or $\forall x$ are called *universal quantifiers* and represent "for all x", "Every x", "for any x". It may be noted that statements remain unchanged if the quantifying variable, say x, is changed or replaced by another variable, say y, throughout. For example, the statements $(x)(D(x) \rightarrow A(x))$ and (y) $(D(y) \rightarrow A(y))$ are equivalent.

Now let us introduce another quantifier which symbolizes the expression such as "there exists some" or "there is at least one". This quantifier is called *existential quantifier* and symbolized as $(\exists x)$. The area of logic that deals with predicates and quantifiers is called *predicate calculus*.

Example 1.35

(a) Symbolize the expression "Some roses are red".

(b) Symbolize the expression "Some numbers are irrational".

Solution: (a) $(\exists x)\,(C(x) \wedge R(x))$

(b) Let I: x is irrational.

N: x is a number.

Then, the above statement can be symbolized as

$$(\exists x)\,(N(x) \wedge I(x))$$

It may be observed that a conjunction is used with the existential quantifier and an implication is used with the universal quantifier. ∎

1.16.1 Predicate Formulas

From the earlier discussions, we know that $P(x_1, x_2, ..., x_n)$ denotes an n-place predicate formula in which P is the predicate and $(x_1, x_2, ..., x_n)$ are n individual variables or objects. Normally, the expression $P(x_1, x_2, ..., x_n)$ is called an *atomic formula* of predicate calculus. Now, we present some examples of atomic formulas in Example 1.36.

Example 1.36 S $M(y)$, $P(b, a, x)$, $M(x, y, z)$ ∎

Some rules should be kept in mind while obtaining a well-formed formula (wff) of a predicate calculus. The rules are:

1. An atomic formula is a well formed formula.

2. If A and B are well formed formulas (well-formed formulas), then $(A \wedge B)$, $(A \vee B)$, $(A \to B)$ and $(A \equiv B)$ are also well-formed formulas.

3. If M is a well formed formula then $\overline{M}$ is also a well-formed formula.

4. If M is a well formed formula then $(x)M$ and $(\exists x)M$ are also well-formed formulas, where x is any variable.

5. Only the formulas which are obtained by applying rules (1) to (4) are well formed formulas.

Note: As mentioned earlier, we shall use the term "formula" for "well-formed formula" in rest of the chapter.

1.17 FREE AND BOUND VARIABLES

If any formula contains a part like $(\exists x)\,M(x)$ or $(\forall x)\,M(x)$ then that part is called *x-bound* part of the formula. Any occurrence of x in an x-bound part, is known as a *bound occurrence* of x. Any occurrence of x which is not a bound occurrence is known as *free occurrence*. The formula that immediately follows the quantifier is known as the *scope of the quantifier*. In other words, the *scope of a quantifier* is the part of a logical expression to which the quantifier is applied. So, a variable is free if it lies outside the scope of all quantifiers in the formula which specifies this variable. For example, the formula $M(x)$ in $(\exists x)\,M(x)$ or $(\forall x)\,M(x)$ is known as the *scope of the quantifier*.

Example 1.37

(i) $(x) M(x)$

Here, $M(x)$ is the scope of the quantifier.

(ii) $(\exists x) (M(x) \wedge N(x))$

Here, $[M(x) \wedge N(x)]$ is the scope of quantifier and all occurrences of x are bound.

(iii) $M(x) \wedge \exists (x) N(x)$

Here, scope of $(\exists x)$ is $N(x)$ and it contains bound occurrence of x while occurrence of x in M is free. ■

It should be kept in mind that bound variable can be replaced by any other variable but not by a constant. Hence, the formulas $(x) M(y, x)$ and $(z) M(y, z)$ are same.

It may be observed that, if there is a free variable in the formula then we have a statement function and in the case when every occurrence of a variable is bound and no variable has free occurrence then we get a statement.

Example 1.38 Write the following predicate in symbolic form: "Someone in your school has visited Agra".

Solution: Let $\quad S(x)$: x is in your school.

$\qquad A(x)$: x has visited Agra.

We symbolize the predicate as

$$(\exists x) (S(x) \wedge A(x)).$$ ■

Example 1.39 Symbolize the expression "Everyone has exactly one favorite language".

Solution: Let $M(y, x)$: y is the favorite language of x.

Then, we can symbolize the statement as

$$(\forall x) (\exists y) (M(y, x) \wedge ((\forall z) (z \neq y) \rightarrow \overline{M}(z, x))).$$ ■

1.17.1 The Universe of Discourse

Example 1.39 indicates that symbolizing a statement in predicate calculus could be very much complex. The complexity can be reduced to some extent by restricting the class of individuals or objects under consideration. According to this restriction, the quantified variables represent only those objects which belong to a specific domain or class. This restricted class is known as the *universe of discourse* or simply *universe*. For example, if the present discussion is on integers only, then the universe of discourse could be the set of integers. If the discussion is based on fruits only, then the universe of discourse is the class of fruits. Now, we explain the concept of the universe of discourse with some examples.

Example 1.40   Symbolize the statement "All dogs are animals".

Solution: Let $D(x)$: x is a dog.

              $A(x)$: x is an animal.

Then the given statement can be symbolized as

$$(x)\,(D(x) \rightarrow A(x))$$

If the universe of discourse is taken into account and the universe is the set of all dogs then the above statement can be symbolized as $(x)\,A(x)$.   ∎

Example 1.41   Symbolize the statement "Everyone in the final-year class has a cellular phone".

Solution: Let $C(x)$: x is in the final-year class.

              $P(x)$: x has a cellular phone.

Then the given statement can be symbolized as

$$(x)\,(C(x) \rightarrow P(x)) \text{ (without using universe)}$$

Let the universe be the set of all students in the final-year class. Then the above statement can be symbolized as $(x)\,P(x)$.

The universe of discourse must be defined clearly as the truth value of a statement depends on it. In order to illustrate this, let us consider the following example.   ∎

Example 1.42   Consider the predicate

$$P(x): x \text{ is greater than 2.}$$

and the statements $(x)\,P(x)$ and $(\exists x)\,P(x)$. Suppose, the universe of discourse is stated as:

  (a) $\{-5, -3, 0, 1, 2\}$

  (b) $\{3, 5, 7, 10\}$

  (c) $\{-1, 0, 2, 6\}$

Then, the statement $(x)\,P(x)$ is true only for the universe of discourse (b) and false for (a) and (c). Similarly, the statement $(\exists x)\,P(x)$ is true for both (b) and (c) and false for (a).   ∎

1.18   INFERENCE THEORY OF PREDICATE CALCULUS

In this section, we discuss the inference theory of predicate calculus. We will use the same terminologies and notations as that used for statement calculus.

1.18.1   Valid Formulas and Equivalences

A formula P is said to be a valid formula in the universe of discourse S if, for every assignment of object names from S to the corresponding variable names in P and for every assignment of statements to statement variables, the resulting statements have truth value T.

Let P and Q be two predicate formulas defined over the universe S. We define the equivalence of P and Q as follows:

If, for every assignment of object names from the universe of discourse S to every variable of P and Q, the resulting statements have identical truth values, then the predicate formulas P and Q are said to be equivalent over the universe S. We denote this as $P \equiv Q$.

All possible substitutions of the object variables can be enumerated, if the universe of discourse is a finite set. But this is not possible in the case of infinite universe of discourse.

Let the universe of discourse be denoted by the finite set S such that $S = \{q_1, q_2, ..., q_n\}$.

From the concepts of quantifiers and by the process of enumeration of all the objects in S, it can be observed that,

$$(x)\,P(x) \equiv P(q_1) \wedge P(q_2) \wedge ... \wedge P(q_n)$$
$$(\exists x)\,P(x) \equiv P(q_1) \vee P(q_2) \vee ... \vee P(q_n)$$

Now, we will prove the following two important equivalences by using the above two expressions and De Morgan's law.

(i) $\sim((x)\,P(x)) \equiv (\exists x) \sim P(x)$

(ii) $\sim((\exists x)\,P(x)) \equiv (x) \sim P(x)$

Proof:

(i) $\sim((x)\,P(x)) \equiv \sim[P(q_1) \wedge P(q_2) \wedge ... \wedge P(q_n)]$

$\equiv \sim P(q_1) \vee \sim P(q_2) \vee ... \vee \sim P(q_n)$

(by using De Morgan's law)

$\equiv (\exists x) \sim P(x)$

(ii) $\sim((\exists x)\,P(x)) \equiv \sim[P(q_1) \vee P(q_2) \vee ... \vee P(q_n)]$

$\equiv \sim P(q_1) \wedge \sim P(q_2) \wedge ... \wedge \sim P(q_n)$

(by using De Morgan's law)

$\equiv (x) \sim P(x).$ ■

Assuming that the negation symbol appearing before the quantifier negates not the quantifier but the entire quantified statement, we may omit some parentheses in (i) and (ii) and rewrite them as

(i) $\sim(x)\,P(x) \equiv (\exists x) \sim P(x)$

(ii) $\sim(\exists x)\,P(x) \equiv (x) \sim P(x)$

If the universal and existential quantifiers are said to be *duals* of each other, then, from (i) and (ii), we can state that the negation of the quantified formula is equivalent to a formula in which the quantifier is replaced by its *dual* and the scope of the quantifier by its *negation*.

Example 1.43   Express the negation of following statements in English.

(a) Some drivers do not obey the speed limit.

(b) All Swedish movies are serious.

(c) There is someone in the class who does not have good attitude.

Solution:

(a) Every driver obeys the speed limit.

(b) Some Swedish movies are not serious.

(c) Everyone in the class has good attitude.   ■

Example 1.44   Express the following statements using quantifiers. Then construct the negation of the statement. Express the negation in simple English.

(a) Every bird can fly.

(b) Some birds can talk.

Solution:

(a) Let $P(x)$: x can fly.

Let the universe of discourse be birds.

Then, the above statement can be expressed as, $\forall x\, P(x)$. The negation is, $\exists x$ ~ $P(x)$. This can be expressed as, "There is a bird that cannot fly".

(b) Let $Q(x)$: x can talk.

Let the universe of discourse be birds.

Then, the above statement can be expressed as, $\exists x\, Q(x)$. The negation is, $\forall x$ ~ $Q(x)$. This can be expressed as, "No bird can talk".   ■

1.18.2   Theory of Inference for Predicate Calculus

We have already discussed the rules of inference for statement calculus. While deriving the conclusion in predicate calculus, the rules of inference given for the statement calculus along with some additional rules for handling quantifiers can be used. We shall now present some rules of inference for predicate calculus involving quantifiers.

Rule US (Universal Specification):   This rule of inference is used to conclude that $P(a)$ is true, where a is a particular member of the universe of discourse, given the premise $\forall x\, P(x)$. For example, this rule can be used when we conclude from the statement "All students are brilliant" that "Ram is brilliant", where Ram is a member of the universe of discourse of all students. This rule of inference is also known as *universal instantiation*.

Rule UG (Universal Generalization):   This rule of inference states that $\forall x\, P(x)$ is true when the given premise $P(a)$ is true for all elements a belonging to the universe of discourse. This rule can be used when we want to prove that $\forall x$ $P(x)$ is true by taking an arbitrary element a from the universe of discourse and using $P(a)$ is true. The selected element a must be an arbitrary element, and not a specific element of the universe of discourse.

Rule ES (Existential Specification): This rule of inference permits us to conclude that there exists an element *a* in the universe of discourse for which $P(a)$ is true, if the premise $\exists x\, P(x)$ is true. Here, the selected element *a* cannot be arbitrary, but it should be an element, for which $P(a)$ is true. This rule of inference is also known as *existential instantiation*.

Rule EG (Existential Generalization): This rule of inference is used to conclude that the premise $\exists x\, P(x)$ is true when a particular element *a* with $P(a)$ true is given. In other words, if we know one element *a* in the universe of discourse for which $P(a)$ is true, then we can say that $\exists x\, P(x)$ is true.

We have summarized these rules of inference in Table 1.3.

Table 1.3 Rules of Inference for Predicate Calculus Involving Quantifiers

Tautology	Name of Rule of Inference
$\forall x\, P(x) \rightarrow P(a)$	Universal Specification (*US*)
$P(a) \rightarrow \forall x\, P(x)$, for an arbitrary *a*	Universal Generalization (*UG*)
$\exists x\, P(x) \rightarrow P(a)$, for some element *a*	Existential Specification (*ES*)
$P(a) \rightarrow \exists x\, P(x)$, for some element *a*	Existential Generalization (*EG*)

The restrictions on *UG* and *ES* if not imposed may lead to invalid conclusion. Let us understand this through an example.

Example 1.45 Let $S(a, b)$: *a* is divisible by *b*. Let the universe of discourse be $\{3, 5, 9, 13\}$, so that the statement $(\exists a)\, S(a, 3)$ is true. However, $(\forall a)\, S(a, 3)$ is false.

Now, consider the following derivation.

{1}	(1)	$(\exists a)\, S(a, 3)$	*P*
{1}	(2)	$S(y, 3)$	*T*, ES, (1)
{1}	(3)	$\forall x\, S(x, 3)$	*T*, UG, (2)

In the third step the restriction on UG is neglected. Since 'a' is not free in the premise (in first step), so the restriction on ES is satisfied. But 'y' is free in step 2 and resulted from the use of ES, hence it cannot be generalized and so we get an invalid conclusion. ∎

Example 1.46 Prove that
$$(\forall x\, (P(x) \rightarrow Q(x)) \wedge \forall x\, (Q(x) \rightarrow S(x))) \rightarrow \forall x\, (P(x) \rightarrow S(x))$$

Solution:

{1}	(1) $\forall x$	$(P(x) \rightarrow Q(x))$	*P*
{1}	(2)	$P(a) \rightarrow Q(a)$	*T*, US, (1)
{3}	(3)	$\forall x\, (Q(x) \rightarrow S(x))$	*P*

$\{3\}$	(4)	$Q(a) \rightarrow S(a)$	T, US, (3)
$\{1, 3\}$	(5)	$P(a) \rightarrow S(a)$	T, (2), (4), hypothetical syllogism.
$\{1, 3\}$	(6)	$\forall x\, (P(x) \rightarrow S(x))$	UG, (5) ∎

Example 1.47   Show that the premises "Every one in this college has purchased a computer" and "Hari is a student in this college" imply the conclusion "Hari has purchased a computer".

Solution: Let $P(x)$ denote "x is in this college" and let $Q(x)$ denote "x has purchased a computer". Then the premises can be written as $\forall x\, (P(x) \rightarrow Q(x))$ and $P(\text{Hari})$. The conclusion is $Q(\text{Hari})$.

In the following, we present the steps which are used to establish the conclusion from the given premises.

	Induction Step		**Basis of Induction**
$\{1\}$	(1)	$\forall x\, (P(x) \rightarrow Q(x))$	P
$\{1\}$	(2)	$P(\text{Hari}) \rightarrow Q(\text{Hari})$	US, (1)
$\{3\}$	(3)	$P(\text{Hari})$	P
$\{1, 3\}$	(4)	$Q(\text{Hari})$	(2), (3), modus ponens ∎

1.18.3   Formulas Involving More Than One Quantifier

Till now, we have written only those formulas in which the universal and existential quantifiers occur singly. Now, we shall, consider some cases where the quantifiers occur multiple times. Many such cases are possible when the quantifier occurs in combination. In the case of 2-place predicate, they become specifically more important. If $A(x, y)$ is a 2-place predicate formula then the following possibilities exist:

$(x)(y)\, A(x, y),$ $(x)(\exists y)\, A(x, y)$ $(\exists x)(y)\, A(x, y)$

$(\exists x)(\exists y)\, A(x, y)$ $(y)\,(x)\, A(x, y)$ $(\exists y)(x)\, A(x, y)$

$(y)(\exists x)\, A(x, y)$ $(\exists y)(\exists x)\, A(x, y)$

We can also construct some formulas involving multiple quantifiers. Following are some examples of formulas containing more than one quantifier.

$$(x)(y)\, A(x, y) \rightarrow (y)(x)\, A(x, y)$$
$$(x)(y)\, A(x, y) \rightarrow (\exists y)\,(x)\, A(x, y)$$
$$(y)(x)\, A(x, y) \rightarrow (\exists x)\,(y)\, A(x, y)$$
$$(\exists y)(x)\, A(x, y) \rightarrow (x)(\exists y)\, A(x, y)$$
$$(\exists x)(y)\, A(x, y) \rightarrow (y)(\exists x)\, A(x, y)$$
$$(x)(\exists y)\, A(x, y) \rightarrow (\exists y)(\exists x)\, A(x, y)$$
$$(y)(\exists x)\, A(x, y) \rightarrow (\exists x)(\exists y)\, A(x, y)$$
$$(\exists x)(\exists y)\, A(x, y) \rightarrow (\exists y)(\exists x)\, P(x, y)$$

Using De Morgan's law, negation of any of the above formulas can be done. For example,

$$\sim [(x)(y)\, A(x, y)]$$

$$\Leftrightarrow (\exists x)(\sim(y)\, A(x, y))$$
$$\Leftrightarrow (\exists x)(\exists y) \sim A(x, y)$$

The following implication of rules should be carefully used:

(1) $(x)(\exists y)\, A(x, y)$

Applying *US*, we can write, $(\exists y)\, A(x, y)$ or $(\exists y) A(w, y)$.

But we should not write $(\exists y)\, A(y, y)$ since y is a bound variable i,e. $(\exists y)$ $A(x, y)$ is not free.

(2) Now consider the statement $(x)\, A(x, y)$

Using *EG*, it can be generalized as

$$(\exists y)\,(x)\, A(x, y) \text{ or } (\exists z)\,(x)\, A(x, z).$$

But we should not generalize it as

$$(\exists x)\,(x)\, A(x, x)$$

Similar care should be taken while using *UG* and *ES* rules.

1.19 METHODS OF PROOF

In this section, we shall discuss some important methods for proving theorems. A theorem is a statement which can be shown to be true. Theorems are also known as *propositions, facts* or *results*.

1. Trivial Proof In an implication $p \to q$, if we can establish that q is true, then regardless of the truth-value of p, the implication $p \to q$ will be true. So, the construction of a trivial proof of $p \to q$ needs to show that the truth-value of q is true. For example, If $x = 2$, then $x^2 = 4$. So, If $x^2 = 4$ is true, then $x = 2 \to x^2 = 4$ is true.

2. Vacous Proof If the hypothesis p of an implication $p \to q$ is false, then $p \to q$ is true for any proposition q.

Example 1.48 Prove the proposition $P(0)$ where $P(n)$ is the proposition "If n is a positive integer greater than 1, then $n^2 > n$".

Solution: The proposition $P(0)$ is the implication "If 0 is a positive integer greater than 1, then $0^2 > 0$". Since 0 is not a positive integer, so the proposition is true. ∎

3. Direct Proof Suppose, the hypothesis p is true. Then, the implication $p \to q$ can be proved if we can prove that q is true by using the rules of inference and some other theorems. This represents that the combination p true and q false never occurs.

Example 1.49 Let $P(n)$ be the proposition "If a and b are positive real numbers, then $(a + b)^n \geq a^n + b^n$." Prove that $P(1)$ is true.

Solution: Suppose the hypothesis of this implication is true, i.e. a and b are positive real numbers. Then $P(1)$ is true, since $(a + b)^1 = a + b \geq a^1 + b^1 = a + b$. ∎

Example 1.50 Prove that the sum of two odd integers is even.

Solution: Let us assume that n and m are two odd integers. So, we can express them as $n = 2k + 1$ and $m = 2l + 1$, where k and l are any integers. So, $n + m = 2(k + l + 1)$, which is even. Thus, the sum of two odd integers is even. ■

Example 1.51 Prove the statement: "If x is a number such that $x^2 + 7x + 12 = 0$, then $x = -4$ or $x = -3$".

Solution: A direct proof of the statement proceeds as follows:

Assume $x^2 + 7x + 12 = 0$. Using the rules of algebra, we have $x^2 + 7x + 12 = (x + 3)(x + 4) = 0$. It is known that if the product of two numbers is zero, then one or the other of the two factors must be zero. Hence, $x + 3 = 0$, or $x + 4 = 0$ implies $x = -3$ or $x = -4$. ■

4. Indirect Proof This method is also known as *direct proof of contra positive*. We know that the implication $p \rightarrow q$ is equivalent to its contrapositive $\sim q \rightarrow \sim p$. So, we can prove the implication by showing that its contrapositive $\sim q \rightarrow \sim p$ is true. So, an indirect proof of $p \rightarrow q$ proceeds as follows:

(a) First assume q is false.

(b) Then, prove on the basis of this assumption and other available information from the frame of reference that p is false.

Example 1.52 Prove that if n is an integer and $n^3 + 5$ is odd then n is even.

Solution: Let us assume that n is odd, so $n = 2k + 1$, for some integer k. Then, $n^3 + 5 = 2(4k^3 + 6k^2 + 3k + 3)$. Since $n^3 + 5$ is two times some integer, so it is even and therefore not odd. Since the negation of the conclusion of the implication implies that the hypothesis is false, the original implication is true. ■

Example 1.53 Prove that if x is irrational then $1/x$ is irrational.

Solution: If $1/x$ were rational, then by definition $1/x = p/q$ for some integers p and q with $q \neq 0$. Since $1/x$ cannot be 0 (if it were then we would have the contradiction $1 = x.0$ by multiplying both sides by x), so $p \neq 0$. Now $x = 1/(1/x) = 1/(p/q) = q/p$, by the usual rules of algebra and arithmetic. Hence, x can be written as the quotient of two integers with the denominator nonzero. Thus by definition, x is rational. ■

5. Proof by Contradiction There are some other methods which can be used when neither a direct proof nor an indirect proof is successful. Now, we discuss some additional methods of proof.

If a contradiction q can be found so that $\sim p \rightarrow q$ is true, then the proposition $\sim p$ must be false. So, p must be true. This method can be used when a contradiction, such as $r \wedge \sim r$, can be found so that it is possible to show that the implication $\sim p \rightarrow (r \wedge \sim r)$ is true. This type of argument is known as *proof by contradiction*.

The proof by contradiction proceeds as follows:

(a) First assume $p \wedge (\sim q)$ is true.

(b) Then find some conclusion (on the basis of this assumption) that is patently false or violates some other fact already established.

(c) Then the contradiction found out in step (b) leads us to conclude that $p \wedge (\sim q)$ is false. Hence, $p \rightarrow q$ is true.

Very often, one obtains the proposition $p \wedge (\sim p)$ in a proof by contradiction. So, in this case, one should give a proof by contra positive.

Example 1.54 Prove that the sum of an irrational number and a rational number is irrational.

Solution: Suppose that r is a rational number and i is an irrational number and $s = r + i$ is rational. We know that the sum of two rational numbers is rational. So, $s + (-r) = i$ is rational, which is a contradiction. Hence, the proof. ∎

Example 1.55 Show that at least 10 of any 64 days chosen must fall on the same day of the week.

Solution: If there were 9 or fewer days on each day of the week, this would account for at most $9.7 = 63$ days. But we choose 64 days. This contradiction shows that at least 10 of the days must be on the same day of the week. ∎

6. Proof by Cases We can use the tautology $(p_1 \vee p_2 \vee \dots \vee p_n) \rightarrow q] \leftrightarrow [(p_1 \rightarrow q) \wedge (p_2 \rightarrow q) \wedge \dots \wedge (p_n \rightarrow q)]$ as a rule of inference to proof an implication of the form $(p_1 \vee p_2 \vee \dots \vee p_n) \rightarrow q$.

This implies that the original implication with a hypothesis made up of the disjunction of the propositions $p_1, p_2, \dots, p_n$, can be proved by proving each of the n implications $p_i \rightarrow q$, $i = 1, 2, \dots n$, separately. Such an argument is called a *proof by cases*. It may be noted that the method of proof by cases is valid when $n = 2$. For example, the statements $(p_1 \vee p_2) \rightarrow q$ and $(p_1 \rightarrow q) \wedge (p_2 \rightarrow q)$ may be considered which are equivalent.

Example 1.56 Prove that if x and y are real numbers then $\max(x, y) + \min(x, y) = x + y$.

Solution: There are two possible cases, i.e. $x \leq y$ and $x \geq y$. If $x \leq y$, then $\max(x, y) + \min(x, y) = y + x = x + y$. If $x \geq y$ then $\max(x, y) + \min(x, y) = x + y$. Since these are the only two cases, the equality always holds. Hence the proof. ∎

Example 1.57 Prove the triangle inequality, which states that if x and y are real numbers then $|x| + |y| \geq |x + y|$ (where $|x|$ represents the absolute value of x, which equals x if $x \geq 0$ and equals $-x$ if $x < 0$).

Solution: There are four cases:

Case 1: $x \geq 0$ and $y \geq 0$. Then $|x| + |y| = x + y = |x + y|$.

Case 2: $x < 0$ and $y < 0$. Then $|x| + |y| = -x + (-y) = -(x + y) = |x + y|$ since $x + y < 0$.

Case 3: $x \geq 0$ and $y < 0$. Then $|x| + |y| = x + (-y)$. If $x \geq -y$ then $|x + y|$ $= x + y$. But since $y < 0$, $-y > y$ so that $|x| + |y| = x + (-y) > x + y = |x + y|$. If $x < -y$ then $|x + y| = -(x + y) = -x + (-y)$. But, since $x \geq 0$, $x \geq -x$, so that $|x| + |y|$ $= x + (-y) \geq -x + (-y) = |x + y|$.

Case 4: $x < 0$ and $y \geq 0$. This is identical to case 3 with the roles of x and y reversed.

Hence the proof. ∎

7. *Proof by Elimination of Cases* Very often, while solving a problem or in constructing a proof, we are confronted with two alternatives: either p has to be true or q has to be true. If we verify that p is false, then obviously we must conclude that q is true.

This method of proof is identical to the rule of inference *disjunctive syllogism,* i.e. $[(p \vee q) \wedge (\sim p)] \to q$, and, it can be extended to any finite number of cases:

$$[\{(p_1 \vee p_2 \vee p_3 \vee \dots \vee p_n) \vee q\} \wedge (\sim p_1) \wedge (\sim p_2) \wedge (\sim p_3) \wedge \dots (\sim p_n)] \to q$$

Similarly, a proof by elimination of cases can take another form based on the following tautology:

$$\{[p \to (q \vee r)] \wedge (\sim q)\} \to (p \to r)$$

In other words, if we are given that p implies two possible conclusions q or r, and if one of the conclusions q is definitely false, then, we may conclude that p implies the other conclusion r.

Finally, there is a third form of a proof by elimination of cases. In this situation, a statement of the form $p \to (q \vee r)$ is proved instead of proving the equivalent statement $(p \wedge \sim q) \to r$.

For example, we can prove the following statement for a real number X: if x^2 $+ 7x + 12 = 0$ and $x \neq 3$ and then $x = 4$.

We might observe that this method of proof of $p \to (q \vee r)$ by elimination of cases is quite similar in form to proof by contradiction; however, a proof by contradiction of $p \to (q \vee r)$ would go one step further and assume $p \wedge (\sim q) \wedge$ $(\sim r)$ is true (since $\sim(q \vee r) = (\sim q) \wedge (\sim r)$, by De Morgan's law), and then attempt to find a contradiction.

8. *Conditional Proof* This method of proof is actually just another form of elimination of cases.

We know that the two propositions $p \to (q \to r)$ and $(p \wedge q) \to r$ are equivalent. So, a proof of the conditional $p \to (q \to r)$ can proceed as follows:

(a) First, join the two antecedents p and q.
(b) Then prove r on the basis of these assumptions and other available information.

9. *Proof of Equivalence* We can use the tautology

$$(p \leftrightarrow q) \leftrightarrow [(p \to q) \wedge (q \to p)]$$

to prove a theorem which is a biconditional, i.e. a statement of the form $p \leftrightarrow q$, where p and q are propositions.

In other words, the proposition "p iff q" can be proved if both the implications "if p, then q" and "if q then p" are proved.

To do this, we break the proof into two halves: first we prove $p \rightarrow q$, and then we prove $q \rightarrow p$. However, one may prove $q \rightarrow p$ first.

Example 1.58   Prove that if n is a positive integer, then n is odd if and only if $5n + 6$ is odd.

Solution: This theorem has the form "p iff q" where p is "n is odd" and q is "$5n + 6$ is odd". To prove this theorem we need to show that $p \rightarrow q$ and $q \rightarrow p$ are true.

First, assume that n is odd, so that $n = 2k + 1$ for some integer k. Then, $5n + 6 = 5(2k + 1) + 6 = 10k + 11 = 2(5k + 5) + 1$. Hence $5n + 6$ is odd. To prove the converse, suppose that n is even, so that $n = 2k$ for some integer k. Then $5n + 6 = 10k + 6 = 2(5k + 3)$, so that $5n + 6$ is even. Hence n is odd, if and only if $5n + 6$ is odd. ∎

1.20   EUCLIDEAN ALGORITHM

Possibly, the oldest recorded nontrivial algorithm is the *Euclidean Algorithm*. Euclid devised an algorithm for computing the Greatest Common Divisor (GCD) of two non-negative integers. If the two integers M and N are non-negative, i.e. $M \geq 0$ and $N \geq 0$, then the Greatest Common Divisor is the largest integer P(say) ≥ 0 such that M and N both are divisible by P.

The Euclidean Algorithm to compute the Greatest Common Divisor (GCD) of two integers M and N is a recursive definition and is as follows:

$$GCD\ (M, N) = \begin{cases} GCD(N, M) & \text{If } N > M \\ M, & \text{If } N = 0 \\ GCD(N, R), & \text{otherwise} \end{cases}$$

where, R is the remainder when M is divided by N, or $M = aN + R$, a is some constant.

Example 1.59   By applying the Euclidean Algorithm, compute $GCD(25, 6)$.

Solution:

$= GCD(25, 6)$	here $M = 25, N = 6$
$= GCD(6, 1),$	since $6 < 25, N < M$
$= GCD(1, 0),$	since $1 < 6, N < M$
$= 1,$	since $N = 0$

So, $GCD(25, 6) = 1$. ∎

Example 1.60   By applying the Euclidean Algorithm, compute

  (a) $GCD(18, 4)$

  (b) $GCD(26, 2)$

  (c) $GCD(28, 8)$

Solution:

  (a) $GCD(18, 4) = GCD(4, 2) = GCD(2, 0) = 2$

  (b) $GCD(26, 2) = GCD(2, 0) = 2$

  (c) $GCD(28, 8) = GCD(8, 4) = GCD(4, 0) = 4$ ■

Figure 1.20 shows the code for computing GCD of two numbers using Euclidean Algorithm.

The **least common multiple** (also called the Lowest common multiple) of two integers M and N, usually denoted by **LCM (M, N)** is the smallest positive integer that is a multiple of both M and N. The LCM of two integers can be easily computed using the Euclidean Algorithm (for finding GCD of two numbers) as follows:

$$LCM (M, N) = \frac{M \times N}{GCD(M, N)}$$

```
/* Program to compute Greatest Common Divisor* /

# include<stdio.h>
# include<conio.h>

int GCD(int , int);

/* Definition of the Greatest Common Divisor Function */

int GCD( int n, int m)
{
        if(( n >= m) && (( n % m) == 0))
                return(m);
        else
                GCD(m,(n % m));
}



void main()
{
        int n, m;
        int result;
        printf("\n Input the first integer number: ");
        scanf("%d", &n);

        printf("\n Input the second integer number: ");
        scanf("%d", &m);

        result = GCD(n, m);
        printf("\n Greatest Common Divisor of : %d and %d is = %d", n, m, result);
        getch();
}
```

Fig. 1.20   The code for computing GCD of two numbers using Euclidean Algorithm

Example 1.61 By using Euclidean Algorithm, compute

   (a) LCM (18, 4)

   (b) LCM (26, 2)

   (c) LCM (28, 8)

Solution:

(a) $\text{LCM}(18,4) = \dfrac{18 \times 4}{\text{GCD}(18,4)} = \dfrac{72}{\text{GCD}(4,2)} = \dfrac{72}{\text{GCD}(2,0)} = \dfrac{72}{2} = 36$

(b) $\text{LCM}(26,2) = \dfrac{26 \times 2}{\text{GCD}(26,2)} = \dfrac{52}{\text{GCD}(2,0)} = \dfrac{52}{2} = 26$

(c) $\text{LCM}(28,8) = \dfrac{28 \times 8}{\text{GCD}(28,8)} = \dfrac{224}{\text{GCD}(8,4)} = \dfrac{224}{\text{GCD}(4,0)} = \dfrac{224}{4} = 56$

The program for computing the LCM of two numbers from their GCD using Euclidean Algorithm is given in Fig. 1.21.

```c
//finding LCM of two numbers from their GCD
#include<stdio.h>
#include<conio.h>
int gcd(int m,int n)
{
  int ans;
   if(m<n)
      ans=gcd(n,m);
   else if(n==0)
      ans=m;
   else
      ans=gcd(n,m%n);
   return(ans);
}
int main()
{
  int m,n,lcm1,hcf1;
  char a='y';
  printf("Calclating LCM of two positive numbers from their GCD\n");
  do
  {
    printf("\nEnter the two numbers:\n");
    scanf("%d%d",&m,&n);
    hcf1=gcd(m;n);
    lcm1=m*n/hcf1;
    printf("\nLCM of %d and %d is: %d\n Do you want to find LCM of two more
       Numbers?\ny/n\n",m,n,lcm1);
    a=getch();
    }while(a=='y');
  return 0;
}
OUTPUT:
Calclating LCM of two positive numbers from their GCD:
Enter the two numbers:
12
18
LCM of 12 and 18 is: 36
Do you want to find LCM of two more numbers?
y/n
n
```

Fig. 1.21 The code for computing LCM of two numbers using Euclidean Algorithm

The above two figures compute the GCD and LCM of two numbers. The GCD (LCM) of more than two numbers can also be found easily. For this, first compute the GCD (LCM) of the first two numbers. Suppose, the result comes to be a_1. Then, compute the GCD (LCM) of a_1 and the third number. This process may be repeated till all the numbers are exhausted. Finally, the desired GCD (LCM) will be obtained.

Example 1.62   Find the GCD, and LCM of 12, 27 and 9.

Solution: First, we find the GCD of 12 and 27 as follows:

$$GCD\ (12,27) = GCD\ (27,\ 12)$$
$$= GCD\ (12,\ 3)$$
$$= GCD\ (3,\ 0)$$
$$= 3$$

Then, we find the GCD of 3 and 9 as follows:

$$GCD\ (3,\ 9) = GCD\ (9,\ 3)$$
$$= GCD\ (3,0)$$
$$= 3$$

Now, let us find the LCM of the above three numbers. First, we find the LCM of 12 and 27 as follows:

$$LCM(12,27) = 12*27/GCD(12,27)$$
$$= 12*27/3$$
$$= 108$$

Then, we find the LCM of 108 and 9 as follows:

$$LCM(108,9) = 108*9/GCD(108,9)$$
$$= 108*9/GCD(9,0)$$
$$= 108*9/9$$
$$= 108$$

So, GCD and LCM of 12, 27 and 9 are 3 and 108 respectively. ■

The readers can write programs to find the GCD and LCM of more than two numbers, themselves.

1.20.1   Euclidean Prime

Let n be a prime number. Let $P(n)$ be 1 added to the product of all prime numbers up to and including P, i.e. $P(n) = \{2*3*5* \ldots *n\} + 1$. We call n, a *Euclidean prime*, if $P(n)$ is a prime number. For example, it may be verified that 13 is not a Euclidean prime.

Solve This   Find all the Euclidean primes less than or equal to 21, 33, 43.

Problems

1.1 Determine whether each of the following statements is true or false. Briefly explain your answer.

(a) $\phi \subseteq \phi$
(b) $\phi \in \phi$
(c) $\phi \subseteq \{\phi\}$
(d) $\phi \in \{\phi\}$
(e) $\{\phi\} \subseteq \phi$
(f) $\{\phi\} \in \phi$
(g) $\{\phi\} \subseteq \{\phi\}$
(h) $\{\phi\} \in \{\phi\}$
(i) $\{a, b\} \subseteq \{a, b, c, \{a, b, c\}\}$
(j) $\{a, b\} \in \{a, b, c, \{a, b, c\}\}$
(k) $\{a, b\} \subseteq \{a, b, \{\{a, b\}\}\}$
(l) $\{a, b\} \in \{a, b, \{\{a, b\}\}\}$
(m) $\{a, \phi\} \subseteq \{a, \{a, \phi\}\}$
(n) $\{a, \phi\} \in \{a, \{a, \phi\}\}$

1.2 Determine the following sets:

(a) $\phi \cup \{\phi\}$
(b) $\phi \cap \{\phi\}$
(c) $\{\phi\} \cup \{a, \phi, \{\phi\}\}$
(d) $\{\phi\} \cap \{a, \phi, \{\phi\}\}$
(e) $\phi \oplus \{a, \phi, \{\phi\}\}$
(f) $\{\phi\} \oplus \{a, \phi, \{\phi\}\}$

1.3 (a) Let A and B be sets such that $(A \cup B) \subseteq B$ and $B \subsetneqq A$. Draw the corresponding Venn diagram.

(b) Let A, B. and C be sets such that $A \subseteq B$, $A \subseteq C$, $(B \cap C) \subseteq A$, and $A \subseteq (B \cap C)$. Draw the corresponding Venn diagram.

(c) Let A, B, and C be sets such that $(A \cap B \cap C) = \phi$, $(A \cap B) \neq \phi$, $(A \cap C) \neq \phi$, and $(B \cap C) \neq \phi$. Draw the corresponding Venn diagram.

1.4 Give an example of sets A, B. and C such that $A \in B$, $B \in C$, and $A \notin C$.

1.5 Determine whether each of the following statements is true for arbitrary sets A, B, C. Justify your answer.

(a) If $A \in B$ and $B \subseteq C$, then $A \in C$.
(b) If $A \in B$ and $B \subseteq C$, then $A \subseteq C$.
(c) If $A \subseteq B$ and $B \in C$, then $A \in C$.
(d) If $A \subseteq B$ and $B \in C$, then $A \subseteq C$.

1.6 Let A, B, C be subsets of U. Given that

$$A \cap B = A \cap C$$
$$\overline{A} \cap B = \overline{A} \cap C$$

Is it necessary that $B = C$? Justify your answer.

1.7 Given that

$$(A \cap C) \subseteq (B \cap C)$$
$$(A \cap \overline{C}) \subseteq (B \cap \overline{C})$$

show that $A \subseteq B$.

1.8 What can you say about the sets P and Q if

(a) $P \cap Q = P$?
(b) $P \cup Q = P$?
(c) $P \oplus Q = P$?
(d) $P \cap Q = P \cup Q$?

1.9 (a) Let $A \subseteq B$ and $C \subseteq D$. Is it always the case that $(A \cup C) \subseteq (B \cup D)$? Is it always the case that $(A \cap C) \subseteq (B \cap D)$?

(b) Let $W \subset X$ and $Y \subset Z$. Is it always the case that $(W \cup Y) \subset (X \cup Z]$? Is it always the case that $(W \cap Y) \subset (X \cap Z)$?

1.10 (a) Given that $A \cup B = A \cup C$, is it necessary that $B = C$?

(b) Given that $A \cap B = A \cap C$, is it necessary that $B = C$?

(c) Given that $A \oplus B = A \oplus C$, is it necessary that $B = C$?

Justify your answers.

1.11 For $A = \{a, b, \{a, c\}, \phi\}$, determine the following sets:

(a) $A - \{a\}$ (b) $A - \phi$

(c) $A - \{\phi\}$ (d) $A - \{a, b\}$

(e) $A - \{a, c\}$ (f) $A - \{\{a, b\}\}$

(g) $A - \{\{a, c\}\}$ (h) $\{a\} - A$

(i) $\phi - A$ (j) $\{\phi\} - A$

(k) $\{a, c\} - A$ (l) $\{\{a, c\}\} - A$

(m) $\{a\} - \{A\}$

1.12 Let A, B, C be arbitrary sets.

(a) Show that

$$(A - B) - C = A - (B \cup C)$$

(b) Show that

$$(A - B) - C = (A - C) - B$$

(c) Show that

$$(A - B) - C = (A - C) - (B - C)$$

1.13 Let A, B, C be sets. Under what condition is each of the following statements true?

(a) $(A - B) \cup (A - C) = A$ (b) $(A - B) \cup (A - C) = \phi$

(c) $(A - B) \cap (A - C) = \phi$ (d) $(A - B) \oplus (A - C) = \phi$

1.14 Let A, B be two sets.

(a) Given that $A - B = B$, what can be said about A and B?

(b) Given that $A - B = B - A$, what can be said about A and B?

1.15 Let A denote the set of all automobiles that are manufactured domestically. Let B denote the set of all imported automobiles. Let C denote the set of all automobiles manufactured before 1977. Let D denote the set of all automobiles with a current market value of less than \$2000. Let E denote the set of all automobiles owned by students at the university. Express the following statements in set-theoretic notation:

(a) The automobiles owned by students at the university are either domestically manufactured or imported.

(b) All domestic automobiles manufactured before 1977 have a market value of less than \$2000.

(c) All imported automobiles manufactured after 1977 have a market value of more than \$2000.

1.16 Let A denote the set of all freshmen, B denotes the set of all sophomores, C denote the set of all mathematics majors, D denote the set of all computer science majors, E denote the set of all students in the course Elements of Discrete Mathematics, F denote the set of all students who went to a rock concert on Monday night, and G denote the set of all students who stayed up late Monday night. Express the following statements in set-theoretic notation:

(a) All sophomores in computer science are in the course Elements of Discrete Mathematics.

(b) Those and only those who are in the course Elements of Discrete Mathematics or who went to the rock concert stayed up late Monday night.

(c) No student in the course Elements of Discrete Mathematics went to the rock concert Monday night. (The obvious reason is the long problem sets in the course Elements of Discrete Mathematics.)

(d) The rock concert was only for freshmen and sophomores.

(e) All sophomores who are neither mathematics nor computer science majors went to the rock concert.

1.17 Determine the power sets of the following sets.

    (a) $\{a\}$ (b) $\{\{a\}\}$

    (c) $\{\phi, \{\phi\}\}$

1.18 Let $A = \{\phi, b\}$. Construct the following sets:

    (a) $A - \phi$ (b) $\{\phi\} - A$

    (c) $A \cup \mathscr{P}(A)$ (d) $A \cap \mathscr{P}(A)$

1.19 Let $A = \{\phi\}$. Let $B = \mathscr{P}(\mathscr{P}(A))$.

    (a) Is $\phi \in B$? $\phi \subseteq B$?   (b) Is $\{\phi\} \in B$? $\{\phi\} \subseteq B$?

    (c) Is $\{\{\phi\}\} \in B$? $\{\{\phi\}\} \subseteq B$?

1.20 Let $A = \{\phi, \{\phi\}\}$. Determine whether each of the following statements is true or false.

    (a) $\phi \in \mathscr{P}(A)$ (b) $\phi \subseteq \mathscr{P}(A)$

    (c) $\{\phi\} \subseteq \mathscr{P}(A)$ (d) $\{\phi\} \subseteq A$

    (e) $\{\phi\} \in \mathscr{P}(A)$ (f) $\{\phi\} \in A$

    (g) $\{\{\phi\}\} \subseteq \mathscr{P}(A)$ (h) $\{\{\phi\}\} \subseteq A$

    (i) $\{\{\phi\}\} \in \mathscr{P}(A)$ (j) $\{\{\phi\}\} \in A$

1.21 Let $A = \{a, \{a\}\}$. Determine whether each of the following statements is true or false.

    (a) $\phi \in \mathscr{P}(A)$ (b) $\phi \subseteq \mathscr{P}(A)$

    (c) $\{a\} \in \mathscr{P}(A)$ (d) $\{a\} \subseteq \mathscr{P}(A)$

    (e) $\{\{a\}\} \in \mathscr{P}(A)$ (f) $\{\{a\}\} \subseteq \mathscr{P}(A)$

    (g) $\{a, \{a\}\} \in \mathscr{P}(A)$ (h) $(a, \{a\}) \subseteq \mathscr{P}(A)$

    (i) $\{\{\{a\}\}\} \in \mathscr{P}(A)$ (j) $\{\{\{a\}\}\} \subseteq \mathscr{P}(A)$

1.22 Determine whether each of the following statements is true or false. Briefly explain your answer.

    (a) $A \cup \mathscr{P}(A) = \mathscr{P}(A)$ (b) $A \cap \mathscr{P}(A) = A$

    (c) $\{A\} \cup \mathscr{P}(A) = \mathscr{P}(A)$ (d) $\{A\} \cap \mathscr{P}(A) = A$

    (e) $A - \mathscr{P}(A) = A$ (f) $\mathscr{P}(A) - \{A\} = \mathscr{P}(A)$

1.23 Let A and B be two arbitrary sets.

    (a) Show that $\mathscr{P}(A \cap B) = \mathscr{P}(A) \cap \mathscr{P}(B)$ or give a counter example.

    (b) Show that $\mathscr{P}(A \cup B) = \mathscr{P}(A) \cup \mathscr{P}(B)$ or give a counter example.

1.24 Determine the cardinalities of the sets:

    (a) $A = \{n^7 | n \text{ is a positive integer}\}$ (b) $B = \{n^{109} | n \text{ is a positive integer}\}$

    (c) $A \cup B$ (d) $A \cap B$

Justify your answers.

1.25 Show that at most a countably infinite number of books can ever be written in English. (We define a book to be a finite sequence of words, divided into sentences, paragraphs, and chapters.)

1.26 (a) Show that the set of all positive rational numbers is a countably infinite set. (*Hint*: Consider all the points in the first quadrant of the plane whose x coordinate and y coordinate are integral values.)

    (b) Show that the union of a countably infinite number of countably infinite sets is a countably infinite set.

1.27 Let N denote the set of all natural numbers. Let S denote the set of all *finite* subsets of N. What is the cardinality of the set S? Justify your answer.

1.28 (a) Give an example to show that the cardinality of a set that is the intersection of two countably infinite sets may also be countably infinite.

   (b) Give an example to show that the cardinality of a set that is the intersection of two countably infinite sets may be finite.

1.29 Mr. Kantor built a machine that tells "lucky" numbers from "unlucky" numbers. That is, given a natural number, the machine will respond with the answer "lucky" or "unlucky." Two such machines are considered different if there is at least one number which one machine considers lucky but the other considers unlucky. Prove that there are more than a countably infinite number of such machines.

1.30 Solve the postage stamp problem in Example 1.9 by showing how postages of $3k$, $3k + 1$, $3k + 2$ cents can be made up with 3-cent and 5-cent stamps.

1.31 Mr. J. E. Roberts claims that he is a one-third Indian. When asked how this is possible, his answer was, "My father was a one-third Indian and my mother was a one-third Indian." Is this a correct proof by induction?

1.32 We present a proof of the statement "Any n billiard balls are of the same color" by induction.

Basis of induction. For $n = 1$, the statement is trivially true.

Induction step. Suppose we are given $k + 1$ billiard balls which we number 1, 2, ..., ($k + 1$). According to the induction hypothesis, balls 1, 2, ..., k are of the same color. Also, balls 2, 3, ..., ($k + 1$) are of the same color. Consequently, balls 1, 2, ..., k, ($k + 1$) are all of the same color.

What is wrong with the proof?

1.33 Prove by induction that for $n \geq 0$ and $a \neq 1$

$$1 + a + a^2 + \ldots + a^n = \frac{1 - a^{n+1}}{1 - a}$$

1.34 Show that $n^3 + 2n$ is divisible by 3 for all $n \geq 1$ by induction.

1.35 Show that $n^4 - 4n^2$ is divisible by 3 for all $n \geq 2$ by induction.

1.36 Show that $2^n \times 2^n - 1$ is divisible by 3 for all $n \geq 1$ by induction.

1.37 Show that

$$1 + 2 + 2^2 + 2^3 + \ldots + 2^n = 2^{n+1} - 1$$

by induction.

1.38 Determine the sum

$$1 + 3 + 5 + \ldots + (2n - 1)$$

by (a) guessing a general formula on the basis of the values of the sum for $n = 1, 2, 3, 4, 5$; (b) proving that the general formula is valid by induction.

1.39 Prove by induction that for $n \geq 1$

$$1 \cdot 1! + 2 \cdot 2! + 3 \cdot 3! + \ldots + n \cdot n! = (n + 1)! - 1$$

where $n!$ stands for the product $1 \cdot 2 \cdot 3 \ldots n$.

1.40 Prove by induction that for $n \geq 1$

$$1 \cdot 2 + 2 \cdot 3 + \ldots + n(n + 1) = \frac{n(n + 1)(n + 2)}{3}$$

1.41 Show that

$$1^2 - 2^2 + 3^2 - 4^2 + \ldots (-1)^{n-1} n^2 = (-1)^{n-1} \frac{n(n+1)}{2}$$

   (a) By induction.

   (b) By using the result in Example 1.13.

1.42 Show that

$$1^2 + 3^2 + 5^2 + \ldots + (2n-1)^2 = \frac{n(2n-1)(2n+1)}{3}$$

1.43 Show that

$$1^3 + 2^3 + \ldots + n^3 = (1 + 2 + 3 + \ldots + n)^2$$

1.44 Show that

$$\frac{1^2}{1 \cdot 3} + \frac{2^2}{3 \cdot 5} + \ldots + \frac{n^2}{(2n-1)(2n+1)} = \frac{n(n+1)}{2(2n+1)}$$

1.45   (a) Show that

$$\frac{1}{1 \cdot 2} + \frac{1}{2 \cdot 3} + \frac{1}{3 \cdot 4} + \ldots + \frac{1}{n(n+1)} = \frac{n}{n+1}$$

   (b) Show that

$$\frac{1}{1 \cdot 3} + \frac{1}{3 \cdot 5} + \ldots + \frac{n^2}{(2n-1)(2n+1)} = \frac{n}{2n+1}$$

   (c) Show that

$$\frac{1}{1 \cdot 4} + \frac{1}{4 \cdot 7} + \frac{1}{7 \cdot 10} + \ldots + \frac{1}{(3n-2)(3n+1)} = \frac{n}{3n+1}$$

   (d) Determine and prove a general formula that includes the results in (a), (b), and (c) as special cases.

1.46 Show that

$$1 \cdot 2 \cdot 3 + 2 \cdot 3 \cdot 4 + 3 \cdot 4 \cdot 5 + \ldots + n(n+1)(n+2) = \frac{n(n+1)(n+2)(n+3)}{4}$$

1.47 Formulate and prove by induction a general formula stemming from the observations that

$$1^3 = 1$$
$$2^3 = 3 + 5$$
$$3^3 = 7 + 9 + 11$$
$$4^3 = 13 + 15 + 17 + 19$$

1.48 Prove by induction that the sum of the cubes of three consecutive integers is divisible by 9.

1.49 Show that for any integer n

$$(11)^{n+2} + (12)^{2n+1}$$

is divisible by 133.

1.50 It is known that for any positive integer $n \geq 2$

$$\frac{1}{n+1} + \frac{1}{n+2} + \ldots + \frac{1}{2n} - A > 0$$

where A is a constant. How large can A be?

1.51 Show that for any positive integer $n > 1$

$$\frac{1}{\sqrt{1}} + \frac{1}{\sqrt{2}} + \ldots + \frac{1}{n} > \sqrt{n}$$

1.52 When n couples arrived at a party, they were greeted by the host and hostess at the door. After rounds of handshaking, the host asked the guests as well as his wife (the hostess) to indicate the number of hands each of them had shaken. He got $2n + 1$ different answers. Given that no one shook hands with his or her spouse, how many hands had the hostess shaken? Prove your result by induction.

1.53 (a) Let S be a set of natural numbers such that: (1) The natural number n_0 is in S. (2) If the natural numbers n_0, $n_0 + 1$, $n_0 + 2$, ..., k are in S, then the natural number $k + 1$ is also in S.

         Show that S is the set of all natural numbers larger than or equal to n_0.

         Hint: Assume that n_1 is the smallest natural number not in S.

     (b) Use the result in part (a) to show that the principle of strong mathematical induction is indeed valid.

1.54 Among the integers 1–300, how many of them are not divisible by 3, nor by 5, nor by 7? How many of them are divisible by 3, but not by 5 nor by 7?

1.55 N toys are to be distributed randomly among N children. There is an interesting way for the children to choose the toys so that no two of them will choose the same toy. A graph such as that shown in Fig. 1P.1(a) is drawn where there are N vertical lines and an arbitrary number of random horizontal segments between adjacent vertical lines with the stipulation that no two horizontal segments meet at the same point. The N toys are assigned to the bottoms of the vertical lines, and each child chooses as a starting point the top of a vertical line. From this starting point, the child will trace a path downward. However, whenever the child runs into a horizontal segment, he or she must turn

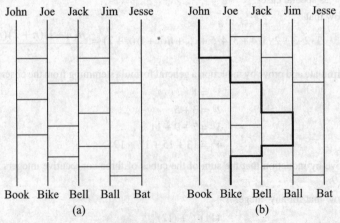

(a)   (b)

Fig. 1P.1

horizontally, and then turn downward again when the adjacent vertical line is reached. For example, Fig. 1P.1(*b*) shows the path that John follows. It is claimed that no matter how many horizontal segments are drawn, in whatever possible way, no two children will reach the same toy. Prove this claim by induction on the number of horizontal segments drawn.

1.56 A survey was conducted among 1000 people. Of these 595 are Democrats, 595 wear glasses, and 550 like ice cream; 395 of them are Democrats who wear glasses, 350 of them are Democrats who like ice cream, and 400 of them wear glasses and like ice cream; 250 of them are Democrats who wear glasses and like ice cream. How many of them who are not Democrats, do not wear glasses, and do not like ice cream? How many of them are Democrats who do not wear glasses, and do not like ice cream?

1.57 It is known that at the university 60 percent of the professors play tennis, 50 percent of them play bridge, 70 percent jog, 20 percent play tennis and bridge, 30 percent play tennis and jog, and 40 percent play bridge and jog. If someone claimed that 20 percent of the professors jog and play bridge and tennis, would you believe this claim? Why?

1.58 The 60,000 fans who attended the homecoming football game bought up all the paraphernalia for their cars. Altogether, 20,000 bumper stickers, 36,000 window decals, and 12,000 key rings were sold. We know that 52,000 fans bought at least one item and no one bought more than one of a given item. Also, 6000 fans bought both decals and key rings, 9000 bought both decals and bumper stickers, and 5000 bought both key rings and bumper stickers.

(a) How many fans bought all three items?

(b) How many fans bought exactly one item?

(c) Someone questioned the accuracy of the total number of purchasers; 52,000 (given that all the other numbers have been confirmed to be correct). This person claimed the total number of purchasers to be either 60,000 or 44,000. How do you dispel the claim?

1.59 Out of a total of 130 students, 60 are wearing hats to class, 51 are wearing scarves, and 30 are wearing both hats and scarves. Of the 54 students who are wearing sweaters, 26 are wearing hats, 21 are wearing scarves, and 12 are wearing both hats and scarves. Everyone wearing neither a hat nor a scarf is wearing gloves.

(a) How many students are wearing gloves?

(b) How many students not wearing a sweater are wearing hats but not scarves?

(c) How many students not wearing a sweater are wearing neither a hat nor a scarf?

1.60 Among 100 students, 32 study mathematics, 20 study physics, 45 study biology, 15 study mathematics and biology, 7 study mathematics and physics, 10 study physics and biology, and 30 do not study any of the three subjects.

(a) Find the number of students studying all three subjects.

(b) Find the number of students studying exactly one of the three subjects.

1.61 At a DAR (Daughters of the American Revolution) meeting of 30 women, 17 are descended from George Washington, 16 are descended from John Adams, and 5 are not descended from Washington or Adams. How many of the 30 women are descended from both Washington and Adams?

1.62 Seventy-five children went to an amusement park where they can ride on the merry-go-round, roller coaster, and ferris wheel. It is known that 20 of them have taken all three rides, and 55 of them have taken at least two of the three rides. Each ride costs $0.50, and the total receipt of the amusement park was $70. Determine the number of children who did not try any of the rides.

1.63 (a) Among 50 students in a class, 26 got an A in the first examination and 21 got an A in the second examination. If 17 students did not get an A in either examination, how many students got an A in both examinations?

(b) If the number of students who got an A in the first examination is equal to that in the second examination, if the total number of students who got an A in exactly one examination is 40, and if 4 students did not get an A in either examination, determine the number of students who got an A in the first examination only, who got an A in the second examination only, and who got an A in both examinations.

1.64 A possible way to define the symmetric difference of two multisets P and Q, denoted $P \oplus Q$, is to let the multiplicity of an element in $P \oplus Q$ be equal to the absolute value of the difference between the multiplicities of the element in P and Q. What is a possible inconsistency with such a definition?

Hint: Consider the multisets $(P \oplus Q) \oplus R$ and $P \oplus (Q \oplus R)$.

1.65 To describe the various restaurants in the city, we let p denote the statement, "The food is good," q denote the statement, "The service is good," and r denote the statement, "The rating is three-star." Write the following statements in symbolic form.

(a) Either the food is good, or the service is good, or both.

(b) Either the food is good or the service is good, but not both.

(c) The food is good while the service is poor.

(d) It is not the case that both the food is good and the rating is three-star.

(e) If both the food and services are good, then the rating will be three-star.

(f) It is not true that a three-star rating always means good food and good service.

1.66 Let p denote the statement, "The material is interesting," and q denote the statement, "The exercises are challenging," and r denote the statement, "The course is enjoyable." Write the following statements in symbolic form:

(a) The material is interesting and the exercises are challenging.

(b) The material is uninteresting, the exercises are not challenging, and the course is not enjoyable.

(c) If the material is not interesting and the exercises are not challenging, then the course is not enjoyable.

(d) The material is interesting means the exercises are challenging, and conversely.

(e) Either the material is interesting or the exercises are not challenging, but not both.

1.67 Write the following statements in symbolic form:

(a) The sun is bright and the humidity is not high.

(b) If I finish my homework before dinner and it does not rain, then I will go to the ball game.

(c) If you do not see me tomorrow, it means I have gone to Chicago.

(d) If the utility cost goes up or the request for additional funding is denied, then a new computer will be purchased if and only if we can show that the current computing facilities are indeed not adequate.

1.68 Let p denote the statement, "The weather is nice" and q denote the statement, "We have a picnic." Translate the following in English and simplify if possible:

(a) $p \wedge \bar{q}$ (b) $p \leftrightarrow q$

(c) $\bar{q} \rightarrow \bar{p}$ (d) $(\overline{p \vee q})\,(\overline{p \wedge q})$

1.69 (a) Write a compound statement that is true when exactly two of the three statements p, q, r are true.

(b) Write a compound statement that is true when none, or one, or two of the three statements p, q, r are true.

1.70 Construct the truth tables for the folllowing statements:

(a) $p \to p$

(b) $(p \to p) \vee (p \to \bar{p})$

(c) $(p \to p) \to (p \to \bar{p})$

(d) $(p \vee \bar{q}) \vee \bar{p}$

(e) $(p \vee \bar{q}) \to \bar{q}$

(f) $p \leftrightarrow (\bar{p} \vee \bar{q})$

(g) $(p \to (q \to r)) \to ((p \to q) \to (p \to r))$

(h) $(\bar{q} \to \bar{p}) \to (p \to q)$

1.71 (a) Given that the value of $p \to q$ is false, determine the value of $(\bar{p} \vee \bar{q}) \to q$.

(b) Given that the value of $p \to q$ is true, can you determine the value of $\bar{p} \vee (p \leftrightarrow q)$?

1.72 Consider the following advertisement for a game:

(a) There are three statements in this advertisement.

(b) Two of them are not true.

(c) The average increase in IQ scores of people who learn this game is more than 20 points. Is statement (c) true?

1.73 A certain country is inhabited only by people who either always tell the truth or always tell lies, and who will respond to questions only with a "yes" or a "no." A tourist comes to a fork in the road, where one branch leads to the capital and the other does not. There is no sign indicating which branch to take, but there is an inhabitant, Mr. Z, standing at the fork. What single question should the tourist ask him to determine which branch to take?

Hint: Let p stand for "Mr. Z always tells the truth" and let q stand for "The left-hand branch leads to the capital." Formulate a proposition A involving p and q such that Mr. Z's answer to the question "Is A true?" will be "yes" when and only when q is true.

1.74 Tony, Mike, and John belong to the Alpine Club. Every club member is either a skier or a mountain climber or both. No mountain climber likes rain, and all skiers like snow. Mike dislikes whatever Tony likes and likes whatever Tony dislikes. Tony likes rain and snow. Is there a member of the Alpine Club who is a mountain climber but not a skier?

1.75 What is the truth value of the quantification $\forall x\, Q(x)$, if the statement $Q(x)$ and universe of discourse given as follows:

(a) $Q(x): x + 1 > x,$ $U = \{\text{all real numbers}\}$

(b) $Q(x): x < 5,$ $U = \{\text{all real numbers}\}$

(c) $Q(x): x^2 < 12,$ $U = \{\text{positive integer not exceeding 3}\}$

1.76 What is the truth value of the quantification $(\exists x)\, Q(x)$, if the statement $Q(x)$ and universe of discourse is given as follows:

(a) $Q(x): x > 3?,$ $U = \{\text{all real number}\}$

(b) $Q(x): x = x + 2$ $U = \{\text{all real number}\}$

(c) $Q(x): x^2 < 12,$ $U = \{\text{positive integer not exceeding 3}\}$

1.77 Translate these statements into English:

$(x): x$ is a cat

$A(x): x$ is an animal

(a) $\forall x((x) \to A(x))$

(b) $\forall x((x) \wedge A(x))$

(c) $\exists x((x) \to A(x))$

(d) $(\forall x)\, ((x) \wedge \sim A(x))$

1.78 Translate each of these statements into logical expression using predicates, quantifiers and logical connectives.
  (a) Someone in your class can speak Oriya.
  (b) Everyone in your class is honest.
  (c) There is a person in the class who was not born in India.
  (d) A student in your class has been in NCC.

1.79 Express the negation of these propositions using quantifier and then express the negation in English.
  (a) Some people do not follow the rules.
  (b) Some people are very serious.
  (c) No one can keep a secret.
  (d) There is someone in this class who is very intelligent.

1.80 Establish these logical equivalences, where P is a proposition not involving any quantifier.
  (a) $(\forall x Q(x)) \vee P \equiv \forall x (Q(x) \vee P)$ (b) $(\exists x Q(x)) \vee P \equiv \exists x (Q(x) \vee P)$
  (c) $(\forall x Q(x)) \wedge P \equiv \forall x (Q(x) \wedge P)$ (d) $(\exists x Q(x)) \wedge P \equiv \exists x (Q(x) \wedge P)$

1.81 Translate these statements into English.
  Let $Q(x, y) = $ 'x has sent a letter to y', where universe of discourse for both x and y consist of all students in your class.
  (a) $\exists x \, \exists y \, Q(x, y)$ (b) $\exists x \, \forall y \, Q(x, y)$
  (c) $\forall x \, \exists y \, Q(x, y)$ (d) $\exists y \, \exists x \, Q(x, y)$
  (e) $\exists y \, \forall x \, Q(x, y)$ (f) $\forall y \, \exists x \, Q(x, y)$

1.82 Use quantifier and predicate with more than one variable to express these statements:
  (a) Many students in this class can speak Hindi.
  (b) There is a student in this class who plays golf.
  (c) Some students in this class belong to the same town.
  (d) All students in this class have visited Agra.
  (e) Every student in this class has chatted with at least one other student, in at least one chat group.

1.83 Translate the following into a logical expression.
  (a) Every positive integer has exactly two square roots.
  (b) A negative real number does not have a square root that is a real number.
  (c) The difference of a real number and itself is zero.
  (d) The product of two negative real numbers is positive.

1.84 Which of the following are statements?
  (a) $(x) (A(x) \vee B(x)) \wedge C$ (b) $(x) (A(x) \wedge B(x)) \wedge (\exists x) D(x)$
  (c) $(y) (P(y) \wedge Q(y)) \wedge R(y)$

1.85 Indicate free and bound variables with scope of quantifier.
  (a) $(x) (A(x) \wedge B(x)) \rightarrow (x) A(x) \wedge B(x)$
  (b) $(x) (A(x) \wedge (\exists x) B(x)) \vee ((x) A(x) \rightarrow B(x))$
  (c) $(x) (A(x) \leftrightarrow B(x) \wedge (\exists x) R(x)) \wedge D(x)$

1.86 If the universe of discourse is set $\{1, 2, 3\}$, eliminate the quantifier in the following formulas.
  (a) $(x) Q(x)$ (b) $(\exists x) M(x)$

(c) $(x) A(x) \wedge (x) B(x)$ (d) $(x) A(x) \wedge \exists x\, M(x)$

(e) $(x) \sim A(x) \vee (x) A(x)$

1.87 Demonstrate the following implication.

(i) $(\exists x)(A(x) \wedge B(x)) \to (\exists x) A(x) \wedge (\exists x) B(x)$

(ii) $(x)(A(x) \vee B(x)) \to (x) A(x) \vee (\exists x) B(x)$

(iii) $(x)(A(x) \to B(x)) \wedge (x)(B(x) \to C(x)) \to (A(x) \to C(x))$

(iv) $(\exists x)(P(x) \wedge Q(x) \to (y) R(y) \to S(y))$
 and $(\exists y)(R(y) \wedge \sim S(y)) \to (x)(P(x) \to \sim Q(x))$

(v) $\sim(x)(P(x) \wedge Q(x)), (x) P(x) \to \equiv\, \sim(x) Q(x)$

1.88 Check the validity of the following conclusions:

(a) $(x)(A(x) \to B(x)), (\exists x) A(x)$ $\qquad C : (\exists z) B(z)$

(b) $(\exists y)(A(y) \wedge B(y))$ $\qquad C : (y) A(y)$

(c) $(\exists y) A(y), (\exists y) B(y)$ $\qquad C : (\exists y)(A(y) \wedge B(y))$

1.89 Using *CP* or otherwise, show the following implications:

(a) $((\exists y) P(y) \to (y) Q(y)) \to (y)(P(y) \to Q(y))$

(b) $(y)(A(y) \to B(y)), (y)(R(y) \to \sim B(y)) \to (y)(R(y) \to \sim A(y))$

(c) $(y)(A(y) \to B(y)) \to (y) A(y) \to (y) B(y)$

1.90 Show that, if m is an odd integer then m^2 is an odd integer.

1.91 Show that if $3m + 2$ is odd then m is odd.

1.92 Suppose $P(m)$ represents the statement "If x and y are positive integers with $x \geq y$ then $x^m \geq y^m$." Prove that the proposition $P(0)$ is true.

1.93 Prove that the sum of two rational numbers is rational.

1.94 Prove that, if m is an integer, and m^2 is odd, then m is odd.

1.95 Show that at least two of any eight days must fall on the same day of the week.

1.96 Show that $|ab| = |a|\,|b|$, where a and b are real numbers and $|a|$ represents the absolute value of a, which equals a when $a \geq 0$ and equals $-a$ if $a < 0$.

1.97 Prove that the integer m is odd if m^2 is odd.

1.98 Prove that there exist irrational numbers p and q such that p^q is rational.

1.99 Show that every rational number has a multiplicative inverse.

Objective
....

To discuss the
basic concepts of
permutations,
combinations,
discrete
probability and
conditional
probability.

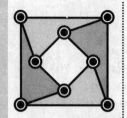

CHAPTER

TWO

PERMUTATIONS, COMBINATIONS, AND DISCRETE PROBABILITY

2.1 INTRODUCTION

In Sec. 1.5 we discussed some results on the size of finite sets. We shall present in this chapter some further results along this line. For example, let A be a finite set of size n. We might wish to know the number of distinct subsets of the set A, that is, the size of the power set of A, $\mathscr{P}(A)$. Furthermore, among all subsets of A, we might wish to know the number of subsets that are of size k. We might also wish to know the number of ordered sets with the components of the ordered sets being the elements of A. For example, let A be a set of 10 senators. The number of subsets in $\mathscr{P}(A)$, which is equal to 2^{10}, is the number of different committees the senators can form [including a committee with no members, corresponding to the empty set in $\mathscr{P}(A)$]. Moreover, the number of subsets of size 6 in $\mathscr{P}(A)$, which is equal to 210, is the number of different 6-member committees they can form. An ordered set of size 3 with distinct components from A might represent the 3 highest vote getters among the 10 senators in the election. There are 720 such ordered sets, corresponding to the 720 different possible outcomes. An ordered set of size 3 with not necessarily distinct components from A might represent the 3 chairpersons of 3 different senate committees consisting of some of the 10 senators. In this chapter, we shall discuss these and related problems in the context of permutations and combinations of objects.

2.2 THE RULES OF SUM AND PRODUCT

By an *experiment*, we mean a physical process that has a number of observable outcomes. For example, placing a ball in a box, placing a certain number of balls in a certain number of boxes, selecting a representative among a group of students, assigning offices to professors, placing bets on a horse race, tossing a coin, rolling a pair of dice and dealing a poker hand are all experiments. For example, for the experiment of placing a ball in a box, there is only one possible outcome. (There is only one way to place a ball in a box.) The two possible outcomes of tossing a coin are *head* and *tail*, the six possible outcomes of rolling a dice are 1, 2, 3, 4, 5, and 6, and both the experiments of dealing a poker hand and selecting five student representatives from 35,000 students have many possible outcomes. When we consider the outcomes of several experiments, we shall follow the rules stated below:

Rule of Product   If one experiment has m possible outcomes and another experiment has n possible outcomes then there are $m \times n$ possible outcomes when both of these experiments take place.

Rule of Sum   If one experiment has m possible outcomes and another experiment has n possible outcomes then there are $m + n$ possible outcomes when exactly one of these experiments takes place.

For example, if there are 52 ways to select a representative for the junior class and 49 ways to select a representative for the senior class then according to the rule of product, there will be 52×49 ways to select the representatives for both the junior and senior classes. On the other hand, according to the rule of sum, there will be $52 + 49$ ways to select a representative for either the junior or the senior class. As another example, suppose there are seven different courses offered in the morning and five different courses offered in the afternoon. There will be 7×5 choices for students who want to enroll in one course in the morning and one in the afternoon. On the other hand, they will have $7 + 5$ choices if they want to enroll in only one course.

2.3   PERMUTATIONS

Consider the simple problem of placing three balls colored red, blue, and white in 10 boxes numbered 1, 2, 3, ..., 10. We want to know the number of distinct ways in which the balls can be placed in the boxes, if each box can hold only one ball. Let us place the balls one at a time, beginning with the red ball, then the blue ball, and then the white ball. Since the red ball can be placed in any of the 10 boxes, the blue ball can be placed in any of the nine remaining boxes, and the white ball can be placed in any of the eight remaining boxes, the total number of distinct ways to place these balls is $10 \times 9 \times 8 = 720$.

The result of this numerical example can be generalized immediately:

Suppose we are to place r distinctly colored balls in n distinctly numbered boxes with the condition that a box can hold only one ball. Since the first ball can be placed in any one of the n boxes, the second ball can be placed in any one of the remaining $(n - 1)$ boxes, ..., and the rth ball can be placed in any one of the remaining $(n - r + 1)$ boxes, the total number of distinct ways to place the balls is

$$n(n-1)(n-2) \dots (n-r+1)$$

which can also be written as*

$$\frac{n!}{(n-r)!}$$

We use the notation $P(n, r)$ for the quantity $n(n-1)(n-2) \dots (n-r+1)$.

The following examples show that the problem of placing balls in boxes is not as uninteresting as it might seem.

Example 2.1 In how many ways can three examinations be scheduled within a five-day period so that no two examinations are scheduled on the same day? Considering the three examinations as distinctly colored balls and the five days as distinctly numbered boxes, we obtain the result $5 \times 4 \times 3 = 60$. ∎

Example 2.2 Suppose that we have seven rooms and want to assign four of them to four programmers as offices and use the remaining three rooms for computer terminals. The assignment can be made in $7 \times 6 \times 5 \times 4 = 840$ different ways because we can view the problem as that of placing four distinct balls (the programmers) into seven distinct boxes (the rooms), with the three boxes that are left empty being the rooms for computer terminals. (We assume that the programmers are distinct but that all computer terminals are identical.) ∎

A problem equivalent to placing balls in boxes is that of arranging or permuting distinct objects. By permuting r of n distinct objects, we mean to arrange r of these n objects in some order. For example, there are six ways to permute two of the three objects a, b, c. They are ab, ba, ac, ca, bc, and cb. Since to arrange r of n objects amounts to filling r positions with r of the n objects, there are n choices of an object for the first position, $n-1$ choices of an object (from the $n-1$ remaining objects) for the second position, ..., and $n-r+1$ choices of an object (from the $n-r+1$ remaining objects) for the rth position. Consequently, there are $n(n-1) \dots (n-r+1)$ ways to arrange r of n objects in order.[†] In the terminology of ordered sets, there are $n(n-1) \dots (n-r+1)$ ordered r-tuples that have *distinct* components which are elements from a set of size n.

Consider the following examples:

Example 2.3 Let us determine the number of four-digit decimal numbers that contain no repeated digits. Since this is a problem of arranging 4 of the 10 digits

---

* $n!$ reads "n factorial" and is defined to be $n(n-1)(n-2) \dots 2 \times 1$. We also have the convention that 0! is equal to 1.

[†] A slightly different point of view which might cause some initial confusion but will prove to be useful eventually is to consider the problem as that of placing balls in boxes. Consider n boxes corresponding to the n objects, and r balls corresponding to the r positions in the arrangement. The placement of a ball in a certain box is equivalent to putting the object corresponding to the box in a position corresponding to the ball in an arrangement. Consequently, the number of ways to permute r of n objects is $P(n, r)$.

0, 1, 2, ..., 9, the answer is $P(10, 4) = 5040$. Among these 5040 numbers, $9 \times 8 \times 7 = 504$ of them have a leading 0. Consequently, $5040 - 504 = 4536$ of them do not have a leading 0. The result can also be computed as

$$9 \times 9 \times 8 \times 7 = 4536$$

using the argument that the first digit can be any one of the nine digits 1, 2, ..., 9, the second digit can be any of the *nine* remaining digits, and so on. ∎

Example 2.4 We note that the number of ways in which we can make up strings of four distinct letters followed by three distinct digits is

$$P(26, 4) \times P(10, 3) = 258{,}336{,}000 \qquad ∎$$

Let us return to the problem of placing 3 distinctly colored balls into 10 distinctly numbered boxes. Suppose a box can hold as many balls as we wish. Since the red ball can be placed in any of the 10 boxes, as can the blue ball, and as can the white ball, the total number of ways of placement is

$$10 \times 10 \times 10 = 1000$$

In general, there are n^r ways to place r colored balls into n numbered boxes if a box can hold as many balls as we wish.

We consider now some other examples:

Example 2.5 If we are to schedule three examinations within a five-day period with no restriction on the number of examinations scheduled each day, the total number of ways is $5^3 = 125$. ∎

Example 2.6 Let us determine the number of subsets of a set A whose size is r. Consider the problem of placing the r elements of A in two boxes. Corresponding to each placement, we can define a subset of A by taking the elements placed in box 1 and discarding the elements placed in box 2. Since there are 2^r ways to place the r elements, there are 2^r subsets in $\mathscr{P}(A)$. ∎

Similarly, in terms of permutation of objects, we say that, if there are n distinct kinds of objects with an infinite supply of each kind, then there are n^r ways to arrange r of these n kinds of objects, because there are n choices of an object for the first position, n choices of an object for the second position, ..., and n choices of an object for the rth position. Again, in the terminology of ordered sets, there are n^r ordered r-tuples with their components being elements from a set of size n. For example, there are 10^4 four-digit decimal sequences. Consequently, $10^4 - P(10, 4) = 4960$ of them contain one or more repeated digits.

Example 2.7 We observe first that there are 2^r r-digit binary sequences. We now ask among the 2^r r-digit binary sequences how many of them have an even number of 1s? We can pair off these binary sequences such that two sequences in a pair differ only in the rth digits. Clearly, one of the two sequences in a pair has an even number of 1s and the other has an odd number of 1s. It follows that there are $\frac{1}{2} \cdot 2^r$ r-digit binary sequences that contain an even number of 1s.

There is a slightly different way to derive the same result. There are $2^{r-1}(r-1)$-digit binary sequences. To an $(r-1)$-digit sequence that has an even number of 1s, we can append a 0 to obtain an r-digit sequence that has an even number of 1s. To an $(r-1)$-digit sequence that has an odd number of 1s, we can append a 1 to obtain an r-digit sequence that has an even number of 1s. Furthermore, in these two ways, we shall obtain all r-digit sequences that have an even number of 1s. Consequently, there are 2^{r-1} of them. Such an idea can be employed to enhance the reliability of computers. Inside a computer, data are represented by sequences of binary digits. In the course of manipulating and transmitting these binary sequences, an error is said to occur if a 0 becomes a 1, or a 1 becomes a 0. So that errors will be detected, we shall use $(r-1)$-digit binary sequences to represent the data and append an rth digit to each sequence so that the resultant r-digit sequence always has an even number of 1s. The occurrence of an error (as a matter of fact, the occurrence of an odd number of errors) will yield a binary sequence with an odd number of 1s. The detection of a binary sequence with an odd number of 1s will signify the presence of an error condition.

We now ask for the number of r-digit quintary sequences (sequences made up of the digits 0, 1, 2, 3, 4) that contain an even number of 1s. We note that among the 5^r r-digit quintary sequences, there are 3^r of them that contain only the digits 2, 3, and 4. These sequences are, of course, counted as sequences containing an even number of 1s. The remaining $5^r - 3^r$ sequences can be divided into groups according to the patterns of 2s, 3s, and 4s in the sequences. (For instance, all sequences of the form $23xx344xx2xxx$ will be in one group, where each x is either 0 or 1.) Since half of the sequences in each group has an even number of 1s, the total number of r-digit quintary sequences with an even number of 1s is $3^r + \frac{1}{2}(5^r - 3^r)$. ∎

Example 2.8 Suppose we print all five-digit numbers on slips of paper with one number on each slip. However, since the digits 0, 1, 6, 8, and 9 become 0, 1, 9, 8, and 6 when they are read upside down, there are pairs of numbers that can share the same slip if the slips are read right side up or upside down. For example, we can make up one slip for the numbers 89166 and 99168. The question is then how many distinct slips will we have to make up for all five-digit numbers. We note first that there are 10^5 distinct five-digit numbers. Among these numbers, 5^5 of them can be read either right side up or upside down. (They are made up of the digits 0, 1, 6, 8, and 9.) However, there are numbers that read the same either right side up or upside down, for example, 16091, and there are $3(5^2)$ such numbers. (The center digit of these numbers must be either 1, 0, or 8; furthermore, the fifth digit must be the first digit turned upside down, and the fourth digit must be the second digit turned upside down.) Consequently, there are $5^5 - 3(5^2)$ numbers that can be read either right side up or upside down but will read differently. These numbers can be divided into pairs so that every pair of numbers can share one slip. It follows that the total number of distinct slips we need is $10^5 - [5^5 - 3(5^2)]/2$. ∎

Example 2.9 We now give an example on the application of the principle of inclusion and exclusion. Suppose a student wants to make up a schedule for a seven-day period during which she will study one subject each day. She is taking four subjects: mathematics, physics, chemistry, and economics. Clearly, there are 4^7 different schedules. We want to know the number of schedules that devote at least one day to each subject?*

Let A_1 denote the set of schedules in which mathematics is never included. Let A_2 denote the set of schedules in which physics is never included. Let A_3 denote the set of schedules in which chemistry is never included. Let A_4 denote the set of schedules in which economics is never included. Then

$$A_1 \cup A_2 \cup A_3 \cup A_4$$

is the set of schedules in which one or more of the subjects is not included. Since

$$|A_1| = |A_2| = |A_3| = |A_4| = 3^7$$
$$|A_1 \cap A_2| = |A_1 \cap A_3| = |A_1 \cap A_4| = |A_2 \cap A_3|$$
$$= |A_2 \cap A_4| = |A_3 \cap A_4| = 2^7$$
$$|A_1 \cap A_2 \cap A_3| = |A_1 \cap A_2 \cap A_4| = |A_1 \cap A_3 \cap A_4|$$
$$= |A_2 \cap A_3 \cap A_4| = 1^7$$
$$|A_1 \cap A_2 \cap A_3 \cap A_4| = 0$$

we obtain

$$|A_1 \cup A_2 \cup A_3 \cup A_4| = 4(3^7) - 6(2^7) + 4$$

Consequently, the number of schedules in which all subjects will be included is

$$4^7 - 4(3^7) + 6(2^7) - 4 \qquad \blacksquare$$

Let us consider the problem of placing four balls, two red, one blue, and one white, in 10 numbered boxes. Suppose we repaint the two red balls with two shades of red, light and dark, so that they become distinguishable. The number of ways to place these balls in the 10 boxes is then $P(10, 4) = 5040$. Among these 5040 placements, let us consider the placement in which the light red ball is in the first box, the dark red ball is in the second box, the blue ball is in the third box, and the white ball is in the fourth box, and the placement in which the dark red ball is in the first box, the light red ball is in the second box, the blue ball is in the third box, and the white ball is in the fourth box. If we do not distinguish between the two shades of red, that is, if the two red balls are indistinguishable, these two ways of placement actually become one. Indeed, the 5040 placements can be paired off in a similar way so that every pair of placements becomes one when we do not distinguish the two shades of red. Consequently, there are $\frac{5040}{2} = 2520$ ways to place two red balls, one blue ball, and one white ball in 10 numbered boxes. Following the same argument, we see that the number of ways of placing

---

* We ask the reader to convince himself that $P(7, 4) \times 4^3$ is not the right answer. There is a flaw in the argument that there are $P(7, 4)$ ways to schedule four subjects for four of the seven days, and 4^3 ways to schedule three subjects for the three remaining days.

three red balls, one blue ball, and one white ball in 10 numbered boxes is

$$\frac{P(10,5)}{3!} = 5040$$

because each way to place three *indistinguishable* red balls, one blue ball, and one white ball corresponds to 3! ways of placing three *distinguishable* red balls, one blue ball, and one white ball.

We derive now a general formula for the number of ways to place r colored balls in n number boxes, where q_1 of these balls are of one color, q_2 of them are of a second color, ..., and q_t of them are of a tth color. We note that a placement of the r balls is not changed by rearranging the q_1 balls of the same color among the boxes in which they are placed, or rearranging the q_2 balls of the same color among the boxes in which they are placed, ..., or rearranging the q_t balls of the same color among the boxes in which they are placed. On the other hand, if the r balls were distinctly colored, any rearrangement will yield a different placement. It follows that each way to place the r not completely distinctly colored balls corresponds to $q_1!q_2!...q_t!$ ways to place r distinctly colored balls. Since there are $P(n, r)$ ways to place r distinctly colored balls in n numbered boxes, the total number of ways to place r colored balls in n numbered boxes, where q_1 of these balls are of one color, q_2 of them are of a second color, ..., and q_t of them are of a tth color, is

$$\frac{P(n,r)}{q_1!\,q_2!\,q_t!} \tag{2.1}$$

Example 2.10   We observe that the number of ways to paint 12 offices so that 3 of them will be green, 2 of them pink, 2 of them yellow, and the remaining ones white is

$$\frac{12!}{3!2!2!5!} = 166,320 \qquad \blacksquare$$

In terms of arrangement of objects, we say that there are

$$\frac{n!}{q_1!q_2!.....!} \tag{2.2}$$

ways to arrange n objects, where q_1 of them are of one kind, q_2 of them are of a second kind, ..., and q_t of them are of a tth kind. Again, if the n objects were all distinct, there are $n!$ ways to arrange them. On the other hand, in an arrangement of objects that are not completely distinct, permuting the objects of the same kind among themselves will not change the arrangement. We thus obtain the formula in (2.2).

Example 2.11   We note that the number of different messages that can be represented by sequences of three dashes and two dots is

$$\frac{5!}{3!2!} = 10 \qquad \blacksquare$$

2.4 COMBINATIONS

Consider now the problem of placing three balls, all of them colored red, in 10 boxes that are numbered 1, 2, 3, ..., 10. We want to know the number of ways the balls can be placed, if each box can hold only one ball. According to (2.1), the answer is

$$\frac{10 \times 9 \times 8}{3!}$$

In general, the number of ways of placing r balls of the same color in n numbered boxes is

$$\frac{n(n-1)(n-2)\dots(n-r+1)}{r!} = \frac{n!}{r!(n-r)!}$$

The quantity $\frac{n!}{r!(n-r)!}$ is also denoted $C(n, r)$ or $\left(\frac{n}{r}\right)$.

Let us consider some examples:

Example 2.12 Suppose a housekeeper wants to schedule spaghetti dinners three times each week. Imagine the spaghetti dinners as three balls and the seven days in the week as seven boxes; then the number of ways of scheduling is

$$\frac{7!}{3!4!} = 35 \qquad \blacksquare$$

Example 2.13 We note that there are $C(32, 7)$ binary sequences of length 32 in each of which there are exactly seven 1s, because we can view the problem as placing seven 1s in 32 numbered boxes (and then fill the empty boxes with 0s).

$\blacksquare$

A problem equivalent to placing r indistinguishable balls in n numbered boxes is that of selection of r objects from n distinct objects. If we are to select r objects from n distinct objects, we can imagine the n objects as boxes and mark the selected objects with r identical markers, the balls. Consequently, the number of ways to select r objects from n distinct objects is also $C(n, r)$. In other words, for a set of size n there are $C(n, r)$ subsets of size r.

According to the definition of $C(n, r)$, it is clear that $C(n, r) = C(n, n-r)$. There is also a simple combinatorial argument that confirms this result: since to select r objects from n objects is the same as to pick out the $n - r$ objects that are not to be selected, we have $C(n, r) = C(n, n-r)$.

Example 2.14 Among 11 senators there are $C(11, 5) = 462$ ways to select a committee of 5 members. Moreover, there are $C(10, 4) = 210$ ways to select a committee of five members so that a particular senator, senator A, is always included, and there are $C(10, 5) = 252$ ways to select a committee of five members so that senator A is always excluded. We now ask in how many ways we can select a committee of five members so that at least one of senator A and senator B

will be included. The number of selections including both senator A and senator B is $C(9, 3) = 84$. The number of selections including senator A but excluding senator B is $C(9, 4) = 126$, as is the number of selections including senator B but excluding senator A. Consequently, the total number of ways of selection is

$$84 + 126 + 126 = 336$$

Alternatively, since the total number of committees excluding both A and B is $C(9, 5)$, the total number of ways of selection is

$$C(11, 5) - C(9, 5) = 462 - 126 = 336$$

The problem can also be solved by applying the principle of inclusion and exclusion. Among the 462 ways of selecting 5 senators, let A_1 and A_2 be the set of ways of selection that include senator A and senator B, respectively. Since

$$|A_1| = C(10, 4) = 210$$
$$|A_2| = C(10, 4) = 210$$
$$|A_1 \cap A_2| = C(9, 3) = 84$$

it follows that

$$|A_1 \cup A_2| = 210 + 210 - 84 = 336 \qquad \blacksquare$$

Example 2.15 If no three diagonals of a convex decagon meet at the same point inside the decagon, into how many line segments are the diagonals divided by their intersections? First of all, the number of diagonals is equal to

$$C(10, 2) - 10 = 45 - 10 = 35$$

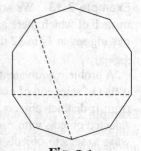

as there are $C(10, 2)$ straight lines joining the $C(10, 2)$ pairs of vertices, but 10 of these 45 lines are the sides of the decagon. Since for every four vertices we can count exactly one intersection between the diagonals, as Fig. 2.1 shows (the decagon is convex), there are a total of $C(10, 4) = 210$ intersections between the diagonals. Since a diagonal is divided into $k + 1$ straight-line segments when there are k intersecting points lying on it, and since each intersecting point lies on two diagonals, the total number of straight-line segments into which the diagonals are divided is $35 + 2 \times 210 = 455$.

Fig. 2.1

Suppose we are to place r balls of the same color in n numbered boxes, allowing as many balls in a box as we wish. The number of ways to place the balls is

$$\frac{(n+r-1)!}{r!(n-1)!} = C(n + r - 1, r)$$

An easy way to see this result is to consider the problem of arranging $n + 1$ 1s and r 0s with a 1 at the beginning and a 1 at the end of each arrangement. If we consider the 1s as interbox partitions and the 0s as balls, then every such arrangement corresponds to a way of placing r balls of the same color in n numbered boxes. For example, let $n = 5$ and $r = 4$, the sequence

$$1011001101$$

can be viewed as a placement of four balls in five boxes having one ball in the first box, no ball in the second box, two balls in the third box, no ball in the fourth box, and one ball in the fifth box. According to (2.1), the number of ways of arranging r 0s and $n + 1$ 1s with 1s at both ends of an arrangement is

$$\frac{(n+r-1)!}{r!(n-1)!}$$

We note that the problem of selecting r objects from n distinct objects, allowing repeated selections, can be viewed as that of using r identical markers to mark the n distinct objects while each object can be marked with arbitrarily many markers. Therefore, the number of ways to select r objects from n distinct objects, allowing repeated selections, is

$$\frac{(n+r-1)!}{r!(n-1)!} = C(n+r-1, r) \tag{2.3}$$

Consider the following examples:

Example 2.16 The number of ways to choose three out of seven days (with repetitions allowed) is

$$C(7 + 3 - 1, 3) = C(9, 3) = 84$$

The number of ways to choose seven out of three days (with repetitions necessarily allowed) is

$$C(3 + 7 - 1, 7) = C(9, 7) = 36 \qquad \blacksquare$$

Example 2.17 A domino is made up of two squares each of which is marked with one, two, three, four, five, or six spots, or is left blank. We note that there are 28 different dominoes in a set, because the number of distinct dominoes is the same as the number of ways of selecting two subjects from the seven objects "one," "two," "three," "four," "five," "six," and "blank," with repetitions allowed. Thus, according to (2.3), the number of distinct dominoes is

$$C(7 + 2 - 1, 2) = C(8, 2) = 28 \qquad \blacksquare$$

Example 2.18 We note that when three dice are rolled, the number of different outcomes is

$$C(6 + 3 - 1, 3) = C(8, 3) = 56$$

because rolling three dice is equivalent to selecting three numbers from the six numbers 1, 2, 3, 4, 5, 6, with repetitions allowed. $\qquad \blacksquare$

Example 2.19 We ask for the number of different paths for a rook* to move from the southwest corner of a chessboard to the northeast corner by moving eastward and northward only. If we let a 0 denote an eastward step and a 1 denote a northward step, then the number of paths is equal to the number of ways of arranging seven 0s and seven 1s, which is

$$\frac{14!}{7!7!} = 3432$$

We ask now how many of these paths consist of four eastward moves and three northward moves. (By an eastward move we mean a certain number of consecutive eastward steps. A northward move is defined similarly.) The number of ways of making up a path with four eastward moves is the same as that of placing seven indistinguishable balls in four distinct boxes with no box left empty. Let us place a ball in each of the four boxes and then distribute the three remaining balls. Since the number of ways to distribute three indistinguishable balls in four distinct boxes with each box holding as many balls as we wish is

$$C(4 + 3 - 1, 3) = 20$$

the number of ways to place the seven balls in four boxes with no box left empty is also equal to 20. Similarly, the number of ways of making up a path with three northward moves is

$$C(3 + 4 - 1, 4) = 15$$

Therefore, the answer to our question is

$$20 \times 15 = 300 \qquad \blacksquare$$

Example 2.20 We want to determine the number of ways to seat five boys in a row of 12 chairs. The problem can be viewed as that of arranging 12 objects that are of six different kinds, with each boy being an object of a distinct kind and the seven unoccupied chairs being objects of the same kind. According to (2.2), the number of arrangements is

$$\frac{12!}{7!}$$

There is an alternative way to obtain the same result. Suppose we first arrange the five boys in a row (there are 5! ways to do so), and then distribute the seven unoccupied chairs arbitrarily either between any two boys or at the two ends. The distribution problem then becomes that of placing seven balls of the same color in six boxes. Thus, the number of ways to do so is

$$5! \times C(6 + 7 - 1, 7) = 5! \times \frac{12!}{7!5!} = \frac{12!}{7!}$$

Suppose we want to seat the boys so that no two boys are next to each other. We ask the reader to confirm that the number of ways to seat the boys is

---

* A rook is a chesspiece that can move horizontally and vertically on a chessboard.

$$5! \times C(6 + 3 - 1, 3) = 5! \times \frac{8!}{3!5!} = \frac{8!}{3!} \qquad \blacksquare$$

Example 2.21 We want to determine the number of ways to place $2t + 1$ indistinguishable balls in three distinct boxes so that any two boxes together will contain more balls than the other one. The total number of ways to place the balls disregarding the constraint is

$$C(3 + 2t + 1 - 1, 2t + 1) = C(2t + 3, 2t + 1)$$

The total number of ways to place the balls so that the first box will have more balls than the second and third boxes combined is

$$C(3 + t - 1, t) = C(t + 2, t)$$

(We place $t + 1$ balls in the first box and then place the t remaining balls in the three boxes arbitrarily.) The same result applies to the case that the second box has more balls than the first and third boxes combined, and to the case that the third box has more balls than the first and second boxes combined. Thus, the answer to our question is

$$C(2t + 3, 2t + 1) - 3C(t + 2, t) = C(2t + 3, 2) - 3C(t + 2, 2)$$

$$= \frac{1}{2}(2t + 3)(2t + 2) - \frac{3}{2}(t + 2)(t + 1)$$

$$= \frac{t(t+1)}{2} \qquad \blacksquare$$

*2.5 GENERATION OF PERMUTATIONS AND COMBINATIONS

Suppose we want to write down the $n!$ permutations of n distinct objects. For $n = 3$, there are only six permutations, so there clearly is little difficulty. For $n = 4$, there are 24 permutations, and it is no longer a totally trivial task to keep track of what we have written down and to make sure we shall write down all the permutations with no omissions or repetitions. An interesting problem is to find systematic procedures that exhaustively generate all the permutations of n objects. As an illustration, we shall present one such procedure. Before we describe our procedure, let us point out an important question one might raise: If we are to design a procedure or to examine a procedure presented to us, how can we ascertain that the procedure will indeed do what it purports to do, namely, to generate all permutations of n objects? Note that there is no way for us to test exhaustively the procedure, since it is supposed to perform correctly for all positive integers n. One way to make sure that a procedure will generate all the permutations exhaustively with no repetition is to introduce an ordering of the $n!$ permutations. If we have a procedure that generates the permutations one by one according to this order then we can be assured that the procedure will correctly generate all the permutations when it starts with the first permutation in the order and stops at the last permutation in the order. One order we can use is the *lexicographic order.* Without loss of generality, let $\{1, 2, 3, ..., n\}$ be the n objects to be permuted. For two permutations $a_1 a_2 ... a_n$ and $b_1 b_2 ... b_n$, we shall say $a_1 a_2 ... a_n$ comes before $b_1 b_2 ... b_n$ in the lexicographic order if, for some $1 \leqq m < n$, $a_1 = b_1$, $a_2 = b_2$, ..., $a_{m-1} = b_{m-1}$, and $a_m < b_m$. For example, the permutation 124635 comes before the permutation 125643, and the permutation 125463 comes after the permutation 125346.

Suppose we were given a permutation $a_1 a_2 ... a_n$. Our question is what the next permutation is according to the lexicographic order. It is not difficult to show that the next permutation $b_1 b_2 ... b_n$ must be such that:

1. $a_i = b_i$, $1 \leqq i \leqq m - 1$, and $a_m < b_m$, for the largest possible m.

2. b_m is the smallest element among a_{m+1}, a_{m+2}, ..., a_n that is larger than a_m.

3. $b_{m+1} < b_{m+2} < ... < b_n$.

For example, the permutation following 124653 in the lexicographic order is 125346. For a given permutation $a_1 a_2 ... a_n$, we note that the largest possible m for which (1) is satisfied is the largest possible m for which a_m is less than at least one of a_{m+1}, a_{m+2}, ..., a_n. A moment's reflection shows that this is also the largest possible m for which $a_m < a_{m+1}$.* Therefore, if we examine the permutation $a_1 a_2 ... a_n$ element by element from *right to left*, the first time we observe a decrement, we know the value of m and can determine $b_m b_{m+1} ... b_m$ according to (2) and (3). For example, suppose we were given the permutation 124653. When we scan the permutation from right to left element by element, according to (1), we determine that the next permutation is of the form $12xxxx$. In other words, the subscript m is equal to 3. According to (2), we can further determine that the next permutation is of the form $125xxx$. Finally, according to (3), we determine that the next permutation is 125346. (Actually, we can make use of the fact that $a_{m+1} > a_{m+2} > ... > a_n$ to carry out steps 2 and 3 in a rather simple manner. The interested reader is referred to Prob. 2.55.)

Our observation leads immediately to a systematic procedure for generating the $n!$ permutations of n objects by starting with the permutation 1234 ... n and stopping at the permutation n ... 4321. Moreover, we know that the procedure is indeed a correct one. We ask the reader to convince herself that our procedure will indeed generate the permutations of the four objects 1, 2, 3, 4 in the following order:

$$1234 \rightarrow 1243 \rightarrow 1324 \rightarrow 1342 \rightarrow 1423 \rightarrow 1432 \rightarrow 2134 \rightarrow 2143 \rightarrow$$
$$2314 \rightarrow 2341 \rightarrow 2413 \rightarrow 2431 \rightarrow 3124 \rightarrow 3142 \rightarrow 3214 \rightarrow 3241 \rightarrow$$
$$3412 \rightarrow 3421 \rightarrow 4123 \rightarrow 4132 \rightarrow 4213 \rightarrow 4231 \rightarrow 4312 \rightarrow 4321$$

---

* Suppose that m is the largest possible subscript for which a_m is less than one of a_{m+1}, a_{m+2}, ..., a_n. Let us assume, however, that $a_m > a_{m+1}$ and $a_m < a_{m+j}$ for some $j > 1$. We then have $a_{m+1} < a_{m+j}$ contradicting the assumption that m is the largest possible subscript for which a_m is less than one of a_{m+1}, a_{m+2}, ..., a_n. The converse argument is left to the reader.

Suppose we want to generate all k-subsets* of the set $\{1, 2, 3, ..., n\}$. So that we can introduce a lexicographic order of the subsets, let us agree first that each subset will be represented by a sequence with the elements in the subset arranged in increasing order. We can then arrange the sequences according to the lexicographic order.[†] For example, the 4-subsets of $\{1, 2, 3, 4, 5, 6\}$ are represented and ordered as

$$1234$$
$$1235$$
$$1236$$
$$1245$$
$$1246$$
$$1256$$
$$1345$$
$$1346$$
$$1356$$
$$1456$$
$$2345$$
$$2346$$
$$2356$$
$$2456$$
$$3456$$

Along exactly the same line as our procedure to generate permutations, let us observe how we can design a procedure to generate all k-subsets of the set $\{1, 2, ..., n\}$. Let $a_1 a_2 ... a_k$ be a k-subset. It can be shown that the next k-subset $b_1 b_2 ... b_k$ according to the lexicographic order must be such that

1. $a_i = b_i$, $1 \leq i \leq m - 1$, and $a_m < b_m$ for the largest possible m.
2. $b_m = a_m + 1$.
3. $b_{j+1} = b_j + 1$ for $m \leq j \leq k - 1$.

In the sequence $a_1 a_2 ... a_k$, we define the maximum possible value of a_j to be $n - k + j$. Thus, the maximum possible value of a_k is n, the maximum possible value of a_{k-1} is $n - 1$, the maximum possible value of a_{k-2} is $n - 2$, ..., and the maximum possible value of a_1 is $n - k + 1$. Since in $a_1 a_2 ... a_k$ the largest m for which a_m is not equal to its maximum possible value is the largest m that satisfies (1), we can determine m by examining $a_1 a_2 ... a_k$ from *right to left*, element by element. Once the value of m is determined we can determine $b_m b_{m+1} ... b_k$ according to (2) and (3). We ask the reader to confirm that the 4-subsets of $\{1, 2, 3, 4, 5, 6\}$ shown above were indeed generated by our procedure.

---

* A subset of size k is abbreviated as a k-subset.
[†] For two k-subsets $a_1 a_2 ... a_k$ and $b_1 b_2 ... b_k$, we shall say $a_1 a_2 ... a_k$ comes before $b_1 b_2 ... b_k$ in the lexicographic order if for some $1 \leq m \leq k$, $a_1 = b_1$, $a_2 = b_2$, ..., $a_{m-1} = b_{m-1}$, and $a_m < b_m$.

2.6 BINOMIAL THEOREM

Binomial theorem can be used to find the coefficients of the terms in the expansion of power of binomial expression $(p + q)^n$. A binomial expression is a simple algebraic expression involving two terms, such as $p + q$. We know that the number of r combinations from a set of n elements is denoted by ^nC_r or $\binom{n}{r}$. This number is also termed *binomial coefficient* in the expansion of $(p + q)^n$. Below, first we discuss the binomial theorem which shows the power of a binomial expression as the sum of terms involving binomial coefficients. Then, we prove the binomial theorem by using the principle of mathematical induction.

Let p and q be two variables. Let us compute the power of the simple algebraic expression $(p + q)$. We start with powers 2 and 3.

Now,

$$(p + q)^2 = p^2 + 2pq + q^2,$$

$$(p + q)^3 = (p + q)(p + q)(p + q) = (p + q)(p^2 + 2pq + q^2) = p^3 + 3p^2q + 3pq^2 + q^3$$

and so on.

We can see that the coefficients we get are integers. Let us make this observation precise. We illustrate the argument for the next value of n, i.e., $n = 4$.

$$(p + q)^4 = (p + q)\,(p + q)\,(p + q)\,(p + q).$$

We get each term in the expansion by selecting one of the two terms in each factor and multiplying them. If we choose p one time then we have to choose q three times because the sum of powers of p and q should be 4 for expansion of $(p + q)^4$ and hence we get pq^3. How many times do we get the same term? Clearly, as many times as the number of ways to select the factor that supplies p (the remaining factors supply q).

Thus to obtain a term of the form pq^3, p must be chosen from one of the four sums (and consequently, q in the other sums). Hence, the number of such terms will be $4C_1$. Similarly, the number of terms for p^2q^2, p^3q, p^4, will be $4C_2$, $4C_3$, $4C_4$ and $4C_0$ respectively.

Hence, the expansion of $(p + q)^4$ will look like the following:

$$(p + q)^4 = \binom{4}{0}q^4 + \binom{4}{1}pq^{4-1} + \binom{4}{2}p^2q^{4-2} + \binom{4}{3}p^3q^{4-3}\binom{4}{4}p^4$$

$$= 4C_0q^4 + 4C_1pq^3 + 4C_2p^2q^2 + 4C_3pq^3 + 4C_4q^4.$$

If we choose q first in each term then the expansion of $(p + q)^4$ will look like the following:

$$(p + q)^4 = 4C_0p^4 + 4C_1p^3q + 4C_2p^2q^2 + 4C_3p^3q + 4C_4p^4.$$

Now, we generalize the above expansion for any value of n, where n is a positive integer. We consider the identity

$$(p + q)^n = (p + q)\,(p + q)...p + q) \text{ (up to n times)} \qquad (2.4)$$

The product on the right-hand side gives $2n$ terms; but not all the terms are different. Each term is of the form $p^x q^y$ such that $x + y = n$. How many such terms are there? Think that you have n boxes and each box can be filled up with either p or q. How many ways can this be done? Definitely one has to choose r boxes out of n and fill all of them with q's and remaining boxes with p's. From the general combinatorial theory, this can be done in $\binom{n}{r}$ ways. In other words, out of $2n$ terms in the right-hand side of Eq. (2.4), there are $\binom{n}{r}$ terms each equal to $p^r q^{n-r}$. Since r can take any value from 0 to n, we have

$$(p + q)^n = \sum_{r=0}^{n} \binom{n}{r} p^{n-r} q^r$$

This is called the binomial theorem for positive integral index. This can also be proved by mathematical induction. We observe that the theorem is true for $n = 1, 2$. Assume that it is true for $n = m$. Then,

$$(p + q)^m = \sum_{r=0}^{n} \binom{n}{r} p^{n-r} q^r$$

For $n = m + 1$, we have

$$(p + q)^{m+1} = (p + q)(p + q)^m$$

$$= (p + q) \sum_{r=0}^{m} \binom{m}{r} p^{m-r} q^r$$

$$= \sum_{r=0}^{m} \binom{m}{r} p^{m+1-r} q^r + \sum_{r=0}^{m} \binom{m}{r} p^{m-r} q^{r+1}$$

$$= \sum_{r=0}^{m} \binom{m}{r} p^{m+1-r} q^r + \sum_{s=1}^{m+1} \binom{m}{s-1} p^{m+1-s} q^s$$

(where $s = r + 1$)

$$= p^{m+1} + \sum_{r=1}^{m} \left[\binom{m}{r-1} + \binom{m}{r} \right] p^{m+1-r} q^r + q^{m+1}$$

$$= p^{m+1} + \sum_{r=1}^{m} \binom{m+1}{r} p^{m+1-r} q^r + q^{m+1}$$

$$= \sum_{r=0}^{m+1} \binom{m+1}{r} p^{m+1-r} q^r.$$

Thus the assertion is also true for $n = m + 1$ and hence holds for every n.

Corollary-1 If n is a positive integer then $\sum_{r=0}^{n} \binom{n}{r} = 2^n$

Proof: According to binomial theorem,

$$(p + q)^n = \sum_{r=0}^{n} \binom{n}{r} p^{n-r} q^r$$

Putting $p = q = 1$, we get

$$(1+1)^n = \sum_{r=0}^{n} \binom{n}{r} 1^{n-r} 1^r$$

Thus,
$$2^n = \sum_{r=0}^{n} \binom{n}{r} \cdot 1.1$$

or,
$$\sum_{r=0}^{n} \binom{n}{r} = 2^n$$

Corollary-2   If n be a positive integer then $\sum_{r=0}^{n} (-1)^r \binom{n}{r} = 0$.

Proof: According to binomial theorem,

$$(p+q)^n = \sum_{r=0}^{n} \binom{n}{r} p^{n-r} q^r.$$

Putting $p = 1$ and $q = -1$, we get

$$(1+(-1))^n = \sum_{r=0}^{n} \binom{n}{r} 1^{n-r} (-1)^r.$$

Thus,
$$0 = \sum_{r=0}^{n} \binom{n}{r} (-1)^r,$$

or,
$$\sum_{r=0}^{n} (-1)^r \binom{n}{r} = 0.$$

Another important corollary of the binomial theorem is as follows:

$$\binom{n}{0} + \binom{n}{2} + \binom{n}{4} + \dots = \binom{n}{1} + \binom{n}{3} + \binom{n}{5} + \dots$$

where n is a positive integer. We leave the proof as an exercise to the reader.

Example 2.22 What will be the coefficient of $p^{11}q^{12}$ in the expansion of $(p+q)^{23}$?

Solution: From binomial theorem, it follows that the coefficient of $p^{11}q^{12}$ in the expansion of $(p+q)^{23}$ is

$$\binom{23}{11} = \frac{23!}{11!12!} = 1352078 \qquad \blacksquare$$

Example 2.23 What will be the coefficient of p^5q^6 in the expansion of $(3p - 2q)^{11}$?

Solution: According to the Binomial Theorem, we have

$$(3p - 2q)^{11} = \sum_{r=0}^{11} \binom{11}{r} (3p)^{11-r} (-2q)^r.$$

When $x = 6$ we get the term p^5q^6. So, coefficient of p^5q^6 in the expansion of

$$(3p - 2q)^{11} = \binom{11}{6} 3^{11-6} (-2)^6 = 7185024 \qquad \blacksquare$$

Example 2.24 Show that $1.\binom{n}{1} + 2.\binom{n}{2} + ... + n.\binom{n}{n} = n.2^{n-1}$.

Solution: By binomial theorem,

$$(1+x)^n = 1 + \binom{n}{1}.x + \binom{n}{2}.x^2 + ... + \binom{n}{n}.x^n.$$

Differentiating both sides with respect to x, we get

$$n(1+x)^{n-1} = 1 + \binom{n}{1}. + 2.\binom{n}{2}.x + ... + n.\binom{n}{n}.x^{n-1}.$$

Putting $x = 1$ in both sides, we get

$$n.2^{n-1} = 1.\binom{n}{1}. + 2.\binom{n}{2} + ... + n.\binom{n}{n}. \quad \blacksquare$$

Example 2.25 Show that $1.\binom{n}{1} - 2.\binom{n}{2} + ... + (-1)^{n-1}n.\binom{n}{n} = 0$.

Solution: Using binomial theorem, we can write

$$(1+x)^n = 1 + \binom{n}{1}x + \binom{n}{2}x^2 + ... + \binom{n}{n}x^n.$$

Differentiating both the sides with respect to x, we get

$$n.(1+x)^{n-1} = 1.\binom{n}{1} + 2.\binom{n}{2} + ... + n.\binom{n}{n}x^{n-1}.$$

Putting $x = -1$, we get

$$1.\binom{n}{1} - 2.\binom{n}{2} + ... + (-1)^{n-1}.n.\binom{n}{n} = 0. \quad \blacksquare$$

Example 2.26 Find the term independent of x in the expansion of $(x^2 + \frac{1}{x^3})^5$.

Solution: Let us denote the terms in the binomial theorem as $t_0, t_1, t_2, ..., t_n$, where $t_r = \binom{n}{r}p^{n-r}q^r$. In the present case, let t_r be the term free from x. Then,

$$t_r = \binom{5}{r} \times (x^2)^{5-r} \times \left(\frac{1}{x^3}\right)^r$$

$$= \binom{5}{r} \times x^{(10-2r)} \times \frac{1}{x^{3r}}$$

$$= \binom{5}{r} \times x^{10-5r}$$

Since t_r is free from x, we must have $10 - 5r = 0$ imply that $x = 2$. Hence, the term free from x is $\binom{5}{2} = 10$. $\quad \blacksquare$

Example 2.27 Prove that

$$\binom{n}{0}\binom{m}{r} + \binom{n}{1}\binom{m}{r-1} + \binom{n}{2}\binom{m}{r-2} + ... + \binom{n}{r}\binom{m}{0} = \binom{n+m}{r}.$$

Solution: Let us consider the identity

$$(1+x)^n (1+x)^m = (1+x)^{n+m}.$$

By virtue of binomial theorem, the coefficient of x^r in $(1 + x)^{n+m}$ is $\binom{n+m}{r}$. In the left-hand side, x^r can be constructed by collecting the coefficient of x^k from $(1 + x)^n$ and the coefficient of x^{r-k} from $(1 + x)^m$, $r = 0, 1, 2, \ldots, k$. Hence, we have the following table:

k	Coefficient of x^k from $(1 + x)^n$	Coefficient of x^{r-k} from $(1 + x)^m$	Coefficient of x^r
0	$\binom{n}{0}$	$\binom{m}{r}$	$\binom{n}{0}\binom{m}{r}$
1	$\binom{n}{1}$	$\binom{m}{r-1}$	$\binom{n}{1}\binom{m}{r-1}$
$\cdot$	$\cdot$	$\cdot$	$\cdot$
s	$\binom{n}{s}$	$\binom{m}{r-s}$	$\binom{n}{s}\binom{m}{r-s}$
$\cdot$	$\cdot$	$\cdot$	$\cdot$
r	$\binom{n}{r}$	$\binom{m}{0}$	$\binom{n}{r}\binom{m}{0}$

Hence, the coefficient of x^r in the left-hand side of the above identity is

$$\binom{n}{r}\binom{m}{r} + \binom{n}{1}\binom{m}{r-1} + \ldots + \binom{n}{r}\binom{m}{0}.$$

Since the coefficients of x^r in both sides of the above identity must be same, we have

$$\binom{n}{0}\binom{m}{r} + \binom{n}{1}\binom{m}{r-1} + \ldots + \binom{n}{r}\binom{m}{0} = \binom{m+n}{r}$$

Note that when $m = n$, we have

$$\binom{n}{0}\binom{n}{r} + \binom{n}{1}\binom{n}{r-1} + \ldots + \binom{n}{r}\binom{n}{0} = \binom{2n}{r}. \qquad \blacksquare$$

Example 2.28 For any natural number $n \geq 2$, prove that $17^n - 128n^2 + 112n$ always leaves remainder 1 when divided by 16^3.

Solution: Using binomial theorem, we can write

$$17^n = (1 + 16)^n$$

$$= 1 + \binom{n}{1} \times 16 + \binom{n}{2} \times 16^2 + \binom{n}{3} \times 16^3 + \ldots + 16^n$$

$$= 1 + 16n + 128\,(n^2 + n) - 16^3\,k \quad (k \text{ is a positive integer})$$

$$= 1 - 112n + 128\,n^2 + 16^3\,k$$

Therefore, $17^n - 128n^2 + 112n = 1 + 16^3\,k$. Hence, for any natural number $n \geq$ 2, $17^n - 128\,n^2 + 112n$ always leaves the remainder 1 when divided by 16^3. ∎

Example 2.29 For any natural number n, show that $21^n - 2^n - 19n \times 2^{n-1}$ is a multiple of 361.

Solution: Using binomial theorem, we can write

$$21^n = (2 + 19)^n$$

$$= 2^n + \binom{n}{1}.2^{n-1} \times 19 + \binom{n}{2} \times 2^{n-2} \times 19^2 + \ldots + 19^n$$

$$= 2^n + 19\,n \times 2^{n-1} + 19^2 \times k \quad (k \text{ is a positive integer})$$

Therefore, $21^n - 2^n - 19n \times 2^{n-1} = 361\,k$. So, for any natural number n, $21^n - 2^n - 19n \times 2^{n-1}$ is a multiple of 361. ∎

Example 2.30 For any positive integer n, show that $12^n - 11n$ leaves the remainder 1 when divided by 121.

Solution: Using binomial theorem we can write

$$12^n = (1 + 11)^n$$

$$= \binom{n}{0} + \binom{n}{1} \times 11 + \binom{n}{2} \times 11^2 + \ldots + 11^n$$

$$= 1 + 11n + 11^2 k \quad (k \text{ is a positive integer})$$

Therefore, $12^n - 11n = 1 + 121\,k$. Hence, for any positive integer n, $12^n - 11n$ leaves remainder 1 when divided by 121. ∎

Example 2.31 Show that $25^{100} + 2599$ is divisible by 676.

Solution: Using binomial theorem, we can write

$$25^{100} = (-1 + 26)^{100}$$

$$= 1 - \binom{100}{1} \times 26 + \binom{100}{2} \times 26^2 - \cdots + 26^{100}$$

Therefore, $25^{100} - 1 + 2600 = 26^2\,k \quad (k \text{ is an integer})$

So, $26^2 = 676$ divides $25^{100} + 2599$. ∎

2.6.1 Binomial Theorem for Negative Integral Index

Let x be any real number. It is well known that

$$1 + x + \ldots + x^{n-1} = \frac{1 - x^n}{1 - x}. \tag{2.5}$$

Also it is well known that if $|x| < 1$ then $x^n \rightarrow 0$. Now taking limit as $n \rightarrow \infty$ in both sides of (2.5), we get

$$1 + x + x^2 + \ldots = \frac{1}{1-x},$$

which is the formula for an infinite geometric series with common ratio x whose absolute value less than 1. Also, this gives the binomial theorem for negative index $n = -1$; i.e.

$$(1-x)^{-1} = 1 + x + x^2 + \ldots = \sum_{r=0}^{\infty} x^r \tag{2.6}$$

Valid for $|x| < 1$. Differentiating both sides of Eq. (2.6) with respect to x, we get (this is possible by the properties of convergent power series)

$$(1-x)^{-2} = 1 + 2x + 3x^2 + 4x^2 + \ldots \tag{2.7}$$

$$= \sum_{r=1}^{\infty} r x^{r-1}.$$

Once again differentiating with respect to x, we get

$$2(1-x)^{-3} = 2 + 6x + 2x^2 + 20x^2 + \ldots$$

$$= 2(1 + 3x + 6x^2 + 10x^3 + \ldots).$$

This gives

$$(1-x)^{-3} = 1 + 3x + 6x^2 + 10x^3 + \ldots$$

$$= 1 + \binom{3}{1}x + \binom{4}{2}x^2 + \binom{5}{3}x^3 + \ldots$$

To write a general formula for $(1-x)^{-r}$, let us study the binomial coefficient $\binom{n}{r}$ more closely. By definition, if n and r are non-negative integers and $r \leq n$ then $\binom{n}{r} = \frac{n!}{r!(n-r)!}$ which can be further simplified to $\binom{n}{r} = \frac{n(n-1)(n-2)\ldots(n-r+1)}{r!}$. But in this form, if n is negative and r is a non-negative integer, we can still define $\binom{n}{r}$. For example, if n is positive, we can write

$$\binom{-n}{r} = \frac{(-n)(-n-1)(-n-2)\ldots(-n-r+1)}{r!}$$

where we need not restrict $r \leq n$. But, we can very well see that

$$\binom{-n}{r} = \frac{(n+r-1)(n+r-2)\ldots(n+1)\,n(-1)^r}{r!}$$

$$= (-1)^r \binom{n+r-1}{r},$$

which is a direct link to usual combinations. Using this negative binomial coefficient, we can guess the formula.

$$(1+x)^{-n} = \sum_{r=0}^{\infty} \binom{-n}{r} x^r \quad \text{(for } |x| < 1)$$

$$= \sum_{r=0}^{\infty} (-1)^r \binom{n+r-1}{r} x^r.$$

If $n = 3$ and we write $|x|$ in place of x then we get

$$(1-x)^{-3} = \sum_{r=0}^{\infty} \binom{-3}{r} (-x)^r$$

$$= \sum_{r=0}^{\infty} \binom{3+r-1}{r} (-1)^r (-x)^r$$

$$= \sum_{r=0}^{\infty} \binom{r+2}{r} x^r$$

$$= 1 + \binom{3}{1} x + \binom{4}{2} x^2 + \binom{5}{3} x^3 + \dots$$

$$= 1 + 3x + 6x^2 + 10x^3 + \dots$$

which is same as what we earlier obtained otherwise.

The general proof of

$$(1+x)^{-n} = \sum_{r=0}^{\infty} (-1)^r \binom{n+r-1}{r} x^r$$

can be achieved by using principle of mathematical induction which is beyond the scope of this book. Indeed, for $|x| < 1$, we can still have

$$(1+x)^a = \sum_{r=0}^{\infty} \binom{a}{r} x^r$$

where a is an arbitrary index and $0 < a < 1$

$$\binom{a}{r} = \frac{a(a-1)\dots(a-r+1)}{r!}; \quad r = 0, 1, 2, \dots$$

For example, for $x = 1$, $a = \frac{1}{2}$, we have

$$(1+1)^{1/2} = \sum_{r=0}^{\infty} \binom{1/2}{r} x^r$$

$$= 1 + \frac{1}{2} + \frac{\frac{1}{2}\left(-\frac{1}{2}\right)}{2!} + \frac{\frac{1}{2}\left(-\frac{1}{2}\right)\left(-\frac{3}{2}\right)}{3!} + \dots$$

$$= 1 + \frac{1}{2} - \frac{1}{8} + \frac{3}{48} - \dots$$

The series on the right-hand side converges to positive square root of 2. It may be observed that the sum of the first six terms of the series is equal to 1.425 which is very close to the rational approximation of $\sqrt{2}$.

2.6.2 Pascal's Identity and Triangle

Binomial coefficients satisfy many identities. One such important identity is *Pascal's Identity*, which states that if n and m be positive integers with $n \geq m$, then,

$$\binom{n+1}{m} = \binom{n}{m-1} + \binom{n}{m}.$$

The triangle shown in Fig. 2.2 is known as *Pascal's triangle*. The $(n+1)^{th}$ row in Pascal's triangle consists of the binomial coefficients

$$\binom{n}{m}, m = 0, 1, ..., n.$$

```
              1
           1     1
        1     2     1
     1     3     3     1
   1    4     6     4     1
  1   5   10    10   5    1
1   6   15   20   15   6    1
```

Fig. 2.2

One of the important characteristics of *Pascal's triangle* is that the sum of two consecutive binomial coefficients in any row in this triangle is equal to the binomial coefficient in the next row between these two coefficients. The rows in this triangle represent the binomial coefficients for positive integral index whereas the diagonals represent the binomial coefficients for negative integral index. The rth row in Pascal's triangle represents binomial coefficients in the expansion of $(1 + x)^{r-1}$. The rth diagonal represents binomial coefficients in the expansion of $(1 - x)^{-r}$. For example, the entries on the fifth horizontal line are 1, 4, 6, 4, 1 and hence, $(1 + x)^4 = 1 + 4x + 6x^2 + 4x^3 + x^4$. Also the entries in the third diagonal are 1,3,6,10,15, ... and hence,

$$(1 - x)^{-3} = 1 + 3x + 6x^2 + 10x^2 + 15x^4 + ... \, .$$

2.7 DISCRETE PROBABILITY

As an illustration of the application of some of the concepts and tools studied in Chapter 1 and this chapter, we present a brief introduction to discrete probability theory. We recall that an *experiment* is a physical process that has a number of observable outcomes. In previous sections of this chapter, we studied various ways to compute the number of outcomes of an experiment. As examples, we note that dealing a poker hand has $C(52, 5) = 2,598,960$ possible outcomes; and examining a student's transcript has 5^4 possible outcomes (assuming that the student takes four courses, and the five possible grades are A, B, C, D, F). In our model of a physical process, these outcomes are considered to be *mutually exclusive* and *exhaustive*; that is, exactly one outcome will take place in any particular instance of the experiment. Thus, when we toss a coin, either a head or a tail will show. It is not possible that both of them will show, nor is it possible that none of them will show. (If, indeed, we believe that the coin might stand on its side, we should include in our model three possible outcomes when a coin is tossed— namely, *head, tail*, and *standing on its side*.)

Formally, we refer to the set of all possible outcomes of an experiment as the *sample space* of the experiment. We also refer to the outcomes in the sample space as *samples* or *sample points*. We shall use the notation $S = \{x_1, x_2, \ldots, x_i, \ldots\}$ for a sample space S consisting of the samples $x_1, x_2, \ldots, x_i$, and so on. A sample space that has a finite number or a countably infinite number of samples is called a *discrete sample space*. We shall restrict our discussion to discrete sample spaces. (An in-depth discussion of the general case of sample spaces with an uncountably infinite number of samples would require some advanced concepts and tools from mathematical analysis.) For example, for the experiment of tossing a coin, the sample space is a set $S = \{h, t\}$, which consists of the two possible outcomes h (head) and t (tail). For the experiment of tossing two coins, the sample space is a set $S = \{hh, ht, th, tt\}$, which consists of the four possible outcomes head-head, head-tail, tail-head, and tail-tail. Also, for the experiment of waiting for the arrival of a bus at a bus stop, the sample space is a set $S = \{0, 1, 2, 3, \ldots, 30\}$ in which the outcomes are the waiting times ranging from 0 to 30 minutes. Consider the experiment of shooting at a target until there is a hit. The sample space is a countably infinite set $S = \{h, mh, mmh, mmmh, \ldots\}$, where h denotes a hit, mh denotes a miss followed by a hit, mmh denotes two misses followed by a hit, and so on.

As another example, let us consider the experiment of rolling a die. Here, the sample space is a set $S = \{1, 2, 3, 4, 5, 6\}$, which consists of the six possible outcomes: 1, 2, 3, 4, 5 and 6.

Associated with each sample in a sample space is a real number called the *probability* of that sample. For the sample x_i, we shall use $p(x_i)$ to denote the probability associated with x_i. The probabilities associated with the samples must satisfy two conditions:

1. The probability of each sample is a nonnegative number less than or equal to 1. That is, for each x_i in S, $0 \leq p(x_i) \leq 1$.

2. The sum of the probabilities of all the samples in the sample space is equal to 1. That is, $\Sigma_{x_i \varepsilon S} p(x_i) = 1$.

The probability of a sample is a measure of the likelihood of occurrence of that sample. A sample with a larger probability is more likely to take place, while a sample with a smaller probability is less likely to take place. Quantitatively, if we conduct an experiment a large number of times, the probability of a certain sample is a measure of the fraction of times in which the particular outcome takes place. For example, in the sample space of the experiment of tossing a fair coin, the probability of the outcome *head* is $\frac{1}{2}$, and the probability of the outcome *tail* is also $\frac{1}{2}$. Thus, if we toss the coin many times, approximately half of the outcomes will be *heads* and half will be *tails*. On the other hand, in the sample space of the experiment of tossing an unfair coin, the probability of the outcome *head* might be $\frac{2}{3}$, while the probability of the outcome *tail* might be $\frac{1}{3}$. In that case, when we toss the coin many times, approximately two-thirds of the outcomes will be *heads*, and approximately one-third of the outcomes will be *tails*. Also, for the experiment of tossing two coins with the sample space being $S = \{hh, ht, th, tt\}$, we might have

$$p(hh) = \frac{1}{4}$$

$$p(ht) = \frac{1}{4}$$

$$p(th) = \frac{1}{4}$$

$$p(tt) = \frac{1}{4}$$

if the coin is fair. Or we might have

$$p(hh) = \frac{4}{9}$$

$$p(ht) = \frac{2}{9}$$

$$p(th) = \frac{2}{9}$$

$$p(tt) = \frac{2}{9}$$

if the coin is unfair. For the experiment of shooting at a target until there is a hit with the sample space being $S = \{h, mh, mmh, mmmh, \ldots\}$, we might have

$$p(h) = \frac{1}{2}$$

$$p(mh) = \frac{1}{4}$$

$$p(mmh) = \frac{1}{8}$$

$$\ldots\ldots\ldots\ldots$$

$$\underbrace{p(mm\ldots mh)}_{k} = 2^{-(k+1)}$$

Also, in the sample space of any experiment, a sample with probability 1 corresponds to an outcome that will take place with certainty; a sample with probability 0 corresponds to an outcome that will never take place.

We can now explain the physical significance of the two conditions imposed on the probabilities associated with the samples in a sample space stated above. Clearly, if the probability associated with a sample is a measure of the frequency of occurrence of the outcome of an experiment, it is meaningless for it to assume a negative value, or to assume a value larger than 1. Also, since the sample space contains all possible outcomes of an experiment, the sum of probabilities of the samples should equal exactly 1.

We assume that the probabilities of the outcomes of an experiment are given to us, either based on statistical data or simply on one's intuitive *guesstimation*.

An *event* is a subset of the outcomes of an experiment. An event is said to occur if any one of the samples in the event occurs. Thus, when we roll a die, getting a 1 is an event, getting an odd number (1, 3, or 5) is another event. An event that contains one sample is referred to as a *simple* event, and an event that contains more than one sample is referred to as a *compound* event. The probability of occurrence of an event is defined as the sum of probabilities of the samples in the subset. Since samples are mutually exclusive outcomes of an experiment, the probability of an event is a measure of the frequency of occurrence of the event. Thus, in set-theoretic notations, an event A is a subset of the sample space S. The probability of event A, denoted $p(A)$, is equal to $\Sigma_{x_i \varepsilon A}\, p(x_i)$.

We consider some illustrative examples:

Example 2.32 For the experiment of rolling a die, the sample space consists of six samples. If we suppose the probability of occurrence of each of these samples is $\frac{1}{6}$; then the probability of getting an odd number is equal to

$$\frac{1}{6} + \frac{1}{6} + \frac{1}{6} = \frac{1}{2}$$

On the other hand, suppose that we have a "crooked" die such that the probability of getting a 1 is $\frac{1}{3}$ and the probability of getting each of the remaining numbers is $\frac{2}{15}$. Consequently, the probability of getting an odd number is

$$\frac{1}{3} + \frac{2}{15} + \frac{2}{15} = \frac{3}{5}$$

and the probability of getting an even number is

$$\frac{2}{15} + \frac{2}{15} + \frac{2}{15} = \frac{2}{5} \qquad\blacksquare$$

Example 2.33 For the experiment of rolling two dice, the sample space consists of 36 samples. Suppose we want to find the probability of getting a sum 9 in this experiment. We can get the sum 9 in four different ways such as {(3, 6), (4, 5), (5, 4), (6, 3)}. So, the probability of getting a sum 9 is 4/36. $\blacksquare$

Example 2.34 Consider the problem of dealing a poker hand out of a deck of 52 cards. The sample space consists of $C(52, 5)$ sample points corresponding to the $C(52, 5)$ different hands that can be dealt. We assume that these outcomes have equal probabilities; that is, the probability that a particular hand was dealt is equal to $1/C(52, 5)$. To determine the probability of getting four aces, we note that 48 of the $C(52, 5)$ possible outcomes contain four aces; thus, the probability is $48/C(52, 5) = 0.0000185$. ∎

Example 2.35   We shall confirm the observation that out of 23 people the chance is less than 50-50 that no two of them will have the same birthday. Consider the sample space consisting of 366^{23} samples corresponding to all possible distributions of birthdays of 23 people. Let us assume that these distributions are equiprobable. Since out of the 366^{23} samples, $P(366, 23)$ of them correspond to distributions of birthdays such that no two of the 23 people have the same birthday, the probability that no two people have the same birthday is

$$\frac{P(366, 23)}{366^{23}} = 0.494$$ ∎

Example 2.36   Eight students are standing in line for an interview. We want to determine the probability that there are exactly two freshmen, two sophomores, two juniors, and two seniors in the line. The sample space consists of 4^8 samples corresponding to all possibilities of classes the students are from. Let us assume these are equiprobable samples. There are $8!/2! 2! 2! 2!$ samples corresponding to the case in which there are two students from each class. Thus, the probability is

$$\frac{8!}{2!2!2!2!4^8} = 0.0385$$ ∎

Example 2.37   For the experiment of shooting at a target until there is a hit, we assume the probability of occurrence of the sample that has k misses before a hit to be $2^{-(k+1)}$. Let A denote the event that there is a hit before no more than 5 misses, then $A = \{h, mh, mmh, mmmh, mmmmh, mmmmmh\}$ and

$$p(A) = \sum_{k=0}^{5} 2^{-(k+1)} = 0.984$$

Let B denote the event that there is a hit after an odd number of misses. Then

$$p(B) = \sum_{i=1}^{\infty} 2^{-2i} = \frac{1}{3}$$

Yet, on the other hand, let C denote the event that there is a hit after an even number of misses (including no misses). Then

$$p(C) = \sum_{i=0}^{\infty} 2^{-2i+1} = \frac{2}{3}$$ ∎

Once again, we shall observe how elementary set-theoretic concepts enable us to introduce new definitions precisely and concisely. Given two events A and B, the event that both A and B occur corresponds to the set of samples $A \cap B$. We shall use $A \cap B$ to denote such an event. If A and B have no sample points in common, i.e., $A \cap B = \phi$, where ϕ is empty set then A and B are said to be *mutually exclusive* or disjoint events because the occurrence of A excludes that of B and vice versa. For example, if the tossing of a die turns up an even number, it cannot turn up an odd number in the same trial. So, these two events are mutually *exclusive* or *disjoint* events. Furthermore, the probability of occurrence of the event, denoted $p(A \cap B)$, is equal to $\Sigma_{x_i \varepsilon A \cap B} \, p(x_i)$. Similarly, given two events A and B, the event that either A or B or both occur corresponds to the set of samples $A \cup B$. Also, the event that A occurs but B does not correspond to the set of samples $A - B$; the event that one but not both of them occurs corresponds to the set of samples $A \oplus B$. Of course, these events are denoted by $A \cup B$, $A - B$, and $A \oplus B$, and their corresponding probabilities can be computed as $\Sigma_{x_i \varepsilon A \cup B} \, p(x_i), \Sigma_{x_i \varepsilon A - B} p(x_i), \Sigma_{x_i \varepsilon A \oplus B} p(x_i)$, respectively.

If the occurrence or non-occurrence of the event A does not affect the occurrence or non-occurrence of the event B then the two events A and B are said to be *independent events*. For example, if three students appeared in an examination then the first one passing in the examination is independent of passing of the other students in the same examination. Similarly, drawing of two cards one after another from a pack of cards with replacement are independent.

Let A be an event of a given sample space S. The event A^C is said to be a *complementary event* iff A^C consists of all the sample points of S which are not in A.

Thus $A \cap A^C = \phi$ and $A \cup A^C = S$

Example 2.38 Let us consider rolling of a die.

Here the sample space is $S = \{1, 2, 3, 4, 5, 6\}$

Let the events be A and B, where

$$A = \{\text{even numbers}\}$$

$$B = \{\text{odd numbers}\}$$

Hence, $A^C = \text{B}$ and $A^C = \text{A}$

Also, $A \cap A^C = A \cap B = \phi$ and $A \cap A^C = A \cup B = S$ ∎

We see now some examples:

Example 2.39 Digital data received from a remote site might fill up 0 to 32 buffers. Let the sample space be $S = \{0, 1, 2, ..., 32\}$, where the sample i denotes that i of the buffers are full. It is given that

$$p(i) = \frac{1}{561}(33 - i)$$

Let A denote the event that at most 16 buffers are full, and B denote the event that an odd number of buffers are full. Then

$$A = \{0, 1, 2, ..., 16\}$$
$$B = \{1, 3, 5, ..., 31\}$$
$$A \cap B = \{1, 3, 5, ..., 15\}$$

and

$$p(A) = \frac{1}{561} \sum_{i=0}^{16} (33 - i) = \frac{425}{561} = 0.758$$

$$p(B) = \frac{1}{561} \sum_{\substack{i=1 \\ i \text{ is odd}}}^{31} (33 - i) = \frac{272}{561} = 0.485$$

$$p(A \cap B) = \frac{1}{561} \sum_{\substack{i=1 \\ i \text{ is odd}}}^{15} (33 - i) = \frac{200}{561} = 0.357 \qquad \blacksquare$$

Example 2.40   Out of 100,000 people, 51,500 are female and 48,500 are male. Among the females 9,000 are bald, and among the males 30,200 are bald. Suppose we are going to choose a person at random. We shall have $S = \{fb, fh, mb, mh\}$ as the sample space with fb denoting a bald female, fh a female with hair, mb a bald male, and mh a male with hair. Also, we have

$$p(fb) = 0.090$$
$$p(fh) = 0.425$$
$$p(mb) = 0.302$$
$$p(mh) = 0.183$$

Let A denote the event that a bald person was chosen, and B denote the event that a female was chosen. Then $A \cap B$ is the event that a bald female was chosen, $A \cup B$ the event that a bald person or a female was chosen, $A \oplus B$ the event that a female with hair or a bald male was chosen, and $B - A$ the event that a female with hair was chosen. Thus, we have

$$p(A) = 0.090 + 0.302 = 0.392$$
$$p(B) = 0.090 + 0.425 = 0.515$$
$$p(A \cap B) = 0.090$$
$$p(A \cup B) = 0.090 + 0.425 + 0.302 = 0.817$$
$$p(A \oplus B) = 0.425 + 0.302 = 0.727$$
$$p(B - A) = 0.425 \qquad \blacksquare$$

Example 2.41   Ten men went to a party and checked their hats when they arrived. The hats were randomly returned to them when they departed. We want to know the probability that no man gets his own hat back. For the experiment of returning the hats to the men, the sample space consists of 10! samples corresponding to the 10! possible permutations of the hats. Let us assume that each permutation occurs with equal probability, that is, 1/10!. Consequently, the probability that no man receives his own hat is equal to 1/10! times the number of permutations in which no man receives his own hat. Let A_i denote the set of samples in which the ith man receives his own hat. The reader can confirm that, using the principle of inclusion and exclusion, we obtain

$$|A_1 \cup A_2 \cup \ldots \cup A_{10}| = \binom{10}{1}9! - \binom{10}{2}8! + \binom{10}{3}7! - \ldots + \binom{10}{9}1! - \binom{10}{10}0!$$

Consequently, the probability that no man receives his own hat is:

$$\frac{1}{10!}\left[10! - \binom{10}{1}9! + \binom{10}{2}8! - \binom{10}{3}7! + \ldots - \binom{10}{9}1! - \binom{10}{10}0!\right]$$

$$= 1 - \frac{1}{1!} + \frac{2}{2!} - \frac{3}{3!} + \dots - \frac{9}{9!} + \frac{10}{10!} = 0.36788$$

Intuitively, one probably would not have guessed that the probability would turn out to be so large. ∎

2.7.1 Discrete Random Variable

A random variable defined over a finite sample space or, countably infinite sample space consisting of discontinuous elements is known as discrete random variable.

Example 2.42 Describe the sample space and random variable corresponding to the number of heads obtained in 4 tosses of a balanced coin.

Solution: Let S = Sample space corresponding to 4 tosses of a balance coin.

$$= \{HHHH, HHHT, \dots TTTT\}$$
$$|S| = 2^4 = 16$$

Let X = The random variables corresponding to the number of heads obtained in 4 tosses of a balanced coin.

∴ $X = \{0, 1, 2, 3, 4\}$ ∎

Example 2.43 Find the random variable corresponding to the sum of numbers appeared in rolling of four dice once. Also find the corresponding sample space.

Solution: Let S = The sample space corresponding to the rolling of 4 dice once.

∴ $S = \{(1, 1, 1, 1), (1, 1, 1, 2), \dots (6, 6, 6, 6)\} = 6^4 = 1296$

Let X = The random variables corresponding to the sum of numbers obtained in rolling of 4 dice once.

So, $X = \{4, 5, 6, 7, \dots, 24\}$ ∎

2.7.2 Probability Distribution Function (p.d.f.)

If X is a discrete random variable with sample space S then a function denoted by $f(x)$ or $P(X = x)$ and defined as

$f(x) = P(X = x) = $ Probability for the random variable $X = x$, is called *probability distribution function* (p.d.f.) or probability function. ∎

Example 2.44 Find the probability distribution function corresponding to the number of heads obtained in 4 tosses of a balanced coin.

Solution: Here, the sample space is

∴ $S = \{HHHH, HHHT, \dots, TTTT\} \Rightarrow |S| = 2^4 = 16$

and $X = \{0, 1, 2, 3, 4\}$

∴ $f(0) = p(X = 0) = $ Probability of getting zero number of heads in 4 tosses of a balanced coin.

$$= \frac{{}^4C_0}{16} = \frac{1}{16}$$

Similarly,
$$f(1) = \frac{^4C_1}{16} = \frac{4}{16} = \frac{1}{4}$$

$$f(2) = \frac{^4C_2}{16} = \frac{6}{16} = \frac{3}{8}$$

$$f(3) = \frac{^4C_3}{16} = \frac{4}{16} = \frac{1}{4}$$

$$f(4) = \frac{^4C_4}{16} = \frac{1}{16}$$

2.7.3 Properties of Probability Distribution Function

Two important properties of probability distribution function are:
1. The probability distribution function is a non-negative real number, i.e.,
   $f(x) \geq 0, \forall x \in X$
2. The sum of the probability distribution functions is 1, i.e. $\sum_{x \in X} f(x) = 1$.

Example 2.45 Verify that the given functions are probability distribution functions.

   i. $f(x) = \frac{x^2 + 1}{35}$,   for $x = 0, 1, 2, 3, 4$.

   ii. $f(x) = \frac{5x - 4}{55}$,   for $x = 1, 2, 3, 4, 5$.

Solution: i. The given function is

$$f(x) = \frac{x^2 + 1}{35}, \text{ for } x = 0, 1, 2, 3, 4.$$

$\therefore$ $f(0) = \frac{1}{35}, \quad f(1) = \frac{2}{35}, \quad f(2) = \frac{5}{35}, \quad f(3) = \frac{10}{35}, \quad f(4) = \frac{17}{35},$

$\Rightarrow$ $f(x) \geq 0, \forall x = 0,1,2,3,4.$

Now, to prove that the given function is a p.d.f. , we have to show

$$\sum_{x=0}^{4} f(x) = 1$$

$$\text{L.H.S} = \sum_{x=0}^{4} f(x)$$

$$= f(0) + f(1) + f(2) + f(3) + f(4)$$

$$= \frac{1}{35} + \frac{2}{35} + \frac{5}{35} + \frac{10}{35} + \frac{17}{35} = 1$$

Hence, the given function is a p.d.f.

Similarly, we can prove (ii). We leave it as an exercise to the readers. ∎

Example 2.46 Find the p.d.f. corresponding to the sum of numbers 2, 3, 4, 5 and 6 which appeared in rolling of two dice once.

Solution: Let S = The sample space corresponding to the rolling of two dice once.

$\therefore \quad S = \{(1, 1), (1, 2), ..., (6, 6)\}$

$\Rightarrow \quad |S| = 6^2 = 36$

Let, X = The discrete random variable corresponding to the sum of numbers obtained in rolling of 2 dice once.

$\therefore \quad X = \{2, 3, 4, 5, ...11, 12\}$

Now, $f(2) = p(X = 2)$ = Probability of getting a sum of 2 in rolling of 2 dice once.

$= \dfrac{1}{36}$ as 2 will be obtained from the outcome (1, 1) which will occur only once.

Similarly, we can get

$$f(3) = p(X = 3) = \frac{2}{36} \text{ \{since 3 can be obtained from the outcomes \}}$$
$$\text{(1, 2) and (2, 1)\}}$$

$$f(4) = p(X = 4) = \frac{3}{36}$$

$$f(5) = p(X = 5) = \frac{4}{36}$$

$$f(6) = p(X = 6) = \frac{5}{36}$$

Similarly, we can find the probability distribution functions for other values. ■

Example 2.47   Find the value of c if

$f(x) = \dfrac{C}{2^{2x}}$; $x = 0, 1, 2,...$ is a probability distribution function.

Solution: Since $f(x)$ is a probability distribution function, so $\displaystyle\sum_{x=1}^{\infty} f(x) = 1$

$\Rightarrow \quad f(0) + f(1) + f(2) + f(3) + ... = 1$

$\Rightarrow \quad c + \dfrac{c}{2^2} + \dfrac{c}{2^4} + \dfrac{c}{2^8} + ... = 1$

$\Rightarrow \quad c\left(1 + \dfrac{1}{2^2} + \dfrac{1}{2^4} + \dfrac{1}{2^8} + ...\right) = 1$

$\Rightarrow \quad c\left(\dfrac{1}{1 - \dfrac{1}{2^2}}\right) = 1$

$\Rightarrow \quad c\left(\dfrac{4}{3}\right) = 1$

$\Rightarrow \quad c = \dfrac{3}{4}$ ■

Example 2.48   For what value of m will the function

$f(x) = m\dbinom{4}{x}$, $x = 0, 1, 2, 3, 4$ be a probability distribution function.

Solution: This example can be solved similarly as the above example. We leave it as an exercise to the readers.

2.7.4   Distribution Function

If X is a discrete random variable defined over the sample space S with p.d.f $f(x)$ then a function given by

$F(x) = p(X \leq x) = \sum_{x_i \leq x} f(x_i)$ is called the distribution function of X.

Example 2.49   Find the distribution function F when $f(0) = f(1) = \frac{1}{3}$, when $f(2) = f(3) = \frac{1}{6}$. Also, prove that the given function is a p.d.f.

Solution: For the given function $f(x)$, the set of random variables is given by $X = \{0, 1, 2, 3\}$.

We have to prove that the given function is a p.d.f.

Here, we observe that the value of $f(x) \geq 0$, $\forall x \in X$.

Also, $\sum_{x=0}^{8} f(x)\, f(x) = f(0) + f(1) + f(2) + f(3) = \frac{1}{3} + \frac{1}{3} + \frac{1}{6} + \frac{1}{6} = 1$

So, the given function is a p.d.f.

Now,

$$F(0) = \sum_{x \leq 0} f(x) = f(0) = \tfrac{1}{3}$$

$$F(1) = \sum_{x \leq 1} f(x) = f(0) + f(1) = \frac{1}{3} + \frac{1}{3} = \frac{2}{3}$$

$$F(2) = \sum_{x \leq 2} f(x) = f(0) + f(1) + f(2) = \frac{1}{3} + \frac{1}{3} + \frac{1}{6} = \frac{5}{6}$$

$$F(3) = \sum_{x \leq 3} f(x) = f(0) + f(1) + f(2) + f(3) = 1$$

Hence, the distribution function is

$$F(x) = \begin{cases} 0 & \text{if } x < 0 \\ \frac{1}{3} & \text{if } 0 \leq x < 1 \\ \frac{2}{3} & \text{if } 1 \leq x < 2 \\ \frac{5}{6} & \text{if } 2 \leq x < 3 \\ 1 & \text{if } x \geq 3. \end{cases}$$

*2.8   CONDITIONAL PROBABILITY

Suppose a die was rolled, and we want to know the probability that the outcome was 4. Assume that the six outcomes are equiprobable. Clearly, the answer is one-sixth. Now, suppose a die was rolled, and we were told that the number was even. Again, we want to know the probability that the outcome is 4. We realize that since only 2, 4, or 6 are the possible outcomes, the probability that 4 has appeared must be larger than one-sixth. As a matter of fact, the reader has probably arrived at the answer: the probability that 4 has appeared is one-third.

Consider again the problem of bald people in Example 2.40. Suppose we choose a person at random. As shown above, the probability that the person is bald is 0.392. Suppose we were told that this person was a female. Then we would say, at least intuitively, that the probability of this person being bald would be less than 0.392. On the other hand, if we were told that the person was male, then the probability that he is bald would be greater than 0.392.

These two examples bring up the notion of conditional probability of an event. Let S be a sample space and A and B be two events in S. The probability that event A occurs given that event B has occurred is defined as the *conditional probability* of event A given the occurrence of event B, which is denoted $p(A|B)$. In the example of rolling a die, let A denote the event, "the outcome is 4," and B denote the event, "the outcome is an even number." The conditional probability $p(A|B)$ is then equal to $\frac{1}{3}$. In the example of bald people, let A denote the event that a bald person is chosen, B denote the event that a female is chosen, and C denote the event that a male is chosen. As mentioned above, we would agree that $p(A|B)$ is smaller than $p(A)$. In other words, given that a female was chosen, there is a smaller chance that a bald person was chosen. However, $p(A|C)$ is larger than $p(A)$, since given that a male was chosen, the chance is better that a bald person was chosen. Also, although the probability $p(B)$ of a woman being chosen is greater than the probability $p(C)$ of a man being chosen, the conditional probability $p(B|A)$ of a woman being chosen given that a bald person was chosen is less than the conditional probability $p(C|A)$ of a man being chosen given that a bald person was chosen. We shall show how to compute these conditional probabilities to confirm all of these intuitive notions later.

The occurrence of event B has effectively changed the probabilities associated with the samples in the sample space. Obviously, the probability associated with a sample not included in event B becomes 0. On the other hand, the probability associated with a sample included in event B increases. Let us examine again the simple example of rolling a dice. If we were told that an even number appeared, the probabilities of the samples 1, 3, and 5 all become 0, since it is certain that none of them could have occurred. On the other hand, the probabilities of the samples 2, 4, and 6 become one-third. (We assume that all possible outcomes are equally likely.) Thus, indeed,

$$p(4 \text{ appeared} \mid \text{even number appeared}) = \frac{1}{3}$$

In general, let $p_B(x_i)$ denote the probability associated with sample x_i given that event B has occurred. As pointed out above, for $x_i \notin B$, $p_B(x_i) = 0$. However, for the samples in event B their *relative* frequencies of occurrence remain the same while the sum of their probabilities should equal to 1, that is, $\Sigma_{x_i \in B}\, p_B(x_i) = 1$.

Consequently, we need to scale the probability of each of these samples up from $p(x_i)$ to $p(x_i)/p(B)$. Thus, we have

$$p_B(x_i) = \begin{cases} 0 & x_i \notin B \\ \dfrac{p(x_i)}{p(B)} & x_i \in B \end{cases}$$

It follows that

$$p(A|B) = \sum_{x_i \varepsilon A \cap B} p_B(x_i)$$

$$= \sum_{x_i \varepsilon A \cap B} \frac{p(x_i)}{p(B)}$$

$$= \frac{1}{p(B)} \sum_{x_i \in A \cap B} p(x_i)$$

$$= \frac{p(A \cap B)}{p(B)}$$

Example 2.50 For the example of choosing a person at random discussed above, let A denote the event that a bald person was chosen, B the event that a female was chosen, and C the event that a male was chosen. We have

$$p(A|B) = \frac{p(A \cap B)}{p(B)} = \frac{0.090}{0.515} = 0.175$$

This is less than $p(A)$, which is 0.392. On the other hand,

$$p(A|C) = \frac{p(A \cap C)}{p(C)} = \frac{0.302}{0.485} = 0.623$$

which is quite a bit larger than $p(A)$. Also,

$$p(B|A) = \frac{p(B \cap A)}{p(A)} = \frac{0.090}{0.392} = 0.23$$

$$p(C|A) = \frac{p(C \cap A)}{p(A)} = \frac{0.302}{0.392} = 0.77$$

Indeed, although $p(B)$ is slightly larger than $p(C)$, $p(B|A)$ is much smaller than $p(C|A)$. ∎

Example 2.51 A coin was chosen at random and tossed. The probability that a fair coin was chosen and head shows is one-third. The probability that a fair coin was chosen and tail shows is also one-third. The probability that an unfair coin was chosen and head shows is one-twelfth. The probability that an unfair coin was chosen and tail shows is one-quarter.

Clearly, the probability that head shows is

$$\frac{1}{3} + \frac{1}{12} = \frac{5}{12}$$

and the probability that an unfair coin was chosen is

$$\frac{1}{12} + \frac{1}{4} = \frac{1}{3}$$

Thus, the conditional probability that an unfair coin was chosen given that head shows is

$$\frac{1/12}{5/12} = \frac{1}{5}$$

and the conditional probability that head shows given that an unfair coin was chosen is

$$\frac{1/12}{1/3} = \frac{1}{4}$$

∎

Example 2.52　Three dice were rolled. Given that no two faces were the same, what is the probability that there was an ace? Let A denote the event that there was an ace, and B the event that no two faces were the same. Note that

$$p(B) = \frac{P(6,3)}{6^3} \quad p(A \cap B) = \frac{3P(5,2)}{6^3}$$

thus,

$$p(A|B) = \frac{3P(5,2)}{P(6,3)} = \frac{1}{2} \qquad \blacksquare$$

We should point out that, in general, $p(A|B)$ is not equal to $p(B|A)$. Let us consider the simple example of rolling a dice. Let A denote the event that 5 appeared, and B the event an odd number appeared. Clearly, $p(A|B) = \frac{1}{3}$, while $p(B|A) = 1$.

2.9　BAYES' THEOREM

Bayes' theorem is one of the important theorems associated with conditional probability. In this section, we state and prove Bayes' theorem along with some examples.

Theorem 2.1　Let $A_1, A_2, \ldots, A_n$ be mutually disjoint events with $P(A_i) \neq 0$, $(i = 1, 2, \ldots, n)$. Then, for any arbitrary event E which is a subset of $\bigcup_{i=1}^{n} A_i$ such that $P(E) > 0$, we have

$$P(A_i|E) = \frac{P(A_i)\,P(E|A_i)}{\sum\limits_{i=1}^{n} P(A_i)\,P(E|A_i)}, \, i = 1, 2, \ldots, n.$$

Proof:　It is given that $E \subset \bigcup_{i=1}^{n} A_i$, so, we have

$$E = E \cap \left(\bigcup_{i=1}^{n} A_i \right) = \bigcup_{i=1}^{n} E \cap A_i \qquad \text{[by distributive law]}$$

Since, $(E \cap A_i) \subset A_i$, $(i = 1, 2, \ldots, n)$ are mutually disjoint events, we have by addition theorem of probability

$$P(E) = P\left[\bigcup_{i=1}^{n} E \cap A_i \right] = \sum_{i=1}^{n} P(E \cap A_i) = \sum_{i=1}^{n} P(A_i)P(E|A_i) \qquad (2.8)$$

Also, we know that

$$P(E \cap A_i) = P(E)\,P(A_i|E)$$

So, $P(A_i|E) = \dfrac{P(E \cap A_i)}{P(E)} = \dfrac{P(A_i)\,P(E|A_i)}{\sum\limits_{i=1}^{n} P(A_i)\,P(E|A_i)}$ 　　[from (2.8)]　■

Observations

1. The probabilities $P(A_1)$, $P(A_2)$, ... $P(A_n)$ are called as the '*a priori probabilities*' because they exist before we get any information from the experiment itself.

2. The probabilities $P(E|A_i)$, $i = 1, 2, ..., n$ are called '*likelihoods*' because they indicate how likely the event E under consideration is to occur, given each and every *a priori* probability.

3. The probabilities $P(A_i|E)$, $i = 1, 2, ... n$ are called '*posterior probabilities*' because they are computed after the results of the experiments are known.

Example 2.53 There were three candidates for the position of the Chairman of a college – Mr. *X*, Mr. *Y*, and Mr. *Z*—whose chances of getting the appointment are in the ratio 4:2:3 respectively. The probability that Mr. *X* if selected would introduce computer education in the college is 0.3. The probabilities of Mr. *Y* and Mr. *Z* doing the same are respectively 0.5 and 0.8. What is the probability that there was computer education in the college?

Solution: We define the events and probabilities as follows:

E : Introduction of computer education
A_1 : Mr. *X* is selected as Chairman.
A_2 : Mr. *Y* is selected as Chairman.
A_3 : Mr. *Z* is selected as Chairman.

Then,

$$P(A_1) = \frac{4}{9}, P(A_2) = \frac{2}{9} \quad \text{and} \quad P(A_3) = \frac{3}{9}$$

$$P(E|A_1) = \frac{3}{10}, P(E|A_2) = \frac{5}{10} \quad \text{and} \quad P(E|A_3) = \frac{8}{10}$$

$\therefore$
$$P(E) = P[(E \cap A_1) \cup (E \cap A_2) \cup (E \cap A_3)]$$

$$= P(E \cap A_1) + P(E \cap A_2) + P(E \cap A_3)$$

$$= P(A_1) P(E|A_1) + P(A_2) P(E|A_2) + P(A_3) P(E|A_3)$$

$$= \frac{4}{9} \cdot \frac{3}{10} + \frac{2}{9} \cdot \frac{5}{10} + \frac{3}{9} \cdot \frac{8}{10} = \frac{23}{45}$$

So, the probability that there was computer education in the college is $\frac{23}{45}$. ∎

Example 2.54 There were three different machines M_1, M_2, and M_3 for producing a large batch of similar manufactured items. Let 20 percent of the items were produced by machine M_1, 30 percent by machine M_2 and 50 percent by machine M_3. Suppose 1 percent of the items produced by machine M_1 are defective, 2 percent of the items produced by machine M_2 are defective, and 3 percent of the items produced by machine M_3 are defective. Suppose, one item is selected at random from the entire batch and it is found to be defective. What is the probability that this item was produced by machine M_3?

Solution: We define the events and probabilities as follows:

A_i : the event that the selected item was produced by machine M_i ($i = 1, 2, 3$).

E : the event that the selected item is defective.

In order to get the answer, we require to evaluate the conditional probability $P(A_3|E)$.

The probability $P(A_i)$ that an item selected at random from the entire batch was produced by machine M_i can be stated as follows, for $i = 1, 2, 3$;

$$P(A_1) = 0.2, \quad P(A_2) = 0.3, \quad P(A_3) = 0.5.$$

Now, the probability $P(E|A_i)$ that an item produced by machine M_i will be defective is:

$$P(E|A_1) = 0.01, \quad P(E|A_2) = 0.02, \quad P(E|A_3) = 0.03$$

By using Bayes' theorem, we get

$$P(A_3|E) = \frac{P(A_3)\,P(E|A_3)}{\sum_{i=1}^{3} P(A_i)\,P(E|A_i)}$$

$$= \frac{(0.5)(0.3)}{(0.2)(0.1) + (0.3)(0.02) + (0.5)(0.03)}$$

$$= 0.652$$

So, the probability that this item was produced by machine M_3 is 0.652. ∎

*2.10 INFORMATION AND MUTUAL INFORMATION

Suppose we were told that a die was rolled and the outcome was 4. Clearly, we were given all the information concerning the outcome of the experiment. If we were told that the outcome was red, we would agree that we were given some information but not as much. (The outcome is narrowed to one of two possibilities.*) On the other hand, if we were told that the outcome was black, we would feel that we were also given some information, but even less. (The outcome is narrowed to one of four possibilities.)

Suppose after six weeks of the semester students were told that there will be a 1-hour examination. Clearly, such an announcement contains a certain amount of information. However, if the students were told after one week of classes that there will be a 1-hour examination, we would say the announcement contains much more information because it is quite unexpected that an examination would be scheduled after only one week of classes.

These examples illustrate that it is desirable to measure quantitatively how much information a certain piece of message carries. (We assume that a message is always an *unerring* assertion.) If a statement tells us the occurrence of a

---

* For the nongamblers, faces 1 and 4 on a die are red, and faces 2, 3, 5, 6 are black.

certain event that is likely to happen, we would say that the statement contains a small amount of information. On the other hand, if a statement tells us the occurrence of a certain event that is not likely to happen, then we would say that the statement contains a large amount of information. Such an observation suggests that the information contained in a statement asserting the occurrence of an event depends on the probability of occurrence of the event. We define the information contained in a statement asserting the occurrence of an event to be

$$-\lg p^{\dagger}$$

where p is the probability of occurrence of that event. We note first that because p is always less than or equal to 1, $\lg p$ is always a nonpositive number. Consequently, $-\lg p$ is always a non-negative number. Furthermore, it is immediately obvious that the smaller the value of p, the larger the quantity $-\lg p$, which is exactly what we wanted.*

Thus, for example, when we were told that the outcome of rolling a dice was 4, the amount of information we received can be computed as

$$-\lg \frac{1}{6} = \lg 6 = 2.585$$

On the other hand, when we were told that the outcome was red, the amount of information we received can be computed as

$$-\lg \frac{2}{6} = \lg 3 = 1.585$$

Suppose that we receive from the computer as output a binary digit that is either 0 or 1 with equal probability of occurrence. When we are told that the output is indeed 1, the amount of information we receive is

$$-\lg \frac{1}{2} = 1$$

Similarly, when we are told that the output is 0, the amount of information we receive is also

$$-\lg \frac{1}{2} = 1$$

Indeed, when we use the formula $-\lg p$ to compute information contained in a statement, the unit is referred to as a *bit* (short for binary digit), since it is the amount of information carried by one (equally likely) binary digit.

Now, suppose we receive 32 binary digits from the computer as output. Assuming all 2^{32} possibilities are equally likely, the information we receive is

$$-\lg \frac{1}{2^{32}} = 32 \text{ bits}$$

---

† We use lg to denote logorithm of base 2.

* However, a reader might immediately point out that there are many other ways to define a measure of information which increases as the value of p decreases. For example, $1/p$, $1/p^2$, and $1 - p$ are just some of the many possibilities that we can choose. As one will see in a course on information theory, our choice is a natural one because it has other properties that match our intuition very well.

Our discussion also enables us to introduce the notion of mutual information. Suppose we were told that the outcome of rolling a die is red. How much does that help us to determine that the outcome is a 4? Suppose we were told that the professor will be out of town tomorrow. How much does that help us to determine that there will be a 1-hour examination tomorrow? Thus, we want to know the amount of information concerning the occurrence of event A that is contained in the statement asserting the occurrence of event B, which we shall denote $I(A, B)$. Since $-\lg p(A)$ is the amount of information contained in a statement asserting the occurrence of A and $-\lg p(A|B)$ is the amount of information contained in a statement asserting the occurrence of A given that B has occurred, the difference between these two quantities is the amount of information on the occurrence of A provided by the assertion that B has occurred. In other words, we need $-\lg p(A)$ bits of information to assert the occurrence of event A, and we still need $-\lg p(A|B)$ bits of information to assert the occurrence of event A after we were told that event B has occurred. Thus, the information provided by the occurrence of event B on the occurrence of event A is

$$I(A, B) = [-\lg p(A)] - [-\lg p(A|B)] = -\lg p(A) + \lg p(A|B) \qquad (2.9)$$

For example, let A be the event that 4 appeared and B be the event that red appeared when a dice was rolled. Then

$$\begin{aligned} I(A, B) &= -\lg p(A) + \lg p(A|B) \\ &= -\lg \frac{1}{6} + \lg \frac{1}{2} \\ &= 2.585 - 1 \\ &= 1.585 \text{ bits} \end{aligned}$$

On the other hand, let C be the event that an even number appeared. Then

$$\begin{aligned} I(A, C) &= -\lg p(A) + \lg p(A|C) \\ &= -\lg \frac{1}{6} + \lg \frac{1}{3} \\ &= 2.585 - 1.585 \\ &= 1 \text{ bit} \end{aligned}$$

Let us examine (2.9) more closely so that we can better understand the significance of the definition of mutual information. If $p(A|B)$ is large, it means that the occurrence of B indicates a strong possibility of the occurrence of A. Consequently, $I(A, B)$ is large.* However, if $p(A|B)$ is small, it means that the occurrence of B does not tell us much about the occurrence of A. Consequently, $I(A, B)$ is small. As a matter of fact, the occurrence of event B may mean that event A is less likely to occur. In that case, $p(A|B)$ is smaller than $p(A)$ and $I(A, B)$ is a negative quantity, as we shall see in Example 2.55.

Let us also examine some extreme cases. Suppose that B is a subset of A in S. In that case, intuitively, the occurrence of B assures the occurrence of A. Since

---

* We remind the reader that $\lg p(A|B)$ is a negative quantity, and $|\lg p(A|B)|$ is small when $p(A|B)$ is large.

we have $p(A \cap B) = p(B)$, it follows that $p(A|B) = 1$ and $-\lg p(A|B) = 0$; that is, the mutual information provided by the assertion that B has occurred on the occurrence of A is equal to the information provided by the assertion that A has occurred. However, suppose that B is the whole sample space. In that case, $p(A \cap B) = p(A)$ and $-\lg p(A|B)$ is equal to $-\lg p(A)$. Indeed, that $I(A, B) = 0$ means that the occurrence of B tells us nothing about the occurrence of A.

Let us consider some more examples:

Example 2.55 Consider the problem of estimating the likelihood that there will be a 1-hour examination when the professor is scheduled to go out of town. Let $S = \{x_1, x_2, x_3, x_4\}$ be the sample space, where the samples represent the four possible outcomes:

x_1 : professor out of town and examination given
x_2 : professor out of town and examination not given
x_3 : professor in town and examination given
x_4 : professor in town and examination not given

Furthermore,

$$p(x_1) = \frac{1}{2}$$

$$p(x_2) = \frac{1}{16}$$

$$p(x_3) = \frac{3}{16}$$

$$p(x_4) = \frac{1}{4}$$

Let A denote the event that an examination is given, and B the event that the professor is out of town. Note that

$$p(A) = \frac{1}{2} + \frac{3}{16} = \frac{11}{16}$$

$$p(A|B) = \frac{1/2}{1/2 + 1/16} = \frac{8}{9}$$

The information needed to determine that an examination will be given is

$$-\lg p(A) = -\lg \frac{11}{16}$$

$$= -\lg 11 + \lg 16$$

$$= -3.46 + 4$$

$$= 0.54 \text{ bits}$$

and the information provided by the fact that the professor is out of town on the fact that an examination will be given is

$$I(A, B) = -\lg \frac{11}{16} + \lg \frac{8}{9}$$

$$= -\lg 11 + \lg 16 + \lg 8 - \lg 9$$

$$= -3.46 + 4 + 3 - 3.17$$

$$= 0.37 \text{ bits}$$

Let C denote the event that the professor is in town. Since

$$p(A|C) = \frac{3/16}{3/16 + 1/4} = \frac{3}{7}$$

we have

$$I(A, C) = -\lg\frac{11}{16} + \lg\frac{3}{7}$$
$$= -3.46 + 4 + 1.58 - 2.81$$
$$= -0.69 \text{ bits}$$

The fact that the professor is in town makes it less likely that an examination will be given. Consequently, the mutual information provided by the presence of the professor on the occurrence of an examination is a negative quantity. ∎

Example 2.56   Figure 2.3 shows a simple model of a communication channel, known as the *binary symmetric channel*. At the transmission end, either 0 or 1 is transmitted, and at the receiving end either 0 or 1 will be received. Specifically, when 0 is transmitted the probability that 0 will be received is $1 - \varepsilon$, and the probability that 1 will be received is ε. When 1 is transmitted the probability that 1 will be received is $1 - \varepsilon$, and the probability that 0 will be received is ε. Suppose we have two equally likely messages m_1 and m_2 that will be transmitted over the channel using the representations 000 and 111, respectively. If 010 was received, we can compute the mutual information between the event that message m_1 was transmitted and the event that either part or the whole of the sequence 010 was received.

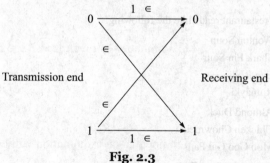

Fig. 2.3

$$I(m_1, 0) = -\lg\frac{1}{2} + \lg\frac{\frac{1}{2}(1-\varepsilon)}{\frac{1}{2}(1-\varepsilon)+\frac{1}{2}\varepsilon} = 1 + \lg(1-\varepsilon)$$

$$I(m_1, 01) = -\lg\frac{1}{2} + \lg\frac{\frac{1}{2}(1-\varepsilon)\varepsilon}{\frac{1}{2}\varepsilon(1-\varepsilon)+\frac{1}{2}\varepsilon(1-\varepsilon)} = 0$$

$$I(m_1, 010) = -\lg\frac{1}{2} + \lg\frac{\frac{1}{2}(1-\varepsilon)^2\varepsilon}{\frac{1}{2}\varepsilon(1-\varepsilon)^2+\frac{1}{2}\varepsilon^2(1-\varepsilon)} = 1 + \lg(1-\varepsilon)$$

Note that knowing that either 0 or 010 was received tells us exactly the same amount of information on the transmission of message m_1. However, knowing that the sequence 01 was received tells us nothing about the transmission of message m_1. Intuitively, this is what we would expect, since the transmission of either m_1 or m_2 would yield the sequence 01 at the receiving end with the same probability. ∎

Note that

$$I(A, B) = -\lg p(A) + \lg p(A \mid B)$$
$$= -\lg p(A) - \lg p(B) + \lg p(A \cap B)$$
$$= -\lg p(B) + \frac{\lg p(A \cap B)}{\lg p(A)}$$
$$= -\lg p(B) + \lg p(B \mid A)$$
$$= I(B, A)$$

We realize that mutual information is a symmetric measure on the information concerning two events. In other words, what the occurrence of B tells us about the occurrence of A is equal to what the occurrence of A tells us about the occurrence of B. Thus, $I(A, B)$ is a measure of the *mutual information* from B to A as well as from A to B.

Problems

2.1 A menu in a restaurant reads like the following:

Group A : Wonton Soup
              Shark Fin Soup
              Egg Rolls
              Rumayki

Group B : Almond Duck
              Chicken Chowmein
              Moo Goo Gai Pan

Group C : Sweet and Sour Pork
              Pepper Steak
              Dragon Beef
              Butterfly Shrimp
              Shrimp with Lobster Sauce
              Egg Foo Young

Group D : Coffee
              Tea
              Milk

(a) Suppose you select one course from each group without omission or substitution. How many different "complete four-course dinners" can you make out of this menu?

(b) Suppose the waiter will not force you to make a selection if you desire to omit a group completely. (After all, you are going to pay for it.) How many different dinners can you make out of this menu?

(c) Suppose you select one course from each of groups *A*, *B*, and *D* and two courses from group *C* without omission or substitution. How many different dinners can you devise? Suppose you select one or two from group *C* without any other omission or substitution. How many dinners can you devise?

2.2 (a) In how many ways can two integers be selected from the integers 1, 2, ... , 100 so that their difference is exactly seven?

(b) Repeat part (a) if the difference is to be seven or less.

2.3 In how many ways can two adjacent squares be selected from an 8 × 8 chessboard?

2.4 A variable name in a programming language must be either a letter or a letter followed by a decimal digit. How many different variable names are there in this language?

2.5 Five boys and five girls are to be seated in a row. In how many ways can they be seated if:

(a) All boys must be seated in the five leftmost seats?

(b) No two boys can be seated together?

(c) John and Mary must be seated together?

2.6 (a) In how many ways can 10 boys and 5 girls stand in a line so that no two girls are next to each other? (All boys and girls are distinct)

(b) Repeat part (a) if they stand around a circle.

2.7 In how many ways can the letters in the English alphabet be arranged so that there are exactly seven letters between the letters *a* and *b*?

2.8 (a) In how many ways can the letters *a*, *a*, *a*, *a*, *a*, *b*, *c*, *d*, *e* be permuted such that no two *a*'s are adjacent?

(b) Repeat part (a) if no two of *b*, *c*, *d*, *e* can be adjacent.

2.9 (a) In how many ways can the letters in the word *MISSISSIPPI* be arranged?

(b) In how many ways can they be arranged if the two *P*'s must be separated?

2.10 (a) In how many ways can the letters *a*, *b*, *c*, *d*, *e*, *f* be arranged so that the letter *b* is always to the immediate left of the letter *e*?

(b) Repeat part (a) if the letter *b* is always to the left of the letter *e*.

2.11 (a) Suppose that repetitions are not permitted, How many four-digit numbers can be formed from the six digits 1, 2, 3, 5, 7, 8?

(b) How many of the numbers in part (a) are less than 4000?

(c) How many of the numbers in part (a) are even?

(d) How many of the numbers in part (a) are odd?

(e) How many of the numbers in part (a) are multiples of 5?

(f) How many of the numbers in part (a) contain both the digit 3 and the digit 5?

2.12 There are 15 "true or false" questions in an examination. In how many different ways can a student do the examination if he or she can also choose not to answer some of the questions?

2.13 A palindrome is a word that reads the same forward or backward. How many seven-letter palindromes can be made out of the English alphabet?

2.14 (a) How many different automobile license plates made up of two letters followed by four digits are there?

    (b) Repeat part (a) if the two letters must be distinct.

2.15 (a) In how many ways can we make up the pattern

$$
\begin{array}{ccccc}
 & & \times & & \\
\times & \times & \times & \times & \times \\
 & & \times & & \\
 & & \times & & \\
 & & \times & &
\end{array}
$$

with 0s and 1s?

    (b) How many of these patterns are not symmetrical with respect to the vertical axis?

2.16 (a) Cards are drawn from a deck of 52 cards with replacements. In how many ways can 10 cards be drawn so that the 10th card is the first repetition?

    (b) Repeat part (a) if the 10th card is a repetition.

2.17 In a row of 20 seats, in how many ways can three blocks of consecutive seats with five seats in each block be selected?

2.18 (a) Show that the total number of permutations of p red balls and 0, or 1, or 2, ... , or q white balls is

$$
\frac{p!}{p!} + \frac{(p+1)!}{p!\,1!} + \frac{(p+2)!}{p!\,2!} + \dots + \frac{(p+q)!}{p!\,q!}
$$

    (b) Show that the sum in part (a) is

$$
\frac{(p+q+1)!}{(p+1)!\,q!}
$$

    (c) Show that the total number of permutations of 0, or 1, or 2, ..., or p red balls with 0, or 1, or 2, ..., or q white balls is

$$
\frac{(p+q+2)!}{(p+1)!\,(q+1)!} - 2
$$

2.19 In a class of 100 students, 40 were boys.

    (a) In how many ways can a 10-person committee be formed?

    (b) Repeat part (a) if there must be an equal number of boys and girls in the committee.

    (c) Repeat part (a) if the committee must consist of *either* six boys and four girls *or* four boys and six girls.

2.20 A student must answer 8 out of 10 questions in an examination.

    (a) How many choices does the student have?

    (b) How many choices does she have if she must answer the first three questions?

    (c) How many choices does she have if she must answer at least four of the first five questions?

2.21 A delegation of four students is to be selected from a total of 12 students to attend a meeting.

    (a) In how many ways can the delegation be chosen?

    (b) Repeat part (a) if there are two students who refuse to be in the delegation together?

    (c) Repeat part (a) if there are two students who will only attend the meeting together?

    (d) Repeat part (a) if there are two students who refuse to be in the delegation together and two other students who will only attend the meeting together?

2.22 (a) From 200 automobiles, 30 are selected to test whether they meet the safety requirements. Also, 30 (from the same 200 automobiles) are selected to test whether they meet the antipollution requirements. In how many ways can the selection be made?

(b) In how many ways can the selection be made so that there are exactly five automobiles that undergo both tests?

2.23 A man has 10 friends. In how many ways can he go to dinner with two or more of them?

2.24 (a) Fifteen basketball players are to be drafted by the three professional teams in Boston, Chicago, and New York such that each team will draft five players. In how many ways can this be done?

(b) Fifteen basketball players are to be divided into three teams of five players each. In how many ways can this be done?

2.25 In how many ways can we distribute 15 different books among Pun, Khim, and Leong so that Pun and Khim together receive twice as many books as Leong?

2.26 Among all seven-digit decimal numbers, how many of them contain exactly three 9s?

2.27 (a) In how many ways can two numbers be selected from the integers 1, 2, ..., 100 so that their sum is an even number? An odd number?

(b) Use a combinatorial argument to show that
$$C(2n, 2) = 2C(n, 2) + n^2$$

2.28 There are 50 students in each of the junior and the senior classes. Each class has 25 male and 25 female students. In how many ways can eight representatives be selected so that there are four females and three juniors?

2.29 Three integers are selected from the integers 1, 2, ..., 1000. In how many ways can these integers be selected such that their sum is divisible by 4?

2.30 In how many ways can a group of eight people be divided into committees, subject to the constraint that each person must belong to exactly one committee, and each committee must contain at least two people. (Note that a division into committees of three, three, and two people is considered the same as a division into committees of two, three, and three people.)

2.31 From 100 students two groups of 10 students each are selected. In how many ways can the selection be made so that the tallest student in the first group is shorter than the shortest student in the second group? (Assume all 100 students are of different heights.)

2.32 How many n-digit decimal numbers have their digits in nondecreasing order? (Note that the first digit of an n-digit number must not be 0.)

2.33 In how many ways can 22 different books be given to 5 students so that 2 of them will have 5 books and the other 3 will have 4 books?

2.34 In how many ways can $2n$ people be divided into n pairs?

2.35 (a) In how many ways can two squares be selected from an 8×8 chessboard so that they are not in the same row or the same column?

(b) In how many ways can four squares, not all in the same row or column, be selected from an 8×8 chessboard to form a rectangle?

2.36 Show that the product of k successive integers is divisible by $k!$ (*Hint:* Consider the number of ways of selecting k objects from $n + k$ objects.)

2.37 (a) Show that
$$C(2n + 2, n + 1) = C(2n, n + 1) + 2C(2n, n) + C(2n, n - 1)$$

(b) Give a combinatorial interpretation to the equality in part (a).

2.38 (a) Among $2n$ objects, n of them are identical. Find the number of ways to select n objects out of these $2n$ objects.

(b) Among $3n + 1$ objects, n of them are identical. Find the number of ways to select n objects out of these $3n + 1$ objects.

2.39 In how many ways can two integers be selected from $1, 2, \ldots, n - 1$ so that their sum is larger than n?

2.40 Out of a large number of pennies, nickels, dimes, and quarters, in how many ways can five coins be selected?

2.41 (a) Show that the number of ways to place r indistinguishable balls in n distinct boxes, $n \leqq r$, with no box left empty is $C(r - 1, n - 1)$. (A box can hold arbitrarily many balls.)

(b) In how many ways can a student schedule 15 hours of study in a 5-day period so that she will study at least an hour each day?

(c) In how many ways can r indistinguishable balls be placed in n distinct boxes with each box holding at least q balls?

(d) Repeat part (b) if she must study at least two hours each day.

2.42 In how many ways can we place r red balls and w white balls in n boxes so that each box contains at least one ball of each color?

2.43 In how many ways can we distribute $2t$ marbles among four distinct boxes A, B, C, and D such that boxes A and B contain at most t marbles while boxes C and D may contain any number of marbles?

2.44 (a) How many sequences of m 0s and n 1s are there?

(b) How many sequences are there in which each 1 is separated by at least two 0s? [Assume for this part that $m \geqq 2(n - 1)$.]

2.45 Suppose n different games are to be distributed among n children. In how many ways can this be done so that exactly one child gets no game?

2.46 We are given a red box, a blue box, and a green box. We are also given 10 red balls, 10 blue balls, and 10 green balls. Balls of the same color are considered identical. Consider the following constraints:

1. No box contains a ball that has the same color as the box.
2. No box is empty.

Determine the number of ways in which we can put the 30 balls into boxes so that:

(a) No constraint has to be satisfied; that is, every combination is permitted

(b) Constraint 1 is satisfied.

(c) Constraint 2 is satisfied.

(d) Constraints 1 and 2 are satisfied.

2.47 (a) r distinct balls are to be placed in n distinct boxes with balls in each box arranged in order. Show that there are

$$(n + r - 1)(n + r - 2) \ldots (n + 1)n$$

ways to do so.

(b) In how many ways can the letters a, b, c, d, e, f, g, h be arranged so that a is to the left of b and b is to the left of c?

2.48 Find the number of permutations of the letters a, b, c, d, e, f, g so that neither the pattern *beg* nor the pattern *cad* appears.

2.49 How many permutations of the 10 digits 0, 1, 2, ..., 9 are there in which the first digit is greater than 1 and the last digit is less than 8?

2.50 How many permutations of the 26 letters $a, b, c, ..., x, y, z$ are there in which the first letter is not $a, b,$ or c and the last letter is not $w, x, y,$ or z?

2.51 For the set of letters $\{a, b, c, ..., z\}$, how many 12-subsets (that is, subsets containing 12 elements) are there that do not contain any of the sets $\{h, o, n, w, a, i,\}\{r, o, n, a\}$, and $\{l, i, u\}$ as subsets?

2.52 Ten books were arranged on a shelf in alphabetical order of the names of the authors. In how many ways can a monkey rearrange the books so that no book is put in its original place?

2.53 Among all n-digit numbers, how many of them contain the digits 2 and 7 but not the digits 0, 1, 8, 9?

2.54 If we write all decimal numbers from 1 to 1 million, how many times would we have written the digit 9?

2.55 Steps 2 and 3 in the procedure for generating all permutations of a set in Sec. 2.5 can be carried out as follows:

    (a) Examine the permutatation $a_1 a_2 ... a_n$ element by element from right to left. Let a_m be the rightmost element such that $a_m < a_{m+1}$.

    (b) Examine the permutation element by element from right to left again. Let a_p denote the rightmost element such that $a_m < a_p$.

    (c) Interchange a_m and a_p.

    (d) Interchange a_{m+1} and a_n, a_{m+2} and a_{n-1}, a_{m+3} and a_{n-2} and so on. [Note that after step (c), the original a_m becomes a_p.]

    Convince yourself that these steps indeed will yield the next permutation in the lexicographic order.

2.56 Seven (distinct) car accidents occurred in a week. What is the probability that they all occurred on the same day?

2.57 Ten (distinct) passengers got into an elevator on the ground floor of a 20-story building. What is the probability that they will all get off at different floors?

2.58 When the McGraw-Hill Book Company decided to order a reprint of this book, they were told by the author that there were 50 misprints to be corrected. (Actually, there were many more misprints than those that the author discovered. However, that is beside the point.) Out of the 422 pages in the book, what is the probability that these 50 misprints appear on 10 or fewer pages?

2.59 From the numbers 1, 2 ..., 100, a first number is chosen and then a second number is chosen from the remaining numbers. Assuming all 9900 possibilities are equally likely, what is the probability that the sum of the two numbers is divisible by 3?

2.60 One of ten keys opens the door. If we try the keys one after another, what is the probability that the door is opened on the first attempt? On the second attempt? On the tenth attempt?

2.61 There are 10 adjacent parking spaces in the parking lot. When you arrive in your new Rolls Royce, there are already seven cars in the lot. What is the probability that you can find two adjacent unoccupied spaces for your Rolls Royce?

2.62 A number is chosen at random from the 30 numbers $\{10, 11, ..., 19, 20, 21, ..., 30, 31, ..., 39,\}$. It is known that numbers with the same first digit have an equal chance of being chosen. Also, a number with 2 as the first digit is twice as likely to be chosen as one with 1 as the first digit, and a number with 3 as the first digit is three times as likely to be chosen as one with 1 as the first digit.

(a) Describe the sample space.

(b) What is the probability that a number with 2 as its first digit is chosen?

(c) What is the probability that a number with 2 as its second digit is chosen?

(d) What is the probability that a number with 2 as its first or second digit or both is chosen?

(e) What is the probability that a number divisible by 3 is chosen?

(f) What is the probability that a number divisible by 5 is chosen?

(g) What is the probability that a number divisible either by 3 or 5 but not by both is chosen?

2.63 An insurance company is interested in the age distribution of married couples when both the husband's and the wife's ages range from 21 to 25. Consider the sample space consisting of 25 sample points, each of which is represented by an ordered pair of numbers (x, y), where x is the age of the husband and y is the age of the wife:

$$S = \{(x, y)/21 \leq x \leq 25, 21 \leq y \leq 25\}$$

The probability associated with the sample point (x, y) is equal to kx/y if $x \leq y$, and is equal to ky/x if $y \leq x$.

(a) Determine the value of k.

(b) Suppose that a couple from this age group is selected at random, what is the probability that the husband is 21 years old and the wife is 22 years old? That the husband and wife are the same age? That the husband is older than the wife? That the husband is 25 years old?

(c) Suppose that a couple from this age group is selected at random. What is the probability that at least one of them is 22 years or older, or both the husband and the wife are the same age?

(d) Suppose that a couple from this age group is selected at random. Given that the husband is 23 years old, what is the probability that the wife is 24 years old? What is the probability that the wife is older than the husband?

(e) Suppose that a couple from this age group is selected at random. Given that both the husband and wife are at least 22 years old, what is the probability that both of them are at least 24 years old? That one or both of them is at least 24 years old?

(f) Suppose that a couple from this age group is selected at random. Given that at least one of them is 23 years old or younger, what is the probability that both of them are 22 years old or younger?

2.64 Consider the experiment of tossing a fair coin until two heads or two tails appear in succession.

(a) Describe the sample space.

(b) What is the probability that the experiment ends before the sixth toss?

(c) What is the probability that the experiment ends after an even number of tosses?

(d) Given that the experiment ends with two heads, what is the probability that the experiment ends before the sixth toss?

(e) Given that the experiment does not end before the third toss, what is the probability that the experiment does not end after the sixth toss?

2.65 There are 10 pairs of shoes in a closet. If eight shoes are chosen at random, what is the probability that no complete pair of shoes is chosen? That exactly one complete pair of shoes is chosen?

2.66 There is a 30 percent chance that it rains on any particular day. What is the probability that there is at least one rainy day within a 7-day period? Given that there is at least one rainy day, what is the probability that there are at least two rainy days?

2.67 A company purchased 100,000 transistors—50,000 from supplier A, 30,000 from supplier B, and 20,000 from supplier C. It is known that 2 percent of supplier A's transistors are defective, 3 percent of supplier B's transistors are defective, and 5 percent of supplier C's transistors are defective.

(a) If a transistor from the 100,000 transistors is selected at random, what is the probability that it is defective?

(b) Given that a transistor selected at random is defective, what is the probability that it is from supplier A?

(c) Given that a transistor selected at random is not from supplier A, what is the probability that it is defective?

2.68 A computer system consists of six subsystems. Each subsystem might fail independently with a probability of 0.2. The failure of any subsystem will lead to a failure of the whole computer system. Given that the computer system fails, what is the probability that subsystem 1 and only subsystem 1 fails?

2.69 There is a radar, a computer, and a gyroscope on board an airplane. The probability that the radar fails is 0.2. If the radar fails, the gyroscope will also fail, and the probability that the computer fails is 0.3. If the radar functions correctly, then the computer will also function correctly, and the probability that the gyroscope fails is 0.2.

(a) Describe the sample space.

(b) What is the probability that the computer or the gyroscope functions correctly while the other does not?

(c) What is the probability that the radar functions correctly if one of the other two systems fails?

2.70 Consider the problem of selecting a number out of 30 numbers described in Prob. 2.62. Determine the information in each of the assertions in (a), (b), (c), and (d).

(a) The number 27 was chosen.

(b) A number with 1 as its first digit was chosen.

(c) A number between 25 and 30 (inclusive) was chosen.

(d) A two-digit number the sum of whose digits is 9 was chosen.

(e) What is the mutual information between the two events in (a) and (b)? In (a) and (c)? In (a) and (d)? Compute the mutual information in two different ways.

2.71 Consider the problem on the distribution of ages of married couples in Prob. 2.63. Determine the information in each of the assertions in (a), (b), and (c).

(a) The husband is older than the wife.

(b) The difference between the husband's and the wife's ages is less than or equal to 2.

(c) The husband is 25 years old or the wife is at least 22 years old or both.

(d) What is the mutual information between the two events in (a) and (b)? In (a) and (c)? In (b) and (c)? Compute the mutual information in two different ways.

2.72 State and prove Bayes' theorem.

2.73 The set of events A_k, $(k = 1, 2 \ldots n)$, are (i) exhaustive and (ii) pairwise mutually exclusive. If for all k the probabilities $P(A_k)$ and $P(E|A_k)$ are known, calculate $P(A_k|E)$, where E is an arbitrary event. Indicate where conditions (i) and (ii) are used.

2.74 The events $E_1, E_2, E_3 \ldots E_n$ are mutually exclusive and $E = E_1 \cup E_2 \cup \ldots \cup E_n$. Show that if $P(A|E_i) = P(B|E_i)$; $i = 1, 2 \ldots n$, then $P(A|E) = P(B|E)$. Is this conclusion true if the events E_i are not mutually exclusive?

2.75 What are the criticisms against the use of Bayes' theorem in probability theory.

2.76 Using the fundamental addition and multiplication rules of probability, show that

$$P(B|A) = \frac{P(B)\, P(A|B)}{P(B)\, P(A|B) + P(\bar{B})\, P(A|\bar{B})}$$

where $\bar{B}$ is the event complementary to the event B.

2.77 Suppose the contents of urns I, II, III are as follows:

1 white, 2 black and 3 red balls,

2 white, 1 black and 1 red ball,

4 white, 5 black and 3 red balls.

One urn is chosen at random and two balls drawn. They happen to be white and red. What is the probability that they come from urns I, II, or III?

2.78 In answering a question on a multiple choice test, a student either knows the answer or he guesses. Let p be the probability that he knows the answer and $1-p$ is the probability that he guesses. Assume that a student who guesses at the answer will be correct with probability 1/5, where 5 is the number of multiple-choice alternatives. What is the conditional probability that a student knew the answer to a question given that he answered it correctly?

2.79 In a bolt factory machines A, B, and C manufacture respectively 25%, 35%, and 40% of the total. Of their output 5, 4, 2 percent are defective bolts. A bolt is drawn at random from the product and is found to be defective. What are the probabilities that it was manufactured by machines A, B and C?

Objective

To discuss the basic concepts associated with relations and functions, and their applications.

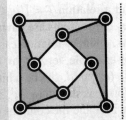

CHAPTER

THREE

RELATIONS AND FUNCTIONS

3.1 INTRODUCTION

In many problems concerning discrete objects, it is often the case that there is some kind of relationship among the objects. Among a set of computer programs, we might say that two of the programs are related if they share some common data and are not related otherwise. Among a group of students, we might say two students are related if the first letters of their last names are the same. On the other hand, in a different situation we might want to say that two students are related if the first letters of their last names are different. Also, consider the set of integers $\{1, 2, 3, ..., 15\}$. We might say that three integers in the set are related if their sum is divisible by 5. Thus, the integers 2, 3, 5 are related and integers 5, 10, 15 are related, but the integers 1, 2, 4 are not. We study in this chapter relations among discrete objects.

Let A and B be two sets. The *cartesian product* of A and B, denoted $A \times B$, is the set of all ordered pairs of the form (a, b) where $a \in A$ and $b \in B$. For example,

$$\{a, b\} \times \{a, c, d\} = \{(a, a), (a, c), (a, d), (b, a), (b, c), (b, d)\}$$

A *binary relation* from A to B is a subset of $A \times B$. A binary relation is indeed only a formalization of the intuitive notion that some of the elements in A are related to some of the elements in B. As a matter of fact, if R is a binary relation from A to B and if the ordered pair (a, b) is in R, we would say that the element a *is related to* the element b. For example, let $A = \{a, b, c, d\}$ be a set of four students, let $B = \{CS121, CS221, CS257, CS264, CS273, CS281\}$ be a set of six courses. The cartesian product $A \times B$ gives all the possible pairings of students and courses. On the other hand, a relation $R = \{(a, CS121), (b, CS221), (b, CS264), (c, CS221), (c, CS257), (c, CS273), (d, CS257), (d, CS281)\}$ might describe the courses the students are taking, and a relation $T = \{(a, CS121), (c, CS257), (c, CS273)\}$ might describe the courses the students are having difficulty with.

Besides a list of the ordered pairs, a binary relation can also be represented in tabular form or graphical form. For example, let $A = \{a, b, c, d\}$ and $B = \{\alpha, \beta, \gamma\}$, and let $R = \{(a, \alpha), (b, \gamma), (c, \alpha), (c, \gamma), (d, \beta)\}$ be a binary relation from A to B. R can be represented in tabular form, as shown in Fig. 3.1a, where the rows of the table correspond to the elements in A and the columns of the table correspond to the elements in B, and a check mark in a cell means the element in the row containing the cell is related to the element in the column containing the cell. If the elements of A and B appear in a certain order then the relation R can also be represented in the form of a matrix whose elements are 1s and 0s. We can place a 1 in the ith row and jth column if the element $a_i \in A$ is related to the element $b_j \in B$, otherwise a 0 is placed. The matrix for a relation R is usually termed as a *relation matrix* and is denoted as M_R. Mathematically, we can define the relation matrix, M_R as follows:

$$M_R = [m_{ij}] \quad \text{where } m_{ij} = \begin{cases} 1, & \text{if } (a_i, b_j) \in R \\ 0, & \text{if } (a_i, b_j) \notin R \end{cases}$$

The relation matrix for the given R is shown in Fig. 3.1b. We can also obtain Fig. 3.1b from Fig. 3.1a by replacing the checkmarks with 1's and the other cells with 0's. R can also be represented in graphical form as shown in Fig. 3.1c, where the points in the left-hand column are the elements in A, the points in the right-hand column are the elements in B, and an arrow from a point in the left-hand column to a point in the right-hand column indicates that the corresponding element in A is related to the corresponding element in B. Here, the points are also known as vertices or nodes and the arrows are known as edges of the graph. Since these graphs contain arrows (directions), they are known as *directed graphs* or *digraphs*.

Since binary relations are sets of ordered pairs, the notions of the intersection of two relations, the union of two relations, the symmetric difference of two relations, and the difference of two relations follow directly from that of sets.

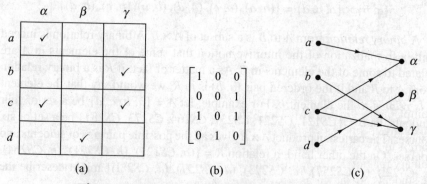

	α	β	γ
a	✓		
b			✓
c	✓		✓
d		✓	

$$\begin{bmatrix} 1 & 0 & 0 \\ 0 & 0 & 1 \\ 1 & 0 & 1 \\ 0 & 1 & 0 \end{bmatrix}$$

(a)   (b)   (c)

Fig. 3.1 Different representations of a relation

To be specific, let R_1 and R_2 be two binary relations from A to B. Then $R_1 \cap R_2$, $R_1 \cup R_2$, $R_1 \oplus R_2$, and $R_1 - R_2$ are also binary relations from A to B, which are known as the intersection, the union, the symmetric difference, and the difference of R_1 and R_2. For example, let $A = \{a, b, c, d\}$ be a set of students and $B = \{CS121, CS221, CS257, CS264, CS273, CS281\}$ be a set of courses. We might have a binary relation R_1 from A to B describing the courses the students are taking, and a binary relation R_2 from A to B describing the courses the students are interested in, as shown in Fig. 3.2. Then the binary relations $R_1 \cap R_2$, which is $\{(a, CS121), (b, CS221), (d, CS264), (d, CS281)\}$, describes the courses that the students are taking and are also interested in. The binary relation $R_1 \cup R_2$, which is $\{(a, CS121), (a, CS264), (b, CS221), (b, CS257),$ $(b, CS273), (c, CS221), (c, CS273), (c, CS281), (d, CS5264), (d, CS273),$ $(d, CS281)\}$, describes the courses the students are either taking or interested in. The binary relation $R_1 \oplus R_2$, which is $\{(a, CS264), (b, CS257), (b, CS273), (c,$ $CS221), (c, CS273), (c, CS281), (d, CS273)\}$, describes the courses the students are interested in but not taking or are taking but not interested in. The binary relation $R_1 - R_2$, which is $\{(b, CS257), (c, CS221), (c, CS273), (c, CS281)\}$, describes the courses the students are taking but not interested in.

	CS121	CS221	CS257	CS264	CS273	CS281
a	✓					
b		✓	✓			
c		✓			✓	✓
d				✓		✓ ✓

R_1

	CS121	CS221	CS257	CS264	CS273	CS281
a	✓			✓		
b		✓			✓	
c						
d				✓	✓	✓

R_2

Fig. 3.2

As another example, let $A = \{a, b, c, d\}$ be a set of students and $B = \{BT\&T,$ CompComm, GEE, JBM, Orange$\}$ be a set of companies that came to the university to interview students for jobs. We might have a binary relation R_1 from A to B describing the interviews the companies had with the students, and a binary relation R_2 from A to B describing the job offers the companies made to the students, as shown in Fig. 3.3. We ask the reader to give the meanings of the binary relations $R_1 \cap R_2$, $R_1 \cup R_2$, $R_1 \oplus R_2$, and $R_1 - R_2$.

	BT&T	Compcomm	GEE	JBM	Orange
a	✓	✓		✓	
b	✓	✓	✓	✓	✓
c				✓	✓
d	✓		✓	✓	

$$R_1$$

	BT&T	Compcomm	GEE	JBM	Orange
a					
b			✓	✓	
c		✓		✓	✓
d			✓	✓	✓

$$R_2$$

Fig. 3.3

As binary relations describe the relationship between pairs of objects, we would like to define ternary relations to describe the relationship among triples of objects, and quaternary relations to describe the relationship among quadruples of objects, and so on. Thus, a *ternary relation* among three sets A, B, and C is defined as a subset of the cartesian product of the two sets $A \times B$ and C, denoted $(A \times B) \times C$. Note that $(A \times B) \times C$ is the set of all ordered triples of the form $((a, b), c)$, where $(a, b) \in A \times B$ and $c \in C$. For example, let $A = \{a, b\}$, $B = \{\alpha, \beta\}$, and $C = \{1, 2\}$. We have

$$(A \times B) \times C = \{((a, \alpha), 1), ((a, \alpha), 2), ((a, \beta), 1), ((a, \beta), 2),$$
$$((b, \alpha), 1), ((b, \alpha), 2), ((b, \beta), 1), ((b, \beta), 2)\}$$

Also, let A be a set of students, B be a set of courses, and C be a set of all possible grades. Then a ternary relation among A, B, and C can be defined to describe the grades the students obtained in the courses they took. Similarly, a *quarternary relation* among four sets A, B, C, and D is defined as a subset of $((A \times B) \times C) \times D$. In general, an *n-ary relation* among the sets $A_1, A_2, A_3, ..., A_n$ is defined as a subset of $((A_1 \times A_2) \times A_3) ... \times A_n$. In other words, an *n-ary relation* among the sets $A_1, A_2, A_3, ..., A_n$ is a set of ordered n-tuples in which the first component is an element of A_1, the second component is an element of A_2, ..., and the nth component is an element of A_n.

3.2   A RELATIONAL MODEL FOR DATA BASES

As an example of relations among discrete objects, we present a brief introduction to a relational model for data bases. Modern large-scale computing systems are capable of handling large amounts of data, such as the records of charge account transactions of customers in a department store, the employment history and personal data of employees in a company, and the records of parts ordered and received in a factory. So that large amounts of data can be handled effectively, they must be organized in some form suitable for the more frequent operations, such as inserting new data, deleting old data, updating existing data, and searching for items with special attributes. One general way to view the organization of large varieties of data is with a *relational data model*. Let A_1, A_2, ... , A_n be n (not necessarily distinct) sets. An n-ary relation among A_1, A_2, ..., A_n is known as a *tablet** on A_1, A_2, ..., A_n in the language of relational data models. The sets $A_1, A_2, ..., A_n$ are called the *domains* of the table, and n is called the *degree* of the table. For example, let SUPPLIER $= \{s_1, s_2, s_3, s_4\}$ be the set of suppliers of parts, PART $= \{p_1, p_2, p_3, p_4, p_5, p_6, p_7\}$ be the set of parts, PROJECT $= \{j_1, j_2, j_3, j_4, j_5\}$ be the set of projects, and QUANTITY be the set of positive integers. We may have a table named SUPPLY on the sets SUPPLIER, PART, PROJECT, and QUANTITY describing the names of suppliers who supply parts to the various projects and the quantities they supply. Thus,

$$\text{SUPPLY} = \{(s_1, p_2, j_5, 5), (s_1, p_3, j_5, 17), (s_2, p_3, j_3, 9), (s_2, p_1, j_5, 5),$$
$$(s_4, p_1, j_1, 4)\}$$

is an example of a table. We shall also represent a table in tabular form, as shown in Fig. 3.4.

As another example, consider a table ASSEMBLE on PART, PART, and QUANTITY, where PART $= \{p_1, p_2, ..., p_7\}$ is the set of parts and QUANTITY is the set of positive integers. An ordered triple (p_i, p_j, c) in the table ASSEMBLE means that part p_i is a subcomponent of part p_j; moreover, it takes c units of part p_i to assemble each unit of part p_j. Therefore, we might have the table shown in Fig. 3.5.

SUPPLY

SUPPLIER	PART	PROJECT	QUANTITY
s_1	p_2	j_5	5
s_1	p_3	j_5	17
s_2	p_3	j_3	9
s_2	p_1	j_5	5
s_4	p_1	j_1	4

Fig. 3.4

ASSEMBLE

PART	PART	QUANTITY
p_1	p_5	9
p_2	p_5	7
p_3	p_5	2
p_2	p_6	12
p_3	p_6	3
p_4	p_7	1
p_6	p_7	1

Fig. 3.5

A domain of a table is called a *primary key** if its value in an ordered n-tuple uniquely identifies the ordered n-tuple in the table. In the table EMPLOYEES in Fig. 3.6, EMPLOYEE NO. is a primary key; so is NAME. On the other hand, DEPARTMENT is

---

* The term relation is also used. Here, we choose to use a more intuitive term.

* Since, in general, ordered n-tuples are added to and deleted from a table from time to time, being a primary key could be a *time-varying* property of a domain.

EMPLOYEES

EMPLOYEE NO.	NAME	DEPARTMENT	HOURLY WAGE
20835	Bernstein, E. M.	2	5.00
11273	Jones, D. J.	1	7.00
10004	Smith, C. W.	1	7.35
21524	Vögeli, W. J.	2	8.00
17734	Wong, J. W. S.	1	5.00
30219	Yamamoto, S.	3	6.50

Fig. 3.6

not a primary key and neither is HOURLY WAGE. If a table does not have a domain that can serve as a primary key, we might wish to use a combination of domains to identify the ordered n-tuples in the table. We define a *composite primary key* as the cartesian product of two or more domains such that its value[†] in an ordered n-tuple uniquely identifies the ordered n-tuple in the table. For example, in the table SUPPLY in Fig. 3.4, SUPPLIER × PART is a composite primary key.

Given a collection of tables, we might wish to manipulate the tables in various ways. As an illustration, we describe two important operations on tables—*projection* and join. We frequently want to abstract subtables from a table. The operation *projection* enables us to do so. Let R be a table of degree n. A projection of R is an m-ary relation, $m \leq n$, obtained from R by deleting $n - m$ of the components in each ordered n-tuple in R. We use the notation $\pi_{i1\,i2} \cdots i_m(R)$, $1 \leq i_1 < i_2 < \cdots < i_m \leq n$, to denote a projection of R, that is, a table of degree m obtained from R such that for each ordered n-tuple in R there is a corresponding ordered m-tuple in $\pi_{i1\,i2} \cdots i_m(R)$ with the kth component of the ordered m-tuple being the i_kth component of the ordered n-tuple. For example, for the table SUPPLY in Fig. 3.4, the projection $\pi_{1,3}$ (SUPPLY) is shown in Fig. 3.7.

$\pi_{1,3}$(SUPPLY)

SUPPLIER	PROJECT
s_1	j_5
s_2	j_3
s_2	j_5
s_4	j_1

Fig. 3.7

Note that, as illustrated in this example, there might be fewer ordered m-tuples in a projection of a table than there are ordered n-tuples in the table, because several distinct ordered n-tuples in the table might yield the same ordered m-tuple in the projection.

Tables can also be combined to yield bigger tables. The operation *join* combines two tables into one. Let R be a table of degree n and S be a table of degree m. For p less than n and m, we can construct a *join* of R and S, that is, a table denoted $\tau_p(R * S)$ such that

$$\tau_p(R * S) = \{(a_1, a_2, \ldots, a_{n-p}, b_1, b_2, \ldots, b_p, c_1, c_2, \ldots, c_{m-p}) |$$
$$(a_1, a_2, \ldots, a_{n-p}, b_1, b_2, \ldots, b_p) \in R,$$
$$(b_1, b_2, \ldots, b_p, c_1, c_2, \ldots c_{m-p}) \in S\}$$

[†] By the values of a composite primary key, we mean the ordered tuples in the cartesian product.

As an example, for the tables SUPPLY and COLOR of Fig. 3.8*a*, we have the join τ_2(SUPPLY * COLOR) shown in Fig. 3.8*b*.

SUPPLY

SUPPLIER	PART	PROJECT
s_1	p_1	j_1
s_2	p_1	j_1
s_2	p_2	j_2

COLOR

PART	PROJECT	COLOR
p_1	j_1	c_1
p_2	j_2	c_2
p_2	j_2	c_3

(a)

τ_2(SUPPLY * COLOR)

SUPPLIER	PART	PROJECT	COLOR
s_1	p_1	j_1	c_1
s_2	p_1	j_1	c_1
s_2	p_2	j_2	c_2
s_2	p_2	j_2	c_3

(b)

Fig. 3.8

A great deal more can be said about the relational data model, especially concerning other operations on tables, its implementation on computer systems, and so on; many of the details can be found in Codd [1] and Date [3].

3.3 PROPERTIES OF BINARY RELATIONS

A binary relation from a set A to A is said to be a *binary relation on A*. For example, let A be a set of positive integers. We may define a binary relation R on A such that (a, b) is in R if and only if $a - b \geq 10$. Thus, $(12, 1)$ is in R, but $(12, 3)$ is not; neither is $(1, 12)$. As another example, let $B = \{CS121, CS221, CS257, CS264, CS273, CS281\}$. A binary relation on $B = \{(CS121, CS221), (CS121, CS257), (CS257, CS281)\}$ might describe the prerequisite structure of these courses in that an ordered pair in the binary relation means the first course in the pair is a prerequisite of the second course in the pair. For the rest of this chapter, we shall study binary relations on a set because this is the case that we shall encounter most often.

Let R be a binary relation on A. R is said to be a *reflexive relation* if (a, a) is in R for every a in A. In other words in a reflexive relation every element in A is related to itself. For example, let A be a set of courses and R be a binary relation on A so that for two courses a and b in A, (a, b) is in R if and only if their final examinations are scheduled in the same time period. Clearly, for any course a, (a, a) is in R. Thus, R is a reflexive relation. As another example, let A be a set of positive integers, and let us define a binary relation R on A such that (a, b) is in R if and only if a divides b. Since an integer always divides itself, R is a reflexive relation. On the other hand, let us define a binary relation T on a set of integers A

such that (a, b) is in T if and only if $a > b$. Clearly, T is not a reflexive relation. As another example, let A be a set of students and R be a binary relation on A such that (a, b) is in R if a nominates b as a candidate for class president. R is a reflexive relation if *everyone* nominates himself or herself. On the other hand, R is not a reflexive relation if one or more of the students did not. When a binary relation on a set is represented in tabular form, it is very simple to determine whether the binary relation is a reflexive relation. To be specific, a binary relation on a set is reflexive if and only if all the cells on the main diagonal of the table contain check marks or 1s. For example, the binary relation in Fig. 3.9a is reflexive while that in Fig. 3.9b is not. Similarly, in a digraph, if each vertex contains a loop, then the corresponding relation is a *reflexive relation*. For example, the relation in Fig. 3.9c is a reflexive relation.

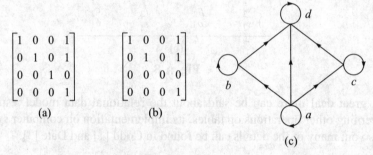

$$\begin{bmatrix} 1 & 0 & 0 & 1 \\ 0 & 1 & 0 & 1 \\ 0 & 0 & 1 & 0 \\ 0 & 0 & 0 & 1 \end{bmatrix}$$
(a)

$$\begin{bmatrix} 1 & 0 & 0 & 1 \\ 0 & 1 & 0 & 1 \\ 0 & 0 & 0 & 0 \\ 0 & 0 & 0 & 1 \end{bmatrix}$$
(b)

(c)

Fig. 3.9   Representations for reflexive relations

Let R be a binary relation on A. R is said to be a *symmetric* relation if (a, b) in R implies that (b, a) is also in R. For example, let A be a set of students and let R be a binary relation on A such that (a, b) is in R if and only if a is in a class that b is in. If a is in a class that b is in, then, clearly, b is also in a class that a is in. Thus, the relation R is a symmetric relation. As another example let A be a set of positive integers and T be a binary relation on A such that (a, b) is in T if and only if $a \geq b$. Since, for instance, $(10, 9)$ is in T but $(9, 10)$ is not in T, T is not a symmetric relation. As another example, let $A = \{a, b, c\}$. Let $U = \{\ \}$, $V = \{(a, a), (b, b)\}$, $W = \{(a, b), (b, a)\}$, and $X = A \times A$ be four binary relations on A. We note that all four of these are symmetric relations. When a binary relation on a set is represented in tabular form, we can determine whether it is symmetric by observing whether the check marks are in cells that are symmetrical with respect to the main diagonal. For example, the binary relation in Fig. 3.10a is symmetric while that in Fig. 3.10b is not.

Let R be a binary relation on A. R is said to be an *antisymmetric relation* if (a, b) in R implies that (b, a) is not in R unless $a = b$. In other words, if both (a, b) and (b, a) are in R then it must be the case that $a = b$.

$$\begin{bmatrix} 0 & 1 & 0 & 1 \\ 1 & 0 & 1 & 0 \\ 0 & 1 & 0 & 1 \\ 1 & 0 & 1 & 1 \end{bmatrix}$$
(a)

$$\begin{bmatrix} 0 & 1 & 0 & 1 \\ 1 & 0 & 0 & 0 \\ 0 & 0 & 0 & 0 \\ 0 & 0 & 0 & 1 \end{bmatrix}$$
(b)

Fig. 3.10

For example, let A be a set of tests to be performed on a patient in the hospital and let R be a binary relation on A such that if (a, b) is in R then test a must be performed before test b. Clearly, if test a must be performed before test b then test b must not be performed before test a for two distinct tests a and b. Thus, R is an antisymmetric relation. As another example, let A be a set of positive integers and R be a binary relation on A such that (a, b) is in R if and only if $a \geq b$. We note that R is an antisymmetric relation. Let $A = \{a, b, c\}$. Let $S = \{(a, a), (b, b)\}$ and $N = \{(a, b), (a, c), (c, a)\}$ be binary relations on A. Note that S is both symmetric and antisymmetric, yet N is neither symmetric nor antisymmetric.

Let R be a binary relation on A. R is said to be a transitive relation if (a, c) is in R whenever both (a, b) and (b, c) are in R. For example, let $A = \{a, b, c\}$ and $X = \{(a, a), (a, b), (a, c), (b, c)\}$. We note that X is a transitive relation. We also note that $Y = \{(a, b)\}$ is a transitive relation, yet $Z = \{(a, b), (b, c)\}$ is not.* As another example, let A be a set of people, and let R be a binary relation on A such that (a, b) is in R if and only if a is an ancestor of b. Clearly, R is a transitive relation. On the other hand, if we let T be a binary relation on A such that (a, b) is in T if and only if a is the father of b, then T is not a transitive relation.

3.4 CLOSURE OF RELATIONS

Before discussing the closure of relations, let us consider the following example: A software company has centers in Kolkata, Hyderabad, Bangalore, Pune, Tokyo and Los Angeles. There are direct one-way routes from Kolkata to Pune, from Hyderabad to Pune, from Pune to Bangalore and from Tokyo to Los Angeles. Let R be the relation such that $(a, b) \in R$, if there is a direct route from the center at a to the center at b. But, how can we determine whether there is some (possibly indirect) other route consisting of one or more routes from one center to another center. Since all the routes are not direct (like the route from Kolkata to Bangalore that goes through Pune), R cannot be used directly to answer this. According to the language of relations, R is not transitive. So, it does not contain all the pairs that can be linked. As we will show in this section, we can find all pairs of centers that have a route by constructing the smallest transitive relation that contains R. This relation is known as the *transitive closure* of R.

The *closure of* a relation is the smallest extension of the relation that has certain specific properties such as reflexivity, symmetry and transitivity. Let R be a relation on a set A. R may or may not have certain property P such as reflexivity, symmetry or transitivity. If there exists a relation T with property P containing R such that T is a subset of every relation with property P containing R, then T is known as the *closure of R* with respect to P. In the following sections, we define reflexive, symmetric and transitive closures of relations.

---

* At this point, a reader probably becomes aware of the problem of checking whether a given binary relation is transitive or not. This clearly can be done by an exhaustive search, but looking for efficient procedures for checking transitivity is still a topic of current research.

Reflexive Closure   A relation R' is the reflexive closure of a relation R if and only if,

(a) R' is reflexive
(b) $R \subseteq R'$
(c) For any relation R'', if $R \subseteq R''$ and R'' is reflexive then $R' \subseteq R''$, i.e. R' is the smallest relation that satisfies (a) and (b). The reflexive closure of a relation R is denoted as $r(R)$.

Example 3.1   Let us consider the relation $R = \{(a, b), (b, a), (b, b), (c, b)\}$ on the set $A = \{a, b, c\}$. It is clear that the relation R is not reflexive. Now consider the relation R' which contains R as well as (a, a) and (c, c) i.e. $R' = \{(a, b), (b, a), (b, b), (c, b), (a, a), (c, c)\}$. Clearly, R' is reflexive and $R \subseteq R'$. Furthermore, any other reflexive relation say R'' containing R must also contain (a, a) and (c, c). (Otherwise it will not be reflexive). So, $R' \subseteq R''$. As, R' contains R, is reflexive and is contained in every reflexive relation that contains R, so R' is the reflexive closure of R.   ∎

Example 3.2   Let R be the greater than (>) relation on the set of integers Z, that is

$$R = \{(a, b) | a \in Z \wedge b \in Z \wedge a > b\}$$

Let $S = \{(a, a) | a \in Z\}$

Then, the reflexive closure $r(R)$ of R is the union of R and the equality relation S on Z, i.e.

$$r(R) = \{(a, b) | a \in Z \wedge b \in Z \text{ and } a \geq b\}.$$ ∎

Symmetric Closure   A relation R' is the symmetric closure of a relation R if and only if

(a) R' is symmetric
(b) $R \subseteq R'$
(c) For any relation R'', if $R \subseteq R''$ and R'' is symmetric, then $R' \subseteq R''$, i.e. R' is the smallest relation that satisfies (a) and (b).

The symmetric closure of a relation R is denoted as $s(R)$.

Example 3.3   Let us consider a relation $R = \{(a, a), (a, b), (c, c), (b, c), (b, a), (a, c)\}$. Clearly R is not symmetric. To be symmetric, R needs (c, b) and (c, a). Let the relation R' contains R as well as (c, b) and (c, a), i.e.,

$$R' = \{(a, a), (a, b), (c, c), (b, c), (b, a), (a, c), (c, b), (c, a)\}$$

Clearly R' is symmetric and $R \subseteq R'$. Furthermore, any other symmetric relation, say R'' containing R must also contain (c, b) and (c, a). Now, R' contains R, it is symmetric and it is contained within every symmetric relation that contains R, i.e. $R' \subseteq R''$. So, R' is the symmetric closure of R.   ∎

Example 3.4   Let R be the greater than (>) relation on the set of integers Z, i.e. $R = \{\langle a, b \rangle | a \in Z \wedge b \in Z \wedge a > b\}$

Then the symmetric closure of R denoted by $s(R)$ is given by

$$s(R) = \{\langle a, b\rangle | a > b\} \cup \{\langle b, a\rangle | a < b\}$$
$$= \{\langle a, b\rangle | a \in Z, b \in Z \wedge a > b \cup a < b\} \qquad \blacksquare$$

Transitive Closure A relation R' is the transitive closure of a relation R if and only if

(a) R' is transitive

(b) $R \subseteq R'$

(c) For any relation R'', if $R \subseteq R''$ and R'' is transitive then $R' \subseteq R''$, i.e. R' is the smallest relation that satisfies (a) and (b)

The transitive closure of a relation R is denoted as $t(R)$.

Example 3.5 The transitive closure of the less than relation on the set of integers is the less than relation itself. $\qquad \blacksquare$

The above definition of transitive closure of a relation can be expressed in another way. Let R be a binary relation on A. The *transitive extension of R*, denoted R_1, is a binary relation on A such that R_1 contains R, and moreover, if (a, b) and (b, c) are in R, then (a, c) is in R_1. For example, let $A = \{a, b, c, d\}$ and R be the binary relation shown in Fig. 3.12a. The transitive extension of R, (say R_1), is shown in Fig. 3.12b, where the ordered pairs in R_1 but not in R are marked with **1s**. Note that if R is a transitive relation, R is equal to R_1. Let R_2 denote the transitive extension of R_1, and, in general, let R_{i+1} denote the transitive extension of R_i. We define the *transitive closure* of R, denoted R^*, to be the set union of $R, R_1, R_2, \ldots$. Mathematically, we can write, $R^* = R \cup R_1 \cup R_2 \cup R_3 \cup \ldots$. The matrix for the transitive closure R^* is denoted as M_R^*. The program for computing the transitive closure of a relation using transitive extensions is given in Figure 3.11. For example, the transitive closure of the binary relation R in Fig. 3.12a is shown in Fig. 3.12c. As another example, let A be a set of cities and R be a binary relation on A so that the ordered pair (a, b) is in R if there is a communication link from city a to city b for the transmission of messages. Thus, the transitive extension of R, (say R_1), describes how messages can be transmitted from one city to another, either on a direct communication link or through one intermediate city. Similarly, the transitive extension of R_1, (say R_2), describes how messages can be transmitted from one city to another, either on a direct communication link or through at most three intermediate cities.* Finally, the transitive closure of R, (say R^*), describes how messages can be transmitted from one city to another, either through a direct communication link or through as many intermediate cities as we wish.

As another example, let A be a set of males and R be a binary relation on A so that the ordered pair (a, b) is in R if a is the father of b. Note that, in general, R is not a transitive relation since if a is the father of b and b is the father of c then a

---

* See Problem 3.23.

```
/*FINDING THE TRANSITIVE CLOSURE OF A RELATION USING TRANSITIVE EXTENSIONS*/
#include<stdio.h>
#include<conio.h>
int main()
{
    int R[10][10],n,i,j,k,flag,temp;
    printf("relation matrix R declared on the set A");
    printf("\n enter the no. of elements of set A ");
    scanf("%d", &n);
    printf("the relation matrix is of order %d",n);

    /*To enter the relation matrix*/
    printf("\n enter the elements into matrix R(row wise)\n");
    for(i=0;i<n;i++)
    for(j=0;j<n;j++)
    scanf("%d", &R[i][j]);//enter 0 or 1

    /*To print the entered relation matrix */
    printf("\n matrix R is:\n");
    for(i=0;i<n;i++)
    {
                    for(j=0;j<n;j++)
                    printf("%d  ",R[i][j]);
                    printf("\n");
    }
    /*To find the transitive closure*/
        printf("\n MATRIX FORMS IN THE VARIOUS STEPS WHILE FINDING THE TRANSITIVE
            CLOSURE: ");
    do
    {
        flag=0;
        for(i=0;i<n;i++)
        for(j=0;j<n;j++)
        {
                if(R[i][j]==1)
                {
                    for(k=0;k<n;k++)
                    if(R[j][k]==1)
                    {
                        temp=R[i][k];
                        R[i][k]=1;
                        if(temp==0)
                        flag=1;
                    }
                }
        }
        printf("\n\n");
        for(i=0;i<n;i++)
        {
                    for(j=0;j<n;j++)
                    printf("%d  ",R[i][j]);
                    printf("\n");
        }
    }while(flag==1);
    printf("\n END OF PROCEDURE WHEN NO FURTHER CHANGE IN THE MATRIX OCCURS\n");

    /*To print the required transitive closure matrix*/
    printf("\n the transitive closure matrix is:\n");
    for(i=0;i<n;i++)
    {
                    for(j=0;j<n;j++)
                    printf("%d  ",R[i][j]);
                    printf("\n");
    }
    getch();
    return 0;
}
```

Fig. 3.11   C code for computing transitive closure using transitive extension

$$\begin{bmatrix} 0 & 1 & 0 & 0 \\ 0 & 0 & 1 & 0 \\ 0 & 1 & 0 & 1 \\ 0 & 0 & 0 & 0 \end{bmatrix} \qquad \begin{bmatrix} 0 & 1 & 1 & 0 \\ 0 & 1 & 1 & 1 \\ 0 & 1 & 1 & 1 \\ 0 & 0 & 0 & 0 \end{bmatrix} \qquad \begin{bmatrix} 0 & 1 & 1 & 1 \\ 0 & 1 & 1 & 1 \\ 0 & 1 & 1 & 1 \\ 0 & 0 & 0 & 0 \end{bmatrix}$$

(a) (b) (c)

Fig. 3.12

is definitely not the father of c. On the other hand, the transitive closure of R, R^*, is a transitive relation that describes the ancestor-descendant relationship among the people in A. We note that for any binary relation R, R^* is always a transitive relation.

3.5 WARSHALL'S ALGORITHM

Stephen Warshall proposed an efficient algorithm to compute the transitive closure of a relation. Before presenting Warshall's technique, we define a path in a diagraph.

Path A path from x to y in a directed graph G is a sequence of edges (a_0, a_1), (a_1, a_2), ... (a_{n-1}, a_n) in G, where $n > 0$, and $a_0 = x$ and $a_n = y$. The path is denoted by $a_0, a_1, ..., a_{n-1}, a_n$ and has length n.

Suppose R is a relation in a set with n elements. Warshall's algorithm is based on the construction of a sequence of matrices for the relation. These matrices are represented by $W_0, W_1, W_2, ..., W_n$, where $W_0 = M_R$ is the relation matrix of R.

Here, $W_k = [w_{ij}^{(k)}]$

where $w_{ij}^{(k)} = \begin{cases} 1, \text{ if there exists a path from vertex } v_i \text{ to } v_j \\ \quad \text{in the corresponding diagraph, such that all} \\ \quad \text{the intermediate vertices of this path are} \\ \quad \text{in the set } \{v_1, v_2, ..., v_k\} \\ 0, \text{ otherwise} \end{cases}$

It may be noted that, $W_n = M_R^*$, as the (i, j)th entry of M_R^* is 1, iff there exists a path from v_i to v_j, with all intermediate vertices in the set $\{v_1, v_2, ..., v_n\}$. We explain Warshall's algorithm with the help of the following examples.

Example 3.6 Let R be the relation on the set $A = \{a, b, c, d\}$ with directed graph shown in Fig. 3.13. Find the transitive closure of R using Warshall's algorithm.

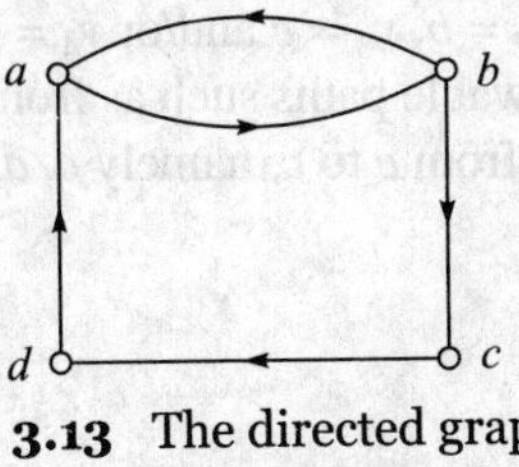

Solution: Let $v_1 = a$, $v_2 = b$, $v_3 = c$, and $v_4 = d$. $W_0 = M_R$ is the relation matrix of R. So,

Fig. 3.13 The directed graph of the relation R

$$W_0 = \begin{bmatrix} 0 & 1 & 0 & 0 \\ 1 & 0 & 1 & 0 \\ 0 & 0 & 0 & 1 \\ 1 & 0 & 0 & 0 \end{bmatrix}$$

W_1 has 1 as its (i, j)th entry if there is a path from v_i to v_j, that has only $v_1 = a$ as an interior vertex, if any. It may be noted that all paths of length one can still be used since they have no interior vertices. Now, there are two allowable paths such as from b to b, namely b, a, b, and from d to b, namely d, a, b. So,

$$W_1 = \begin{bmatrix} 0 & 1 & 0 & 0 \\ 1 & 1 & 1 & 0 \\ 0 & 0 & 0 & 1 \\ 1 & 1 & 0 & 0 \end{bmatrix}$$

W_2 has 1 as its (i, j)th entry if there is a path from v_i to v_j, that has only $v_1 = a$ and/or $v_2 = b$ as its interior vertices, if any. Here, there are three allowable paths such as from a to a, namely a, b, a and from a to c, namely a, b, c and from d to c, namely d, a, b, c. So,

$$W_2 = \begin{bmatrix} 1 & 1 & 1 & 0 \\ 1 & 1 & 1 & 0 \\ 0 & 0 & 0 & 1 \\ 1 & 1 & 1 & 0 \end{bmatrix}$$

W_3 has 1 as its (i, j)th entry if there is a path from v_i to v_j, that has only $v_1 = a$, $v_2 = b$ and/or $v_3 = c$ as its interior vertices, if any. Here, there are three allowable paths such as from a to d, namely a, b, c, d and from b to d, namely b, c, d and from d to d, namely d, a, b, c, d. So,

$$W_3 = \begin{bmatrix} 1 & 1 & 1 & 1 \\ 1 & 1 & 1 & 1 \\ 0 & 0 & 0 & 1 \\ 1 & 1 & 1 & 1 \end{bmatrix}$$

W_4 has 1 as its (i, j)th entry if there is a path from v_i to v_j, that has only $v_1 = a$, $v_2 = b$, $v_3 = c$ and/or $v_4 = d$ as its interior vertices, if any. Here, there are three allowable paths such as from c to a, namely c, d, a, from c to b, namely c, d, a, b and from c to c, namely c, d, a, b, c. So,

$$W_4 = \begin{bmatrix} 1 & 1 & 1 & 1 \\ 1 & 1 & 1 & 1 \\ 1 & 1 & 1 & 1 \\ 1 & 1 & 1 & 1 \end{bmatrix}$$

This last matrix W_4 is the matrix of the transitive closure of the relation R. ∎

Example 3.7 Let $R = \{(a, b), (a, c), (a, d), (b, c), (b, d), (c, d)\}$ be a relation on the set $A = \{a, b, c, d\}$. Find the transitive closure of R using Warshall's algorithm.

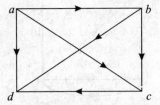

Fig. 3.14 The directed graph of the relation R

Solution: Fig. 3.14 shows the directed graph of relation R. Let $v_1 = a$, $v_2 = b$, $v_3 = c$ and $v_4 = d$. Here, $W_0 = M_R$ – the relation matrix of R. So,

$$W_0 = \begin{bmatrix} 0 & 1 & 1 & 1 \\ 0 & 0 & 1 & 1 \\ 0 & 0 & 0 & 1 \\ 0 & 0 & 0 & 0 \end{bmatrix}$$

W_1 has 1 as its $(i, j)th$ entry if there is a path from v_i to v_j that has only $v_1 = a$ as an interior vertex, if any. It may be noted that all paths of length one can still be used since they have no interior vertices. But, in this case, there are no allowable paths when we consider $v_1 = a$ as the interior vertex. So, $W_1 = W_0$.

W_2 has 1 as its $(i, j)th$ entry if there is a path from v_i to v_j that has only $v_1 = a$ and/or $v_1 = b$ as its interior vertices, if any. Here, there are two allowable paths such as from a to d, namely a, b, d and from a to c, namely a, b, c. But this results in a matrix which is same as the previous matrix W_1. So, $W_2 = W_1$.

W_3 has 1 as its $(i, j)th$ entry if there is a path from v_i to v_j that has only $v_1 = a$, $v_2 = b$ and/or $v_3 = c$ as its interior vertices, if any. Here, there are three allowable paths such as from a to d namely a, b, c, d, from a to d namely a, c, d and from b to d, namely b, c, d. But this results in a matrix which is same as the previous matrix W_2. So, $W_3 = W_2$.

W_4 has 1 as its $(i, j)th$ entry if there is a path from v_i to v_j that has only $v_1 = a$, $v_2 = b$ $v_3 = c$ and/or $v_4 = d$ as its interior vertices, if any. Here, there are no allowable paths. So, $W_4 = W_3$.

Now, $$W_4 = \begin{bmatrix} 0 & 1 & 1 & 1 \\ 0 & 0 & 1 & 1 \\ 0 & 0 & 0 & 1 \\ 0 & 0 & 0 & 0 \end{bmatrix}$$

This last matrix W_4 is the matrix of the transitive closure of the given relation R. In this case it may be observed that the transitive closure of the given relation R is the relation R itself. ∎

Example 3.8 Let R be the relation on the set $A = \{a, b, c, d\}$ as given in Fig. 3.15. Find the transitive closure of R using Warshall's algorithm.

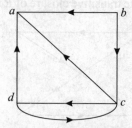

Fig. 3.15 The directed graph of the relation R

Solution: Fig. 3.15 shows the directed graph of the relation R. Let $v_1 = a$, $v_2 = b$, $v_3 = c$ and $v_4 = d$. Here, $W_0 = M_R$ - the relation matrix of R. So,

$$W_0 = \begin{bmatrix} 0 & 0 & 0 & 0 \\ 1 & 0 & 1 & 0 \\ 1 & 0 & 0 & 1 \\ 1 & 0 & 1 & 0 \end{bmatrix}$$

W_1 has 1 as its $(i, j)th$ entry if there is a path from v_i to v_j that has only $v_1 = a$ as an interior vertex, if any. It may be noted that all paths of length one can still be used since they have no interior vertices. But, in this case, there are no allowable paths when we consider $v_1 = a$ as the interior vertex. So, $W_1 = W_0$.

W_2 has 1 as its $(i, j)th$ entry if there is a path from v_i to v_j, that has only $v_1 = a$ and/or $v_2 = b$ as its interior vertices, if any. But, in this case, there are no allowable paths. So, $W_2 = W_1$.

W_3 has 1 as its $(i, j)th$ entry if there is a path from v_i to v_j, that has only $v_1 = a$, $v_2 = b$ and/or $v_3 = c$ as its interior vertices, if any. Here, there are two allowable paths such as from b to d namely b, c, d and from d to d, namely d, c, d. So,

$$W_3 = \begin{bmatrix} 0 & 0 & 0 & 0 \\ 1 & 0 & 1 & 1 \\ 1 & 0 & 0 & 1 \\ 1 & 0 & 1 & 1 \end{bmatrix}$$

W_4 has 1 as its $(i, j)th$ entry if there is a path from v_i to v_j, that has only $v_1 = a$, $v_2 = b$, $v_3 = c$ and/or $v_4 = d$. as its interior vertices, if any. Here, there is only one allowable path from c to c, namely c, d, c. So,

So, $$W_4 = \begin{bmatrix} 0 & 0 & 0 & 0 \\ 1 & 0 & 1 & 1 \\ 1 & 0 & 1 & 1 \\ 1 & 0 & 1 & 1 \end{bmatrix}$$

Now, W_4 is the matrix of the transitive closure of the given relation R. ∎

Example 3.9 Let R be the relation on the set $A = \{a, b, c, d, e\}$ as given in Fig. 3.16. Find the transitive closure of R using Warshall's algorithm.

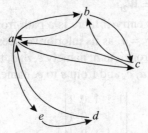

Fig. 3.16 The directed graph of the relation R

Solution: The corresponding directed graph for the above relation R is shown in Fig. 3.16. Let $v_1 = a$, $v_2 = b$, $v_3 = c$, $v_4 = d$, and $v_5 = e$. $W_0 = M_R$ is the relation matrix of R. So,

$$W_0 = \begin{bmatrix} 0 & 1 & 1 & 0 & 1 \\ 1 & 0 & 1 & 0 & 0 \\ 1 & 1 & 0 & 0 & 0 \\ 1 & 0 & 0 & 0 & 0 \\ 0 & 0 & 0 & 1 & 0 \end{bmatrix}$$

W_1 has 1 as its $(i, j)th$ entry if there is a path from v_i to v_j, that has only $v_1 = a$ as an interior vertex, if any. Note that all paths of length one can still be used since they have no interior vertices. Here, there are seven allowable paths such as from b to b, namely b, a, b, from b to e, namely b, a, e, from c to c, namely c, a, c, from c to e, namely c, a, e, from d to b, namely d, a, b, from d to c, namely d, a, c, and from d to e, namely d, a, e. So,

$$W_1 = \begin{bmatrix} 0 & 1 & 1 & 0 & 1 \\ 1 & 1 & 1 & 0 & 1 \\ 1 & 1 & 1 & 0 & 1 \\ 1 & 1 & 1 & 0 & 1 \\ 0 & 0 & 0 & 1 & 0 \end{bmatrix}$$

W_2 has 1 as its $(i, j)th$ entry if there is a path from v_i to v_j, that has only $v_1 = a$ and/or $v_2 = b$ as its interior vertices, if any. Here, there are two allowable paths such as from a to a, namely a, b, a, and from c to c, namely c, b, c. But the second path does not yield a new entry. So, we consider only the first path. Hence,

$$W_2 = \begin{bmatrix} 1 & 1 & 1 & 0 & 1 \\ 1 & 1 & 1 & 0 & 1 \\ 1 & 1 & 1 & 0 & 1 \\ 1 & 1 & 1 & 0 & 1 \\ 0 & 0 & 0 & 1 & 0 \end{bmatrix}$$

W_3 has 1 as its $(i, j)th$ entry if there is a path from v_i to v_j, that has only $v_1 = a$, $v_2 = b$ and/or $v_3 = c$ as its interior vertices, if any. But, in this case, there are no allowable paths. So, $W_3 = W_2$.

W_4 has 1 as its $(i, j)th$ entry if there is a path from v_i to v_j, that has only $v_1 = a$, $v_2 = b$, $v_3 = c$, and/or $v_4 = d$, as its interior vertices, if any. Here, there are four allowable paths such as from e to a, namely e, d, a, from e to b, namely e, d, a, b, from e to c, namely e, d, a, c, and from e to e, namely e, d, a, e. So,

$$W_4 = \begin{vmatrix} 1 & 1 & 1 & 0 & 1 \\ 1 & 1 & 1 & 0 & 1 \\ 1 & 1 & 1 & 0 & 1 \\ 1 & 1 & 1 & 0 & 1 \\ 1 & 1 & 1 & 1 & 1 \end{vmatrix}$$

W_5 has 1 as its $(i, j)th$ entry if there is a path from v_i to v_j, that has only $v_1 = a$, $v_2 = b$, $v_3 = c$, $v_4 = d$, and/or $v_5 = e$, as its interior vertices, if any. Here, there are four allowable paths such as from a to d, namely a, e, d, from b to d namely b, a, e, d, from c to d, namely c, a, e, d, and from d to d, namely d, a, e, d. So,

$$W_5 = \begin{vmatrix} 1 & 1 & 1 & 1 & 1 \\ 1 & 1 & 1 & 1 & 1 \\ 1 & 1 & 1 & 1 & 1 \\ 1 & 1 & 1 & 1 & 1 \\ 1 & 1 & 1 & 1 & 1 \end{vmatrix}$$

This last matrix W_5 is the matrix of the transitive closure of the above relation R. ∎

Example 3.10   Let $R = \{(b, c), (b, e), (c, e), (d, a), (e, b), (e, c)\}$ be a relation on the set $A = \{a, b, c, d, e\}$. Find the transitive closure using Warshall's algorithm.

Solution: The corresponding directed graph for the relation $R = \{(b, c), (b, e), (c, e), (d, a), (c, b), (e, c)\}$ is shown in Fig. 3.17.

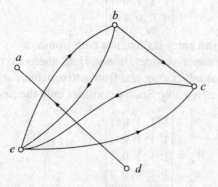

Fig. 3.17   The directed graph of the relation R

Let $v_1 = a$, $v_2 = b$, $v_3 = c$, $v_4 = d$ and $v_5 = e$. $W_0 = M_R$ is the relation matrix of R. So,

$$W_0 = \begin{bmatrix} 0 & 0 & 0 & 0 & 0 \\ 0 & 0 & 1 & 0 & 1 \\ 0 & 0 & 0 & 0 & 1 \\ 1 & 0 & 0 & 0 & 0 \\ 0 & 1 & 1 & 0 & 0 \end{bmatrix}$$

W_1 has 1 as its (i, j)th entry if there is a path from v_i to v_j, that has only $v_1 = a$ as an interior vertex, if any. Note that all paths of length one can still be used since they have no interior vertices. But, in this case, there are no allowable paths when we consider $v_1 = a$ as the interior vertex. So, $W_1 = W_0$.

W_2 has 1 as its (i, j)th entry if there is a path from v_i to v_j, that has only $v_1 = a$ and/or $v_2 = b$ as its interior vertices, if any. Here, there is one allowable path such as, from e to e, namely e, b, e. So,

$$W_2 = \begin{bmatrix} 0 & 0 & 0 & 0 & 0 \\ 0 & 0 & 1 & 0 & 1 \\ 0 & 0 & 0 & 0 & 1 \\ 1 & 0 & 0 & 0 & 0 \\ 0 & 1 & 1 & 0 & 1 \end{bmatrix}$$

W_3 has 1 as its (i, j)th entry if there is a path from v_i to v_j, that has only $v_1 = a$, $v_2 = b$ and/or $v_3 = c$ as its interior vertices, if any. Here, there is a allowable path from e to e, namely e, c, e. But this results in a matrix which is same as the previous matrix W_2. So, $W_3 = W_2$.

W_4 has 1 as its (i, j)th entry if there is a path from v_i to v_j, that has only $v_1 = a$, $v_2 = b$, $v_3 = c$ and/or $v_4 = d$ as its interior vertices, if any. But, in this case, there are no allowable paths. So, $W_4 = W_3$.

W_5 has 1 as its (i, j)th entry if there is a path from v_i to v_j, that has only $v_1 = a$, $v_2 = b$, $v_3 = c$, $v_4 = d$ and/or $v_5 = e$ as its interior vertices, if any. Here, there are three allowable paths such as, from b to b, namely b, e, b, from c to b, namely c, e, b and from c to c, namely c, e, c. So,

$$W_5 = \begin{bmatrix} 0 & 0 & 0 & 0 & 0 \\ 0 & 1 & 1 & 0 & 1 \\ 0 & 1 & 1 & 0 & 1 \\ 1 & 0 & 0 & 0 & 0 \\ 0 & 1 & 1 & 0 & 1 \end{bmatrix}$$

This last matrix W_5 is the matrix of the transitive closure of the relation R. ■

The program for computing the transitive closure of a relation using Warshall's algorithm is given in Fig. 3.18.

```
/*C program for Warshall's algorithm to find transitive closure of a relation */
#include<stdio.h>
#include<conio.h>
void main()
{
 int n,i,j,k,p[10][10].
 clrscr();
 printf("\n enter the number of nodes:");
 scanf("%d",&n);
 printf("\n enter the elements into the matrix(row wise): \n");      //W₀ = Mᵣ
 //enter 1 or 0
 for(i=0;i<n;i++)
 {
  for(j=0;j<n;j++)
  {
   scanf("%d",&p[i][j]);
  }
 }

 //to print the given matrix
 printf("\n\n the given matrix is:\n");
 for(i=0;i<n;i++)
 {
  for(j=0;j<n;j++)
  {
   printf("%d    ",p[i][j]);
  }
  printf("\n");
 }

 //to find the transitive relation matrix
 for(k=0;k<n;k++)
 {
  for(i=0;i<n;i++)
  {
   for(j=0;j<n;j++)
   {
    p[i][j]=p[i][j] || (p[i][k] && p[k][j]);
   }
  }
 }

 //to print the required transitive relation matrix
 printf("\n\n the required transitive relation matrix is: \n");
 for(i=0;i<n;i++)
 {
  for(j=0;j<n;j++)
  {
   printf("%d    ",p[i][j]);
  }
  printf("\n");
 }
 getch();
}
```

Fig. 3.18   C code for Warshall's algorithm

3.6 EQUIVALENCE RELATIONS AND PARTITIONS

A binary relation might have one or more of the following properties: reflexivity, symmetry, antisymmetry, and transitivity. For example, the binary relation in Fig. 3.19a is a reflexive and transitive relation, and the binary relation in Fig. 3.19b is a reflexive and symmetric relation. We shall study in this and the next sections two important classes of binary relations, namely, equivalence relations and partial ordering relations.

$$\begin{bmatrix} 1 & 1 & 0 & 1 \\ 0 & 1 & 0 & 1 \\ 0 & 0 & 1 & 0 \\ 0 & 1 & 0 & 1 \end{bmatrix} \qquad \begin{bmatrix} 1 & 1 & 0 & 0 \\ 1 & 1 & 1 & 0 \\ 0 & 1 & 1 & 0 \\ 0 & 0 & 0 & 1 \end{bmatrix}$$

(a)   (b)

Fig. 3.19

A binary relation on a set is said to be an *equivalence relation* if it is reflexive, symmetric, and transitive. For example, the binary relation on in Fig. 3.20 is an equivalence relation. Let A be a set of students and R be a binary relation of A such that (a, b) is in R if and only if a lives in the same dormitory as b. Since everybody lives in the same dormitory as himself or herself, R is a reflexive relation. Note that if a lives in the same dormitory as b, then b lives in the same dormitory as a. Thus, R is a symmetric relation. Note that if a lives

$$\begin{bmatrix} 1 & 1 & 0 & 0 & 0 & 0 \\ 1 & 1 & 0 & 0 & 0 & 0 \\ 0 & 0 & 1 & 0 & 0 & 0 \\ 0 & 0 & 0 & 1 & 1 & 1 \\ 0 & 0 & 0 & 1 & 1 & 1 \\ 0 & 0 & 0 & 1 & 1 & 1 \end{bmatrix}$$

Fig. 3.20

in the same dormitory as b and b lives in the same dormitory as c, then a lives in the same dormitory as c. Thus, R is a transitive relation. Consequently, R is an equivalence relation. Also, let A be a set of strings of 0s and 1s the lengths of which are at least three. Let R be a binary relation on A such that for two strings a and b, (a, b) is in R if and only if the last three digits in a are the same as the last three digits in b. Again, we leave it to the reader to check that R is an equivalence relation. Intuitively, in an equivalence relation two objects are related if they share some common properties or satisfy some common requirements, and are thus "equivalent" with respect to these properties or requirements.

Example 3.11 Show that the relation "congruence modulo m" ($\equiv$) over the set of positive integers is an equivalence relation. Also show that if $x_1 \equiv y_1$ and $x_2 \equiv y_2$, then $(x_1 + x_2) \equiv (y_1 + y_2)$.

Solution: Congruence modulo m is given by

$$\equiv = \{<x, y> \mid x - y \text{ is divisible by } m\}.$$

Clearly $a - a = 0$ is divisible by m, i.e. $a \equiv a \pmod{m}$
So $\equiv$ is reflexive.

Let $a \equiv b \pmod{m}$
$\Rightarrow$ $a = b + km$, where $k \in z$
$\Rightarrow$ $b = a - km$
$\Rightarrow$ $b = a + (-k)m$

$$\Rightarrow \qquad\qquad b \equiv a \;(\text{mod } m)$$

Hence, $\equiv$ is symmetric.

Again, $\qquad\qquad$ let $a \equiv b \;(\text{mod } m)$, $b \equiv c \;(\text{mod } m)$

$$\Rightarrow \qquad\qquad a - b \equiv km \quad \text{and} \quad b - c = k'm, \text{ where } k, k' \in Z$$

$$\Rightarrow \qquad a - b + b - c = km + k'm$$

$$\Rightarrow \qquad\qquad a - c = (k + k')m$$

$$\Rightarrow \qquad\qquad a \equiv c \;(\text{mod } m).$$

So, $\equiv$ is transitive.

Hence, $\equiv$ is an equivalence relation.

Now, suppose, $\qquad\qquad x_1 \equiv y_1 \text{ and } x_2 \equiv y_2$

i.e. $\qquad\qquad x_1 \equiv y_1 \;(\text{mod } m) \text{ and } x_2 \equiv y_2 \;(\text{mod } m)$

$$\Rightarrow \qquad\qquad x_1 = y_1 + k_1 m \quad \text{and} \quad x_2 = y_2 + k_2 m. \text{ where } k_1, k_2 \in z.$$

$$\Rightarrow \qquad x_1 + x_2 = y_1 + y_2 + k_1 m + k_2 m$$

$$\Rightarrow \qquad x_1 + x_2 = (y_1 + y_2) + (k_1 + k_2)m$$

$$\Rightarrow \qquad (x_1 + x_2) \equiv (y_1 + y_2) \qquad\qquad\blacksquare$$

Example 3.12 Let $A = Z$, the set of integers, and let R be defined by $a\,R\,b$ if and only if $a \le b$. Is R an equivalence relation?

Solution: Since $a \le a$, R is reflexive. If $a \le b$, it need not follow that $b \le a$, so R is not symmetric. Incidentally, R is transitive, since $a \le b$ and $b \le c$ imply that $a \le c$. Hence, R is not an equivalence relation as it is not symmetric. $\qquad\blacksquare$

We define now the notion of a *partition* of a set. A *partition* of a set A is a set of non-empty subsets of A denoted $\{A_1, A_2, ..., A_k\}$ such that the union of A_i's is equal to A and the intersection of A_i and A_j is empty for any distinct A_i and A_j. In other words, a partition of a set is a division of the elements in the set into disjoint subsets. These subsets are also called *blocks* of the partition. For example, let $A = \{a, b, c, d, e, f, g\}$, then $\{\{a\}, \{b, c, d\}, \{e, f\}, \{g\}\}$ is a partition of A. As another example, we note that a deck of playing cards is partitioned into the four suits. It is also partitioned into the 13 ranks. We also introduce the notation $\{\overline{a},$ $\overline{bcd}, \overline{ef}, \overline{g}\}$ for a partition where we place an overbar above the elements that are in the same block. We see now a connection between an equivalence relation on a set A and a partition of the set A. From an equivalence relation on A, we can define a partition of A so that every two elements in a block are related and any two elements in different blocks are not.* This partition is said to be the partition induced by the equivalence relation, and the blocks in the partition are called the *equivalence classes*. Conversely, from a partition of a set A we can define an equivalence relation on A so that every two elements in the same block of the partition are related, and any two elements in different blocks are not related.[†]

---

* See Prob. 3.24, part (a)

[†] See Prob. 3.24, part (b)

[‡] We assume that no two families have the same family name.

For example, let A be a set of people and R be a binary relation on A such that (a, b) is in R if and only if a and b have the same family name. We note that R is an equivalence relation which induces a partition of A where the equivalence classes are families.[‡] As another example, let A be the set of all natural numbers. Let n be a fixed integer. Let R be a binary relation on A so that (a, b) is in R if the remainders of a divided by n and b divided by n are the same. R is an equivalence relation which divides A into n equivalence classes. These equivalence classes are those numbers that are divisible by n; those numbers that leave a remainder of 1 when divided by n; those numbers that leave a remainder of 2 when divided by n ; … ; and those numbers that leave a remainder of $n - 1$ when divided by n. Two numbers a and b that are in the same equivalence class are said to be *equal modulo n*, and the notation $a \equiv b \pmod{n}$ is frequently used.

Let π_1 and π_2 be two partitions of a set A. Let R_1 and R_2 be the corresponding equivalence relations. We say that π_1 is a *refinement* of π_2, denoted $\pi_1 \leq \pi_2$, if $R_1 \subseteq R_2$. In other words, if π_1 is a refinement of π_2, then any two elements that are in the same block of π_1 must also be in the same block of π_2. We define the *product* of π_1 and π_2, denoted $\pi_1 \cdot \pi_2$, to be the partition corresponding to the equivalence relation $R_1 \cap R_2$. (We leave it to the reader to show that the intersection of two equivalence relations is always an equivalence relation.) In other words, the product of π_1 and π_2 is a partition of A such that two elements a and b are in the same block of $\pi_1 \cdot \pi_2$ if a and b are in the same block of π_1 and also in the same block of π_2. Thus, $\pi_1 \cdot \pi_2$ is a refinement of π_1, and also a refinement of π_2. We define the sum of π_1 and π_2, denoted $\pi_1 + \pi_2$, to be the partition corresponding to the equivalence relation $(R_1 \cup R_2)^*$. (We leave it to the reader to show that the union of two equivalence relations is always a reflexive and symmetric relation.) In other words, the sum of π_1 and π_2 is a partition of A such that two elements a and b are in the same block of $\pi_1 + \pi_2$ if there exist elements $c_1, c_2, c_3, …, c_k$ such that a and c_1 are in the same block of π_1 or π_2, c_1 and c_2 are in the same block of π_1 or π_2, c_2 and c_3 are in the same block of π_1 or π_2, …, and c_k and b are in the same block of π_1 or π_2. That is, two elements a and b are in the same block of $\pi_1 + \pi_2$ if they are chain-connected, by which we mean there exists a sequence of elements $a, c_1, c_2, …, c_k, b$ such that each pair of successive elements in the sequence is in the same block of π_1 or π_2. Thus, both π_1 and π_2 are refinements of $\pi_1 + \pi_2$.

For example, let $A = \{a, b, c, d, e, f, g, h, i, j, k\}$.

Let $\quad \pi_1 = \{\overline{abcd}, \overline{efg}, \overline{hi}, \overline{jk}\} \qquad \pi_2 = \{\overline{abch}, \overline{di}, \overline{efjk}, \overline{g}\}$

be two partitions of A. We then have

$$\pi_1 \cdot \pi_2 = \{\overline{abc}, \overline{d}, \overline{ef}, \overline{g}, \overline{h}, \overline{i}, \overline{jk}\}$$

and

$$\pi_1 + \pi_2 = \{\overline{abcdhi}, \overline{efgjk}\}$$

An interesting physical interpretation can be given to the product and sum of partitions. For the set A and the partitions π_1 and π_2 given in the foregoing, suppose that A is a set of people, π_1 is a partition of them into age groups, and π_2

is a partition of them into height groups. Suppose we wish to identify a certain person in A. If we are told what age group she is in, then we can identify her up to the blocks of π_1. In other words, we shall be able to identify her as one of a, b, c, d, as one of e, f, g, as one of h, i, or as one of j, k, depending on the age group she is in. Similarly, if we are told what height group she is in, we can identify her up to the blocks of π_2. If we are told the age group and the height group she is in, then we can identify her up to the blocks of $\pi_1 \cdot \pi_2$. In other words, we shall be able to identify her as one of a, b, c, as d, as one of e, f, as g, as h, as i, or as one of j, k. If we are told either the age group or the height group she is in, but not both, we can identify her up to the blocks of $\pi_1 + \pi_2$. In other words, whether we are provided with the information on the age group or with the information on the height group the person to be identified is in, we never have any ambiguity on the identity of the person beyond the blocks of $\pi_1 + \pi_2$. That is, we are assured that we can distinguish someone in the a, b, c, d, h, i group from someone in the e, f, g, j, k group, no matter whether we are given the age group information or the height group information. Indeed, a partition on a set can be viewed either as possessing some *information* on the identification of one of the objects in the set (two objects in different blocks can always be distinguished) or as possessing some *ambiguity* on the identification of one of the objects in the set (two objects in the same block can never be distinguished). It follows that the product of two partitions $\pi_1 \cdot \pi_2$ represents the total information we have on the identification of one of the objects when we have the information from both π_1 and π_2, and the sum of two partitions $\pi_1 + \pi_2$ represent the *most** ambiguity we might have when we are only sure that either the information from π_1 or that from π_2 will be available to us.

3.7 PARTIAL ORDERING RELATIONS AND LATTICES

A binary relation is said to be a *partial ordering relation* if it is reflexive, anti-symmetric, and transitive. For example, the binary relation in Fig. 3.22a is a partial ordering relation. As another example, let A be a set of positive integers, and let R be a binary relation on A such that (a, b) is in R if a divides b. Since any integer divides itself, R is a reflexive relation. Since if a divides b means b does not divide a unless $a = b$, R is an antisymmetric relation. Since if a divides b and b divides c, then a divides c, R is a transitive relation. Consequently, R is a partial ordering relation. Consider also the example of a set of books, A, each of which possesses a certain number of attributes. Let R be a binary relation on A such that (a, b) is in R if and only if every attribute of book a is also an attribute of book b. Note that R is a partial ordering relation. As another example, let A be a set of food items of different prices. Let R be a binary relation on A such that (a, b) is in R if a is not inferior to b in terms of both nutritional value and price. Again, R is a partial ordering relation. Intuitively, in a partial ordering relation two objects

---

* Note the word *most*. In many cases, the ambiguity will be less than that in $\pi_1 + \pi_2$.

are related if one of them is smaller (larger) than, or inferior (superior) to, the other object according to some properties or criteria. Indeed, the word *ordering* implies that the objects in the set are ordered according to these properties or criteria. However, it is also possible that two given objects in the set are not related in the partial ordering relation. In that case, we cannot compare these two objects and identify the small or inferior one. That is the reason the term *partial ordering* is used.

The C code to test whether a relation is an equivalence relation or a partial ordering relation is given in Fig. 3.21.

```
/* To check whether a given relation is an equivalence relation or a partial ordering
relation. */
        #include<stdio.h>
        int main()
        {
        system("clear");
        int a[10][10],m,i,j,k,r=1,ir=1,s=1,ans=1,tr=1;
        printf("\nEnter the order of the square matrix :");
        scanf("%d",&m);
        printf("\nEnter the relation in matrix format(0/1):\n");
        for(i=0;i<m;i++)
        for(j=0;j<m;j++)
        scanf("%d",&a[i][j]);
        //To check reflexive
        for(i=0;i<m;i++)
        {
        if(a[i][i]!=1)
        r=0;
        if(a[i][i]!=0)
        ir=0;
        }
        //To check symmetric
        for(i=0;i<m;i++)
        for(j=0;j<m;j++)
        {
        if(a[i][j]==1 && a[j][i]!=1)
        s=0;
        if(a[i][j]==1 && a[j][i]==1 && i!=j)
        ans=0;
        }
        //To check transitive
        for(i=0;i<m;i++)
        for(j=0;j<m;j++)
        for(k=0;k<m;k++)
        if(a[i][j]==1 && a[j][k]==1 && a[i][k]!=1)
        tr=0;
        if(r= =1)
        printf("\n\nRelation is Reflexive.");
        else if(ir= =1)
        printf("\n\nRelation is Irreflexive.");
        else
        printf("\n\nRelation is niether Reflexive nor Irreflexive");
        if(s= =1)
        printf("\n\nRelation is Symmetric.");
        if(ans==1)
        printf("\n\nRelation is Antisymmetric.");
```

```
if(s!=1 && ans!=1)
printf("\n\nRelation is Not Symmetric.");
if(tr= =1)
printf("\n\nRelation is Transitive.");
else
printf("\n\nRelation is Not Transitive.");
if(r= =1 && s= =1 && tr= =1)
printf("\n\nRelation is Equivalence.");
else
printf("\n\nRelation is Not A Equivalence Relation.");
if(r= =1 && ans= =1 && tr= =1)
printf("\n\nRelation is Partial Ordering Relation.");
else
printf("\n\nRelation is Not a Partial Ordering Relation.");
printf("\n\n");
return 0;
}
```

Fig. 3.21 Program to check whether a relation is an equivalence relation or a partial ordering relation

It was pointed out in Sec. 3.1 that a binary relation from a set A to a set B can be represented graphically as illustrated in Fig. 3.1c. For a binary relation R on a set A, we can have a slightly simpler graphical representation. Instead of having two columns of points as in Fig. 3.1c, we represent the elements in A by points and use arrows to represent the ordered pairs in R. For example, the binary relation in Fig. 3.23a is represented graphically in Fig. 3.23b. When the binary relation is a partial ordering relation, the graphical representation can be further simplified. Since the relation is understood to be reflexive, we can omit arrows from points back to themselves. Since the relation is understood to be transitive, we can omit arrows between points that are connected by sequences of arrows. For example, such a simplified representation for the partial ordering relation in Fig. 3.22a is shown in Fig. 3.22b. In many cases, when the graphical representation is so oriented that all arrowheads point in one direction (upward, downward, left to right, or right to left), we can even omit the arrowheads as the example in Fig. 3.22c shows. Such a graphical representation of a partial

$$\begin{bmatrix} 1 & 1 & 1 & 1 & 1 \\ 0 & 1 & 1 & 0 & 1 \\ 0 & 0 & 1 & 0 & 1 \\ 0 & 0 & 0 & 1 & 1 \\ 0 & 0 & 0 & 0 & 1 \end{bmatrix}$$

(a)　　　　　(b)　　　　　(c)

Fig. 3.22

$$\begin{bmatrix} 1 & 1 & 1 & 0 \\ 0 & 0 & 1 & 0 \\ 0 & 0 & 0 & 1 \\ 0 & 0 & 1 & 0 \end{bmatrix}$$

(a)　　　　　(b)

Fig. 3.23

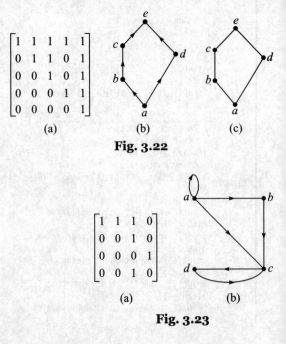

ordering relation in which all arrowheads are understood to be pointing upward is also known as the *Hasse diagram* of the relation.

Example 3.13   Draw the Hasse diagram for the relation R on $A = \{ 1, 2, 3, 4, 5\}$, whose relation matrix is given below.

$$M_R = \begin{bmatrix} 1 & 1 & 1 & 1 & 1 \\ 0 & 1 & 1 & 1 & 1 \\ 0 & 0 & 1 & 1 & 1 \\ 0 & 0 & 0 & 1 & 1 \\ 0 & 0 & 0 & 0 & 1 \end{bmatrix}$$

Solution: Here, $R = \{<1, 1>, <2, 2>, <3, 3>, <4, 4>, <5, 5>, <1, 2>, <1, 3>, <1, 4>, <1, 5>, <2, 3>, <2, 4>, <2, 5>, <3, 4>, <3, 5>, <4, 5>\}$.

The digraph and the Hasse diagram for relation R are given in Fig. 3.24.   ∎

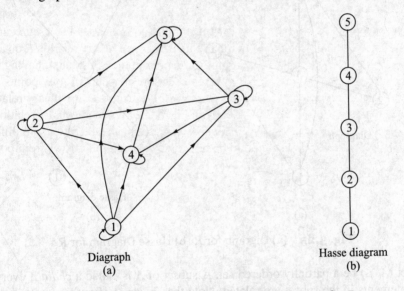

Diagraph
(a)

Hasse diagram
(b)

Fig. 3.24   (a) Digraph for R (b) Hasse Diagram for R

Example 3.14   Draw the Hasse diagram for the relation R on $A = \{ 1, 2, 3, 4, 5\}$, whose relation matrix is given below.

$$M_R = \begin{bmatrix} 1 & 0 & 1 & 1 & 1 \\ 0 & 1 & 1 & 1 & 1 \\ 0 & 0 & 1 & 1 & 1 \\ 0 & 0 & 0 & 1 & 0 \\ 0 & 0 & 0 & 0 & 1 \end{bmatrix}$$

Solution: Here, $R = \{<1, 1>, <1, 3>, <1, 4>, <1, 5>, <2, 2>, <2, 3>, <2, 4>, <2, 5>, <3, 3>, <3, 4>, <3, 5>, <4, 4>, <4, 5>\}$

The digraph and the Hasse diagram for relation R are given in Fig. 3.25. ■

Set A, together with a partial ordering relation R on A, is called a *partially ordered set* and is denoted by (A, R). In the literature, a partially ordered set is also abbreviated as a *poset*. There is also an alternative notation for specifying a partial ordering relation: For each ordered pair (a, b) in R, we write $a \leq b$ instead of $(a, b) \in R$, where $\leq$ is a generic symbol corresponding to the set of ordered pairs R and is commonly read "less than or equal to." (We frequently say a is less than or equal to b to mean $a \leq b$, and say a is less than b to mean $a \leq b$ and $a \neq b$. We also say b is larger than or equal to a and write $b \geq a$ to mean $a \leq b$.) Indeed, a partially ordered set is usually denoted $(A, \leq)$.

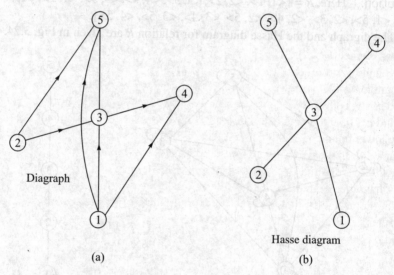

Diagraph

(a)

Hasse diagram

(b)

Fig. 3.25 (a) Digraph for R (b) Hasse Diagram for R

Let $(A, \leq)$ be a partially ordered set. A subset of A is called a *chain* if every two elements in the subset are related. Note that, because of antisymmetry and transitivity, in any chain with a finite number of elements $\{a_1, a_2, ..., a_k\}$ there is an element a_{i1} that is less than every other element in the chain, there is an element a_{i2} that is less than every other element except a_{i1}, there is an element a_{i3} that is less than every other element except a_{i1} and a_{i2}, and so on. We shall use the notation $a_{i1} \leq a_{i2} \leq a_{i3} ... \leq a_{ik}$ as an abbreviation for the list of ordered pairs $a_{i1} \leq a_{i2}, a_{i1} \leq a_{i3}, ..., a_{i1} \leq a_{ik}, a_{i2} \leq a_{i3}, a_{i2} \leq a_{i4}, ..., a_{i2} \leq a_{ik}, ...$ We frequently refer to the number of elements in a chain as the *length* of the chain. A subset of A is called an *antichain* if no two distinct elements in the subset are related. For example, for the partially ordered set in Fig. 3.22a, $\{a, b, c, e\}$, $\{a, b, c\}$, $\{a, d, e\}$, and $\{a\}$ are chains, and $\{b, d\}$, $\{c, d\}$, $\{a\}$ are antichains. Consider a partially ordered set $(A, \leq)$, where A is the set of all employees in a company, and for a

and b in A, $a \leq b$ if and only if b is a or is a superior of a. In this case, a chain is a subset of employees in which there, indeed, exists a chain of command. On the other hand, an antichain is a subset of employees in which no one has command over another. A partially ordered set $(A, \leq)$ is called a *totally ordered set* if A is a chain. In this case, the binary relation $\leq$; is called a *total ordering relation*.

Let $(A, \leq)$ be a partially ordered set. An element a in A is called a *maximal element* if for no b in A, $a \neq b$, $a \leq b$. An element a in A is called a *minimal element* if for no b in A, $a \neq b$, $b \leq a$. For example, in the partially ordered set of Fig. 3.26a, j and k are maximal elements, a, b, e are minimal elements. An element a is said to cover another element b if $b \leq a$ and for no other element c, $b \leq c \leq a$. In the partially ordered set of Fig. 3.26a, f covers b, f also covers c, but f does not cover a.

Let a and b be two elements in a partially ordered set $(A, \leq)$. An element c is said to be an *upper bound* of a and b if $a \leq c$ and $b \leq c$. For example, in the partially ordered set of Fig. 3.26a, h is an upper bound of f and g; so are i, j, and k. An element c is said to be a *least upper bound* of a and b if c is an upper bound of a and b, and if there is no other upper bound d of a and b such that $d \leq c$. For example, in the partially ordered set of Fig. 3.26a, h is a least upper bound of f and g; so is i. Similarly, an element c is said to be a *lower bound* of a and b if $c \leq a$ and $c \leq b$, and an element c is said to be a *greatest lower bound* of a and b if c is a lower bound of a and b, and if there is no other lower bound d of a and b such that $c \leq d$. In the partially ordered set of Fig. 3.26a, elements a, b, c, d, e, f, and g are all lower bounds of h and i, while f and g are greatest lower bounds of h and i. As another example, let A be the set of all positive integers and R be a binary relation on A such that (a, b) is in R if a divides b. We can readily check that R is a partial ordering relation. For two integers a and b, a common multiple of a and b is an upper bound of a and b, and the least common multiple of a and b is

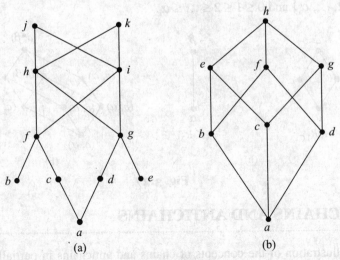

Fig. 3.26

a least upper bound (and the only one) of a and b. Similarly, a common divisor of a and b is a lower bound of a and b, and the greatest common divisor of a and b is a greatest lower bound (and the only one) of a and b.

A partially ordered set is said to be a lattice if every two elements in the set have a unique least upper bound and a unique greatest lower bound. The partially ordered set in Fig. 3.26a is not a lattice, whereas the one in Fig. 3.26b is.

A lattice L is said to be a *bounded lattice,* if it has both an upper bound, denoted by 1 such that $a \leq 1$, $\forall$ a $\in L$ and a lower bound denoted by 0, such that $0 \leq a$, $\forall$ a $\in L$. It may be noted that here we have used the symbol $\leq$, to represent the partial ordering relation.

Let (A, R_1) and (B, R_2) be two partially ordered sets. We define a binary relation R_3 over the set $A \times B$ such that for a_1 and a_2 in A, and b_1 and b_2 in B ((a_1, b_1), (a_2, b_2)) is in R_3 if and only if (a_1, a_2) is in R_1 and (b_1, b_2) is in R_2. We ask the reader to show that R_3 is a partial ordering relation. Consequently, $(A \times B, R_3)$ is a partially ordered set which is usually referred to as the *cartesian product* of the two partially ordered sets (A, R_1) and (B, R_2). Figure 3.27b shows the cartesian product of the two partially ordered sets in Fig. 3.27a. Let A denote the set of all positive divisors of an integer n. Let R be a binary relation on A such that (a, b) is in R if a divides b. Expressing n as a product of powers of primes $p_1^{\alpha 1} p_2^{\alpha 2} \ldots p_t^{\alpha t}$, we note that a positive divisor of n can then be expressed as $p_1^{\beta 1} p_2^{\beta 2} \ldots p_t^{\beta t}$, where $0 \leq \beta_i \leq \alpha_i$, for $i = 1, 2, \ldots, t$. Indeed, the integers in A can all be represented by ordered t-tuples of the form $(\beta_1, \beta_2, \ldots, \beta_t)$, where $0 \leq \beta_i \leq \alpha_i$, $i = 1, 2, \ldots, t$. Furthermore, let the ordered t-tuples corresponding to the integers a and b be $(\beta_1, \beta_2, \ldots, \beta_t)$ and $(\beta'_1, \beta'_2, \ldots \beta'_t)$. That a divides b means $\beta_i \leq \beta'_i$, $i = 1, 2, \ldots, t$. We now ask the reader to check that the partially ordered set (A, R) can be expressed as a cartesian product $(((A_1 \times A_2) \times A_3) \times \ldots) \times A_t$, where, for $i = 1, 2, \ldots, t$, $(A_i, \leq)$ is a totally ordered set such that $A_i = \{0, 1, 2, \ldots, \alpha_i\}$ and $0 \leq 1 \leq 2 \leq \ldots \leq \alpha_i$.

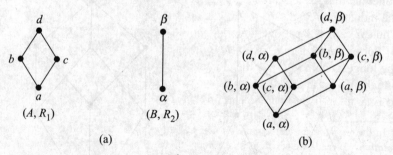

(a)　　　　　　(b)

Fig. 3.27

3.8　CHAINS AND ANTICHAINS

As an illustration of the concepts of chains and antichains in partially ordered sets, let us consider a simple example:

Example 3.15 Let $A = \{a_1, a_2, ..., a_r\}$ be the set of all courses required for graduation. Let R be a *reflexive* binary relation on A such that for $a_i \neq a_j$, (a_i, a_j) is in R if and only if course a_i is a prerequisite of course a_j. We note that R is anti- symmetric and transitive. Consequently, R is a partial ordering relation.* Suppose that the length of the longest chain in the partially ordered set A is c. It means that there are c courses that must be taken one after another. Thus, under no circumstances will a student be able to finish the required courses in less than c semesters. Suppose that the size of the largest antichain in the partially ordered set A is d. It means a student will be able to take at most d required courses in any semester. ■

As another illustration, we present a theorem that shows a close relationship between chains and antichains.†

Theorem 3.1 Let $(P, \leq)$ be a partially ordered set. Suppose the length of the longest chains in P is n. Then the elements in P can be partitioned into n disjoint antichains.

Proof: We shall prove the theorem by induction on n.

Basis of Induction For $n = 1$, no two elements in P are related. Clearly, they constitute an antichain.

Induction Step We assume that the theorem holds when the length of the longest chains in a partially ordered set is $n - 1$. Let P be a partially ordered set with the length of its longest chains being n. Let M denote the set of maximal elements in P. Clearly, M is a nonempty antichain. Consider now the partially ordered set $(P - M, \leq)$. Since there is no chain of length n in $P - M$, the length of the longest chains is at most $n - 1$. On the other hand, if the length of the longest chains in $P - M$ is less than $n - 1$, M must contain two or more elements that are members of the same chain, which is certainly an impossibility. Consequently, we conclude that the length of the longest chain in $P - M$ is $n - 1$, and, according to the induction hypothesis, $P - M$ can be partitioned into $n - 1$ disjoint antichains. Thus, P can be partitioned into n disjoint antichains. ■

For example, for the partially ordered set P in Fig. 3.28a, since the length of the longest chain in P is 4 the elements in P can be partitioned into four disjoint antichains. Figure 3.28b and c shows two such partitions. Applying Theorem 3.1 to Example 3.11 we can be certain that if the length of the longest chain in A is

---

* In the literature an antisymmetric and transitive relation is referred to as a *precedence relation*. Precedence relations share many of the properties of partial ordering relations. However, when a physical situation leads to the definition of a precedence relation, it is often expedient to include the reflexivity property so that the terminologies and results in connection with partial ordering relations can be applied. The prerequisite structure of courses leads naturally to the definition of a precedence relation. However, by adding the reflexivity property, we make R a partial ordering relation.

† Theorem 3.1 is a dual of what is known as *Dilworth's theorem*, which states that if the size of the largest antichains in P is n, then the elements in P can be partitioned into n disjoint chains.

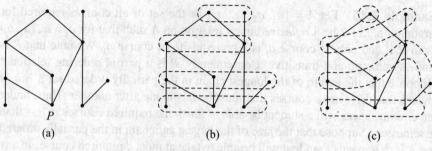

(a) (b) (c)

Fig. 3.28

c, then indeed a student will be able to complete all requirements in *c* semesters. A direct consequence of Theorem 3.1 can be stated as:

Corollary 3.1.1 Let $(P, \leq)$ be a partially ordered set consisting of $mn + 1$ elements. Either there is an antichain consisting of $m + 1$ elements or there is a chain of length $n + 1$ in P.

Proof: Suppose the length of the longest chains in P is n. According to Theorem 3.1, P can be partitioned into n disjoint antichains. If each of these antichains consists of m of fewer elements, the total number of elements in P is at most nm, which is a contradiction to the assumption of the corollary. ∎

Example 3.16 Show that among $ab + 1$ white mice either there is a sequence of $a + 1$ mice, each a descendant of the next, or there is a group of $b + 1$ mice no one of which is a descendant of another. Let us order the mice according to the descendant relationship. Clearly, such an ordering relation is a partial ordering relation. If there is an antichain of size $b + 1$ or larger in this partially ordered set, there is a group of $b + 1$ or more mice, no one of which is a descendant of another. On the other hand, if there is a chain of length $a + 1$ or larger, there is a sequence of $a + 1$ or more mice, each a descendant of the next. ∎

Example 3.17 A point (x, y) in the first quadrant of the xy plane defines a rectangle with the points $(0, 0)$, $(x, 0)$, $(0, y)$, (x, y) as its vertices. (See Fig. 3.29.) We want to show that for the rectangles defined by any five distinct points in the first quadrant either there are three rectangles R_{i1}, R_{i2}, R_{i3} such that R_{i1} and R_{i2} are inside of R_{i3}, and R_{i1} is inside of R_{i2}, or there are three rectangles such that no one is inside of another. Let $P = \{(x_1, y_1), (x_2, y_2), (x_3, y_3), (x_4, y_4), (x_5, y_5)\}$ denote the set of five points in the first quadrant.

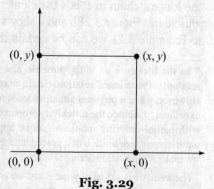

Fig. 3.29

We define a partial ordering relation $\leq$ on P such that $(x_i, y_i) \leq (x_j, y_j)$ if and only if $x_i \leq x_j$ and $y_i \leq y_j$. According to Corollary 3.1.1, either there is a chain of length 3 in P or there is an antichain of size 3 in P. Clearly, a chain of length 3 corresponds to a set of three rectangles R_{i1}, R_{i2}, R_{i3} such that R_{i1} and R_{i2} are inside of R_{i3}, and R_{i1} is inside of R_{i2}. On the other hand, an antichain of size 3 corresponds to a set of three rectangles such that no one is inside of another. ■

3.9 A JOB-SCHEDULING PROBLEM

Consider the problem of scheduling the execution of a set of tasks on a multiprocessor computing system that has a set of identical processors. (The problem can also be phrased as that of making up a schedule for a certain number of workers to complete a given set of tasks.) Let $P_1, P_2, ..., P_n$ denote the n identical processors in a multiprocessor computing system. Let $\mathcal{T} = \{T_1, T_2, ..., T_r\}$ denote a set of tasks to be executed on the computing system. We assume that the execution of a task occupies one and only one processor. Moreover, since the processors are identical, a task can be executed on anyone of the processors. Let $\mu(T_i)$ denote the *execution time* of task T_i, that is, the amount of time it takes to execute T_i on a processor. There is also a partial ordering relation $\leq$ specified over $\mathcal{T}$ such that for $T_i \neq T_j$, $T_i \leq T_j$ if and only if the execution of task T_j cannot begin until the execution of task T_i has been completed. (T_i is said to be a predecessor of T_j and T_j is said to be a successor of T_i.) A partially ordered set of tasks can be described graphically as illustrated in Fig. 3.30a, where the execution time of each task is written next to the name of the task. An obvious interpretation can be given to our model of a set of tasks. Consider the tasks $T_1, T_2, ..., T_r$ to be subprograms of a larger program. Then $T_i \leq T_j$ might mean that subprogram T_j uses some of the data generated by subprogram T_i, so that the execution of T_j must await the completion of T_i. For example, if a computer system is used on a space mission, task T_i might be a subprogram that determines the course of the spacecraft and task T_j might be a subprogram that estimates the total fuel consumption for midcourse adjustment. Clearly, we should complete T_i before executing T_j.[*]

By *scheduling* a set of tasks on a multiprocessor computing system, we mean to specify for each task T_i both the time interval within which it will be executed and the processor P_k on which execution will take place. (Without loss of generality, we assume that execution of the set begins at time $t = 0$.) An explicit way to describe a schedule is a *timing diagram*. For example, the timing diagram of a schedule for execution of the set of tasks in Fig. 3.30a on a three-processor computing system is shown in Fig. 3.30b, where ϕ_1, ϕ_2, ϕ_3, ϕ_4 denote periods within which a processor is left idle. For a given schedule, an *idle period* of

---

[*] Outside of the context of computing, we may also have interpretations such as, "One cannot put on one's shoes before putting on one's socks," or "One should not mop the floor before dusting the furniture," or "The machine cannot be assembled until all its subparts have been built."

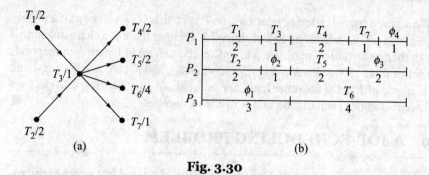

Fig. 3.30

a processor is defined to be a time interval within which the processor is not executing a task. We use ϕ_1, ϕ_2, ... to denote idle periods of the processors, and $\mu(\phi_1)$, $\mu(\phi_2)$, ... to denote the lengths of the idle periods. Notice that in a given schedule, a processor might be left idle either because there is no executable task* at that time or because it is an intentional choice. Clearly, it is never necessary nor beneficial in a given schedule to leave all processors idle at the same time. On the other hand, as we shall see later, it might be beneficial to leave some of the processors idle even though there are tasks that are executable at that time.

The total *elapsed time* of a schedule is the total time it takes to complete the execution of all tasks according to the schedule. Clearly, it is desirable to obtain a schedule that has the minimum total elapsed time. Unfortunately, there is no known procedure (short of exhaustive trial and error) for constructing schedules with minimum total elapsed time. Consequently, an alternative way to approach the problem is to look for schedules that are good but not necessarily the best possible ones. As a matter of fact, there is a very simple and intuitive way to schedule a given set of tasks, namely, never leave a processor intentionally idle. That is, a processor is left idle for a period of time only if no task is executable within that period. Conversely, whenever a processor becomes available at any time, we shall execute on this processor any one of the tasks that are executable at that time. For example, the schedule in Fig. 3.30b for the set of tasks in Fig. 3.30a was obtained this way. At the beginning, since only T_1 and T_2 are executable at that time, they are executed on processors P_1 and P_2 respectively. The completion of T_1 and T_2 lead to the execution of T_3. After the execution of T_3 is completed, T_4, T_5, T_6, T_7 all become executable. An arbitrary choice of executing T_4, T_5, T_6 on P_1, P_2, P_3, respectively, yields the schedule in Fig. 3.30b. We hasten to point out that such a simple way to schedule tasks does not always give us a schedule with minimum total elapsed time. As a matter of fact, Fig. 3.30b shows a schedule for the set of tasks in Fig. 3.31a in which between $t = 9$ and $t = 10$, processor P_2 is left idle although T_3 is executable at $t = 9$. The reader can convince himself or herself

---

* A task is said to be *executable* at a certain instant of time if the execution of its predecessors has been completed at that time.

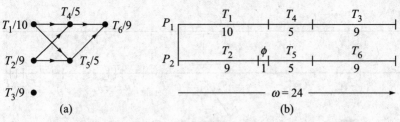

Fig. 3.31

that the schedule in Fig. 3.31*b* is better than any schedule in which processors are not left idle intentionally.

We want to determine how good or how bad such a simple scheduling procedure is. As it turns out, the result is rather surprising.

Theorem 3.2 For a given set of tasks, let ω denote the total elapsed time when the tasks are executed according to a schedule that contains no intentional idle periods, and let ω_0 denote the minimum possible total elapsed time. Then,

$$\frac{\omega}{\omega_0} \le 2 - \frac{1}{n}$$

where n is the number of processors in the computing system. Moreover, the bound is best possible.

Proof: To simplify the presentation, we shall prove the result for $n = 2$. The proof for the general case is analogous. Consider the schedule that contains no intentional idle periods, as illustrated in Fig. 3.32. We observe first that the termination of an idle period in one processor coincides with the completion of the execution of a task in the other processor. (Otherwise, the idle period would not be terminated.) Let ϕ_i be an idle period for a processor. A task T_{ij} is said to overlap ϕ_i if the execution of T_{ij} in the other processor overlaps ϕ_i. For example, in Fig. 3.32, T_{11}, T_{12}, T_{13} overlap ϕ_1. Let $T_{i1}, T_{i2}, T_{i3}, \ldots T_{il}$ be the tasks that overlap ϕ_i. We claim that

$$T_{i1} \le T_{i2} \le T_{i3} \le \ldots \le T_{il}$$

If this was not the case, the tasks $T_{i1}, T_{i2}, \ldots, T_{il}$ would not have to be executed sequentially in P_2, and some of them could be executed in P_1 in place of some portions of the idle period ϕ_i in P_1. Similarly, if ϕ_j is another idle period, and $T_{j1}, T_{j2}, T_{j3}, \ldots, T_{jm}$ are the tasks that overlap ϕ_j, then by repeating the argument, we have

$$T_{j1} \le T_{j2} \le T_{j3} \le \ldots \le T_{jm}$$

It is clear that every task executed after the completion of T_{il} must be a successor of T_{il} (or else it would be executed in ϕ_i). Consequently, there is a subset of tasks $\mathscr{C}$ such that:

1. $\mathscr{C}$ is a chain.
2. $\Sigma_{T_k \in \mathscr{C}} \, \mu(T_k)_j \ge \Sigma_{\phi_i \in \Phi} \, \mu(\phi_i)$,

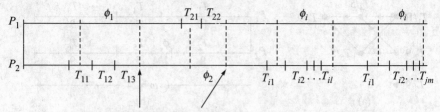

P_1
P_2
ϕ_1
T_{21} T_{22}
ϕ_i
ϕ_i
T_{11} T_{12} T_{13}
ϕ_2
T_{i1} $T_{i2} \ldots T_{il}$
T_{i1} $T_{i2} \ldots T_{jm}$
Termination of an idle period coincides with the completion of the execution of a task

Fig. 3.32

where Φ is the set of all idle periods in the schedule. We note that

$$\omega = \frac{1}{2}\left[\sum_{T_j \in T} \mu(T_j) + \sum_{\phi_i \in \Phi} \mu(\phi_i)\right]$$

$$\leqq \frac{1}{2}\left[\sum_{T_j \in T} \mu(T_j) + \sum_{T_k \in \amalg} \mu(T_k)\right] \tag{3.1}$$

Certainly,

$$\omega_0 \geqq \frac{1}{2}\sum_{T_j \in T} \mu(T_j)$$

and

$$\omega_0 \geqq \sum_{T_k \in \amalg} \mu(T_k)$$

Thus, (3.1) becomes

$$\omega_0 \leqq \omega_0 + \frac{1}{2}\omega_0$$

or

$$\frac{\omega}{\omega_0} \leqq \frac{3}{2} \qquad \blacksquare$$

That this bound is the best possible can be demonstrated by the example in Fig. 3.33, where Fig. 3.33*b* shows two schedules for the set of tasks in Fig. 3.33*a*.

It is interesting to observe that, according to the result we have just proved, the schedule obtained by following the simple rule of not leaving a processor intentionally idle is never worse than a best possible schedule by more than

$T_1/1$
$T_2/1$
$T_3/2$
T_1 T_2
1 1
T_3
2
$\omega_0 = 2$
T_1 T_3
1 2
T_2 ϕ
1 2
$\omega = 3$
(a)
(b)

Fig. 3.33

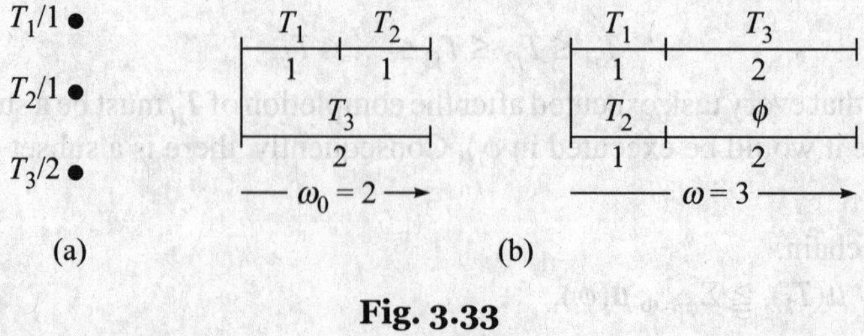

50 percent in a two-processor computing system, and by more than 100 percent in an n-processor computing system. Such a result indeed supports very strongly the idea of employing simple procedures to obtain good, but not necessarily the best possible, results in many optimization problems.

3.10 COMPATIBLE RELATION

Suppose R is a relation on a set A. Then, R is said to be a *compatibility* relation if it is reflexive and symmetric.

Example 3.18 Let A be a set of people and R be a binary relation on A such that (a, b) is in R if a is a friend of b. Show that R is a compatibility relation.

Solution: R is reflexive since a is always a friend of a (i.e. himself). Also, R is symmetric since, if a will be a friend of b then obviously b will be a friend of a. Hence R is a compatibility relation. ■

Example 3.19 Let A be a set of English words and R be a binary relation on A such that two words in A are related if they have one or more letters in common. Show that R is a compatible relation.

Solution: R is reflexive since any word has all the letters common with itself. Also, if x and y are two words such that x has one or more letters common with y, then, obviously y has one or more letters common with x. Hence, R is both reflexive and symmetric. So, R is a compatibility relation. ■

It may be noted that all equivalence relations are compatibility relations. If R and S are two compatibility relations, then $R \cap S$ will be a compatibility relation but $R \cup S$ may or may not be a compatibility relation.

Now, we define the *maximal compatibility block*. Let S be a set and R be a compatibility relation on S. Let T be a subset of S. The subset T is called a maximal compatibility block, if each element of T is compatible to every other element of T and none of the element of $S - T$ is compatible to all the elements of T.

Example 3.20 Let the compatibility relation on a set $\{x_1, x_2, x_3, x_4, x_5, x_6\}$ be given by the following matrix. Construct the graph and find the maximal compatibility blocks of the given relation.

x_2	1				
x_3	1	1			
x_4	0	0	1		
x_5	0	0	1	1	
x_6	1	0	1	0	1
	x_1	x_2	x_3	x_4	x_5

Solution: The compatibility relation is given by

$$
\begin{array}{c|ccccc}
x_2 & 1 & & & & \\
x_3 & 1 & 1 & & & \\
x_4 & 0 & 0 & 1 & & \\
x_5 & 0 & 0 & 1 & 1 & \\
x_6 & 1 & 0 & 1 & 0 & 1 \\
\hline
 & x_1 & x_2 & x_3 & x_4 & x_5
\end{array}
$$

The relation can also be expressed as

$R = \{<x_2, x_1>, <x_3, x_1>, <x_3, x_2>, <x_4, x_3>, <x_5, x_3>, <x_5, x_4>, <x_6, x_1>, <x_6, x_3>,$
$<x_6, x_5>\}.$

The above matrix is the lowyer triangular matrix representing the given relation. From the lowyer triangular matrix, the relation matrix M_R can be obtained. In the relation matrix, all the diagonal elements should be 1. The relation matrix for the above relation is given by

$$
M_R = \begin{array}{c}
\\
x_1 \\
x_2 \\
x_3 \\
x_4 \\
x_5 \\
x_6
\end{array}
\begin{array}{c}
\begin{array}{cccccc}
x_1 & x_2 & x_3 & x_4 & x_5 & x_6
\end{array} \\
\left[
\begin{array}{cccccc}
1 & 1 & 1 & 0 & 0 & 1 \\
1 & 1 & 1 & 0 & 0 & 0 \\
1 & 1 & 1 & 1 & 1 & 1 \\
0 & 0 & 1 & 1 & 1 & 0 \\
0 & 0 & 1 & 1 & 1 & 1 \\
1 & 0 & 1 & 0 & 1 & 1
\end{array}
\right]
\end{array}
$$

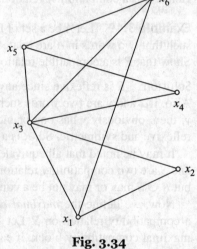

The graph for the relation R is shown in Fig. 3.34. Here, the loops and bidirectional edges are not shown as they are obvious. According to the definition here the maximal compatibility blocks are $\{x_3, x_5, x_6\}$, $\{x_1, x_2, x_3\}$, $\{x_1, x_3, x_6\}$, and $\{x_3, x_4, x_5\}$. ∎

Fig. 3.34

3.11 FUNCTIONS

A binary relation R from A to B is said to be a *function* if for every element a in A, there is a unique element b in B so that (a, b) is in R. For a function R from A to B, instead of writing $(a, b) \in R$, we also use the notation $R(a) = b$, where b is called the *image* of a. The set A is called the *domain* of the function R, and the set B is called the *range* of the function R. The notion of a function is a formalization of the notion of associating or assigning an element in the range to each of the elements in the domain. For example, let A be a set of houses and B be a set of colors. Then a function from A to B is an assignment of colors for painting the houses. A function can often be represented in graphical form. Figure 3.35a shows a function R from $A = \{a, b, c, d, e\}$ to $B = \{\alpha, \beta, \gamma, \delta\}$. Following the convention of representing a binary relation in tabular form that was introduced earlier, we can represent the function in Fig. 3.35a as that in Fig. 3.35b. However, a more convenient tabular form for representing functions is that shown in Fig. 3.35c, where the left column contains all the elements in the domain and the right column contains their corresponding images.

A function from A to B is said to be an *onto* function if every element of B is the image of one or more elements of A. Figure 3.36a shows an example of an onto function. A function from A to B is said to be a *one-to-one* function if no two elements of A have the same image. Figure 3.36b shows an example of a one-to-one function. A function from A to B is said to be a *one-to-one onto* function if it is both an onto and a one-to-one function.* Figure 3.36c shows a one-to-one onto function. Let A be a set of workers and B_1, B_2, and B_3 be sets of jobs. An onto function from A to B_1 is an assignment of the workers to the jobs so that every job has at least one worker assigned to it; a one-to-one function from A to B_2 is an assignment such that no two workers will have the same job; and a one-to-one onto function from A to B_3 is an assignment such that every job has a worker assigned to it, and no two workers are assigned to the same job.

In the literature, an onto function is also called a *surjection*, a one-to-one function is also called an *injection*, and a one-to-one onto function is also called a *bijection*.

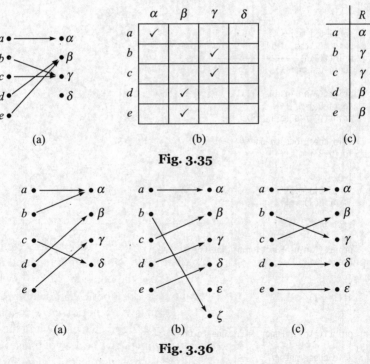

(a) (b) (c)

Fig. 3.35

(a) (b) (c)

Fig. 3.36

---

* Recall that we introduced the notion of a one-to-one correspondence between the elements in two sets. Formally, we say that there is a one-to-one correspondence between the elements of two sets if there exists a one-to-one onto function from one set to the other.

The C code to test whether a function is one-to-one, onto and one-to-one onto is given in Fig. 3.37.

```c
/* Program to check whether a function is one-to-one, onto and one-to-one onto */
#include<stdio.h>
main()
{
int a[10][10],m,i,j,k,l=0,p=0,q=0;
printf("\nEnter the order of the square matrix:");
scanf("%d",&m);
printf("\nEnter the function in 0/1 format:\n");
for(i=0;i<m;i++)
for(j=0;j<m;j++)
scanf("%d",&a[i][j]);
/* To check whether the entered function is valid or not */
for(i=0;i<m;i++)
{
k=0;
for(j=0;j<m;j++)
if(a[i][j]= =1)
k++;
if(k!=1)
{
printf("\n-->>Entered function is Not Valid.\n\n");
return;
}
}
/* To show the function*/
for(i=0;i<m;i++)
printf("\t%d",i+1);
printf("\n-------------------------");
for(i=0;i<m;i++)
{
printf("\n |\n%d|",i+1);
for(j=0;j<m;j++)
printf("\t%d",a[i][j]);
}
/*To check one-to-one*/
for(i=0;i<m;i++)
{
l=0;
for(j=0;j<m;j++)
if(a[i][j]= =1)
l++;
if(l>1)
{
printf("\n\n->Function is Not One-to-One.");
break;
}
}
if(l= =1)
{
p=1;
printf("\n\n->Function is One-to-One.");
}
/*To check onto*/
for(i=0;i<m;i++)
{
l=0;
for(j=0;j<m;j++)
```

```
if(a[j][i]= =1)
l++;
if(l<1)
{
printf("\n\n->Function is not Onto.");
break;
}
}
if(l>0)
{
q=1;
printf("\n\n->Function is Onto.");
}
if(p= =1 && q= =1)
printf("\n\n->Function is One-to-One Onto.");
printf("\n\n\n\n");
}
```

Fig. 3.37   Program to check whether a function is one-to-one, onto and one-to-one onto

3.12 COMPOSITION OF FUNCTIONS

A *composite function*, formed by the composition of one function to another, refers to the combining of functions in a manner where the output from one function becomes the input for the next function. Let f be a function from A to B and g be a function from B to C. The functions $f: A \rightarrow B$ and $g: B \rightarrow C$ can be composed by first applying f to an argument $a \in A$ and then applying g to the result. We can define a function h from A to C such that for every a in A, $h(a) = g(f(a))$. The function h is called the composition of functions or relative product of functions f and g and is denoted as $g \circ f$. Mathematically, if $f: A \rightarrow B$ and $g: B \rightarrow C$ be two functions, then, $h = g \circ f = \{(a, c)|(a \in A) \wedge (c \in C) \wedge (\exists b) (b \in B \wedge b = f(a) \wedge c = g(b))\}$

More precisely, $g \circ f$ is called the left composition of g with f.

Here, we assume that the range R_f of f is a subset of domain D_g of g, which is B, that is $R_f \subseteq D_g$; otherwise, $g \circ f$ is empty. Any function g for which $g \circ f$ can be computed is said to be left-composable with the function f. In such a case, $(g \circ f) (a) = g(f(a))$, where a is in the domain of $g \circ f$. The composition of functions f and g, is shown in Fig. 3.38.

Theorem 3.3   Assuming $g \circ f$ is not empty, show that $g \circ f$ is a function from A to B.

Proof: For this purpose, let us assume that (a, c_1) and (a, c_2) are both in $g \circ f$. This assumption requires that there is a $b \in B$ such that $b = f(a)$ and $c_1 = g(b)$; also $c_2 = g(b)$. Since g is a function, we cannot have $c_1 = g(b)$ and $c_2 = g(b)$; hence $g \circ f$ is a function.   ∎

If $f: A \rightarrow B$ and $g: B \rightarrow C$ then existence of $g \circ f$ does not signify the existence of $f \circ g$. For the existence of $f \circ g$, it is necessary that $R_g \subseteq D_f$.

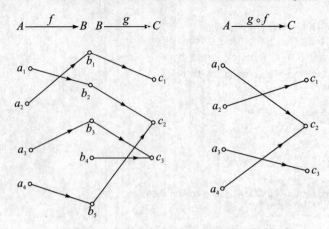

Fig. 3.38 Composition of two functions f and g

Theorem 3.4 Composition of functions is associative.

Proof: Consider three functions $f: A \rightarrow B$, $g: B \rightarrow C$, and $h: C \rightarrow D$. Then, $h \circ (g \circ f)$ and $(h \circ g) \circ f$ are functions from A to D. We have to prove that $h \circ (g \circ f) = (h \circ g) \circ f$. Now, let us assume, $b = f(a)$, $c = g(b)$, and $d = h(c)$. We have, $(a, b) \in f$, $(b, c) \in g$, $(c, d) \in h$ and $(a, c) \in g \circ f$. $(b, d) \in h \circ g$. Making the same argument, we can write, $(a, d) \in h \circ (g \circ f)$. Similarly, we can show, that $(a, d) \in (h \circ g) \circ f$. This fact being true for any a and corresponding d, we have

$$h \circ (g \circ f) = (h \circ g) \circ f \qquad (3.2)$$

Thus, the composition of functions is associative. ∎

We may omit the parentheses from (3.2) and simply, can write $h \circ g \circ f = h \circ (g \circ f) = (h \circ g) \circ f$. The associative property for composition of functions is represented in Fig. 3.39.

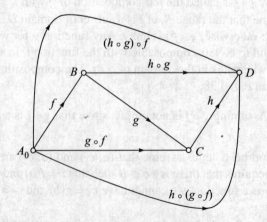

Fig. 3.39 Composition of three functions f, g and h

Example 3.21 Let $A = \{1, 2, 3\}$, $B = \{r, s\}$, and $C = \{m, n\}$. Also, let f_1 be a function from A to B which is given by $f_1 = \{(1, r), (2, r), (3, s)\}$ and f_2 be a function from B to C which is given by $f_2 = \{(r, n), (s, n)\}$. Compute $f_2 \circ f_1$.

Solution: $f_2 \circ f_1 = \{(1, n), (2, n), (3, n)\}$ ∎

Example 3.22 Let $A = \{1, 2, 3\}$ and f_1, f_2, f_3 and f_4 be functions from A to A given by

$$f_1 = \{(1, 2), (2, 3), (3, 1)\} \qquad f_2 = \{(1, 2), (2, 1), (3, 3)\}$$
$$f_3 = \{(1, 1), (2, 2), (3, 1)\} \qquad f_4 = \{(1, 1), (2, 2), (3, 3)\}$$

Compute $f_1 \circ f_2; f_2 \circ f_1; f_1 \circ f_3 \circ f_2; f_4 \circ f_2; f_2 \circ f_4; f_4 \circ f_4;$ and $f_1 \circ f_4$.

Solution:
$$f_1 \circ f_2 = \{(1, 3), (2, 2), (3, 1)\}$$
$$f_2 \circ f_1 = \{(1, 1), (2, 3), (3, 2)\}$$
$$f_1 \circ f_3 \circ f_2 = \{(1, 3), (2, 2), (3, 2)\}$$
$$f_4 \circ f_2 = \{(1, 2), (2, 1), (3, 3)\}$$
$$f_2 \circ f_4 = \{(1, 2), (2, 1), (3, 3)\}$$
$$f_4 \circ f_4 = \{(1, 1), (2, 2), (3, 3)\}$$
$$f_1 \circ f_4 = \{(1, 2), (2, 3), (3, 1)\}$$

It may be observed that in the above example
$f_1 \circ f_2 \neq f_2 \circ f_1$ and $f_4 \circ f_2 = f_2 \circ f_4$. ∎

Example 3.23 Let $f_1(x) = x + 4$, $f_2(x) = x - 4$, and $f_3(x) = 4x$ for $x \in R$, where R is the set of real numbers. Find $f_2 \circ f_1; f_1 \circ f_2; f_1 \circ f_1; f_2 \circ f_2; f_1 \circ f_3; f_3 \circ f_2; f_3 \circ f_1;$ and $f_1 \circ f_3 \circ f_2$.

Solution:
$$f_2 \circ f_1 = \{(x, x) | x \in R\}$$
$$f_1 \circ f_2 = \{(x, x) | x \in R\} = g \circ f$$
$$f_1 \circ f_1 = \{(x, x + 8) | x \in R\}$$
$$f_2 \circ f_2 = \{(x, x - 8) | x \in R\}$$
$$f_1 \circ f_3 = \{(x, 4x + 4) | x \in R\}$$
$$f_3 \circ f_2 = \{(x, 4x - 16) | x \in R\}$$
$$f_3 \circ f_1 = \{(x, 4x + 16) | x \in R\}$$
$$(f_1 \circ f_3) \circ f_2 = \{(x, 4x - 12) | x \in R\} = f_1 \circ (f_3 \circ f_2)$$
$$= f_1 \circ f_3 \circ f_2 \qquad ∎$$

Example 3.24 Let $f_1: R \to R$ be given by $f_1(a) = -a^2$ and $f_2: R^+ \to R^+$ be given by $f_2(a) = \sqrt{a}$ where R^+ is the set of all non-negative real numbers and R is the set of real numbers. Compute $f_1 \circ f_2$. Can $f_2 \circ f_1$ be defined?

Solution: $(f_1 \circ f_2)(a) = f_1(f_2(a)) = f_1(\sqrt{a}) = -a$ for all $a \in R^+$. It is possible to define the function $f_1 \circ f_2: R^+ \to R$ because the range of f_2 is R^+, which is a subset of R and R is the domain of f_1. But, the range of f_1 is not included in the domain of f_2. So, $f_2 \circ f_1$ cannot be defined. ∎

3.13   INVERTIBLE FUNCTION

The converse of a binary relation R from A to B, denoted as R^{-1}, is also a binary relation from B to A such that $R^{-1} = \{(b, a) | (a, b) \in R\}$. The ordered pairs of R^{-1} can be obtained by interchanging the elements of the ordered pairs in R. But, in case of functions the situation is not alike. Let f' represent the converse of f, where f is a function from $A \rightarrow B$. Then, f' may not be a function, due to two reasons. First, the domain of f' may not be B but only a subset of B. Secondly, f' may not be a function from D_f (the domain of f) to A since it may not satisfy the uniqueness condition, which may be expressed as $(a, b) \in f \wedge (a, c) \in f \Rightarrow b = c$. For example, (a_1, b) and (a_2, b) may belong to f, as a result (b, a_1) and (b, a_2) will belong to f'. In some special cases, f' may be a function from a subset of B to A or from B to A directly. Let us consider the following examples:

Example 3.25   Let $A = \{1, 2, 3, 4\}$ and $B = \{a, b, c, d\}$.

1. Let f be a function from A to B which is given by $f = \{(1, a), (2, a), (3, d), (4, c)\}$. Then, $f' = \{(a, 1), (a, 2), (d, 3), (c, 4)\}$, which is clearly not a function.
2. Let $f = \{(1, a), (2, c), (3, b), (4, d)\}$. Here, $f' = \{(a, 1), (c, 2), (b, 3), (d, 4)\}$, which is a function from B to A.   ∎

Example 3.26   Let R be the set of real numbers and let f be a function from R to R, which is given by $f = \{(a, a + 4) | a \in R\}$.

Then, $f' = \{(a + 4, a) | a \in R\}$, which is a function from R to R.

It can be observed that for a function $f: A \rightarrow B$, f' is a function only if f is one-to-one. But, this condition does not ensure that f' is a function from B to A. It can be guaranteed that f' is a function from B to A, if f is one-to-one and onto. In such cases, f' is represented as f^{-1} and f^{-1} is a function from B to A. Mathematically, it can be written as $f^{-1}: B \rightarrow A$ and f^{-1} is called the inverse of the function f. It may be noticed that, f^{-1} is also one-to-one and onto. If f^{-1} exists, then f is called invertible.   ∎

3.13.1   Graph of Inverse Functions

The concept of inverse functions is identical to that of reflections in the plane. We know many examples of reflections in the plane. The reflection of a point (a, b) about the x-axis is $(a, -b)$ and the reflection of (a, b) about the y-axis is $(-a, b)$. Now we want the reflection of the point (a, b) about the identity line $y = x$.

The reflection of the point (a, b) about the line $y = x$ is the point (b, a) as shown in Fig. 3.40. The line segment joining the points (a, b) and (b, a) is bisected at right angle by the line $y = x$ as shown in Fig. 3.41, so that the two points play object-image role around the line $y = x$ which acts as plane mirror.

From the above discussion it follows that the graph of $y = f(x)$ and its inverse written in the form $y = f^{-1}(x)$ are symmetrical about the line $y = x$. If the graphs $y = f(x)$ and $y = f^{-1}(x)$, intersect, then the intersection point is only on the line $y = x$ as shown in Fig. 3.42.

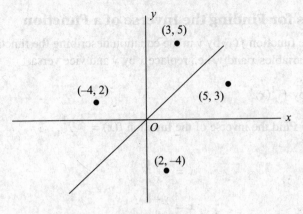

Fig. 3.40

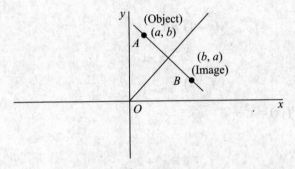

Fig. 3.41

Note: It may be necessary to restrict the domain on certain functions to guarantee that the inverse is also a function. For example, consider the function $y = x^2$. Its inverse is $\sqrt{x}$, which is not a function on the set of integers. So to make the inverse a function, we have to restrict the domain as $x \geq 0$ or $x \leq 0$. So our function should be $f(x) = x^2$, $x \geq 0$ or $f(x) = x^2$, $x \leq 0$.

The graph of f^{-1} is the reflection about the line $y = x$ of the graph of f.

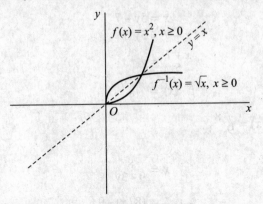

Fig. 3.42

3.13.2 Steps for Finding the Inverse of a Function

1. Replace the function $f(x)$ by y in the equation describing the function.
2. Swap the variables x and y, i.e., replace x by y and vice versa.
3. Solve for y.
4. Replace y by $f^{-1}(x)$.

Example 3.27   Find the inverse of the function $f(x) = \dfrac{x+1}{x}$.

Solution:

Step 1:
$$y = \frac{x+1}{x}$$

Step 2:
$$x = \frac{y+1}{y}$$

Step 3:
$$xy = y + 1$$
$$\Rightarrow \qquad xy - y = 1$$
$$\Rightarrow \qquad y(x-1) = 1$$
$$\Rightarrow \qquad y = \frac{1}{x-1}$$

Step 4:
$$f^{-1}(x) = \frac{1}{x-1}$$

■

Example 3.28 $f(x) = x^3 + 2$

Solution:

Step 1: $\qquad y = x^3 + 2$

Step 2: $\qquad x = y^3 + 2$

Step 3: $\qquad x - 2 = y^3$

$\Rightarrow \qquad y = (x-2)^{1/3}$

Step 4: $\qquad f^{-1}(x) = (x-2)^{1/3}$

■

Example 3.29   Find the inverse of $f(x) = 5x - 7$

Solution:

$$x = 5y - 7$$
$$\Rightarrow \qquad x + 7 = 5y$$
$$\Rightarrow \qquad \frac{x+7}{5} = y$$

So
$$f^{-1}(x) = \frac{x+7}{5}$$

■

Example 3.30 $f(x) = \dfrac{8}{9 - 3x}$

Solution:

$$x = \frac{8}{9 - 3y}$$

So,
$$f^{-1}(x) = \frac{(8/x) - 9}{-3}$$

■

Example 3.31 $f(x) = \dfrac{7+4x}{6-5x}$

Solution:

$$x = \frac{7+4y}{6-5y}$$

$\Rightarrow \qquad (6-5y)x = 7+4y$

$\Rightarrow \qquad 6x - 5xy = 7+4y$

$\Rightarrow \qquad \dfrac{6x-7}{4+5x} = y$

So, $\qquad f^{-1}(x) = \dfrac{6x-7}{4+5x}$

Example 3.32 $f(x) = \sqrt[3]{x-2}$

Solution:

$$x = \sqrt[3]{y-2}$$

$\Rightarrow \qquad x^3 + 2 = y$

$\Rightarrow \qquad f^{-1}(x) = x^3 + 2$ ■

Example 3.33 $f(x) = \dfrac{10}{\sqrt[5]{7-3x}}$

Solution:

$$x = \frac{10}{\sqrt[5]{7-3y}}$$

$\Rightarrow \qquad \sqrt[5]{7-3y} = \dfrac{10}{x}$

$\Rightarrow \qquad 7 - 3y = \left(\dfrac{10}{x}\right)^5$

$\Rightarrow \qquad y = \dfrac{\left(\dfrac{10}{x}\right)^5 - 7}{-3}$

So, $\qquad f^{-1}(x) = \dfrac{\left(\dfrac{10}{x}\right)^5 - 7}{-3}$ ■

Example 3.34 $f(x) = 4e^{(6x+2)}$

Solution:

$$x = 4e^{(6y+2)}$$

$\Rightarrow \qquad \ln\left(\dfrac{x}{4}\right) = \ln(e^{(6y+2)}) = 6y + 2$

$\Rightarrow \qquad y = \dfrac{\ln\left(\dfrac{x}{4}\right) - 2}{6} = f^{-1}(x)$

Example 3.35 $f(x) = 7e^{(3-5x)}$

Solution:

$$y = \frac{\ln\left(\dfrac{x}{7}\right) - 3}{-5} = f^{-1}(x)$$ ∎

Example 3.36 $f(x) = \ln(2 + 4x)$

Solution:

$$x = \ln(2 + 4y)$$

$$\Rightarrow \qquad e^x = e^{\ln(2+4y)}$$

$$\Rightarrow \qquad e^x = 2 + 4y$$

$$\Rightarrow \qquad \frac{e^x - 2}{4} = y$$

So, $$f^{-1}(x) = \frac{e^x - 2}{4}$$ ∎

Example 3.37 $f(x) = 5\ln(7 - 3x)$

Solution:

$$f^{-1}(x) = \frac{e^{x/5} - 7}{-3}$$ ∎

Example 3.38 $f(x) = x^n$ for n is odd.

Solution: For n is odd, the polynomial function $f(x) = x^n$ is an increasing function for all real numbers x. So, f has an inverse. The inverse function is called the nth root function and is denoted by $f^{-1}(x) = x^{1/n}$. ∎

Example 3.39 $f(x) = x^n$ for n is even.

Solution: For n is even, the polynomial function $f(x) = x^n$ is not one-to-one since $f(1) = f(-1) = 1$ and, hence, does not have an inverse. However, recall that f is a increasing function for all $x \geq 0$. If we restrict our domain to the collection of all $x \geq 0$ then, f has an inverse. The inverse function is called the nth root function and is denoted as $f^{-1}(x) = x^{1/n}$. Note that the domain and range of f^{-1} is the collection of all $x \geq 0$. ∎

3.13.3 Properties of Inverse Function

1. The inverse function of a function is unique.
2. The inverse function of a bijective function is also bijective.
3. If $f: A \rightarrow B$ and $g: B \rightarrow C$ are two bijective functions, then $g \circ f: A \rightarrow C$ is also a bijective function and $(g \circ f)^{-1} = f^{-1} \circ g^{-1}$.
4. $f \circ g = g \circ f$, only when either $f^{-1} = g$ or $g^{-1} = f$ and $f \circ g(x) = g \circ f(x) = x$.
5. If $f(x) = y$, then $f^{-1}(y) = x$

6. $(f^{-1})' = 1/f'(f^{-1})$ for any differentiable function f of a real argument and with real values, when the indicated compositions and inverses exist.

7. If the function f is increasing or decreasing then f has an inverse g. In addition, f is increasing, if and only if its inverse g is increasing and f is decreasing, if and only if its inverse g is decreasing.

3.13.4 Left Inverses, Right Inverses

A function f has at least one 'left inverse' if and only if it is a one-to-one (injective) function. A *left inverse* is a function g such that, $\forall x \in X$, $g(f(x)) = x$.

If f is not a surjection, we obtain g by setting $g(f(x)) = x$ for each element in the range of x, and $g(y) = z$, where z is any element, for any y in the co-domain of f but not in its range.

Similarly, f has at least one right-inverse, if and only if it is a onto (surjective) function. A *right-inverse* is a function g such that, $\forall y \in Y$, $f(g(y)) = y$.

Hence, for each x, g assigns one of the elements in the domain of f which produces x. For example, we know that $f(x) = x^2$ is a onto function from R to R^+. Then $g(x) = -\sqrt{x}$ is a famous right inverse to x^2, because $(-\sqrt{x})^2 = x$ for all $x \in R^+$. But it is not a left inverse because $-\sqrt{x^2} = -x$ for all $x \in R^+$.

If f is a bijective function, then the (unique) right inverse equals the left inverse and we have come again to the ordinary inverse described above.

Theorem 3.5 Let $f : A \to B$ be a function.

(a) f^{-1} is a function from B to A if and only if f is one-to-one.

(b) If f^{-1} is a function, then f^{-1} is also one-to-one.

(c) f^{-1} is everywhere defined if and only if f is onto.

(d) f^{-1} is onto if and only if f is everywhere defined.

Proof:

(a) The given statement can be proved by proving the equivalent statement given below: f^{-1} is not a function, if and only if f is not one-to-one. Let f^{-1} is not a function. Then, for some $b \in B$, $f^{-1}(b)$ must contain at least two distinct elements, a_1 and a_2. Then, $f(a_1) = b = f(a_2)$, so f is not one-to-one. Hence, we have, if f^{-1} is not a function then f is not one-to-one.

Now, let f is not one-to-one. Then, $f(a_1) = f(a_2) = b$, for two distinct elements $a_1, a_2 \in A$. Thus, $f^{-1}(b)$ contains both a_1 and a_2. So, f^{-1} cannot be a function. Hence if f is not one-to-one then f^{-1} is not a function. So f^{-1} is not a function if f is not one-to-one. That is, f^{-1} is a function if and only if f is one to one.

(b) Since $(f^{-1})^{-1}$ is the function f, from the above proof, we can easily conclude that f^{-1} is one-to-one.

(c) We know that, $\text{Dom}(f^{-1}) = \text{Ran}(f)$. Thus $B = \text{Dom}(f^{-1})$ if and only if $B = \text{Ran}(f)$. Alternatively, we can express that, f^{-1} is everywhere defined if and only if f is onto.

(d) As, $\text{Ran}(f^{-1}) = \text{Dom}(f)$, so $A = \text{Dom}(f)$ if and only if $A = \text{Ran}(f^{-1})$. That means, f is everywhere defined if and only if f^{-1} is onto. ∎

Example 3.40 Let $A = B = Z$ and let $f: A \rightarrow B$ be defined by $f(a) = a + 1$, for $a \in A$. Is f invertible?

Solution: Since f is everywhere defined, one-to-one, and onto, it is a one-to-one correspondence between A and B. Thus, f is invertible, and f^{-1} is a one-to-one correspondence between B and A. ∎

Example 3.41 Let R be the set of real numbers, and let $f: R \rightarrow R$ be defined by $f(x) = x^2$. Is f invertible?

Solution: Since $f(2) = f(-2) = 4$, hence f is not one-to-one. So f is not invertible. ∎

A function $I_A: A \rightarrow A$ is called an *identity function* if $I_A = \{(a, a) \mid a \in A\}$.

It may be noticed that, for any function $g: A \rightarrow A$, the functions $I_A \circ g = g \circ I_A = g$. Similarly, for any function $f: A \rightarrow B$, we can write $f \circ I_A = f$. These properties of an identity function can be used in expressing the following theorems regarding the inverse of a function.

Theorem 3.6 Let $f: A \rightarrow B$ be any function. Then

(a) $I_B \circ f = f$.

(b) $f \circ I_A = f$.

If $f: A \rightarrow B$ is invertible or f is a one-to-one correspondence between A and B, then

(c) $f^{-1} \circ f = I_A$.   (3.3a)

(d) $f \circ f^{-1} = I_B$.   (3.3b)

Proof:

(a) $(I_B \circ f)(a) = I_B(f(a)) = f(a)$, for all a in $\text{Dom}(f)$. Thus, $I_B \circ f = f$.

(b) $(f \circ I_A)(a) = f(I_A(a)) = f(a)$, for all a in $\text{Dom}(f)$. Hence, $f \circ I_A = f$.

Suppose f is a one-to-one correspondence between A and B. We know that the equation $b = f(a)$ is equivalent to the equation $a = f^{-1}(b)$. Since f and f^{-1} both are everywhere defined and onto, so, for all $a \in A$ and $b \in B$, $f(f^{-1}(b)) = b$ and $f^{-1}(f(a)) = a$. Then,

(c) For all $a \in A$, $I_A(a) = a = f^{-1}(f(a)) = (f^{-1} \circ f)(a)$. Thus, $I_A = f^{-1} \circ f$.

(d) For all $b \in B$, $I_B(b) = b = f(f^{-1}(b)) = (f \circ f^{-1})(b)$. Thus, $I_B = f \circ f^{-1}$. ∎

Theorem 3.7 Let $f: A \rightarrow B$ and $g: B \rightarrow A$. The function g is equal to f^{-1}, only if

$$g \circ f = I_A \quad \text{and} \quad f \circ g = I_B \tag{3.4}$$

Proof: To prove this theorem, first we show that if there exists any other function $h: B \rightarrow A$, such that,

$$h \circ f = I_A \quad \text{and} \quad f \circ h = I_B \tag{3.5}$$

then $h = g$. Once this is shown then $g = f^{-1}$ follows from equations 3(a) and 3(b). Using equations (3.4) and (3.5), we can write $(h \circ f) \circ g = h \circ (f \circ g) = h \circ I_B = h$.

Also, $\qquad\qquad (h \circ f) \circ g = I_A \circ g = g$

So, $\qquad\qquad\qquad\qquad h = g$

Hence, $\qquad\qquad\qquad g = f^{-1}$ ∎

Example 3.42 Verify that the functions $f(a) = a^4$ and $g(a) = a^{1/4}$ for each $a \in R$ are inverses of each other.

Solution: We have, $\qquad (f \circ g)\,(a) = f(a^{1/4}) = a = I_A$

Similarly, $\qquad\qquad (g \circ f)\,(a) = g(a^4) = a = I_A$.

So, $\qquad\qquad\qquad f = g^{-1} \quad \text{or} \quad g = f^{-1}$ ∎

Theorem 3.8

(a) Let $f: A \rightarrow B$ and $g: B \rightarrow A$ be functions such that $g \circ f = I_A$ and $f \circ g = I_B$. Then, f is a one-to-one correspondence between A and B, g is a one-to-one correspondence between B and A, and each is the inverse of the other.

(b) Let $f: A \rightarrow B$ and $g: B \rightarrow C$ be invertible. Then $g \circ f$ is invertible, and $(g \circ f)^{-1} = f^{-1} \circ g^{-1}$.

Proof:

(a) The assumptions can be written as $g(f(a)) = a$ and $f(g(b)) = b$, for all $a \in A$ and $b \in B$. This shows that $\text{Ran}(f) = B$ and $\text{Ran}(g) = A$. So, each function is onto. If $f(a_1) = f(a_2)$ then $a_1 = g(f(a_1)) = g(f(a_2)) = a_2$. Thus, f is one-to-one. In a similar way, we can prove that g is also one-to-one. So, both the functions f and g are invertible. Since, $\text{Dom}(f^{-1}) = \text{Ran}(f) = B$, so f^{-1} is everywhere defined. Now, if b is any element in B, $f^{-1}(b) = f^{-1}(f(g(b))) = (f^{-1} \circ f)\,(g(b)) = I_A(g(b)) = g(b)$.

Thus, $g = f^{-1}$, so also $f = (f^{-1})^{-1} = g^{-1}$. Since g and f are onto, so f^{-1} and g^{-1} are onto. Hence, f and g must be everywhere defined. This proves entire (a) part.

(b) We know that, for any relations f and g, $(g \circ f)^{-1} = f^{-1} \circ g^{-1}$. Since, g^{-1} and f^{-1} are functions by the assumption, so is their composition. So, $(g \circ f)^{-1}$ is a function. Thus, $g \circ f$ is invertible. ∎

Example 3.43 Let $A = B = R$, the set of real numbers and f_1 be a function from A to B given by $f_1(x) = 2x^3 - 1$ and let f_2 be a function from B to A given by $f_2(y) = \sqrt[3]{((1/2)y + 1/2)}$. Show that f_1 is a one-to-one onto function from A to B and f_2 is a one-to-one onto function B to A.

Solution: Let $\qquad\qquad x \in A \quad \text{and} \quad y = f_1(x) = 2x^3 - 1$.

$$\Rightarrow \qquad\qquad (1/2)\,(y + 1) = x^3$$

$$\Rightarrow \qquad x = \sqrt[3]{((1/2)y + 1/2)} = f_2(y) = f_2(f_1(x)) = (f_2 \circ f_1)\,(x).$$

Thus, $f_2 \circ f_1 = I_A$. Similarly, it can be shown that $f_1 \circ f_2 = I_B$. So, both f_1 and f_2 are one-to-one onto functions. ∎

Theorem 3.9 Let A and B be two finite sets with the same number of elements, and let $f: A \to B$ be an everywhere defined function.

(a) If f is one-to-one, then f is onto.

(b) If f is onto, then f is one-to-one.

So, for two finite sets A and B, having equal number of elements, and specifically if $A = B$, we need to only prove that a function is *one-to-one* or *onto* to show that it is a one-to-one onto function. ∎

3.14 RECURSIVE FUNCTIONS

Sometimes we face difficulties in defining objects explicitly; but it may be easy to define an object in terms of itself. This process is called *recursion*. Recursion can be used to define sets, functions, sequences, etc. In this section, we will discuss how to define functions recursively.

The recursive functions, which form a class of computable functions, take their name from the process of "recurrence" or "recursion". In its most general numerical form, the process of recursion involves defining the value of a function by using other values of the same function.

We define the **recursive functions** in two steps. Here, we assume that the domain of the function is the set of non-negative integers. These two steps are:

1st step (Basis step)—Write the value of the function at zero (or any particular value).

2nd step (Recursive step/inductive step)—Define a rule for computing the value of the function at some integer from its values at the previous integers.

This definition is called a **recursive definition**.

Example 3.44 Suppose, the function f is defined recursively by

$$f(0) = 1$$
$$f(x + 1) = 3 \cdot f(x) + 1$$

Compute $f(1), f(2), f(3)$.

Solution: From the above definition, it follows that

$$f(1) = f(0 + 1) = 3 \cdot f(0) + 1 = 3 \cdot 1 + 1 = 4$$
$$f(2) = f(1 + 1) = 3 \cdot f(1) + 1 = 3 \cdot 4 + 1 = 13$$
$$f(3) = f(2 + 1) = 3 \cdot f(2) + 1 = 3 \cdot 13 + 1 = 40$$

∎

A *primitive recursive* function is a function which can be obtained from the initial function by a finite number of composition and recursion operations.

Example 3.45 Show that the function $f(x) = \begin{cases} x/2 & \text{when } x \text{ is even} \\ (x-1)/2 & \text{when } x \text{ is odd} \end{cases}$ is primitive recursive.

Solution: We can take initial functions as $f(1) = (1 - 1)/2 = 0/2 = 0$ as 1 is odd

and $\qquad\qquad\qquad f(2) = 2/2 = 1$ as 2 is even.

For any even number we can have $f(2n) = 2n/2 = n$ for $n \geq 0$

and now $\qquad\qquad f\{2(n + 1)\} = f(2n) + f(2) = f(2n) + 1.$

In general, we can have $f\{2(n + m)\} = f(2n) + f(2m) = f(2n) + m = S(f(2n)).$

Similarly, for any odd number, we can have $f(2n + 1) = (2n + 1 - 1)/2 = n$, for $n \geq 0$.

Now, $\qquad\qquad f\{2(n + 1) + 1\} = n + 1 = f(2n + 1) + 1.$

So, in general $\quad f\{2(n + m) + 1\} = f(2n + 1) + m = S(f(2n + 1)),$ for $n \geq 0$, $m \geq 0$.

Hence, the given function f is primitive recursive. ∎

3.14.1 Recursion in Programming Languages

A programmer's bag of tricks is loaded with heuristics, algorithms and techniques, but of these, few are as powerful as recursions. The Oxford English Dictionary recursively defines recursion as **"The application or use of a recursive procedure or definition!"**.

Here, an account of the class of recursive functions is given with particular emphasis on some basic kinds of recursion.

Recursion is a technique that allows us to break down a problem into one or more sub problems that is similar in form to the original problem.

Let us proceed in our discussion by taking a typical problem. For example, to find factorial of a number.

Recall that factorial, which is written as $n!$, has the following definition:

$$n! = 1 * 2 * 3 * \ldots * (n - 2) * (n - 1) * n$$

We can use this definition to write:

```
int fact(int n) {
    int i;
    int result;
    result = 1;
    for (i = 1; i <= n; i++) {
        result = result * i;
    }
    return result;
}
```

We can write a function that uses recursion as follows:

```
int fact(int n) {
if (n = = 1) return 1;
return n * fact(n - 1);
}
```

Comparing the two versions, we find the following:

- The iterative version has two local variables; the recursive version has none.
- The iterative version has three statements; the recursive version has only one.
- The iterative version must save the solution in an intermediate variable before it can be returned; the recursive version calculates and returns its result as a single expression.

Recursion simplifies the **(fact)** function. It does so by making the computer work more, so that you can work less.

3.14.2   Types of Recursion

The recursive functions are categorized into three types, based on the following:

1. Whether the function calls itself or not (*direct or indirect recursion*).
2. Whether there are pending operations at each recursive call (*tail-recursive or not*).
3. The shape of the calling pattern—whether pending operations are also recursive (*linear or tree-recursive*).

Direct Recursion   A function is *directly* recursive if it contains an explicit call to itself. For example, the function

```
int funct(int x) {
    If (x <= 0) return x;
    return funct(x - 1);
}
```

includes a call to itself, so it is directly recursive. The recursive call will occur for positive values of *x*.

Let us consider another example for direct recursion which is given below. In this example, the function **compute_gcd()** calls itself.

Example 3.46

```
//A recursive function to compute GCD of two numbers …
Void compute_gcd(int x, int y)
{
    if (x > y)
    {
        x = x - y;
        compute_gcd(x, y);
    }
    else if(x < y)
    {
        y = y - x;
        compute_gcd(x, y);
    }
    else
    printf("the gcd of two given numbers is %d ",x);
}
```

Indirect Recursion A function **funct()** is *indirectly recursive* if it contains a call to another function which ultimately calls funct().

The following pair of functions (**funct()** and **method()**) is *indirectly recursive*. Since they call each other, they are also known as *mutually recursive* functions.

```
int funct(int x) {
    if (x <= 0) return x;
    return method(x);
}
int method(int y) {
    return funct(y - 1);
}
```

Tail Recursion A recursive function is said to be *tail recursive* if there are no pending operations to be performed on return from a recursive call.

Tail recursive functions often return the value of the last recursive call as the value of the function. Tail recursion is very desirable because the amount of information which must be stored during the computation is independent of the number of recursive calls. Some modern computing systems will actually compute tail-recursive functions using an iterative process.

The most common factorial function *fact* is usually written in a non-tail-recursive manner:

```
int fact (int n) {/* n >= 0 */
    if (n == 0) return 1;
    return n * fact(n - 1);
}
```

Notice that there is a "pending operation," namely multiplication, to be performed on return from each recursive call. Whenever there is a pending operation, the function is non-tail-recursive. Information about each pending operation must be stored, so the amount of information is not independent of the number of calls.

The factorial function can be written in a tail-recursive way:

```
int fact_tail(int n, int f) {/*n is the given no and f is the factorial of the no.*/
    if (n == 1) return f;
    return fact_tail(n - 1, n * f)
}
int fact(n) {
    return fact_tail(n, 1);
}
```

Note that, **fact_tail()** has no pending operations on return from recursive calls. The value computed by the recursive call is simply returned with no modification. The amount of information which must be stored is constant (the value of n and the value of f), independent of the number of recursive calls.

Linear and Tree Recursion Another way to categorize recursive functions is by observing the way in which the recursion grows. The two basic ways are "linear" and "tree."

A recursive function is said to be *linearly recursive* when no pending operation involves another recursive call to the function.

For example, the **fact()** function is linearly recursive. The pending operation is simply multiplication by a scalar, it does not involve another call to **fact**.

A recursive function is said to be *tree recursive* (or *non-linearly recursive*) when the pending operation involves another recursive call to the function.

Example 3.47   The Fibonacci function **fib()** provides a perfect example of tree recursion. The Fibonacci numbers can be defined by the rule:

$$\text{fib}(n) = 0 \text{ if } n \text{ is } 0,$$
$$= 1 \text{ if } n \text{ is } 1,$$
$$= \text{fib}(n-1) + \text{fib}(n-2), \text{ otherwise}.$$

For example, the first six Fibonacci numbers are

$$\text{fib}(0) = 0$$
$$\text{fib}(1) = 1$$
$$\text{fib}(2) = \text{fib}(1) + \text{fib}(0) = 1$$
$$\text{fib}(3) = \text{fib}(2) + \text{fib}(1) = 2$$
$$\text{fib}(4) = \text{fib}(3) + \text{fib}(2) = 3$$
$$\text{fib}(5) = \text{fib}(4) + \text{fib}(3) = 5$$

The method of getting these Fibonacci numbers is shown in a tree like structure in Fig. 3.43.

This can be implemented as:

```
int fib(int n) {/* n >= 0 */
    if (n == 0) return 0;
    if (n == 1) return 1;
    return  fib(n - 1) + fib(n - 2);
}
```

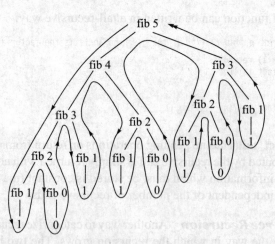

Fig. 3.43   Tree recursion for obtaining Fibonacci numbers

3.15 HASHING

Before entering into the details of the hash function, let us consider an example. Suppose a company with 72 employees assigns a 4-digit employee ID to each employee which is being used by the company as the primary key in the company's employee database. We can use that ID as the address of the corresponding record in memory. The search in fact will not require any comparisons. But the problem is that this technique will require space for a huge number of memory locations whereas space for very few locations would actually be used. So, there is a tradeoff between space and time.

The above idea, i.e., the idea of using the key to determine the address of a record, must be modified so that a great deal of space is not wasted. This can be done by taking a function, H which maps from K, the set of keys to L, the set of memory addresses.

$$H: K \to L$$

Such a function is called a *hash function* or *hashing function*. The memory address computed by the hash function corresponding to a key, is known as hash address. This is possible that two different keys k_1 and k_2 will yield the same hash address. This situation is called *collision* and some method must be introduced to resolve the collision.

3.15.1 Hash Function

Hashing technique uses a table (Array/Vector) of size m to store elements from a set of much larger size. For a given key k, this technique uses a function H to compute the address $H(k)$ for that key. The function H is known as *hash function*. When 2 keys have the same address (in fact same hash value), we say that *collision* occurs. Mathematically, $k_1 \neq k_2 \Rightarrow H(k_1) = H(k_2)$ leads to collision.

A hashing function should possess the following important properties to perform a good search.

(i) The hash function H should execute reasonably fast and should be very easy to execute.

(ii) H should uniformly distribute the hash addresses throughout the set L so that there are minimum number of collisions.

There is no guarantee that the second property can be fully satisfied without knowing the keys and addresses before. However some general techniques may help. One such technique is to chop a key into pieces and combine them in some way to form the hash address $H(k)$.

3.15.2 Some Popular Hash Functions

Division Method   In this method, the hash function is generally expressed as

$$H(k) = k \pmod{m}$$

Here $k(\text{mod } m)$ denotes the reminder when k is divided by m, where m is usually chosen to be a prime number.

Midsquare Method   In this method, first the key k is squared. Then the hash function H is defined by $H(k) = 1$, where 1 is obtained by deleting digits from both ends of k^2.

The program for computing the hash function using midsquare method is given in Fig. 3.44.

```
/***************************************************
Hashing using Midsqure Method
***************************************************/
#include <stdio.h>
#include <math.h>
/*----------------------------------------------------

Function Name   :  MidSquareHash
Purpose         :  To Perform Hashing Using Mid Square Method
Arguments       :  'key' - Key to be hashed (long int )
Returns         :  HashAddress (Two Digit, int )
----------------------------------------------------
Remarks         :  Number of digits in the key must be less than five
----------------------------------------------------------------------*/
int MidSquareHash(long key)
{
/*........................................................
Declaration Section
........................................................*/
long keysquare, temp:
int i, m:
/*........................................................
Code Section
........................................................*/
keysquare= key*key:
/* Find i : the No of Digits in the keysquare */
i=1:
while ( (keysquare / (long) pow(10,i) ) > 0 )
{
  i++:
}
/* Find m : The No Of Digits To Truncate from begining and end */
if (i%2==0)
{
    m=i/2-1:
}
else
{
    m=i/2:
}
/* Truncate m digits from end */
keysquare /= pow(10,m):
```

```
/* In case of even number of digits in Square, return two middle digits and in
case of odd number of digits return the single middle digit */
if (i%2==0)
  return (keysquare % 100);
else
  return (keysquare %10);
}
main()
{
    long int key;
    printf ("\n Hashing Using Mid Square Method");
    printf ("\n Enter Key (4 Digit) :");
    scanf ("%ld",&key);
    printf ("\n Hash Address : %d",MidSquareHash(key));

}
```

Fig 3.44 The program for computing the hash function using midsquare method

Folding Method In this method, the key k is partitioned into a number of parts, say, $k_1, k_2, k_3, \ldots k_r$, where each part, except possibly the last, has the same number of digits as the required address. Then the parts are added together, ignoring the last carry,

i.e., $\quad H(k) = k_1 + k_2 + k_3 + \ldots + k_r$

Example 3.48 Consider the above example about the company of 72 employees where each of them is assigned a unique 4-digit employee ID. Suppose L consists of 100 two-digit addresses: 00, 01, 02, ..., 99. Apply the hash functions to each of the following employee IDs:

$\quad$ 6713 , 4409, 5835.

Solution:

(a) *Division method:* Choose a prime number m close to 99 (i.e. the maximum no. of keys) say, 97.

So $\qquad\qquad m = 97$

Then $\qquad\qquad H(6713) = 6713 \bmod 97 = 20$

$\qquad\qquad\qquad H(4409) = 4409 \bmod 97 = 44$

$\qquad\qquad\qquad H(5835) = 5835 \bmod 97 = 15$

(b) *Midsquare method:* First, we square the key k. Then, the hash addresses can be obtained by deleting 3 digits from both the ends of k^2. Now,

$\qquad\qquad k = 6713 \Rightarrow k^2 = 45064369$

$\qquad\qquad\qquad \Rightarrow H(6713) = 64$

$\qquad\qquad k = 4409 \Rightarrow k^2 = 19439281$

$\qquad\qquad\qquad \Rightarrow H(4409) = 39$

$$k = 5835 \implies k^2 = 34047225$$
$$\implies H(5835) = 47$$

(c) *Folding method:* First, we make a partition of the key k into two parts so that each part contains two digits. Then, we add the parts together, ignoring the last carry. So,

$$6713 = 67 + 13 = 80$$
$$4409 = 44 + 09 = 53$$
$$5835 = 58 + 35 = 93$$

Thus, the obtained addresses are 80, 34 and 93. ■

3.15.3 Collision Resolution

Suppose, we want to add a new record with key value k to a particular file; but the memory location address computed from $H(k)$ is found to be occupied previously. This situation is known as collision. There are 2 general ways of resolving collisions, i.e., (i) open addressing, and (ii) chaining. Selection of a particular procedure depends on many factors; one important factor is the *load factor*. Load factor is nothing but the ratio of the number of keys in the set K (say, n) to the number of hash addresses in L (say, m). This ratio $\lambda = n/m$ is called Load factor.

Open Addressing (Linear Probing and Modifications over That) We assume that the memory table T with m locations is circular; so that $T[1]$ comes after $T[m]$. Suppose a new record R with key k is to be added to the memory table T; but the memory location with hash address $H(k) = h$ is already filled. One natural way to resolve collision is to assign R to the first available location following $T[h]$. In this collision resolution procedure, we search for the record R in the table T by linearly searching the locations $T[h]$, $T[h + 1]$, $T[h + 2]$… until finding R or meeting an empty location, which indicates an unsuccessful search. This particular collision resolution is known as *linear probing*.

Example 3.49 Let the values (keys) be 89, 18, 49, 58, 69 and we have a memory table consisting of 10 partitions or buckets, each having one slot. Assume that the hash function is given by $h(x) = (x \bmod \text{memory size})$ (number of buckets). Find the memory address for each key using a hash function and also find the number of collisions, if any.

Solution: We use the division method to find the memory address for each key. Now, for the given keys, the memory addresses can be computed as given below:

$$89 = 89 \bmod 10 = 9$$
$$18 = 18 \bmod 10 = 8$$
$$49 = 49 \bmod 10 = 9$$
$$58 = 58 \bmod 10 = 8$$
$$69 = 69 \bmod 10 = 9$$

So, keys 89 and 18 will be assigned buckets 9 and 8 respectively as shown in Fig. 3.45. It can be found that, collisions are occurring for the keys 49, 58 and 69. So, we use linear probing technique to resolve the collisions (i.e. to find a memory space for all keys).

So, let us modify the hash function $h(x)$ to $ht_i(x)$. Here, $ht_i(x) = \{h(x) + F(i)\}$ mod table size, where $F(i)$ is known as the collision resolution function. We assume, $F(i) = i$, where i = number of probes or key comparisons. So, $ht_i(x) = \{h(x) + i\}$ mod 10, as there are 10 buckets.

Now for given keys, $ht_1(49) = (h(49) + 1)$ mod 10 = (9 + 1) mod 10 = 0. Since 0th bucket is free, so this can be assigned to the key 49.

$ht_1(58) = (h(58) + 1)$ mod 10 = (8 + 1) mod 10 = 9, thus leading to collision as 9th bucket is already occupied by 89.

Now, $ht_2(58) = (8 + 2)$ mod 10 = 0, again leading to collision as 0th bucket is already occupied by 49.

Again, $ht_3(58) = (h(58) + 3)$ mod 10 = (8 + 3) mod 10 = 1. Since 1st bucket is free, so this can be assigned to the key 58.

Similarly, $ht_1(69) = 9 + 1$ mod 10 = 0, leads to collision.

Now, $ht_2(69) = (9 + 2)$ mod 10 = 1, again lead to collision

Again, $ht_3(69) = (9 + 3)$ mod 10 = 2. Since 2nd bucket is free, so this can be assigned to the key 69.

This is shown in Fig. 3.46. It may be observed that, the total number of collisions occurred here is 7. ■

0	
1	
2	
3	
4	
5	
6	
7	
8	18
9	89

Fig. 3.45

0	49
1	58
2	69
3	
4	
5	
6	
7	
8	18
9	89

Fig. 3.46

Chaining One variation to linear probing is *chaining*. Chaining involves maintaining 2 tables in memory. As usual, there is a table T in memory which contains the records in a file F; except that T has an additional field LINK which is used, to link together all records in T with same hash address h forming a linked list.

Figure 3.47 shows the C code for hashing using linear probing.

```
/*Hashing using Linear Probing*/
#include<stdio.h>>
#include<conio.h>
int main()
{
int a[100],b[100],data,n,m,i,temp,temp2,coll,total_coll=0;
clrscr();
/*CREATING INPUT DATA HASH TABLE*/
n=10;
printf("enter no. of data elements(keys) u want to feed (Maximum  10):");
scanf("%d",&m);
for(i=0;i<n;i++)
  b[i]=0;
for(i=0;i<m;i++)
{
    printf("\n\n enter the data element(key) ");
```

```
          scanf("%d",&data);
          coll=0;
          temp=data%n;
          if(b[temp]==0)
                  a[temp]=data;
          else
          {
                  while(b[temp]==1)
                  {
                   ++coll;
                   ++temp;
                   if(temp>=n)
                          temp=0;
                  }
                  a[temp]=data;
          }
          b[temp]=1;
          printf("number of collisions is %d",coll);
          total_coll=total_coll+coll;
    }
    printf("\n\n Total Number of collisions are: %d",total_coll);
    /*DISPLAYING INPUT DATA HASH TABLE*/
    printf("\n\n INPUT DATA HASH TABLE IS: \n");
    for(i=0;i<n;i++)
    {
      if(b[i]==1)
        printf("location= %d value= %d \n", i, a[i]);
      else
        printf("location= %d value= XXXX\n", i);
    }
    /*SEARCHING*/
    printf("\n enter the data element(key) to be searched ");
    scanf("%d",&data);
    temp=data%n;
    temp2=temp;
    if(a[temp]==data)
    {
        printf("\n SEARCH SUCCESSFUL \n");
        printf("location= %d",temp);
    }
    else
    {
        do
        {
         ++temp;
         if(temp==n)
         temp=0;
        }while((a[temp]!=data)&&(temp!=temp2));
        if(temp==temp2)
        {
         printf("SEARCH UNSUCCESSFUL....NO MATCH FOUND");
        }
        else
        {
         printf("\n SEARCH SUCCESSFUL \n");
         printf("location= %d",temp);
        }
    }
    getch();
    return 0;
}
```

Fig. 3.47 Program for hashing using linear probing

One main disadvantage of linear probing is that the records tend to *cluster*, i.e. appear next to one another, when the load factor is greater than 50%. Such a clustering substantially increases the average search time for a record.

3.15.4 Techniques Used to Minimize Clustering

The following techniques may be used to minimize clustering:
(i) quadratic probing, and (ii) double hashing.

Quadratic Probing Suppose a record R with a key K has the hash address $H(k) = h$. Then, instead of taking collision resolution function as $F(i) = i$, we will take $F(i) = i^2$. In other words, instead of searching the location with address h, $h + 1, h + 2, \ldots$, we linearly search the location $h, h + 1, h + 4, h + 9, \ldots, h + i^2$.

Example 3.50 Let us consider the previous example. Now, we take $F(i) = i^2$.

So, $ht_i(x) = \{h(x) + i^2\} \bmod$ table size, where $h(x) = x \bmod 10$.

So for the given keys, we have

$ht_1(49) = 9 + 1 \bmod 10 = 0$. Since 0th bucket is free, so this can be assigned to the key 49.

$ht_1(58) = (h(58) + 1) \bmod 10 = 8 + 1 \bmod 10 = 9$, thus leading to collision as 9th bucket is already occupied by 89.

Now, $ht_2(58) = (8 + 4) \bmod 10 = 2$. Since 2nd bucket is free, so this can be assigned to the key 58.

$ht_1(69) = 9 + 1 \bmod 10 = 0$, thus leading to collision as 0th bucket is already occupied by 49.

Now, $ht_2(69) = 9 + 4 \bmod 10 = 3$. Since 3rd bucket is free, so this can be assigned to the key 69.

0	49
1	
2	58
3	69
4	
5	
6	
7	
8	18
9	89

Fig. 3.48

This is shown in Fig.3.48. It may be observed that the total number of collisions occurred here is 5. ∎

Figure 3.49 shows the C code for hashing using quadratic probling.

```
/*Hahing using Quadratic Probing*/
#include<stdio.h>
#include<conio.h>
int main()
{
    int a[100],b[100],data,n,m,i,j,temp;
    int temp2,temp3,limit,coll,coll2,total_coll;
    //CREATING INPUT DATA HASH TABLE*/
clrscr();
n=10;       /*Can be set by the user in the code and change limit accordingly in
the code*/
    limit=6;
    printf("no. of hash addresses=n= %d\n",n);
```

```
printf("enter no. of data elements(keys) u want to feed(about n/2
 for a load factor of nearly 50% and maximum= %d)",limit);
scanf("%d",&m);
for(i=0;i<n;i++)
b[i]=0;
for(i=0;i<m;i++)
{
printf("\n\n enter the data element(key) ");
scanf("%d",&data);
coll=0;
            temp=data%n;
            temp2=temp;
            if(b[temp]==0)
                    a[temp]=data;
            else
{
                    j=1;
                    do
                    {
                            ++coll;
                            temp=temp2+j*j;
                            j=j+1;
                            if(temp>=n)
                                    temp=temp%n;
                    }while(b[temp]==1);
                    a[temp]=data;
}
            b[temp]=1;
            printf("number of collisions is %d",coll);
            total_coll=total_coll+coll;
}
    printf("\n\n Total Number of collisions are: %d",total_coll);
    /*DISPLAYING INPUT DATA HASH TABLE*/
    printf("\n\n INPUT DATA HASH TABLE IS:\n");
    for(i=0;i<n;i++)
    {
if(b[i]==1)
                            printf("location= %d value= %d \n", i, a[i]);
            else
                    printf("location= %d value= XXXX\n", i);
    }
    /*SEARCHING*/
    printf("\n enter the data element(key) to be searched ");
    scanf("%d",&data);
    coll2=0;
    temp=data%n;
    temp3=temp;
    if(a[temp]==data)
    {
printf("\nSEARCH SUCCESSFUL\n");
            printf("location= %d",temp);
    }
    else
{
j=1;
do
{
```

```
                   ++coll2;
                   temp=temp3+j*j;
                   j=j+1;
                   if(temp>=n)
                   temp=temp%n;
    }while((a[temp]!=data)&&(coll2<limit));
    if(coll2==limit)
    printf("data cannot be found in the given set of
    buckets..SEARCH UNSUCCESSFUL");
    else
    {
    printf("\nSEARCH SUCCESSFUL\n");
    printf("location= %d",temp);
    }
    }
       getch();
       return 0;
    }
```

Fig. 3.49   Program for hashing using quadratic probing

Double Hashing   Here a second hash function H' is used for resolving a collision as follows: Suppose a record R with a key K has the hash address $H(k) = h$, $H'(k) = h' \neq m$. Then, we linearly search the location with address $h + h'$, $h + 2h'$, $h + 3h'$ ....

Example 3.51   Let us again consider the previous example. We have already known that keys 89 and 18 are assigned with buckets 9 and 8 respectively.

Now, let us assume $H'(x) = R - (x \bmod R)$, where R is a prime number.

We define the collision resolution function as $F(i) = i* H'(x)$. Let us assume $R = 7$.

So, $H'(x) = 7 - (x \bmod 7)$.

Now, $ht_i(x) = \{h(x) + F(i)\} \bmod 10 = [h(x) + i*(7 - (x \bmod 7))] \bmod 10$.

So, $ht_1(49) = [9 + 1(7 - 49 \bmod 7)] \bmod 10 = (9 + 7) \bmod 10 = 6$. Since 6th bucket is free, so this can be assigned to the key 49.

0	69
1	
2	
3	58
4	
5	
6	49
7	
8	18
9	89

Fig. 3.50

$ht_1(58) = [8 + 7 - 58 \bmod 7] \bmod 10 = 8 + (7 - 2)\bmod 10 = (8 + 5) \bmod 10 = 3$. Since 3rd bucket is free, so this can be assigned to the key 58.

$ht_1(69) = [9 + (7 - 69 \bmod 7)] \bmod 10 = 9 + (7 - 6) \bmod 10 = 0$. Since 0th bucket is free, so this can be assigned to the key 69.

This is shown in Fig. 3.50. It may be observed that, the total number of collisions occurred here is 3. ∎

Figure 3.51 shows the *C* code for hashing using double hashing.

```
/*HASHING USING DOUBLE HASHING*/
#include<stdio.h>
#include<conio.h>
int main()
{
    int a[100],b[100],data,n,m,i,j,temp;
    int temp2,temp3,R,coll,coll2,total_coll=0;
    /*CREATING INPUT DATA HASH TABLE*/
    clrscr();
    n=10;    /*Can be set by the user in the code and change R and the
limit for coll2 accordingly in the code*/
    R=7;
    printf("no. of hash addresses=n= %d\n",n);
    printf("enter no. of data elements(keys) u want to feed(about n/2
for a load factor of nearly 50%) ");
    scanf("%d",&m);
    for(i=0;i<n;i++)
            b[i]=0;
    for(i=0;i<m;i++)
    {
            printf("\n\n enter the data element(key) ");
            scanf("%d",&data);
            coll=0;
            temp=data%n;
            temp2=temp;
            if(b[temp]==0)
            a[temp]=data;
            else
            {
                    j=1;
                    do
                    {
                            ++coll;
                            temp=temp2+j*(R-(data%R));
                            j=j+1;
                            if(temp>=n)
                                        temp=temp%n;
                    }while(b[temp]==1);
                    a[temp]=data;
            }
            b[temp]=1;
            printf("number of collisions is %d", coll);
            total_coll=total_coll+coll;
    }
    printf("\n\n Total Number of collisions are: %d",total_coll);
    /*DISPLAYING INPUT DATA HASH TABLE*/
    printf("\n\n INPUT DATA HASH TABLE IS: \n");
    for(i=0;i<n;i++)
    {
            if(b[i]==1)
            printf("location= %d value= %d \n", i, a[i]);
            else
            printf("location= %d value= XXXX\n", i);
    }
}

/*SEARCHING*/
printf("\n enter the data element(key) to be searched ");
scanf("%d",&data);
coll2=0;
temp=data%n;
```

```
        temp3=temp;
        if(a[temp]==data)
        {
                printf("\n SEARCH SUCCESSFUL \n");
                printf("location= %d",temp);
        }
        else
        {
            j=1;
            do
            {
                    ++coll2;
                    temp=temp3+j*(R-(data%R));
                    j=j+1;
                    if(temp>=n)
                    temp=temp%n;
            }while((a[temp]!=data)&&(coll2<10));
            /* The limit for coll2 has been chosen as a sufficiently big no. for breaking
        from the loop*/
            if(coll2==10)
                    printf("data cannot be found in the given set of
                    buckets..SEARCH UNSUCCESSFUL");
            else
            {
            printf("\n SEARCH SUCCESSFUL \n");
            printf("location= %d",temp);
            }
        }
        getch();
        return 0;
}
```

Fig. 3.51 Program for hashing using double hashing

3.16 PIGEONHOLE PRINCIPLE

A well-known proof technique in mathematics is the so-called *pigeonhole principle*, also known as the *shoe box argument* or *Dirichlet drawer principle*. Since there are 10 pigeons but 9 pigeonholes, so, at least one of these 9 pigeonholes, must contain at least 2 pigeons in it. Let us verify this. If each pigeonhole can contain at most one pigeon in it, then at most 9 pigeons could be accommodated and one will be left out. So, there will be at least one hole, which will contain at least 2 pigeons in it. This fact demonstrates the pigeonhole principle. In an informal way the pigeonhole principle says that if there are "many" pigeons and "a few" pigeonholes, then there must be some pigeonhole occupied by two or more pigeons. Suppose, 10 pigeons flew into a set of 9 pigeon holes to take rest.

This principle is also applicable to other objects such as balls and bags, pages and books, etc. Formally, let D and R be finite sets. If $|D| > |R|$, then for any function f from D to R, there exist $d_1, d_2 \in D$ such that $f(d_1) = f(d_2)$. Some trivial applications of the pigeonhole principle are: Among 13 people, there are at least 2 of them who were born in the same month. Here the 13 people are the pigeons, and the 12 months are the pigeonholes. Similarly, if 8 people are randomly selected from a group, then there are at least two of them who were born on the same day. Also, if 11 shoes are selected from 10 pairs of shoes there must be a pair of matched shoes among the selection. Here, the 11 shoes are the pigeons and the 10 pairs are the pigeonholes. The pigeonhole principle can be stated in a slightly more general form: For any function f from D to R, there exist i elements $d_1, \ldots, d_i$ in D, $i = \lceil |D|/|R| \rceil$, such that $f(d_1) = f(d_2) = \ldots = f(d_i)$.* (See Prob. 3.34.)

3.16.1   Extended Pigeonhole Principle

If the number of pigeons is much larger than the number of pigeonholes such as more than double the number of pigeonholes, then "Extended Pigeonhole Principle" is applied.

It says that if there are x pigeons and y pigeonholes then one pigeonhole must be occupied by at least $\lfloor (x - 1)/y \rfloor + 1$ pigeons, where $\lfloor x \rfloor$ stands for the largest integer less than or equal to x.

Proof: Suppose, each pigeonhole is occupied by maximum $\lfloor (x - 1)/y \rfloor$ pigeons. Then, there will be at most $y * \lfloor (x - 1)/y \rfloor \leq y * (x - 1)/y$ number of pigeons in total, i.e. there will be at most $x - 1$ pigeons in total. But this is a contradiction to our assumption as we must have x pigeons. Hence, one of the pigeonholes must contain at least $\lfloor (x - 1)/y \rfloor + 1$ pigeons. ■

The program for the extended pigeonhole principle is given in Fig. 3.52.

```
/*EXTENDED PIGEONHOLE PRINCIPLE*/
#include<stdio.h>
#include<conio.h>
void main()
{
    unsigned int m,n;
    clrscr();
    printf("\n\t enter number of pigeonholes: ");
    scanf("%d",&m);
    printf("\n\t enter number of pigeons: ");
    scanf("%d",&n);
    if(n>m*2)
        printf("\n\t at least one pigeonhole contains %d or more pigeons",
        ((n-1)/m)+1);
    /*here (n-1)/m will find out the greatest integer less than or equal
        to (n-1)/m since both n and m are integer type*/
    else
        printf("\n\t it does not satisfy extended pigeonhole principle");
    getch();
}

Output
    ENTER NO. OF PIGEONHOLES: 40
    ENTER NO. OF PIGEONS: 4068
    AT LEAST ONE PIGEONHOLE CONTAINS 102 OR MORE PIGEONS.
```

*Fig. 3.52 Program with output for the extended pigeonhole principle

*We use $\lceil x \rceil$ to denote the smallest integer not less than x.

Example 3.52 If 30 magazines contain a total of 61,324 pages, then one of the magazine must have at least 2045 pages.

Solution: Let us consider the pages as the pigeons and magazines as the pigeonholes. Assign each page to the magazine in which it appears. Then, by the extended pigeonhole principle, one magazine must contain at least $\lfloor(61,324 - 1)/30\rfloor + 1 = 2045$ pages. ∎

Example 3.53 Show that if seven numbers from 1 to 12 are chosen, then two of them will add up to 13.

Solution: Construct six different sets, each containing two numbers that add up to 13 as follows:

$$S_1 = (1, 12), S_2 = (2, 11), S_3 = (3, 10), S_4 = (4, 9), S_5 = (5, 8), S_6 = (6, 7).$$

Each of the seven numbers chosen must belong to one of these sets, since there are only six sets. According to the pigeonhole principle, the two of the chosen numbers will belong to the same set. These numbers add up to 13. ∎

Example 3.54 Let T be an equilateral triangle whose sides are of length 1 unit. Show that if any 5 points are chosen lying on or inside the triangle, then two of them must be no more than 1/2 unit apart.

Solution: Let T be the equilateral triangle $\triangle ABC$. We are given that $AB = BC = CA = 1$ unit. Let D, E, and F be the mid points of the sides AB, BC, CA respectively. Join DE, EF, FD. Now, we have $AD = DB = BE = EC = AF = FC = DF = DE = EF = 1/2$ unit. The triangle ABC is divided into 4 equilateral triangles ADF, DBE, EFC and DEF, each possessing sides of length 1/2 units. Now, each of the 5 points chosen must belong to one of these triangles (Pigeonholes). Here we may consider the points as the pigeons. Since there are only 4 triangles and any two points chosen from a triangle out of these 4 are not more than 1/2 unit apart, then according to Pigeonhole principle, if 5 points are chosen, then two of them must be no more than 1/2 unit apart (because two points must belong to a single triangle). ∎

Example 3.55 Ten people came forward to volunteer for a three person committee. Every possible committee of three that can be formed from these ten names is written on a slip of paper, one slip for each possible committee and the slips are put in 10 hats. Show that at least 1 hat contains 12 or more slips of paper.

Solution: Now a committee of 3 can be chosen from 10 names in C(10,3) ways that is $10!/(7! * 3!) = 120$ ways. So there are 120 slips (Pigeons) in which these committees are written. The slips are put in 10 hats (Pigeonholes). So by the extended pigeonhole principle, one hat must contain at least $\lfloor(120 - 1)/10\rfloor + 1 = 11 + 1 = 12$ or more slips of paper. ∎

Example 3.56 A store has an introductory sale on 12 types of chocolates. A customer may choose 1 chocolate of any 5 different types and will be charged no more than Rs. 1.75. Show that although different choices may cost different amounts, there must be at least two different ways to choose so that the cost will be the same for both choices.

Solution: Now the customer can choose the chocolates (pigeons) in $C(12,5)$ = 792 ways. The charge is Rs. 1.75 or 175 Paise. Now, by extended pigeonhole principle, we have $\lfloor (792 - 1)/175 \rfloor + 1 = 5$ choices having the same cost. So, there must be at least two different ways to choose, so that the cost will be the same for both choices. ∎

Example 3.57 In Example 3.56, if the store allows repetitions in the choices, show that there must be at least 10 ways to make different choices that have the same cost.

Solution: If repetitions are allowed then we have 5 groups and there are $C(12 + 5 - 1, 5) = C(16, 5) = 4368$ choices (pigeonholes). Now, by extended pigeonhole principle, at least $\lfloor 4367/175 \rfloor + 1 = 25$ choices will have the same cost. So, there are at least 10 ways to make different choices that have the same cost. ∎

Example 3.58 Show that there must be at least 90 ways to choose 6 numbers from 1 to 15 so that all the choices have the same sum.

Solution: 6 numbers out of 1 to 15 can be chosen in $C(15, 6) = 5005$ ways. Consider these as pigeons. Now, the sum varies from 21 to 75 as $(1 + 2 + 3 + 4 + 5 + 6) = 21$ and $(10 + 11 + 12 + 13 + 14 + 15) = 75$. Here, the number of sums (pigeon holes) that can be generated $= 75 - 21 + 1 = 55$. So, by extended pigeonhole principle there are $\lfloor (5005 - 1)/55 \rfloor + 1 = 91$ ways. Hence, there must be at least 90 ways to choose 6 numbers from 1 to 15 so that all the choices have the same sum. ∎

Example 3.59 Show that if 5 points are selected in a square whose sides have length 1 inch, at least two of the points must be no more than $\sqrt{2}$ inches apart.

Solution: Let $ABCD$ be the required square. Join AD and BC. Now, we can get 4 triangles: $\triangle ACD$, $\triangle BCD$, $\triangle ABC$ and $\triangle ABD$ (pigeonholes). According to pigeon hole principle, if 5 points (pigeons) are selected in the square, two points should belong to the same triangle. In any of the triangle, the largest distance would be $\sqrt{(1^2 + 1^2)} = \sqrt{2}$. So, the points must be no more than $\sqrt{2}$ inches apart. ∎

Example 3.60 Let A be an 8 * 8 Boolean matrix. If the sum of the entries in A is 51, prove that there is a row i and a column j in A such that the entries in row i and column j add up to more than 13.

Solution: The sum of the entries in A will be at most 64. Consider the 8 rows. By extended pigeonhole principle, one row must have at least $\lfloor (51 - 1)/8 \rfloor + 1 = 7$ ones. Similarly, one column must have at least 7 ones. The sum of the elements of this row and column is $7 + 7 = 14$. So the sum of the entries will add up to more than 13. ∎

Example 3.61 Prove that if any 14 numbers from 1 to 25 are chosen then one of them will be a multiple of another.

Solution: If we create 13 pigeonholes in such a way that each number chosen can be assigned to only one pigeonhole, and when the numbers x and y are assigned to the same pigeonhole, it is guaranteed that either x divides y or y divides x. There are 9 prime numbers between 1 and 25, but knowing that x and y are multiples of the same prime will not guarantee that either x divides y or y divides x. So, the proof will be as follows:

There are 13 odd numbers between 1 and 25. But we can write every positive integer n as $n = m * 2^k$, where m is odd and $k >= 0$. Now label the pigeonholes with 1, 3, 5… 25, the odd numbers between 1 and 25. Assign each of the selected 14 numbers to the pigeonholes labeled with its odd part. But, there are only 13 pigeonholes. So, by pigeonhole principle, two of them must have the same odd part.

Let us assume n_1 and n_2 have the same odd part. So $n_1 = m * 2^{K1}$ and $n_2 = m * 2^{K2}$ for some k_1 and k_2. If $k_1 > = k_2$ then n_1 is a multiple of n_2; otherwise n_2 is a multiple of n_1. ∎

Example 3.62 Prove that it is not possible to arrange the numbers 1, 2, 3, …, 10 in a circle so that every triplet of consecutively placed numbers has a sum less than 15.

Proof In any arrangement of 1, 2, 3, …, 10 in a circle, there are 10 triplets of consecutively placed numbers. Each number appears in 3 of these triplets. If the sum of each triplet were less than 15, then the total sum of all triplets would be less than 10 times 15, i.e., 150. But, $1 + 2 + 3 + … + 10$ is 55 and since each number appears in 3 triplets, the total sum should be 3 times of 55, i.e. 165. This is a contradiction. So, not all the triplets can have a sum less than 15. ∎

Example 3.63 Show that any sequence of n numbers must contain a subsequence whose sum is divisible by n.

Solution: Let us consider a sequence such as $c_1, c_2, …, c_n$. Let us consider the subsequences $c_1, (c_1, c_2), (c_1, c_2, c_3) … (c_1, c_2, c_3,…, c_n)$. If any one of the subsequences add up to some multiple of n then our proof is done. But, if none of them gives a remainder 0 then according to pigeonhole principle, with $n - 1$ remainders (pigeonholes) and n subsequences (pigeons) at least two subsequences must give same remainder. Thus, the positive difference of the two will give us a subsequence, which is divisible by n. So, any sequence of n numbers must contain a subsequence whose sum is divisible by n. ∎

In the following examples, we ask the reader to observe how the pigeonhole principle is applied, since we shall not make an explicit statement every time we use it.

Example 3.64 A chess player wants to prepare for a championship match by playing some practice games in 77 days. She wants to play at least one game a day but no more than 132 games altogether. We show now that no matter how she schedules the games there is a period of consecutive days within which she plays *exactly* 21 games. Let a_i denote the total number of games she plays up through the ith day. Clearly, the sequence $a_1, a_2, \ldots, a_{77}$ is a monotonically increasing sequence, with $a_1 \geq 1$ and $a_{77} \leq 132$. Let us compute the sequence $a_1 + 21, a_2 + 21, \ldots, a_{77} + 21$, which again is a monotonically increasing sequence with $a_{77} + 21 \geq 153$. Since the values of the 154 numbers $a_1, a_2, \ldots, a_{77}, a_1 + 21, \ldots, a_{77} + 21$ range from 1 to 153, two of them must be the same. Moreover, because both the sequence $a_1, a_2, \ldots, a_{77}$ and the sequence $a_1 + 21, a_2 + 21, \ldots, a_{77} + 21$ are monotonically increasing, we have $a_i = a_j + 21$ for some a_i and a_j. ■

Example 3.65 We want to show that in a sequence of $n^2 + 1$ distinct integers, there is either an increasing subsequence of length $n + 1$ or a decreasing subsequence of length $n + 1$. Let $a_1, a_2, \ldots, a_{n^2+1}$ denote the sequence of integers. Let us label the integer a_k with an ordered pair (x_k, y_k), where x_k is the length of a longest increasing subsequence starting at a_k and y_k is the length of a longest decreasing subsequence starting at a_k. Suppose there is no increasing subsequence or decreasing subsequence of length $n + 1$ in the sequence $a_1, a_2, \ldots, a_{n^2+1}$. That is, the values of x_k and y_k lie between 1 and n for $k = 1, 2, \ldots, n^2 + 1$. With only n^2 distinct ordered pairs as possible labels for the $n^2 + 1$ integers, there must exist a_i and a_j in the sequence that are labeled with the same ordered pair. However, this is impossible because if $a_i < a_j$, we must have $x_i > x_j$; and if $a_i > a_j$, we must have $y_i > y_j$. Consequently, we conclude that there is either an increasing subsequence or a decreasing subsequence of length $n + 1$ in the sequence $a_1, a_2, \ldots, a_{n^2+1}$.* ■

Example 3.66 We want to show that among six persons, either there are three persons who are mutual friends or there are three persons who are complete strangers to each other. Let A be a person in the group. According to the pigeonhole principle, either there are three (or more) persons who are friends of A or there are three (or more) persons who are strangers to A. Let us consider the former case only, since the latter case can be resolved by a similar argument. Let B, C, D denote the friends of A. If any two of B, C, D know each other, then these two, together with A, form a friendly threesome. On the other hand, if no two of B, C, D know each other then they are three persons who are complete strangers to each other. ■

Example 3.67 A rooming house has 90 rooms and 100 guests. Keys are to be issued to the guests so that any 90 guests can have access to the 90 rooms in the sense that each guest will have a key to an unoccupied room. (In other words, we can assign the 90 rooms to any 90 guests so that every guest has a key to the room he is assigned.) We want to use a scheme that will minimize the total number of keys. Although the following scheme seems to be wasteful, it turns out to be a minimal scheme. Ninety of the guests will be given one key each so that

---

* See Prob. 3.41 for a slightly different argument. See also Prob. 3.42.

together they will have access to the 90 rooms. Each of the remaining 10 guests will be given 90 keys, one key to each of the 90 rooms. Clearly such a scheme, which uses a total of 990 keys, works. To show that this is a minimal scheme, we observe that, if 989 or fewer keys were issued, there is a room that has at most 10 outstanding keys. Clearly, the scheme fails when none of the holders of the keys to this room are among the 90 guests. ∎

Example 3.68 The circumference of the two concentric disks are divided into 200 sections each, as shown in Fig. 3.53. For the outer disk, 100 of the sections are painted red and 100 of the sections are painted blue. For the inner disk the sections are painted red or blue in an arbitrary manner. Show that it is possible to align the two disks so that 100 or more of the sections on the inner disk have their colors matched with the corresponding sections on the outer disk. Let us hold the outer disk fixed and rotate the inner disk through the 200 possible alignments. For each alignment, let us count the number of matches. We note that the sum of the counts for the 200 possible alignments is 20,000, because each of the 200 sections on the inner disk

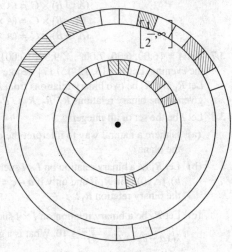

Fig. 3.53

will match its corresponding section on the outer disk in exactly 100 of the alignments. Therefore, there must be an alignment in which there are 100 or more matches. ∎

Problems

3.1 Let A denote the set of shirts and B denote the set of slacks a man owns. What possible interpretation can be given to the cartesian product $A \times B$? To a binary relation from A to B?

3.2 Let $A = \{1, 2\}$. Construct the set $\mathscr{P}(A) \times A$.

3.3 (a) Given that $A \subseteq C$ and $B \subseteq D$, show that $A \times B \subseteq C \times D$.

(b) Given that $A \times B \subseteq C \times D$, does it necessarily follow that $A \subseteq C$ and $B \subseteq D$?

3.4 (a) Let A be an arbitrary set. Is the set $A \times \phi$ well defined?

(b) Given that $A \times B = \phi$, what can one say about the sets A and B?

(c) Is it possible that $A \subseteq A \times A$ for some set A?

3.5 Let A, B, C, D be arbitrary sets.

(a) Show that

$$(A \cap B) \times (C \cap D) = (A \times C) \cap (B \times D)$$

(b) Confirm or disprove the following identities:

$$(A \cup B) \times (C \cup D) = (A \times C) \cup (B \times D)$$
$$(A - B) \times (C - D) = (A \times C) - (B \times D)$$
$$(A \oplus B) \times (C \oplus D) = (A \times C) \oplus (B \times D)$$

3.6 Let A, B, C be arbitrary sets

(a) Show that

$$(A \cap B) \times C = (A \times C) \cap (B \times C)$$

(b) Confirm or disprove the following identities:

$$(A \cup B) \times C = (A \times C) \cup (B \times C)$$
$$(A - B) \times C = (A \times C) - (B \times C)$$
$$(A \oplus B) \times C = (A \times C) \oplus (B \times C)$$

3.7 Let $A = \{6:00, 6:30, 7:00, \ldots, 9:30, 10:00\}$ denote the set of nine half-hour periods in the evening. Let $B = \{3, 12, 15, 17\}$ denote the set of the four local television channels. Let R_1 and R_2 be two binary relations from A to B. What possible interpretations can be given to the binary relations R_1, R_2, $R_1 \cup R_2$, $R_1 \cap R_2$ $R_1 \oplus R_2$, and $R_1 - R_2$?

3.8 Let I be the set of all integers.

(a) Is there a natural way to interpret the ordered pairs in $I \times I$ as geometric points in the plane?

(b) Let R_1 be a binary relation on $I \times I$ such that the ordered pair (of ordered pairs) $((a, b), (c, d))$ is in R_1 if and only if $a - c = b - d$. What is a geometric interpretation of the binary relation R_1?

(c) Let R_2 be a binary relation on $I \times I$ such that $((a, b), (c, d))$ is in R_2 if and only if $\sqrt{(a - c)^2 + (b - d)^2} \leq 10$. What is a geometric interpretation of R_2? of $R_1 \cup R_2$? of $R_1 \cap R_2$? of $R_1 - R_2$? of $R_1 \oplus R_2$?

3.9 Let A be a set of workers and B be a set of jobs. Let R_1 be a binary relation from A to B such that (a, b) is in R_1 if worker a is assigned to job b. (We assume that a worker might be assigned to more than one job and more than one worker might be assigned to the same job.) Let R_2 be a binary relation on A such that (a_1, a_2) is in R_2 if a_1 and a_2 can get along with each other if they were assigned to the same job. State a condition in terms of R_1, R_2 and (possibly) binary relations derived from R_1 and R_2 such that an assignment of the workers to the jobs according to R_1 will not put workers that cannot get along with one another on the same job.

3.10 Let A be a set of books.

(a) Let R_1 be a binary relation on A such that (a, b) is in R_1 if book a costs more and contains fewer pages than book b. In general, is R_1 reflexive? Symmetric? Antisymmetric? Transitive?

(b) Let R_2 be a binary relation on A such that (a, b) is in R_2 if book a costs more or contains fewer pages than book b. In general, is R_2 reflexive? Symmetric? Antisymmetric? Transitive?

3.11 (a) Let R be a binary relation on the set of all positive integers such that

$$R = \{(a, b) \mid a - b \text{ is an odd positive integer}\}$$

Is R reflexive? Symmetric? Antisymmetric? Transitive? An equivalence relation? A partial ordering relation?

(b) Repeat part (a) if $R = \{(a, b) \mid a = b^2\}$

3.12 Let P be the set of all people. Let R be a binary relation on P such that (a, b) is in R if a is a brother of b. (Disregard half-brothers and fraternity brothers.) Is R reflexive? Symmetric? Antisymmetric? Transitive? An equivalence relation? A partial ordering relation?

3.13 Let R be a binary relation on the set of all strings of 0s and 1s such that $R = \{(a, b) | a$ and b are strings that have the same number of 0s}. Is R reflexive? Symmetric? Antisymmetric? Transitive? An equivalence relation? A partial ordering relation?

3.14 Use the fact that "better than" is a transitive binary relation to prove the claim. "A ham sandwich is better than eternal happiness."

Hint: Nothing is better than eternal happiness.

3.15 Let A be a set with 10 distinct elements.

(a) How many different binary relations on A are there?

(b) How many of them are reflexive?

(c) How many of them are symmetric?

(d) How many of them are reflexive and symmetric?

(e) How many of them are total ordering relations?

3.16 Let R be a symmetric and transitive relation on a set A. Show that if for every a in A there exists b in A such that (a, b) is in R, then R is an equivalence relation.

3.17 Let R be a transitive and reflexive relation on A. Let T be a relation on A such that (a, b) is in T if and only if both (a, b) and (b, a) are in R. Show that T is an equivalence relation.

3.18 Let R be a binary relation. Let $S = \{(a, b) | (a, c) \in R$ and $(c, b) \in R$ for some $c\}$. Show that if R is an equivalence relation then S is also an equivalence relation.

3.19 Let R be a reflexive relation on a set A. Show that R is an equivalence relation if and only if (a, b) and (a, c) are in R implies that (b, c) is in R.

3.20 A binary relation on a set that is reflexive and symmetric is called a *compatible relation*.

(a) Let A be a set of people and R be a binary relation on A such that (a, b) is in R if a is a friend of b. Show that R is a compatible relation.

(b) Let A be a set of English words and R be a binary relation on A such that two words in A are related if they have one or more letters in common. Show that R is a compatible relation.

(c) Give more examples of compatible relations.

(d) Let R_1 and R_2 be two compatible relations on A. Is $R_1 \cap R_2$ a compatible relation? Is $R_1 \cup R_2$ a compatible relation?

(e) Let A be a set. A *cover* of A is a set of nonempty subsets of A, $\{A_1, A_2 ..., A_k\}$, such that the union of the A_i's is equal to A. Suggest a way to define a compatible relation on A from a cover of A. Give an interpretation of the notion of a cover in terms of the example in part (a).

(f) Suggest a way to define a cover of A from a compatible relation on A. Does your suggested way define *uniquely* a cover of A?

3.21 (a) Show that the transitive closure of a symmetric relation is symmetric.

(b) Is the transitive closure of an antisymmetric relation always antisymmetric?

(c) Show that the transitive closure of a compatible relation (see Prob. 3.20) is an equivalence relation.

3.22 Let R be a binary relation from A to B. The *converse* of R, denoted R^{-1} is a binary relation from B to A such that

$$R^{-1} = \{(b, a)(a, b) \in R\}$$

(a) Let R_1 and R_2 be binary relations from A to B. Is it true that $(R_1 \cup R_2)^{-1} = R_1^{-1} \cup R_2^{-1}$?

(b) Let R be a binary relation on A. If R is reflexive, is R^{-1} necessarily reflexive? If R is symmetric, is R^{-1} necessarily symmetric? If R is transitive, is R^{-1}, necessarily transitive?

3.23 Let R be a binary relation on A. Let $R_1, R_2, \ldots, R_i, \ldots$ be the successive transitive extensions of R as defined in Sec. 4.3. Prove by induction that if (a, b) is in R_i, there exist n elements in A, $n \leq 2^i - 1$, $x_1, x_2, \ldots, x_n$ such that $(a, x\}, (x_1, x_2), \ldots, (x_{n-1}, x_n), (x_n, b)$ are all in R.

3.24 (a) Let R be an equivalence relation on a set A. Let $\{A_1, A_2, \ldots, A_k\}$ be a set of subsets of A such that $A_i \not\subseteq A_j$ for $i \neq j$ and such that a and b are contained in one of the subsets if and only if the ordered pair (a, b) is in R. Show that $\{A_1, A_2, \ldots, A_k\}$ is a partition of A.

(b) Let $\{A_1, A_2, \ldots, A_k\}$ be a partition of a set A. We define a binary relation R on A such that an ordered pair (a, b) is in R if and only if a and b are in the same block of the partition. Show that R is an equivalence relation.

3.25 Suppose S and T are two sets and f is a function from S to T. Let R_1 be an equivalence relation on T. Let R_2 be a binary relation on S such that $(x, y) \in R_2$ if and only if $(f(x), f(y)) \in R_1$. Show that R_2 is also an equivalence relation.

3.26 Let A be a set and f be a function from A to A. A partition π of A is said to have the *substitution property* with respect to f if for any two elements a and b that are together in one block of π the two elements $f(a)$ and $f(b)$ are also together in one block of π. Let $A = \{1, 2, 3, 4, 5, 6\}$. Let f be a function from A to A such that $f(1) = 3, f(2) = 3, f(3) = 2, f(4) = 5, f(5) = 4, f(6) = 4$.

(a) Does $\pi_1 = \{\overline{123}, \overline{456}\}$ have the substitution property with respect to f? How about $\pi_2 = \{\overline{16}, \overline{25}, \overline{34}\}$? $\pi_3 = \{\overline{12}, \overline{34}, \overline{56}\}$?

(b) Let A be the set of integers and π be a partition of A into even and odd integers. Let $f(a) = a + 1$ for every a in A. Does π have the substitution property with respect to f? Let

$$g(a) = \begin{cases} \dfrac{a}{2} & \text{if } a \text{ is even} \\ \dfrac{a-1}{2} & \text{if } a \text{ is odd} \end{cases}$$

Does π have the substitution property with respect to g?

(c) Let π_1 and π_2 be two partitions that have the substitution property with respect to f. Show that both $\pi_1 \cdot \pi_2$ and $\pi_1 + \pi_2$ also have the substitution property with respect to f.

3.27 Let $(A, \leq)$ be a partially ordered set. Let $\leq_R$ be a binary relation on A such that for a and b in A, $a \leq_R b$ if and only if $b \leq a$.

(a) Show that $\leq_R$ is a partial ordering relation.

(b) Show that if $(A, \leq)$ is a lattice then $(A, \leq_R)$ is also a lattice.

3.28 For a given set A, consider the relation

$$R = \{(x, y) \mid x \in \mathcal{P}(A), y \in \mathcal{P}(A), \text{ and } x \subseteq y\}$$

(a) Show that R is a partial ordering relation.

(b) What is the length of the longest chain in the partially ordered set $(\mathcal{P}(A), R)$?

3.29 Is the cartesian product of two lattices always a lattice? Prove your claim.

3.30 Let P be an arbitrary partially ordered set, and L be a chain of two elements. Let Q denote the cartesian product $P \times L$. Let A be an antichain in Q. Let B be a largest possible subset of P such that B does not contain a chain of length exceeding 2. Show that $|A| \leq |B|$.

3.31 The procedure of scheduling a set of tasks according to the rule of never leaving a processor idle intentionally discussed in Sec. 3.9 did not specify how ties can be broken when several executable tasks compete for a free processor. One way to break ties is to assign distinct priorities to the tasks, and schedule a task that has the highest priority among all executable tasks at any time instant on a processor that is free at that time instant. For example, the set of tasks shown in Fig. 3P.1 is to be executed on a computing system with three processors. Let us assign priorities in decreasing order to the tasks T_1, T_2, T_3, T_4, T_5, T_6, T_7, T_8, T_9.

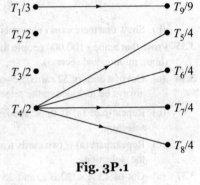

(a) Construct the corresponding schedule.

(b) Suppose we remove the arrows between T_4 and T_5 and between T_4 and T_6 in Fig. 3P.1. Construct the corresponding schedule.

(c) Suppose we reduce the execution time of each task by 1. Construct the corresponding schedule.

(d) Suppose we execute the set of tasks on a computing system with four processors. Construct the corresponding schedule.

Fig. 3P.1

(This problem illustrates some of the *anomalies* when tasks are scheduled according to the rule of never leaving a processor intentionally idle.)

3.32 Let f be a function from A to B and g be a function from B to C. We can define a function h from A to C such that for every a in A, $h(a) = g(f(a))$. h is called the *composition* of f and g and is denoted $g \circ f$.

(a) For the functions f and g in Fig. 3P.2, determine $g \circ f$

(b) For the functions f, g, and h in Fig. 3P.2, determine $h \circ (g \circ f)$ and $(h \circ g) \circ f$.

(c) Show that for any functions f, g, and h, $h \circ (g \circ f) = (h \circ g) \circ f$.

(d) State a necessary and sufficient condition on f and g so that:

    1. $g \circ f$ is an onto function;

    2. $g \circ f$ is a one-to-one function;

    3. $g \circ f$ is one-to-one onto function.

(e) Construct an example to show that for two functions f and g from A to A, in general, $f \circ g \neq g \circ f$.

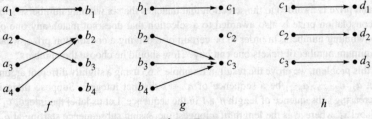

Fig. 3P.2

3.33 Let f, g, h be functions from N to N, where N is the set of natural numbers so that

$$f(n) = n + 1$$
$$g(n) = 2n$$
$$h(n) = \begin{cases} 0 & n \text{ is even} \\ 1 & n \text{ is odd} \end{cases}$$

Determine $f \circ f$, $f \circ g$, $g \circ f$, $g \circ h$, $h \circ g$, $(f \circ g) \circ h$.

3.34 Let f be a function from D to R. Suppose that $|D| > |R|$.

(a) Let i be the quotient and r be the remainder when $|D|$ is divided by $|R|$. Show that

$$\left\lceil \frac{|D|}{|R|} \right\rceil = \begin{cases} i + 1 & \text{if } r \neq 0 \\ i & \text{if } r = 0 \end{cases}$$

(b) Show that there exist i elements $d_1, d_2, \ldots, d_i$ in D such that $f(d_1) = f(d_2) = \ldots = f(d_i)$.

3.35 Prove that among 100,000 people there are two who were born at exactly the same time (hour, minute, and second).

3.36 (a) Out of a deck of 52 cards, how many cards must be chosen so that three spades will always be included in the selection.

(b) Repeat part (a) if three spades and three hearts will always be included in the selection.

(c) Repeat part (a) if two cards from each of *any* two suits will always be included in the selection.

3.37 (a) Out of 15 A's, 20 B's, and 25 C's, how many letters must be chosen so that 12 identical letters will always be included in the selection?

(b) Repeat part (a) if there are 15 A's, 20 B's, 25 C's, 10 D's, and 8 E's.

(c) Repeat part (b) if the D's are considered "wild cards." (That is, i D's together with $12 - i$ of anyone of the other four letters are also considered as 12 "identical letters.")

3.38 How many numbers must be chosen from the integers 10, 11, 12, 13, ..., 97, 98, 99 so that at least a multiple of 3 is included in the selection? So that two numbers with the same first digit are included in the selection? So that two numbers with at least one digit in common (for example, 12 and 52, 12 and 25) are included in the selection?

3.39 There are 35,000 students at the university. Each of them takes four (distinct) courses. The university offers 999 different courses. When a student who has taken a course in discrete mathematics learned that the largest classroom holds only 135 students, she realized that there is a problem. What is the problem?

3.40 To play the game Lotto, one buys a ticket and selects 6 out of the 44 numbers 1, 2, 3, ..., 44. Subsequently, 6 of the 44 numbers are drawn as the winning numbers, and the grand prize is awarded to the selection that matches the six winning numbers. Suppose a consolation prize is also awarded to a selection that does not match any one of the six winning numbers. In order to be certain of receiving a consolation prize, what is a minimum number of tickets one can buy? How should he choose the numbers?

3.41 In this problem, we prove the result in Example 3.65 using a slightly different argument. Let $a_1, a_2, \ldots, a_{n^2+1}$ be a sequence of $n^2 + 1$ distinct integers. Suppose there is no increasing subsequence of length $n + 1$ in the sequence. Let us label the integer a_k with a label x_k, where x_k is the length of a longest increasing subsequence starting at a_k, $1 \leq k \leq n^2 + 1$.

    (a) What is the significance of a chain in the partially ordered set? Of an antichain?

    (b) Show that these integers form a decreasing subsequence.

3.42 In this problem we show how we can apply Corollary 3.1.1 to prove the result in Example 3.65. Let $a_1, a_2, \ldots, a_{n^2+1}$ be a sequence of $n^2 + 1$ distinct integers. We define a partial ordering relation $\leqq$ over the $n^2 + 1$ ordered pairs (a_i, i) such that $(a_i, i) \leqq (a_j, j)$ if and only if $a_i \leqq a_j$ and $i \leqq j$.

    (a) What is the significance of a chain in the partially ordered set of an antichain?

    (b) Apply Corollary 4.1.1 to prove the result in Example 3.65.

3.43 Show that one of any m consecutive integers is divisible by m.

3.44 Show that the decimal expansion of a rational number must, after some point, become periodic.

3.45 A man hiked for 10 hours and covered a total distance of 45 miles. It is known that he hiked 6 miles in the first hour and only 3 miles in the last hour. Show that he must have hiked at least 9 miles within a certain period of two consecutive hours.

3.46 The circumference of a "roulette wheel" is divided into 36 sectors to which the numbers $1, 2, \ldots, 36$ are assigned in some arbitrary manner. Show that there are three consecutive sectors such that the sum of their assigned numbers is at least 56.

3.47 Let $x_1, x_2, \ldots, x_n$ be n arbitrary integers. Show that $x_i + x_{i+1} + x_{i+2} + \ldots x_{i+k}$ is divisible by n for some i and k, $i \leqq 1, k \geqq 0$.

3.48 From the integers 1–200, 101 of them are chosen arbitrarily. Show that, among the chosen numbers, there exist two such that one divides another.

3.49 Show that for an arbitrary integer N, there exists a multiple of N that contains only the digits 0 and 7. (For example, for $N = 3$, we have $259 \times 3 = 777$; for $N = 4$, we have $1925 \times 4 = 7700$; for $N = 5$, we have $14 \times 5 = 70$; for $N = 6$, we have $1295 \times 6 = 7770$.)

  Hint: Consider the remainders when the following integers are divided by N: 7, 77,

$$777, 7777, \ldots, \underbrace{777 \ldots 77}_{N}.$$

3.50 (a) Show that among $n + 1$ arbitrarily chosen integers, there are two whose difference is divisible by n.

    (b) Show that among $n + 2$ arbitrarily chosen integers, either there are two whose difference is divisible by $2n$ or there are two whose sum is divisible by $2n$.

3.51 Consider a sequence of N positive integers containing precisely n distinct integers. If $N \geqq 2n$, show that there is a consecutive block of integers in the sequence whose product is a perfect square. (For example, in the sequence $3, 7, 5, 3, 7, 3, 5, 7$; $7 \cdot 5 \cdot 3 \cdot 7 \cdot 3 \cdot 5$ is a perfect square.)

3.52 Show that among $n + 1$ positive integers less than or equal to $2n$ there are two of them that are relatively prime.

3.53 Let $a_1, a_2, \ldots, a_n$ and $b_1, b_2, \ldots, b_n$ be $2n$ distinct numbers such that $a_i < b_i, i = 1, 2, \ldots, n$. Suppose that $a_1, a_2, \ldots, a_n$ are rearranged as $a'_1, a'_2, \ldots, a'_n$ such that $a'_1 > a'_2 > \ldots > a'_n$ and $b_1, b_2, \ldots, b_n$ are rearranged as $b'_1, b'_2, \ldots, b'_n$ such that $b'_1 > b'_2 > \ldots > b'_n$. Show that $a'_1 < b'_1, i = 1, 2, \ldots, n$.

3.54 The following procedure can be used to select the larger n of $2n$ distinct numbers:

    1. Arrange n of the $2n$ numbers in ascending order. Denote these numbers $a_1, a_2, \ldots, a_n$ such that $a_i < a_2 < a_3 < \ldots < a_n$.

    2. Arrange the remaining n numbers in descending order. Denote these numbers $b_1, b_2, \ldots, b_n$ such that $b_1 > b_2 > b_3 > \ldots > b_n$.

3. Compare a_i and b_i and select the larger one of the two for $i = 1, 2, \ldots, n$.

For example, given eight numbers 4, 2, 7, 6, 5, 3, 1, 8:

1. Arrange 4, 2, 7, 6 in ascending order: $2 < 4 < 6 < 7$.

2. Arrange 5, 3, 1, 8 in descending order: $8 > 5 > 3 > 1$.

3. Compare 2 and 8; select 8. Compare 4 and 5; select 5. Compare 6 and 3; select 6. Compare 7 and 1; select 7.

Prove the procedure is correct.

Hint: Show that exactly one of a_i, and b_i, is among the larger n of the $2n$ numbers.

3.55   (a) Let $A = \{1, 2, 3, 4, 5\}$. If $R = \{(a, b) | a \in A \wedge b \in A \wedge ((a - b)$ is an integral nonzero multiple of 2)$\}$ and $S = \{(a, b) | a \in A \wedge b \in A \wedge ((a - b)$ is an integral nonzero multiple of 3)$\}$, find $R \cup S$ and $R \cap S$.

     (b) If $A = \{1, 2, 3, \ldots\}$, what is $R \cap S$ for R and S as defined in (a)?

3.56   Let $A = \{1, 2, 3, 4\}$ and $R = \{(a, b) | a > b\}$. Draw the graph of R and also give its relation matrix.

3.57   Let $A = \{1, 2, \ldots 7\}$ and $R = \{(a, b) | a - b$ is divisible by 3$\}$. Show that R is an equivalence relation. Draw the graph of R.

3.58   Let R be an equivalence relation on a set A. For any $a \in A$, the set $[a]_R \subseteq A$ given by $[a]_R = \{b \mid b \in A \wedge a \, R \, b\}$ is called an R-equivalence class generated by $a \in A$.

Let I be the set of integers and let R be the relation called "congruence modulo 4" defined by $R = \{(a, b) \mid a \in I \wedge b \in I \wedge (a - b)$ is divisible by 4$\}$.

Determine the equivalence classes generated by the elements of I.

3.59   Let A be the set of all statement functions in n variables and let R be the relation given by $R = \{(a, b) | a \in A \wedge b \in A \wedge a \Leftrightarrow b \}$.

Here, $a \Leftrightarrow b$ represents that the statement a is equivalent to the statement b. Find out the equivalence classes generated by the elements of A.

3.60   Let $A = \{a, b, c, d, e\}$ and let $P = \{\{a, b\}, \{c\}, \{d, e\}\}$. Show that the partition P defines an equivalence relation on A.

3.61   Let $R = \{(1, 2), (3, 4), (2, 2)\}$ and $S = \{(4, 2), (2, 5), (3, 1), (1, 3)\}$. Find $R \circ S$, $S \circ R$, $R \circ (S \circ R)$, $(R \circ S) \circ R$, $R \circ R$, $S \circ S$ and $R \circ R \circ R$.

3.62   Let N be the set of natural numbers including zero. Determine which of the following functions are one-to-one, which are onto, and which are one-to-one onto.

     (a) $f: N \to N$ $f(j) = j^2 + 2$

     (b) $f: N \to N$ $f(j) = j \,(\text{mod } 3)$

     (c) $f: N \to N$ $f(j) = \begin{cases} 1 j & \text{is odd} \\ 0 j & \text{is even} \end{cases}$

3.63   Let I be the set of integers, I_+ be the set of positive integers, and $I_n = \{0, 1, 2, \ldots p - 1\}$. Determine which of the following functions are one-to-one, which are onto and which are one-to-one-onto.

     (a) $f: I \to I$ $f(j) = \begin{cases} j/2 & j \text{ is odd} \\ j(-1)/2 & j \text{ is even} \end{cases}$

     (b) $f: I_+ \to I_+$ $f(x) = $ greatest integer $\leq \sqrt{x}$

     (c) $f: I_7 \to I_7$ $f(x) = 3x \,(\text{mod } 7)$.

3.64   Let $A = \{2, 3, 6, 12, 24, 36\}$ and the relation $\leq$ be such that $a \leq b$ if a divides b. Draw the Hasse diagram of $(A, \leq)$.

3.65 Let A be a given finite set and $p(A)$ its power set. Let $\subseteq$ be the inclusion relation on the elements of $p(A)$. Draw the Hasse diagrams of $(p(A), \subseteq)$ for (i) $A = \{a\}$; (ii) $A = \{a, b\}$; (iii) $A = \{a, b, c\}$; (iv) $A = \{a, b, c, d\}$.

3.66 Give an example of a set A, such that $(p(A), \subseteq)$, (where $p(A)$ is the power set of A), is a totally ordered set.

3.67 Write a relation which is both a partial ordering relation and an equivalence relation on a set.

3.68 Let A be the set of factors of a particular positive integer n and let R be the relation divides, i.e.

$$R = \{(a, b) | a \in A \land b \in A \land (a \text{ divides } b)\}$$

Draw the Hasse diagrams for (i) $n = 2$; (ii) $n = 6$; (iii) $n = 30$; (iv) $n = 210$; (v) $n = 12$; and (vi) $n = 45$.

3.69 Let $f_1: R \to R$ and $f_2: R \to R$ where R is the set of real numbers. Compute $f_1 \circ f_2$ and $f_2 \circ f_1$, where $f_1(y) = y^2 - 2$ and $f_2(y) = y + 4$. Determine whether these functions are one-to-one, onto, or one-to-one onto?

3.70 If $f: A \to B$ and $g: B \to C$ and both f and g are onto, show that $g \circ f$ is also onto. Is $g \circ f$ one-to-one if both g and f are one-to-one?

3.71 Let N be the set of natural numbers including zero. Determine which of the following functions are one-to-one, onto and which are both.

(a) $f: N \to N$, $\quad f(x) = x^2 + 2$

(b) $f: N \to N$, $\quad f(x) = x \pmod 3$

(c) $f: N \to N$, $\quad f(x) = \begin{cases} 1 & x \text{ is odd} \\ 0 & x \text{ is even} \end{cases}$

3.72 Let $A = \{a, b, c\}$, $B = \{0, 1\}$.

Determine all possible functions from A to B. State whether these functions are one-to-one, onto or both.

3.73 Give an example of a relation which is neither reflexive nor irreflexive.

3.74 Give an example of a relation which is both symmetric and antisymmetric.

3.75 If the relations R and S are, show that $R \cup S$ and $R \cap S$ are also reflexive.

3.76 If the relations R and S are reflexive, symmetric, and transitive, then show that $R \cap S$ is also reflexive, symmetric, and transitive.

3.77 Let R denote a relation on the set of ordered pairs of positive integers such that $<x, y> R$ $<u, v>$ iff $xv = yu$. Show that R is an equivalence relation.

3.78 If the function f and g are defined as $f(x) e^x = e^x$ and $g(x) = 3x - 2$, where $f: R \to R$ and $g: R \to R$, then find the function $f \circ g$ and $g \circ f$. Also find $(f \circ g)^{-1}$ and $(g \circ f)^{-1}$.

3.79 If $f: R \to R$; $f(x) = x^2$ and $g: R \to R$; $g(x) = 2x + 1$. Then find $f \circ g$ and $g \circ f$ and show that $f \circ g \neq g \circ f$.

3.80 Let $g(x) = 1 + x - [x]$ and $f(x) = \begin{cases} -1 & x < 0 \\ 0, & x = 0 \\ 1, & x > 0 \end{cases}$. Then for all x find $f(g(x))$.

3.81 Let $f(x) = \begin{cases} x + 1, & 0 \le x \le 2 \\ 3 - x, & 2 \le x \le 3 \end{cases}$. Find $(f \circ f)(x)$.

3.82 Let $f(x) = \begin{cases} x+1, & x \le 1 \\ 2x-1, & 1 < x \le 2 \end{cases}$ and Let $g(x) = \begin{cases} x^2 & -1 < x < 2 \\ x+2, & 2 \le x \le 3 \end{cases}$

Find $(f \circ g)(x)$.\

3.83 If $f(x) = -3x + 2$, $g(x) = |x - 4|$, then find $f \circ g(-2)$.

3.84 $F(x) = (x-1)/(x+2)$, $g(x) = (x+1)/(x-2)$. Find $f \circ g(x)$.

3.85 If $f(x) = x^2 + 2$, $g(x) = \sqrt{x-2}$, find $f \circ g(x)$.

3.86 If $f(x) = x + 1$, $g(x) = 3x$, find $f \circ g(x)$.

3.87 If $f(x) = x^2 + 1$, $g(x) = \sqrt{2x}$, find $f \circ g(x)$.

3.88 $f(x) = \sqrt{-x+1}$, $g(x) = x^2 - 8$. Find $f \circ g(x)$.

3.89 If $f(x) = 2x + 1$, $g(x) = x^2$, find $f \circ g(-2)$.

3.90 If $f(x) = 1/(x+1)$, $g(x) = 1/(x-1)$, find $f \circ g(x)$.

3.91 If $f(x) = 2x$, $g(x) = 3x^2 + 1$, find $f \circ g(x)$.

3.92 If $f(x) = 1/(x+2)$, $g(x) = x/(x-3)$, find $f \circ g(x)$.

3.93 If $f(x) = x + 2$, $g(x) = x^2$, find $f \circ g(x)$.

3.94 If $f(x) = \log_3 x$ and $g(x) = x^4$, find $f \circ g(x)$ and $g \circ f(x)$.

3.95 $f(x) = \sqrt{\sin 2x}$, $g(x) = \sqrt{x}$. Find $f \circ g(x)$ and $g \circ f(x)$.

3.96 Given $f = \{(a, b), (b, a), (c, b)\}$ is a function from x to x where $x = \{a, b, c\}$. Find $f \circ f$ and $f \circ f$ of as sets of ordered pairs.

3.97 $f(x) = x^2$ and $g(x) = 2^x$

Find $f \circ f(x)$, $g \circ g(x)$, $f \circ g(x)$, $g \circ f(x)$.

3.98 Let $f(x) = [2x]$ and $g(x) = x^2$ are the function from R^+ to R^+. Find $f \circ f(x)$, $g \circ g(x)$, $f \circ g(x)$, $g \circ f(x)$.

3.99 Let $f(x) \log_2 x^2$ and $g(x) = 2^x$. Find $f \circ g(x)$, $g \circ f(x)$.

3.100 Let $f(x) = [x]$ and $g(x) = (x-1)/2$. Find $f \circ g(-2)$ and $g \circ f(-2)$ and check whether $f \circ g(-2)$ and $g \circ f(-2)$ are equal or not.

3.101 If $f(x) = e^{x+a}$, $g(x) = x^{b^2}$ and $h(x) = e^{b^2} x$. Prove that $g \circ f(x)/h(x) = e^{ab^2}$.

3.102 If $f(x) = \dfrac{|x|}{x}$, $g(x) = -x^2$, find $f \circ g(x)$ and $g \circ f(x)$.

3.103 Let $X = Y = Z =$ the set of real numbers. Let R and S be the relations from X to Y and Y to Z, respectively, which are defined as follows: $R = \{(a, b) | a \le 2b\}$, $S = \{(b, c) | b \le 3c\}$. Compute $S \circ R$. Is $(1, 5) \in S \circ R$? Is $(2, 3) \in S \circ R$?

3.104 Use Warshall's algorithm to find the transitive closures of the following relations on $A = \{1, 2, 3, 4\}$.

   (i) $\{(1, 2), (2, 1), (2, 3), (3, 4), (4, 1)\}$

   (ii) $\{(2, 1), (2, 3), (3, 1), (3, 4), (4, 1), (4, 3)\}$

   (iii) $\{(1, 2), (1, 3), (1, 4), (2, 3), (2, 4), (3, 4)\}$

   (iv) $\{(1, 1), (1, 4), (2, 1), (2, 3), (3, 1), (3, 2), (3, 4), (4, 2)\}$

3.105 Use Warshall's algorithm to find the transitive closures of the following relations on $A = \{a, b, c, d, e\}$.

   (i) $\{(a, c), (b, d), (c, a), (d, b), (e, d)\}$

   (ii) $\{(a, d), (d, c), (c, d), (c, a), (b, c), (b, a)\}$

(iii) $\{(b, c), (b, e), (c, e), (d, a), (e, b), (e, c)\}$

(iv) $\{(a, b), (a, c), (a, e), (b, a), (b, c), (c, a), (c, b), (d, a), (e, d)\}$

3.106 Suppose that the relation R is reflexive. Show that R^* is reflexive.

3.107 Suppose that the relation R is symmetric. Show that R^* is symmetric.

Find inverse of the quadratic functions given below.

3.108 $f(x) = 2(x - 2)^2 + 3$, for $x \le 2$.

3.109 $f(x) = -2x^2 + 4x + 2$, for $x \ge 1$

3.110 $f(x) = (x - 3)^2 + 3$, for $x \ge 3$

3.111 $f(x) = -x^2 + 4x - 4$, for $x \le 2$

Find the inverse of the following functions.

3.112 $f(x) = x^3 + 2$

3.113 $f(x) = (x - 3)x^2$

3.114 $f(x) = x^3 + 3x^2 + 3x$

3.115 $f(x) = x^{1/3}$

3.116 $f(x) = 6 - \dfrac{x}{2}$

3.117 $f(x) = 1 - 2x^3$

3.118 $f(x) = 3x - 2$

3.119 $-x^2 + 2, x \ge 0$

3.120 $-x^2 - 2x, x \ge 1$

3.121 $2/x$

3.122 $\dfrac{x + 1}{x - 1}$

3.123 $\sqrt{x - 1}$

3.124 $(x + 1)^{1/3}$

3.125 $\ln(x)$

3.126 $e^{x-1} + 3$

3.127 $\ln(x + 2) - 3$

3.128 $2 \ln(x + 4) - 4$

3.129 $2x + 3$

3.130 $-x - 4$

3.131 $(x - 3)^2$, if $x \ge 3$

3.132 If $f: [1, \infty] \to [2, \infty]$ is given by

$$f(x) = x + \frac{1}{x}, \text{ then find } f^{-1}(x).$$

3.133 Find the inverse of the function

$$f(x) = \log_a (x + \sqrt{x^2 + 1}), (a > 1)$$

3.134 $f(x) = \dfrac{e^x - e^{-x}}{2}$ $f: R \to R$. Find $f^{-1}(x)$

3.135 Let $f: \left[\frac{1}{2}, \infty\right) \to \left[\frac{3}{4}, \infty\right), f(x) = x^2 - x + 1,$

then find $f^{-1}(x)$.

3.136 If the function $f: [1, \infty) \to [1, \infty)$ is given by
$$f(x) = 2^{x(x-1)} + \frac{1}{x}, \text{ then find } f^{-1}(x).$$

3.137 $f(x) = \sin^{-1}\left(\frac{x}{3}\right), x \in [-3, 3]$. Compute $f^{-1}(x)$.

3.138 $f(x) = \ln(x^2 + 3x + 1), x \in [1, 3]$. Compute $f^{-1}(x)$.

3.139 Show that the function $f(x) = x!$ is primitive recursive if $0! = 1$ and $n! = n*(n-1)!$.

3.140 Show that the function $f(x, y) = x + y$ is primitive recursive.

3.141 Show that the function $f(x, y) = x^y$ is primitive recursive.

Exercises on Recursive Function

1. Write a recursive function to multiply 2 numbers.
2. Write a program to compute LCM of two numbers using recursion.
3. Write a program to evaluate the value of X^n using recursion.
4. Write a program to evaluate the sum of the following series using recursion: $1 + 2 + 3 + \ldots + n$.
5. Write a program to evaluate the sum of the following series using recursion: $1^2 + 2^2 + 3^2 + \ldots + n^2$.

Exercise on Hash Function

1. Write a function which uses mid-square method, to find the 2-digit hash address of a 9-digit employee number key.
2. Write a function which uses folding method with reversing to find the 2 digit hash address of a 9-digit employee number key.

Exercise on Pigeonhole Principle

1. If $n + 1$ numbers are chosen from $\{1, 2 \ldots, 2n\}$, show that one must divide the other.
2. There are 27 pupils in a class. Each pupil goes for swimming on some of the days from Monday to Friday in a certain week. If each pupil goes for swimming at least twice, then show that there must be two pupils who go for swimming on exactly the same days.
3. Show that if any seven numbers are chosen from 1 to 12, then two of them will add up to 13.
4. Show that if 11 numbers are chosen from the set $\{1, 2, \ldots 20\}$, then one of them will be a multiple of another.
5. How many friends must you have, to guarantee that at least two of them will have birthdays on the same day?
6. Show that if eleven positive integers are chosen, two of them will have the same remainder when divided by ten.
7. Show that if any 30 people are selected from any group, then a subset of 5 can be chosen such that all 5 were born on the same day of the week.
8. Show that if 10 colors are used to paint 101 buildings, then at least 11 buildings have the same color.

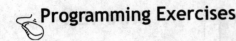

Programming Exercises

1. Write a function to test whether a given relation is reflexive or symmetric or transitive or all.
2. Write a function to test whether a given relation is antisymmetric.
3. Write a program to test whether a given relation is a compatibility relation.
4. Write a program to compute the reflexive closure of a relation.
5. Write a program to compute the symmetric closure of a relation.
6. Write a function to compute the transitive closure of a relation.
7. Write an algorithm using the concept of interior vertices in a path to find the length of the shortest path between two vertices in a directed graph, if such a path exists.
8. Write a program to compute the inverse of a given function.

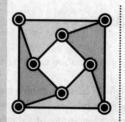

CHAPTER

FOUR

GRAPHS AND PLANAR GRAPHS

4.1 INTRODUCTION

As was pointed out in Chapter 3, there are many real-life problems that can be abstracted as problems concerning sets of discrete objects and binary relations on them. For example, consider a series of public-opinion polls conducted to deter-mine the popularity of the presidential candidates. In each poll, voters' opinions were sought on two of the candidates, and a favorite was determined. The results of the polls will be interpreted as follows: Candidate a is considered to be running ahead of candidate b if one of the following conditions is true:

1. Candidate a was ahead of candidate b in a poll conducted between them.

2. Candidate a was ahead of candidate c in a poll, and candidate c was ahead of candidate b in another poll.

3. Candidate a was ahead of candidate c, and candidate c was ahead of candidate d, and candidate d was ahead of candidate b in three separate polls, and so on.

Given two candidates, we might want to know whether one of them is running ahead of the other.* Let $S = \{a, b, c, \ldots\}$ be the set of candidates and R be a binary relation on S such that (a, b) is in R if a poll between a and b was conducted and a was chosen the favorite candidate. We recall that a binary relation on a set can be represented in tabular form, as in Fig. 4.1a, or in graphical form, as in Fig. 4.1b. Suppose that the binary relation in Fig. 4.1a and Fig. 4.1b represents the

---

* Note that, according to our interpretation of the results of the polls, it is possible that candidate a is running ahead of candidate b, and, at the same time, candidate b is also running ahead of candidate a. (See how politics works!)

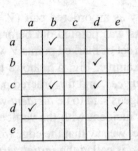

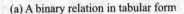

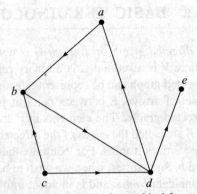

(a) A binary relation in tabular form   (b) A binary relation in graphical form

Fig. 4.1

results of the polls conducted. We observe that candidate *a* is more popular than candidate *e* because of the ordered pairs (*a*, *b*), (*b*, *d*), (*d*, *e*) in *R*. One probably would agree that the graphical representation of the binary relation *R* in Fig. 4.1*b* is quite useful in comparing the popularity of two candidates, since there must be "a sequence of arrows" leading from the point corresponding to the more popular candidate to that corresponding to the less popular one.

As another example, consider a number of cities connected by highways. Given a map of the highways, we might want to determine whether there is a highway route between two cities on the map. Also, consider all the board positions* in a chess game. We might want to know whether a given board position can be reached from some other board position through a sequence of legal moves. It is clear that both of these examples are again concerned with discrete objects and binary relations on them. In the example of the highway map, let $S = \{a, b, c, \ldots\}$ be the set of cities and *R* be a binary relation on *S* such that (*a*, *b*) is in *R* if there is a highway from city *a* to city *b*. In the chess game example, let $S = \{a, b, c, \ldots\}$ be the set of all board positions and *R* be a binary relation on *S* such that (*a*, *b*) is in *R* if board position *a* can be transformed into board position *b* in one legal move. Furthermore, in both of these cases as in the example on the popularity of the presidential candidates, we want to know whether, for given *a* and *b* in *S*, there exist *c*, *d*, *e*, ..., *h* in *S* such that $\{(a, c), (c, d), (d, e), \ldots, (h, b)\} \subseteq R$.

Indeed, in many problems dealing with discrete objects and binary relations, a graphical representation of the objects and the binary relations on them is a very convenient form of representation. This leads us naturally to a study of the theory of graphs.

---

* To be precise, a board position means the position of all pieces together with a specification of whose turn it is (that is, either black or white).

4.2   BASIC TERMINOLOGY

A *directed graph* or *digraph G* is defined abstractly as an ordered pair (V, E), where V is a set and E is a binary relation on V. As was pointed out before, a directed graph can be represented geometrically as a set of marked points V with a set of arrows E between pairs of points.* For example, Fig. 4.5 shows two directed graphs. The elements in V are called the *vertices,* and the ordered pairs in E are called the *edges* of the directed graph. An edge is said to be *incident* with the vertices it joins. For example, the edge (a, b) is incident with the vertices a and b. Sometimes, when we wish to be more specific, we say that the edge (a, b) is incident *from a* and is incident *into b*. The vertex a is called the *initial vertex*, and the vertex b is called the *terminal vertex* of the edge (a, b). An edge that is incident from and into the same vertex, like (c, c) in Fig. 4.5, is called a *loop.* Two vertices are said to be *adjacent* if they are joined by an edge. Moreover, corresponding to an edge (a, b), the vertex a is said to be *adjacent to* the vertex b, and the vertex b is said to be *adjacent from* the vertex a. A vertex is said to be an *isolated* vertex if there is no edge incident with it.

An *undirected graph G* is defined abstractly as an ordered pair (V, E), where V is a set and E is a set of multisets of two elements from V. For example, $G = (\{a, b, c, d\}, \{\{a, b\}, \{a, d\}, \{b, c\}, \{b, d\}, \{c, c\}\})$ is an undirected graph. An undirected graph can be represented geometrically as a set of marked points V with a set of lines E between the points. The undirected graph G above is shown in Fig. 4.6. As another example, let $V = \{a, b, c, d, e\}$ be a set of computer programs. Figure 4.7 shows an undirected graph in which there is an edge between two vertices if the corresponding programs share some common data. From now on, when it is clear from the context, we shall use the term *graph* to mean either a directed graph, or an undirected graph, or both. Now we describe some commonly used graphs.

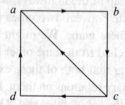

Fig. 4.2 A simple graph

Simple Graph   A graph that has no self-loops or parallel edges is known as simple graph. Figure 4.2 shows a simple graph.

Asymmetric Digraph   Digraphs having only one directed edge between each pair of vertices but can have self-loops are called asymmetric digraphs. Figure 4.3 shows an asymmetric digraph.

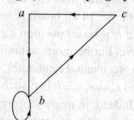

Fig. 4.3 An asymmetric digraph

---

* In fact, we could choose to *define* a directed graph to be a set of marked points V with a set of arrows between the points so that there is at most one arrow from one point to another point.

Symmetric Digraph Digraphs in which for each edge (x, y), there is also an edge (y, x), are known as symmetric digraphs. Figure 4.4 shows a symmetric digraph.

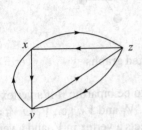

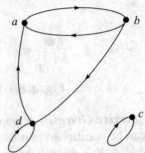

Fig. 4.4 A symmetric digraph

Fig. 4.5 Two directed graphs

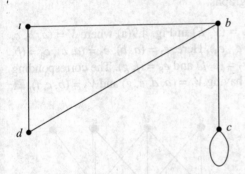

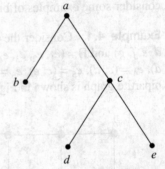

Fig. 4.6 An undirected graph

Fig. 4.7 Another undirected graph

Connected and Disconnected Graphs A graph G is said to be connected if every pair of vertices in G are connected. Otherwise, G is called a disconnected graph. Two vertices in G are said to be connected if there exists at least one path from one vertex to the other.

For example, the graphs in Fig. 4.8 (a), (b), (c) are connected whereas the graphs in Fig. 4.8 (d), and (e) are disconnected.

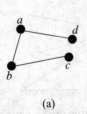

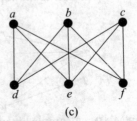

(a)   (b)   (c)

Fig. 4.8 Examples of connected Graphs

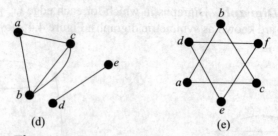

Fig. 4.8   Example of disconnected graphs

Bipartite Graph   A graph $G = (V, E)$ is said, to be bipartite if it's vertex set V can be partitioned into two disjoint subsets, say, V_1 and V_2, i.e., $V_1 \cup V_2 = V$ and $V_1 \cap V_2 = \phi$, such that every edge $e \in E$ connects a vertex in V_1 and a vertex in V_2 i.e., if (x, y) is an edge in E of the graph G then, $x \in V_1$ and $y \in V_2$ and no edge should connect any two vertices in V_1 or any two vertices in V_2. Now, let us consider some examples of bipartite graphs.

Example 4.1   Consider the graph $G = (V, E)$ in Fig. 4.9(a) where $V = (a, b, c, d, e, f, g)$ and E $= (e_1, e_2, e_3, e_4, e_5, e_6, e_7, e_8)$. Here, $e_1 = (a, b)$, $e_2 = (a, c)$, $e_3 = (b, d)$, $e_4 = (c, d)$, $e_5 = (c, e)$, $e_6 = (d, f)$, $e_7 = (e, f)$ and $e_8 = (f, g)$. The corresponding bipartite graph is shown in Fig. 4.9(b) having $V_1 = (a, d, e, g)$ and $V_2 = (b, c, f)$. ■

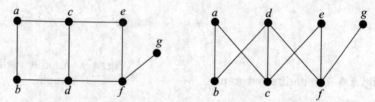

Fig. 4.9   (a) Original graph (b) Corresponding bipartite graph of graph G

Example 4.2   The graph shown in Fig. 4.10 is a bipartite graph as its vertex set can be partitioned into 2 sub sets, $V_1 = \{p, q\}$ and $V_2 = \{r, s, t, u\}$ such that every edge of the graph connects a vertex in V_1 with a vertex in V_2. It may be observed that there are no edges joining any two vertices in V_1 or any two vertices in V_2.

On the other hand, the graph shown in Fig. 4.11 is not a bipartite graph since no such partition of the vertex set is possible.   ■

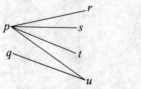

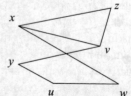

Fig. 4.10   A sample bipartite graph   Fig. 4.11   A sample graph which is not bipartite

Complete Bipartite Graph A complete bipartite graph is a bipartite graph $G = (V, E)$ in which there is an edge between each pair of vertices (x, y) where $x \in V_1$, $y \in V_2$, and $V_1 \cup V_2 = V$ i.e. every vertex in V_1 is connected to every vertex of V_2 by an edge. A complete bipartite graph is denoted by $K_{m,n}$ where $m = |V_1|$ and $n = |V_2|$. The normal order of m and n is such that $m \leq n$. A complete bipartite graph $K_{m,n}$ have $m + n$ number of vertices and $m \cdot n$ number of edges. Figure 4.12 (a) and Figure 4.12 (b) show the complete bipartite graphs $K_{2,3}$, $K_{3,3}$ respectively.

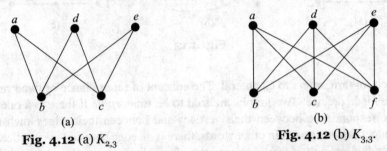

(a)   (b)

Fig. 4.12 (a) $K_{2,3}$ **Fig. 4.12** (b) $K_{3,3}$.

Example 4.3 Let us now consider a practical example of a bipartite graph and complete bipartite graph. Consider a group of children G where each child represents a vertex. An edge connects two children if one of them is a boy and the other is his sister. Clearly, a bipartition of G has occurred. All the boys will be in the first vertex set V_1 and the girls will be in the second set V_2. The resulting graph will become a balanced bipartite graph if the number of boys and girls is the same. Can you think of the situation in which it will become a complete bipartite graph? The answer to this question is that, when all the children have the same parents, i.e, they are all brothers and sisters, then the resulting graph will become a complete bipartite graph. ∎

Isomonphic Graphs Let $V = \{a, b, c, d\}$ be the four players in a round-robin tennis tournament.

Let $E = \{(a, b), (a, d), (b, d), (c, a), (c, b), (d, c)\}$ be a binary relation on V so that (x, y) in E means that x beats y in the match between them. The graph $G = (V, E)$ is shown in Fig. 4.13a. Let $V' = \{1, 2, 3, 4\}$ be the four chapters in a book. Let $E' = \{(1, 2), (2, 3), (3, 1), (3, 4), (4, 1), (4, 2)\}$ be a binary relation on V' such that $(1, 2)$ in E' means that the material in Chapter 1 refers to that in Chapter 2, and so on. The graph $G' = (V', E')$ is shown in Fig. 4.13b. A careful reader might have recognized that the graph in Fig. 4.13b "resembles" the graph in Fig. 4.13a. Indeed, such a "resemblance" becomes even more evident if we redraw the graph in Fig. 4.13b to that shown in Fig. 4.13c. Comparing the graphs in Fig. 4.13a and Fig. 4.13c, we realize that both the tennis tournament problem and the problem of cross reference among chapters can be represented abstractly by the same graph. Consequently, many of the results concerning the tennis players can be rephrased immediately as results concerning the chapters of the book. For example, according to Fig. 4.13a, player b beats player d who, in turn, beats player c, and according to Fig. 4.13c, Chapter 1 refers to Chapter

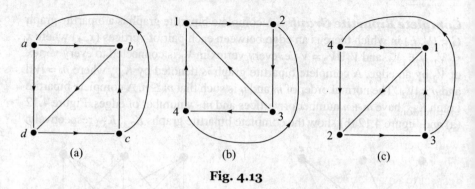

Fig. 4.13

2 which, in turn, refers to Chapter 3. The concept of resemblance of two graphs can be made precise: Two graphs are said to be *isomorphic* if there is a one-to-one correspondence between their vertices and between their edges such that incidences are preserved. In other words, there is an edge between two vertices in one graph if and only if there is a corresponding edge between the corresponding vertices in the other graph. For example, Fig. 4.14a shows a pair of isomorphic undirected graphs, and Fig. 4.14b shows a pair of isomorphic directed graphs. In these two figures, corresponding vertices in the two isomorphic graphs are labeled with the same letter, primed and unprimed. The reader can convince himself that the graphs are isomorphic by checking the incidence relations.

Subgraph   Let $G = (V, E)$ be a graph. A graph $G' = (V', E')$ is said to be a *subgraph* of G if E' is a subset of E and V' is a subset of V such that the edges

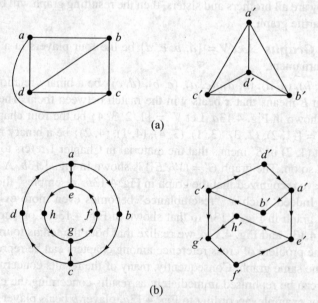

Fig. 4.14   Isomorphic undirected graphs

in E' are incident only with the vertices in V'. For example, Fig. 4.15*b* shows a subgraph of the graph in Fig. 4.15*a*. A subgraph of G is said to be a *spanning subgraph* if it contains all the vertices of G. The *complement of a subgraph* $G' = (V', E')$ with respect to the graph G is another subgraph $G'' = (V'', E'')$ such that E'' is equal to $E - E'$ and V''' contains only the vertices with which the edges in E'' are incident.* For example, Fig. 4.15*c* shows the complement of the subgraph in Fig. 4.15*b*. The *undirected complete graph* of n vertices, denoted K_n, is a graph with n vertices in which there is an edge between each pair of distinct vertices. The *complement of a graph* G of n vertices is defined to be its complement with respect to K_n and is denoted $\overline{G}$. For example, let G be a graph of n vertices. Let the n vertices in G represent n people, and let the set of edges in G represent a compatible relationship such that an edge between two vertices means that the two corresponding persons can work cooperatively as a team. Clearly, the set of edges in $\overline{G}$ will represent the incompatibility relationship among the n people. We also define a *directed complete* graph of n vertices to be a graph with n vertices in which there is exactly one arrow between each pair of distinct vertices.

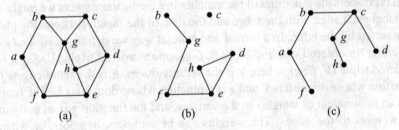

$$\text{(a)} \qquad\qquad \text{(b)} \qquad\qquad \text{(c)}$$

Fig. 4.15 Subgraph and complement of a graph

4.3 MULTIGRAPHS AND WEIGHTED GRAPHS

The definition of a graph can be extended in several ways. Let $G = (V, E)$, where V is a set and E is a multiset of ordered pairs from $V \times V$. G is called a *directed multigraph*. Geometrically, a directed multigraph can be represented as a set of marked points V with a set of arrows E between the points where there is no restriction on the number of arrows from one point to another point. (Indeed, the multiplicity of an ordered pair of vertices in the multiset E is the number of arrows between the corresponding marked points.) For example, Fig. 4.16 shows a multigraph. Also, consider a graphical representation of a highway map in which an edge between two cities corresponds to a lane in a highway

---

* According to our definition, some isolated vertices in G that are not included in G' will not be included in G'' either. However, one can always modify the definition if it is desirable to include such isolated vertices in G''.

between the cities. Since there are often multilane highways between pairs of cities, this representation yields a multigraph. The notion of an *undirected multigraph* can be defined in a similar manner. From now on, when it is clear from the context, we shall use the term *graph* to mean either "graph" or "multigraph" or both. On the other hand, when it is necessary to emphasize that we are referring to a graph (instead of to a multigraph), we shall use the term *linear graph.*

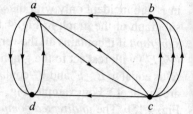

Fig. 4.16 Multigraph

In modeling a physical situation as an abstract graph, there are many occasions in which we wish to attach additional information to the vertices and/or the edges of the graph. For example, in a graph that represents the highway connection among cities, we might wish to assign a number to each edge to indicate the distance between the two cities connected by the edge. We might also wish to assign a number to each vertex to indicate the population of the city. In a graph that represents the outcomes of the matches in a tennis tournament we might wish to label each edge with the score and the date of the match between the players connected by the edge. In a formal and general way we define a *weighted graph* as either an ordered quadruple (V, E, f, g), or an ordered triple (V, E, f), or an ordered triple (V, E, g), where V is the set of vertices, E is the set of edges, f is a function whose domain is V, and g is a function whose domain is E. The function f is an assignment of weights to the vertices, and the function g is an assignment of weights to the edges. The weights can be numbers, symbols, or whatever quantities that we wish to assign to the vertices and edges.

We present some examples:

Example 4.4 Let us consider the problem of modeling the behavior of a vending machine that sells candy bars for 15¢ apiece. For simplicity, we assume that the machine accepts only nickels and dimes and will not return any change when more than 15¢ is deposited. The weighted graph in Fig. 4.17 is a description of the behavior of the machine where the vertices corresponds to the amounts that have already been deposited for the current sale, namely, 0, 5, 10, and 15¢ or more. At any moment, a customer can do one of three things: deposit a nickel, deposit a dime, and press a button for a candy bar of her choice. Correspondingly, in the graph in Fig. 4.17, there are three outgoing edges from each vertex labeled 5, 10, and *P*. An edge with weight 5 updates the total amount deposited in the machine when the customer puts in a nickel, and an edge with weight 10 updates the total amount deposited in the machine when the customer puts in a dime. Clearly, when we are at vertices *a*, *b*, and *c*, nothing will happen when we press a button to select a candy bar; the machine will release a candy bar only when vertex *d* is reached. ∎

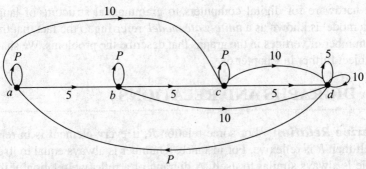

a: 0¢ deposited
b: 5¢ deposited
c: 10¢ deposited
d: 15¢ or more deposited

Fig. 4.17

Example 4.5 We consider the problem of recognizing sentences consisting of an article, followed by at most three adjectives, followed by a noun, and then followed by a verb, as shown in the following.

The train stops.
A little girl laughs.
The large fluffy white clouds appear.

When we examine a sentence word by word, we can determine whether it is in this special form by following the weighted graph in Fig. 4.18, starting at vertex *a*. If vertex *g* is reached, the sentence is in the special form. To simplify the drawing of the graph, we use dotted arrows to indicate the discovery of words that are out of the normal order. In that case we reach vertex *h*, which signifies the detection of an "illegal" sentence. ∎

Examples 4.4 and 4.5 illustrate a general model that is useful in describing many different physical problems ranging from automatic machines and elec-

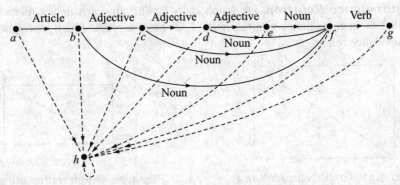

Fig. 4.18 A weighted graph for the problem of recognizing sentences

tronic hardware for digital computers to grammatical structure of languages. Such a model is known as a *finite-state model*, referring to the fact that there is a finite number of vertices in the graphs that describe the problems. We shall study the subject further in Chapter 6.

4.4 DIGRAPHS AND RELATIONS

Reflexive Relation   For some relation R, if every element is in relation R to itself then R is reflexive. For instance, a number is always equal to itself, or a triangle is always similar to itself. A digraph of a reflexive relation will have a self-loop at each of its vertices. Such a digraph is called a *reflexive digraph*. If a digraph does not contain any self-loop then it is called as an irreflexive digraph. Figure 4.19 shows a digraph which represents a reflexive relation.

Symmetric Relation   A digraph representing a symmetric relation on its vertex set is called a symmetric digraph, i.e. a digraph is called a symmetric digraph if for every directed edge from vertex a to b there is a directed edge from b to a. Figure 4.20 shows a digraph which represents a symmetric relation.

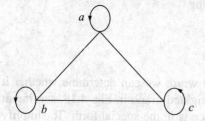

Fig. 4.19 Digraph representing a reflexive relation

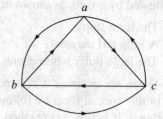

Fig. 4.20 Digraph representing a symmetric relation

Transitive Relation   A graph representing a transitive relation on its vertex set is called a transitive graph. Figure 4.21 shows a graph which represents a transitive relation.

Equivalence Relation   A graph representing an equivalence relation is called as an equivalence graph. Figure 4.22 shows a graph which represents an equivalence relation.

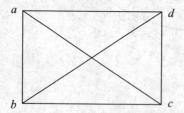

Fig. 4.21 Graph representing a transitive relation

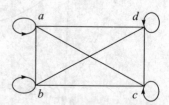

Fig. 4.22 Graph representing an equivalence relation

4.5 REPRESENTATION OF GRAPHS

There are many ways to represent graphs. Out of them, the matrix is the most suitable way for representing graphs in computer memory. Matrices can be easily manipulated. Also, matrices can be applied to study many properties of graphs. In many applications of graph theory, matrices can be considered as the natural way of expressing the problem. In this section, we discuss two important matrices for representing graphs in computer memory: *incidence matrix* and *adjacency matrix*.

4.5.1 Incidence Matrix

The incidence matrix of a graph G with n vertices, e edges and no self-loops is an n by e matrix $M(G) = [m_{ij}]$, whose rows correspond to its vertices and columns correspond to its edges. The elements of the matrix will have values according to the following rule:

$$m_{ij} = 1, \text{ if the } j^{th} \text{ edge } e_j \text{ is incident on the } i^{th} \text{ vertex } v_i$$
$$= 0, \text{ otherwise.}$$

Figure 4.23 shows a graph and its corresponding incidence matrix.

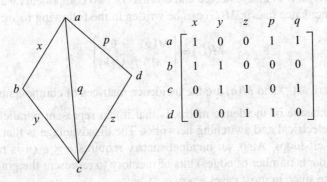

Fig. 4.23 A graph and its corresponding incidence matrix

Similarly, the incidence matrix of a *digraph G* is defined as $M(G) = [m_{ij}]$, such that

$$m_{ij} = 1, \text{ if the } j^{th} \text{ edge } e_j \text{ is incident out of the } i^{th} \text{ vertex } v_i$$
$$= 0, \text{ if the } j^{th} \text{ edge } e_j \text{ is not incident on the } i^{th} \text{ vertex } v_i$$
$$= -1, \text{ if the } j^{th} \text{ edge } e_j \text{ is incident into the } i^{th} \text{ vertex } v_i.$$

Figure 4.24 shows a digraph and its corresponding incidence matrix:

Some observations which directly follow from the above discussions on incidence matrix are:

- As each edge is incident on two vertices, so each column has two 1's (including –1's).

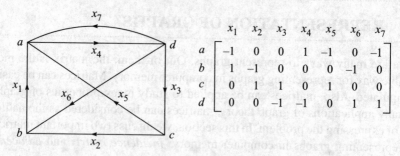

Fig. 4.24 A digraph and its corresponding incidence matrix

- The degree of a vertex is equal to the number of 1's in the corresponding row.
- The row with all 0's is an isolated vertex.
- Identical columns represent presence of parallel edges in the graph.
- Permutation of any two rows and columns simply corresponds to relabeling of vertices and edges.

  This observation suggests that two graphs G_1 and G_2, are isomorphic iff their incidence matrices $M(G_1)$ and $M(G_2)$ differ only by permutations of rows and columns.

- If a graph G is disconnected and consists of two components g and h, then the incidence matrix $M(G)$ can be written in the following form:

$$M(G) = \begin{bmatrix} M(g) & 0 \\ 0 & M(h) \end{bmatrix}$$

  where $M(g)$ and $M(h)$ are the incidence matrices of components g and h.

The advantage of incidence matrix is that it can represent parallel edges. It is used in electrical and switching networks. The disadvantage is that, it cannot represent self-loops. Also, an incident matrix requires $n \times e$ (n is number of vertices and e is number of edges) bits of memory to represent the graph, which is very large since in most cases $e > n$.

4.5.2 Adjacency Matrix

An alternative way to incidence matrix is the adjacency matrix . The adjacency matrix of a graph G with n vertices having no parallel edges is an n by n matrix $A(G) = [a_{ij}]$, whose elements are defined as follows:

    $a_{ij} = 1$, if there is an edge between i^{th} and j^{th} vertices.

         $= 0$, otherwise.

Figure 4.25 shows a grahph and its corresponding adjacency matrix.

Similarly, the adjacency matrix of a *digraph* G is defined as $A(G) = [a_{ij}]$, such that

    $a_{ij} = 1$, if there is an edge directed from i^{th} vertex to j^{th} vertex.

         $= 0$, otherwise.

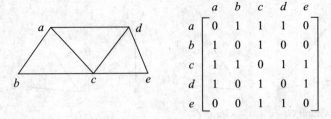

Fig. 4.25   A graph and its corresponding adjacency matrix

Some observations which directly follow from the above discussions on adjacency matrix are:

- The entries along the principal diagonal of matrix $A(G)$ are all 0's iff the graph has no loops.
- The definition makes no provision for parallel edges. That's why $A(G)$ is defined only for graphs without having parallel edges.
- If there exists no loops and no parallel edges, then the degree of a vertex is equal to the number of 1's in the corresponding row or column of $A(G)$.
- Permutations of rows and of the corresponding columns result in reordering the vertices.
- A graph G is disconnected and is in two components g and h, iff the adjacency matrix $A(G)$ can be partitioned as follows:

$$A(G) = \begin{bmatrix} A(g) & 0 \\ 0 & A(h) \end{bmatrix}$$

where $A(g)$ and $A(h)$ are the adjacency matrices of components g and h.

The advantage of adjacency matrix is that it can represent self-loops. As there are n^2 entries in $A(G)$, it requires only n^2 bits of memory (where n is the number of vertices), which is less than $n \times e$ bits of memory to represent the graph (in case of incidence matrix), when $e > n$. The disadvantage is that it cannot represent parallel edges.

4.6   OPERATIONS ON GRAPHS

Since graphs are defined in terms of sets of vertices and edges, so the set operations can be applied to graphs. In this section, we discuss some commonly used operations to graphs.

Union   If $G_1 = (V_1, E_1)$ and $G_2 = (V_2, E_2)$ are two graphs, then their **union** $G_3 = G_1 \cup G_2$ is also a graph, whose vertex set is $V_3 = V_1 \cup V_2$ and edge set is $E_3 = E_1 \cup E_2$. Figure 4.26 shows the union operation.

Intersection   If $G_1 = (V_1, E_1)$ and $G_2 = (V_2, E_2)$ are two graphs then their **intersection** $G_3 = G_1 \cap G_2$ is also a graph, whose vertex set is $V_3 = V_1 \cap V_2$ and edge set is $E_3 = E_1 \cap E_2$. Figure 4.27 shows the intersection operation.

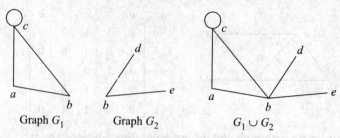

Fig. 4.26 Union of two graphs

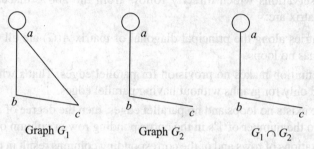

Fig. 4.27 Intersection of two graphs

Ring Sum If $G_1 = (V_1, E_1)$ and $G_2 = (V_2, E_2)$ are two graphs then their **ring Sum** $G_3 = G_1 \oplus G_2$ is a graph consisting of the vertex set $(V_1 \cup V_2)$ and edges that are either in G_1 or G_2, but not in both. Figure 4.28 shows the ring sum operation.

Decomposition A graph G is said to have been decomposed into two subgraphs g and h if $g \cup h = G$ and $g \cap h =$ a null graph, i.e. each edge of G

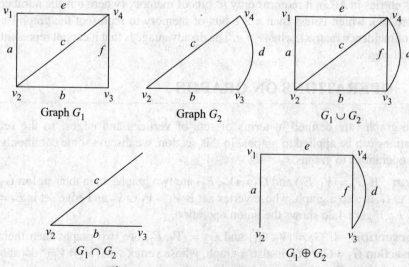

Fig. 4.28 Ring sum of two graphs

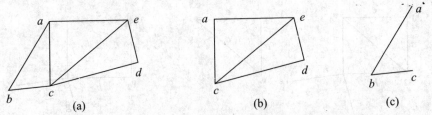

Fig. 4.29 Decomposition of a graph into two subgraphs

occurs either in g or in h but not in both. But, some vertices may occur in both g and h. In decomposition the isolated vertices are not considered. For example, the graph in Fig. 4.29(a) is decomposed into two subgraphs which are shown in Figs. 4.29(b) and (c).

A theorem related with decomposition operation may be stated as follows:

Theorem 4.1 A graph containing m edges $\{e_1, e_2, \ldots e_m\}$ can be decomposed into $2^{m-1} - 1$ different ways into pairs of subgraphs g_1 and g_2.

Proof: Let graph G contain m number of edges ($m \geq 1$).

The number of different subgraphs that can be drawn from G is $^mc_0 + {}^mc_1 + {}^mc_2 + \ldots + {}^mc_m$.

Now, $^mc_0$ – a null graph

$^mc_1$ – graph taking one edge at a time.

$\vdots$

^mc_m – graph taking m edges.

So, total no. of subgraphs $= \Sigma\, {}^mc_x = 2^m$.

While taking pairs the first and last cases, i.e. $^mc_0$ and ^mc_m cannot be considered.

So, total number of cases $= 2^m - {}^mc_0 - {}^mc_m = 2^m - 1$

Total number of pairs $= (2^m - 2)/2 = 2^{m-1} - 1$.

Thus, a graph containing m edges can be decomposed into $2^{m-1} - 1$ different ways into pairs of sub graphs g_1 and g_2. ∎

Deletion If V_i is a vertex in graph G then $G - V_i$ denotes a subgraph of G obtained by deleting V_i from G. Deletion of a vertex implies the deletion of all edges incident on that vertex. But deletion of an edge doesn't imply deletion of its end vertices. Figure 4.30 shows the **deletion** operation.

Fusion A pair of vertices a and b in a graph are said to be **fused** if the two vertices are replaced by a single new vertex such that every edge that was incident on either a or b or in both, is incident on the new vertex.

So, fusion of two vertices doesn't alter the number of edges, but it reduces the number of vertices by one. In Fig. 4.31 vertices b and c are fused together.

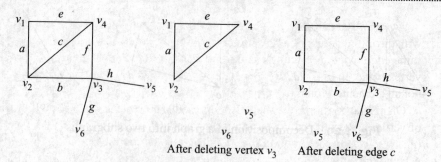

After deleting vertex v_3 After deleting edge c

Fig. 4.30   Deletion operation on a graph

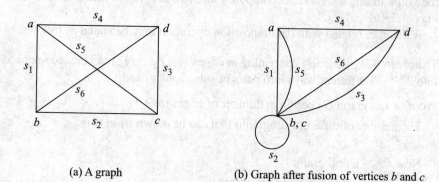

(a) A graph   (b) Graph after fusion of vertices b and c

Fig. 4.31   Fusion operation on a graph

4.7   PATHS AND CIRCUITS

In a directed graph, a *path* is a sequence of edges $(e_{i1}, e_{i2}, \ldots, e_{ik})$* such that the terminal vertex of e_{ij} coincides with the initial vertex of $e_{i(j+1)}$ for $1 \leq j \leq k-1$. A path is said to be *simple* if it does not include the same edge twice. A path is said to be *elementary* if it does not meet the same vertex twice.[†] In Fig. 4.32, (e_1, e_2, e_3, e_4) is a path; $(e_1, e_2, e_3, e_5, e_8, e_3, e_4)$ is a path, but not a simple one; $(e_1, e_2, e_3, e_5, e_9, e_{10}, e_{11}, e_4)$ is a simple path, but not an elementary one. In the example on the popularity of the presidential candidates in Sec. 4.1, that candidate a is more popular than candidate b means the existence of a path from vertex a to vertex b in the graph representing the results of the polls. In the example of the highway map in Sec. 4.1, a path from one vertex to another vertex in the graph representing the highway connections is exactly a highway route between the corresponding cities.

---

* To simplify the notation, we identify the edges of a graph by letter names such as $e_1, e_2, \ldots,$ as shown in Fig. 4.32.

† In other words, no two edges in the sequence have the same terminal vertex.

A *circuit* is a path $(e_{i1}, e_{i2}, ..., e_{ik})$ in which the terminal vertex of e_{ik} coincides with the initial vertex of e_{i1}. A circuit is said to be *simple* if it does not include the same edge twice. A circuit is said to be *elementary* if it does not meet the same vertex twice. In Fig. 4.32, $(e_1, e_2, e_3, e_5, e_9, e_{10}, e_{12}, e_6, e_7)$ is a simple circuit, but not an elementary one; $(e_1, e_2, e_3, e_5, e_6, e_7)$ is an elementary circuit.

On many occasions, we shall also represent a path or a circuit by the sequence of vertices the path or the circuit meets when it is traced. For example, the path (e_1, e_2, e_3, e_4) in the graph in Fig. 4.32 can also be represented as $(v_1, v_2, v_3, v_4, v_7)$, and the circuit $(e_5, e_9, e_{10}, e_{11})$ can be represented as $(v_4, v_5, v_8, v_6, v_4)$.

The notions of paths and circuits in an undirected graph can be defined in a similar way. We shall leave the details to the reader.

As was illustrated in several of the examples in Secs. 4.1 and 4.3, there are many problems in which we want to determine whether there is a path from one vertex to another. We present now a result that is useful in answering the question of existence of such paths. In the next section, we shall see a general procedure for finding such paths.

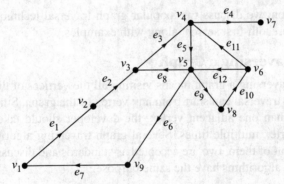

Fig. 4.32 A graph showing various paths

Theorem 4.2 In a (directed or undirected) graph with n vertices, if there is a path from vertex v_1 to vertex v_2 then there is a path of no more than $n - 1$ edges from vertex v_1 to vertex v_2.

Proof: Suppose there is a path from v_1 to v_2. Let $(v_1, ..., v_i, ..., v_2)$ be the sequence of vertices that the path meets when it is traced from v_1 and v_2. If there are l edges in the path, there are $l + 1$ vertices in the sequence. For l larger than $n - 1$, there must be a vertex v_k that appears more than once in the sequence, that is, $(v_1, ..., v_i, ..., v_k, ..., v_k, ..., v_2)$. Deleting the edges in the path that leads v_k back to v_k, we have a path from v_1 to v_2 that has fewer edges than the original one. This argument can be repeated until we have a path that has $n - 1$ or fewer edges. ∎

An undirected graph is said to be *connected* if there is a path between every two vertices, and is said to be *disconnected* otherwise. A directed graph is said to be connected if the undirected graph derived from it by ignoring the directions

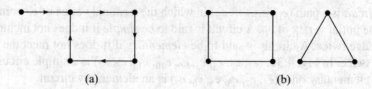

Fig. 4.33   (a) Connected graph (b) Disconnected graph.

of the edges is connected and is said to be disconnected otherwise. It follows that a disconnected graph consists of two or more components each of which is a connected graph. A directed graph is said to be *strongly connected* if for every two vertices *a* and *b* in the graph there is a path from *a* to *b* as well as a path from *b* to *a*. For example, Fig. 4.33*a* shows a connected graph which, however, is not strongly connected, while Fig. 4.33*b* shows a disconnected graph.

4.8   GRAPH TRAVERSALS

In this section, we discuss two popular graph traversal techniques. Depth-first search and breadth-first search, along with examples.

4.8.1   Traversing a Graph

Generally traversing a graph means visiting all the vertices of the graph exactly once. Graph traversal can start from any vertex of the graph. Since a vertex may have more than one adjacent vertex, the developer should take extra care not to visit a vertex multiple times. Several graph traversing algorithms have been proposed. Out of them, two are accepted as standards and discussed below. Both the traversal algorithms have the same purpose.

These algorithms are:

(1) DFS (Depth-First Search)
(2) BFS (Breadth-First Search)

Common Traversal Steps

Step 1 : Start from any vertex of a graph.

Step 2 : From this starting vertex, traverse as deep as you can go. Whenever you cannot go further, then backtrack one vertex and do the same traversal from this vertex until you cannot traverse further, and so on.

Step 3 : Process the information contained in that vertex.

Step 4 : Then move along an edge to process a neighbor (adjacent vertex).

Step 5 : When the traversal finishes, all the above vertices that can be reached from the start vertex are processed.

It may be noted that all the traversal algorithms require the systematical examination of the nodes and edges of the Graph.

4.8.2   Depth-First Search

The key point that lies behind the DFS traversal is: visit the vertex V first, then visit all the vertices that lie along a path which begins at V. That means first visit the vertex V then visit the vertex which is immediate adjacent to V (say V_x). Next, if V_x has any adjacent vertex (say V_y) then visit it and continue till there is a dead end (i.e., a vertex which does not have immediate adjacent vertex or immediate adjacent vertex already been visited). Depth-first search is also called *backtracking*, since the algorithm returns to vertices previously visited to add paths. The following example illustrates the depth-first search technique.

Example 4.6   Consider the graph given in Fig. 4.34. We start with the vertex A. Then, we visit vertex G as it is adjacent to A. (However, it may be noted that one can visit B instead of G as the path of the traversal is not unique.) From G, we visit to vertex F. Then, we back track to A, as there is no path from F to any vertex other than A. From A, we visit the next adjacent vertex B, then from B to C, then C to E, and finally from E to D. As there is no path from D to any other vertex which is not visited, the algorithm stops at this point.

In order to keep track of the adjacent vertices, we use *stack* as the data structure.

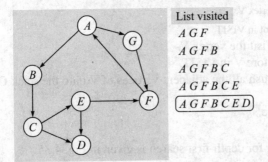

List visited

$A\ G\ F$

$A\ G\ F\ B$

$A\ G\ F\ B\ C$

$A\ G\ F\ B\ C\ E$

$A\ G\ F\ B\ C\ E\ D$

Fig. 4.34   An example showing depth-first search

- It may be noted that, a *stack* is an ordered collection of homogeneous data elements where the insertion and deletion operations take place at one end only. The insertion operation is called PUSH and the deletion operation is called POP.

Now, we present the detailed traversal steps.

Traversal Steps

Step 1 : Start with A.
Step 2 : Pop A from the stack and insert in the list of the visited nodes.
Step 3 : Push A's adjacent vertices B and G on the stack.
Step 4 : Pop G from the stack and insert it in the list of visited nodes.
Step 5 : Push G's adjacent vertex F on the stack.
Step 6 : Pop F from the stack and insert it in the list of visited nodes.

Step 7 : Since *F*'s adjacent vertex *A* is already visited and the stack has the vertex *B*, a new search starts from this vertex *B*.

Step 8 : Pop *B* from the stack and insert it in the list of visited nodes.

Step 9 : Now push *B*'s adjacent vertex *C* onto the stack.

Step 10 : Pop *C* from the stack and insert it in the list of visited nodes.

Step 11 : Push *C*'s adjacent vertices *D* and *E* onto the stack.

Step 12 : Pop *E* from the stack and insert it in the list of visited nodes.

Step 13 : Push *E*'s adjacent vertices *F* and *D* onto the stack.

Step 14 : Pop *D* from the stack and insert it in the list of visited nodes.

Step 15 : Since *D* does not have any neighbors, or vertices which have not yet been visited, so Pop *D* out of stack in order to make the stack empty.

Step 16 : Get the list of visited nodes as **A G F B C E D**. ∎

An Informal Algorithm In the following algorithm we have used OPEN as the stack and VISIT as the list of visited nodes.

Algorithm DFS

1. Push the starting vertex into the stack OPEN.
2. While the stack OPEN is not empty do:
   (a) Pop a vertex V
   (b) if V is not in VISIT
      (i) Visit the vertex V.
      (ii) Store V in VISIT.
      (iii) Push all the adjacent vertices of V onto the stack OPEN.
      endif
   end of while.
3. Stop.

The flow chart for depth-first search is given in Fig. 4.35.

4.8.3 Breadth-First Search

The general idea behind a breadth-first search beginning at a starting node *A* is as follows: First we have to examine the starting node (say *A*).Then we examine all the neighbors of *A*. Then we have to examine all the neighbors of the neighbors of *A* and so on. Generally we have to keep track of the neighbors of a node and care must be taken that no node is visited or processed more than once. This can be done by using a data structure QUEUE to keep track of the nodes visited.

Steps

Step 1 : First choose a starting vertex.

Step 2 : Find all the vertices which are connected to the starting vertex.

Step 3 : Then choose one of the connected vertices and find all the vertices that are connected to this vertex.

Step 4 : Continue this procedure until all the vertices are visited.

The following example illustrates the breadth-first search technique.

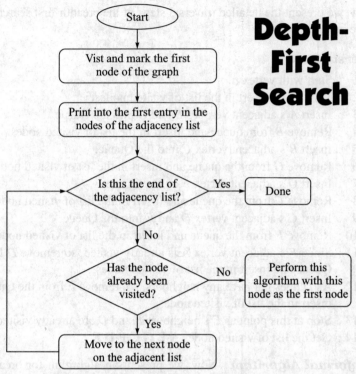

Fig. 4.35 Flow chart for depth-first search

Example 4.7 Consider the graph given in Fig. 4.36. First, we start with vertex *A*. Then, we visit the vertices in the next level, i.e., vertices *B* and *G*. Next, we visit *B*'s adjacent vertex *C*, and *G*'s adjacent vertex *F*. Finally, we visit *D* and *E*, the adjacent vertices of *C*.

In order to keep track of the vertices at a level, we use *queue* as the data structure.

- It may be noted that, like stack, a *queue* is an ordered collection of homogeneous data elements, but in contrast to the stack, in case of the latter, insertion and deletion operations take place at two extreme ends.

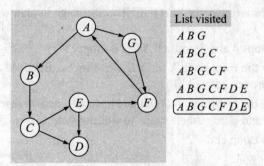

Fig. 4.36 An example showing breadth-first search

Now, we present the detailed traversal steps of the breadth-first search for the above example.

Traversal Steps

Step 1 : Start with vertex A.

Step 2 : Visit A and insert in the list of visited nodes.

Step 3 : Insert A's adjacent vertices B and G into the Queue.

Step 4 : Remove B from queue and insert in the list of visited nodes.

Step 5 : Insert B's adjacent vertex C into the Queue.

Step 6 : Remove G from the queue and insert in the list of visited nodes.

Step 7 : Insert G's adjacent vertex F on the Queue.

Step 8 : Remove C from the queue and insert in the list of visited nodes.

Step 9 : Insert C's adjacent vertex D and E into the Queue.

Step 10 : Remove F from the queue and insert in the list of visited nodes.

Step 11 : Since F's adjacent vertex A is already visited, so remove D from the Queue and insert in the list of visited nodes.

Step 12 : As D does not have any neighbors, so, remove E from the Queue and insert in the list of visited nodes.

Step 13 : Stop at this point as E's neighbors F and D are already visited.

Step 14 : Get the list of visited nodes **A B G C F D E**. ∎

An Informal Algorithm   Now, we present an algorithm for breadth-first search. We have used QUEUE as the data structure in our algorithm. During the execution of the algorithm, we assume each vertex V is in one of the following three states:

Ready State (R): The initial state of the vertex V.

Waiting State (W): The vertex V is in the queue waiting for processing.

Processed State (P): The vertex V has been processed.

Algorithm BFS

1. Initialize all the nodes to ready state (R).

2. Place the starting node A in QUEUE and change its state to the waiting state (W).

3. Repeat steps 4 and 5 until QUEUE is empty.

4. Remove the front node X of QUEUE. Process the node X and change the state to processed state (P).

5. Insert all the neighbors of X that are in steady state to rear (back end) of the QUEUE and change their status to waiting state.

   /* Step 3 Loop ends */

6. Stop.

The flow chart for breadth-first search is given in Fig. 4.37.

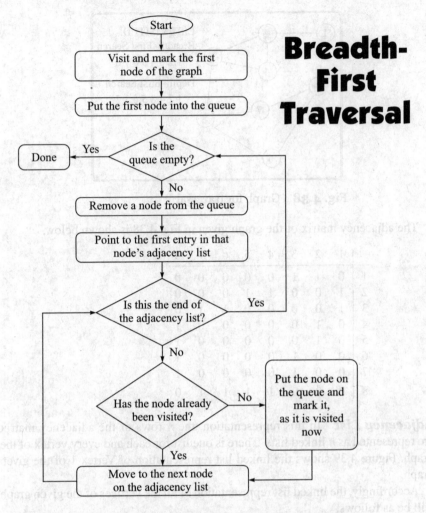

Fig. 4.37 Flow chart for Breadth-First Search

4.8.4 Program Implementations

Find the list of visited nodes of the graph given in Fig. 4.38 using both the BFS and DFS traversal methods.

Graph Representation First, represent the graphs either through adjacency matrices or through adjacency lists.

Adjacency Matrix The adjacency matrix G of a graph is the two dimensional array of size $n * n$ (where n is the number of vertices in the graph). Here, the array has the property that $a[i][j] = 1$, if there is an edge in between the vertices V_1 and V_2. If no such edge exits then the corresponding entry in that matrix will be zero.

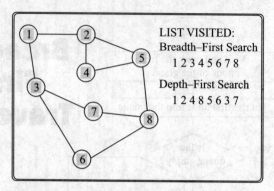

Fig. 4.38   Graph for traversal

The adjacency matrix of the graph given in Fig. 4.38 is shown below.

	1	2	3	4	5	6	7	8
1	0	1	1	0	0	0	0	0
2	1	0	0	1	1	0	0	0
3	1	0	0	0	0	1	1	0
4	0	1	0	0	0	0	0	1
5	0	1	0	0	0	0	0	1
6	0	0	1	0	0	0	0	1
7	0	0	1	0	0	0	0	1
8	0	0	0	1	1	1	1	0

Adjacency List   In this representation, the n rows of the adjacency matrix are represented as n linked lists. There is one list for each and every vertex of the graph. Figure 4.39 shows the linked list representation of Vertex 1 of the given graph.

Accordingly, the linked list representation of all the vertices of the given graph will be as follows:

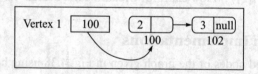

Fig. 4.39   Linked list representation of Vertex 1

Vertex 1.

    2-3

Vertex 2.

    1-4-5

Vertex 3.

    1-6-7

Vertex 4.
    2-8
Vertex 5.
    2-8
Vertex 6.
    3-8
Vertex 7.
    3-8
Vertex 8.
    4-5-6-7

4.8.5 Program that Implements Depth-First Search Algorithm

Figure 4.40 shows the C code for depth-first search.

```c
#include <stdio.h>
#include <conio.h>
#include <alloc.h>

#define TRUE 1
#define FALSE 0
#define MAX 8

struct node
{
    int data ;
    struct node *next ;
} ;

int visited[MAX] ;

void dfs ( int, struct node ** ) ;
struct node * getnode_write ( int ) ;
void del ( struct node * ) ;

void main( )
{
    struct node *arr[MAX] ;
    struct node *v1, *v2, *v3, *v4 ;
    int i ;

    clrscr( ) ;
    //inserting nodes at the vertex v1
    v1 = getnode_write ( 2 ) ;
    arr[0] = v1 ;
    v1 -> next = v2 = getnode_write ( 3 ) ;
    v2 -> next = NULL ;

    //inserting nodes at the vertex v2
    v1 = getnode_write ( 1 ) ;
    arr[1] = v1 ;
    v1 -> next = v2 = getnode_write ( 4 ) ;
    v2 -> next = v3 = getnode_write ( 5 ) ;
    v3 -> next = NULL ;

    //inserting nodes at the vertex v3
    v1 = getnode_write ( 1 ) ;
    arr[2] = v1 ;
```

```
            v1 -> next = v2 = getnode_write ( 6 ) ;
            v2 -> next = v3 = getnode_write ( 7 ) ;
            v3 -> next = NULL ;

            v1 = getnode_write ( 2 ) ;
            arr[3] = v1 ;
            v1 -> next = v2 = getnode_write ( 8 ) ;
            v2 -> next = NULL ;

            v1 = getnode_write ( 2 ) ;
            arr[4] = v1 ;
            v1 -> next = v2 = getnode_write ( 8 ) ;
            v2 -> next = NULL ;

            v1 = getnode_write ( 3 ) ;
            arr[5] = v1 ;
            v1 -> next = v2 = getnode_write ( 8 ) ;
            v2 -> next = NULL ;

            v1 = getnode_write ( 3 ) ;
            arr[6] = v1 ;
            v1 -> next = v2 = getnode_write ( 8 ) ;
            v2 -> next = NULL ;

            v1 = getnode_write ( 4 ) ;
            arr[7] = v1 ;
            v1 -> next = v2 = getnode_write ( 5 ) ;
            v2 -> next = v3 = getnode_write ( 6 ) ;
            v3 -> next = v4 = getnode_write ( 7 ) ;
            v4 -> next = NULL ;
        printf("the list of nodes visited in this traversal are : \n\n\n\t");
            dfs ( 1, arr ) ;

        for ( i = 0 ; i < MAX ; i++ )
            del ( arr[i] ) ;

    getch( ) ;
}
//DFS SEARCH METHOD
void dfs ( int v, struct node **p )
{
        struct node *q ;
        visited[v - 1] = TRUE ;

        printf ( "%d\t", v ) ;
        q = * ( p + v - 1 ) ;

        while ( q != NULL )
        {
            if ( visited[q -> data - 1] == FALSE )
                    dfs ( q -> data, p ) ;
            else
                    q = q -> next ;
        }
}
//Creating a node
struct node * getnode_write ( int val )
{
    struct node *newnode ;
        newnode = ( struct node * ) malloc ( sizeof ( struct node ) ) ;
        newnode -> data = val ;
        return newnode ;
}
```

```
void del ( struct node *n )
{
        struct node *temp ;
    while ( n != NULL )
    {
        temp = n -> next ;
        free ( n ) ;
      n = temp ;
    }
}
```

Fig. 4.40   C code for depth-first search

4.8.6   Program that implements Breadth-First Search Algorithm

Figure 4.41 shows the C code for the breadth-first search.

```
#include <stdio.h>
#include <conio.h>
#include <alloc.h>

#define TRUE 1
#define FALSE 0
#define MAX 8
struct node
{
        int data ;
        struct node *next ;
} ;

int visited[MAX] ;
int q[8] ;
int front, rear ;

void bfs ( int, struct node ** ) ;
struct node * getnode_write ( int ) ;
void addqueue ( int ) ;
int deletequeue( ) ;
int isempty( ) ;
void del ( struct node * ) ;

void main( )
{
        struct node *arr[MAX] ;
        struct node *v1, *v2, *v3, *v4 ;
    int i ;
    clrscr( ) ;
    //represanting the Vertex 1 as linked list node
        v1 = getnode_write ( 2 ) ;
        arr[0] = v1 ;
        v1 -> next = v2 = getnode_write ( 3 ) ;
        v2 -> next = NULL ;
    //represanting the vertex 2 as linked list node
        v1 = getnode_write ( 1 ) ;
        arr[1] = v1 ;
        v1 -> next = v2 = getnode_write ( 4 ) ;
        v2 -> next = v3 = getnode_write ( 5 ) ;
        v3 -> next = NULL ;
```

```
        //represanting the vertex 3 as linked list node
            v1 = getnode_write ( 1 ) ;
            arr[2] = v1 ;
            v1 -> next = v2 = getnode_write ( 6 ) ;
            v2 -> next = v3 = getnode_write ( 7 ) ;
            v3 -> next = NULL ;

            v1 = getnode_write ( 2 ) ;
            arr[3] = v1 ;
            v1 -> next = v2 = getnode_write ( 8 ) ;
            v2 -> next = NULL ;

            v1 = getnode_write ( 2 ) ;
            arr[4] = v1 ;
            v1 -> next = v2 = getnode_write ( 8 ) ;
            v2 -> next = NULL ;

            v1 = getnode_write ( 3 ) ;
            arr[5] = v1 ;
            v1 -> next = v2 = getnode_write ( 8 ) ;
            v2 -> next = NULL ;

            v1 = getnode_write ( 3 ) ;
            arr[6] = v1 ;
            v1 -> next = v2 = getnode_write ( 8 ) ;
            v2 -> next = NULL ;

            v1 = getnode_write ( 4 ) ;
            arr[7] = v1 ;
            v1 -> next = v2 = getnode_write ( 5 ) ;
            v2 -> next = v3 = getnode_write ( 6 ) ;
            v3 -> next = v4 = getnode_write ( 7 ) ;
            v4 -> next = NULL ;

            front = rear = -1 ;
            printf("The list of nodes visited in bfs traversal are ; \n\n\n\t");
            bfs ( 1, arr ) ;

            for ( i = 0 ; i < MAX ; i++ )
                    del ( arr[i] ) ;

            getch( ) ;
}
// BFS SEARCH METHOD
void bfs ( int v, struct node **p )
{
            struct node *u ;

            visited[v - 1] = TRUE ;
            printf ( "%d\t", v ) ;
            addqueue ( v ) ;

            while ( isempty( ) == FALSE )
            {
                    v = deletequeue( ) ;
                    u = * ( p + v - 1 ) ;

                    while ( u != NULL )
                    {
                            if ( visited [ u -> data - 1 ] == FALSE )
                            {
                                    addqueue ( u -> data ) ;
                                    visited [ u -> data - 1 ] = TRUE ;
                                    printf ( "%d\t", u -> data ) ;
                            }
                            u = u -> next ;
```

```
                    }
               }
     }
//creating a node
struct node * getnode_write ( int val )
{
    struct node *newnode ;
         newnode = ( struct node * ) malloc ( sizeof ( struct node ) ) ;
         newnode -> data = val ;
         return newnode ;
}

// the data structure queue is being used to keep track the node visited
void addqueue ( int vertex )
{
         if ( rear == MAX - 1 )
         {
                  printf ( "\nQueue Overflow." ) ;
                  exit( ) ;
         }
         rear++ ;
         q[rear] = vertex ;

         if ( front == -1 )
                  front = 0 ;
}

int deletequeue( )
{
         int data ;

         if ( front == -1 )
         {
                  printf ( "\nQueue Underflow." ) ;
                  exit( ) ;
         }

         data = q[front] ;

         if ( front == rear )
                  front = rear = -1 ;
         else
                  front++ ;

         return data ;
}

int isempty( )
{
         if ( front == -1 )
                  return TRUE ;
         return FALSE ;
}

void del ( struct node *n )
{
         struct node *temp ;

         while ( n != NULL )
         {
              temp = n -> next ;
              free ( n ) ;
              n = temp ;
         }
}
```

Fig. 4.41 C code for breadth-first search

4.9 SHORTEST PATHS IN WEIGHTED GRAPHS

Let $G = (V, E, w)$ be a weighted graph, where w is a function from E to the set of positive real numbers. Consider V as a set of cities and E as a set of highways connecting these cities. The weight of an edge $\{i, j\}$, $w(i, j)$,* is usually referred to as the length of the edge $\{i, j\}$, which has an obvious interpretation as the distance between cities i and j, although other interpretations such as the yearly cost t maintain the highway, or the number of accidents on the highway each month are also possible and meaningful. The *length* of a path in G is defined to be the sum of the lengths of the edges in the path. One problem of significant interest is to determine a shortest path from one vertex to another vertex in V. There are several well-known procedures for solving this problem. We present here one discovered by E. W. Dijkstra [6]. Our presentation is in terms of undirected graphs, although the procedure works also for directed graphs.

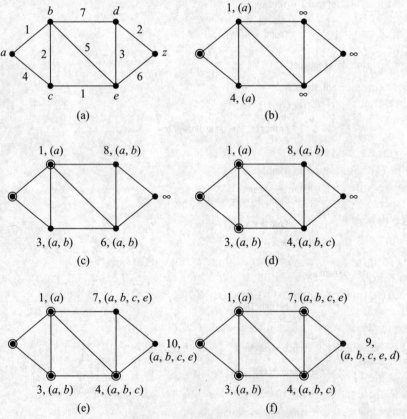

Fig. 4.42

---

* Strictly speaking, we should use the notation $w(\{i, j\})$. However, the notation $w(i, j)$ is simpler and unambiguous.

Suppose we are to determine a shortest path from vertex a to vertex z in G. In our procedure, a shortest path from a to some other vertex is determined, then a shortest path from a to still another vertex is determined, and so on. Eventually, our procedure terminates when a shortest path from a to z is determined.

Our procedure is based on the following observations: Let T be a subset of vertices in V with $a \notin T$. Let P denote the subset of vertices $V - T$. A shortest path from a to one of the vertices in T can be determined as follows: For each vertex t in T let $l(t)$ denote the length of a shortest path among all paths from a to t *that do not include any other vertex in T.** [Notice that $l(t)$ is not necessarily the shortest distance from a to t since there might be a shorter path from a to t that includes other vertices in T]. We call $l(t)$ the *index of t with respect to P.* Among all the vertices in T, let t_1 be a vertex that has the smallest index. We claim that the shortest distance between a and t_1 is indeed equal to $l(t_1)$. To prove our claim, let us assume that there is a path from a to t_1 whose length is less than $l(t_1)$. In this case such a path must include one or more of the vertices in $T - \{t_1\}$. Let t_2 be the first vertex in $T - \{t_1\}$ we encounter when we trace this path from a to t_1. It follows that $l(t_2)$ is less than $l(t_1)$, which is a contradiction. Consequently, if, when computing $l(t)$, we recorded the sequence of vertices in the path that yielded $l(t)$ for each t in T, we would also have determined a shortest path from a to t_1. For example, for the graph in Fig. 4.42a, let $T = \{c, d, e, z\}$. We ask the reader to check that $l(c) = 3$, $l(d) = 8$, $l(e) = 6$, $l(z) = \infty$. It follows that the shortest distance from a to c is 3.

We must also, however, find an efficient way to compute $l(t)$ for each t in T. Again, let T be a subset of V and let $P = V - T$. Suppose that for every vertex p in P, there is a shortest path from a to p that includes only the vertices in P. We assume that for each vertex t in T we have already computed its index with respect to P, $l(t)$. Let x be a vertex in T. Let P' be $P \cup \{x\}$ and T' be $T - \{x\}$. Let $l'(t)$ denote the index of a vertex t in T' with respect to P'. We claim that

$$l'(t) = \min \ [l(t), l(x) + w(x, t)]^{\dagger} \quad (4.1)$$

To show this, we observe that there are two possible ways to obtain a shortest path from a to t that does not include any vertex in T'. The first way is to have a path that includes neither a vertex in T' nor the vertex x. In that case, the index of t with respect to P' is $l(t)$. The second way is to have a path consisting of a path from a to x that includes no vertex in T, followed by the edge $\{x, t\}$. In that case, the index of t with respect to P' is $l(x) + w(x, t)$. We should point out that we need not consider the possibility of having a path that goes from a to x, then to some p_1 in P, and then to t. Because if this is the case, while there is a shortest path from a to p_1 that includes x, there is also one that does not include x which can replace it. Consequently, this is reduced to the first possibility considered above. For example, for the graph in Fig. 4.42a, let $P = \{a, b\}$ and $T = \{c, d, e, z\}$.

---

* We set $l(t)$ to ∞ if no such path exists.

$\dagger$ We set $w(x, t)$ to infinity if there is no edge joining x and t in the graph.

Suppose we have already computed $l(c) = 3$, $l(d) = 8$, $l(e) = 6$, $l(z) = \infty$. Let $P' = \{a, b, c\}$, $T' = \{d, e, z\}$. We have

$$l'(d) = \min (8, 3 + \infty) = 8$$
$$l'(e) = \min (6, 3 + 1) = 4$$
$$l'(z) = \min (\infty, 3 + \infty) = \infty$$

These observations lead to the following procedure for computing the shortest distance from a to any vertex in G:

1. Initially, let $P = \{a\}$ and $T = V - \{a\}$. For every vertex t in T, let $l(t) = w(a, t)$.
2. Select the vertex in T that has the smallest index with respect to P. Let x denote this vertex.
3. If x is the vertex we wish to reach from a, stop. If not, let $P' = P \cup \{x\}$ and $T' = T - \{x\}$. For every vertex t in T', compute its index with respect to P' according to (4.1).
4. Repeat steps 2 and 3 using P' as P and T' as T.

We ask the reader to incorporate into this procedure the necessary computation for keeping track of the path from a to x, whose length is equal to $l(x)$ for each x in T. In that case, we shall be able to determine a shortest path from a to x as well as the shortest distance.

For example, for the weighted graph in Fig. 4.42a, the successive steps for determining a shortest path between a and z are shown in Fig. 4.42b through Fig. 4.42f, where the vertices in P are encircled. Note that the vertices in T are labeled with their indices. Moreover, a vertex whose index is not infinity is also labeled with the sequence of vertices corresponding to a path from a to that vertex whose length is equal to the index of the vertex. We urge the reader's effort to understand fully how these labels of sequences of vertices corresponding to the paths from a are constructed and modified. Thus, the minimum distance between a and z is 9, and moreover, the shortest path is (a, b, c, e, d, z).

Below, we explain two more examples to better understand the application of the above procedure for computing the shortest distance between two vertices of a graph. In our following examples, we use the terms *nodes* and *vertices* interchangeably.

Example 4.8 Find the shortest path between the vertices a and z in the graph shown in Fig. 4.43(a).

Solution: Initially, let $P = \{a\}$ and $T = \{b, c, d, e, z\}$.
Now,

$$l(b) = w(a, b) = 7,$$
$$l(c) = w(a, c) = 3,$$
$$l(d) = w(a, d) = \infty,$$
$$l(e) = w(a, e) = \infty,$$
$$l(z) = w(a, z) = \infty,$$

Fig. 4.43 (b) shows the initialization and the respective indices of the nodes of T.

Iteration 1: Consider the vertex c of T as $l(c)$ is the lowest index with respect to P. Now,

$$P' = P \cup \{c\} = \{a\} \cup \{c\} = \{a, c\} \text{ and}$$
$$T' = T - \{c\} = \{b, c, d, e, z\} - \{c\} = \{b, d, e, z\}.$$

Then, we compute

$$l'(b) = \min [l(b), l(c) + w(c, b)]$$
$$= \min [7, 3 + \infty] = 7$$

$$l'(d) = \min [l(d), l(c) + w(c, b)]$$
$$= \min [\infty, 3 + \infty] = \infty$$

$$l'(e) = \min [l(e), l(c) + w(c, e)]$$
$$= \min [\infty, 3 + 1] = 4$$

$$l'(z) = \min [l(z), l(c) + w(c, z)]$$
$$= \min [\infty, 3 + \infty] = \infty$$

Fig. 4.43 (c) shows the result after iteration 1 and the respective indices of the nodes of T.

Iteration 2: Now, consider $P = P'$, $T = T'$ and the respective indices w.r.t. P as

$$l(b) = l'(b), l(d) = l'(d), l(e) = l'(e), l(z) = l'(z)$$

Consider the vertex e of T as $l(e)$ is the lowest index with respect to P.

$$P' = P \cup \{e\} = \{a, c\} \cup \{e\} = \{a, c, e\} \text{ and}$$
$$T' = T - \{e\} = \{b, d, e, z\} - \{e\} = \{b, d, z\}$$

$$l'(b) = \min [l(b), l(e) + w(e, b)]$$
$$= \min [7, 4 + 2] = 6$$

$$l'(d) = \min [l(d), l(e) + w(e, d)]$$
$$= \min [\infty, 4 + 9] = 13$$

$$l'(z) = \min [l(z), l(e) + w(e, z)]$$
$$= \min [\infty, 4 + 8] = 12$$

Fig. 4.43 (d) shows the result after iteration 2 and the respective indices of the nodes of T.

Iteration 3: Now, consider

$$P = P', T = T' \text{ and the respective indices w.r.t. } P \text{ as}$$
$$l(b) = l'(b), l(b) = l'(d), l(z) = l'(z)$$

Consider the vertex b of T as $l(b)$ is the lowest index with respect to P. Now,

$$P' = P \cup \{b\} = \{a, c, e\} \cup \{b\} = \{a, c, e, b\} \text{ and}$$
$$T' = T - \{b\} = \{b, d, z\} - \{b\} = \{d, z\}$$

$$l'(d) = \min [l(d), l(b) + W(b, d)]$$
$$= \min [13, 6 + 2] = 8$$

$$l'(z) = \min [l(z), l(b) + W(b, z)]$$
$$= \min [12, 6 + \infty] = 12$$

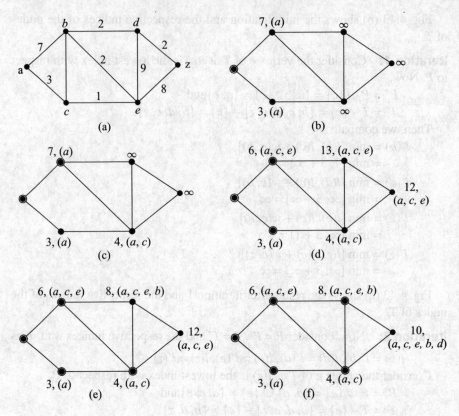

Fig. 4.43

Fig. 4.43 (e) shows the result after iteration 3 and the respective indices of the nodes of T.

Iteration 4: Now, consider

$P = P'$, $T = T'$ and the respetive indices w.r.t. P as

$$l(d) = l'(d), l(z) = l'(z)$$

Consider the vertex d of T as $l(d)$ is the lowest index with respect to P. Now,

$$P' = P \cup \{d\} = \{a, c, e, b\} \cup \{d\} = \{a, c, e, b\} \text{ and}$$

$$T' = T - \{d\} = \{b, z\} - \{d\} = \{z\}$$

$$l'(z) = \min [l(z), l(d) + W(d, z)]$$

$$= \min [12, 8 + 2] = 10$$

Fig. 4.43 (f) shows the result after iteration 4 and the respective indices of the nodes of T.

Iteration 5: Now, let

$P = P'$, $T = T'$ and the respective indices w.r.t. P as $l(z) = l'(z)$.

Consider the vertex z of T. Since z is the destination node, so the process stops here.

Thus, minimum distance between a and z is 10, and moreover, the shortest path is (a, c, e, b, d, z). ∎

Example 4.9 Find the shortest path between the vertices a and z in the graph shown in Fig. 4.44(a).

Solution:

Initially, let P = (a) and T = $\{b, c, d, e, f, g, z\}$. Now,

$l(b) = w(a, b) = 5, l(c) = w(a, c) = 2, l(d) = w(a, d) = \infty, l(e) = w(a, e) = \infty,$
$l(f) = w(a, f) = \infty, l(g) = w(a, g) = \infty, l(z) = w(a, z) = \infty,$

Fig. 4.44 (b) shows the initialization and the respective indices of the nodes of T.

Iteration 1: Consider the vertex c of T as $l(c)$ is the lowest index with respect to P. Now,

$$P' = P \cup \{c\} = \{a\} \cup \{c\} = \{a, c\} \text{ and}$$
$$T' = T - \{c\} = \{b, c, d, e, f, g, z\} - \{c\} = \{b, d, e, f, g, z\}.$$

Then, we compute

$$l'(b) = \min [l(b), l(c) + W(c, b)] = \min [5, 2 + 2] = \min [5, 4] = 4$$
$$l'(d) = \min [l(d), l(c) + W(c, d)] = \min [\infty, 2 + 5] = \min [\infty, 7] = 7$$
$$l'(e) = \min [l(e), l(c) + W(c, e)] = \min [\infty, 2 + 6] = \min [\infty, 8] = 8$$
$$l'(f) = \min [l(f), l(c) + W(c, f)] = \min [\infty, 2 + \infty] = \min [\infty, \infty] = \infty$$
$$l'(g) = \min [l(g), l(c) + W(c, g)] = \min [\infty, 2 + \infty] = \min [\infty, \infty] = \infty$$
$$l'(z) = \min [l(z), l(c) + W(c, z)] = \min [\infty, 2 + \infty] = \min [\infty, \infty] = \infty$$

Fig. 4.44 (c) shows the result after iteration 1 and the respective indices of the nodes of T.

Iteration 2: Now, consider $P = P', T = T'$ and the respective indices w.r.t. P as

$l(b) = l'(b), l(d) = l'(d), l(e) = l'(e), l(f) = l'(f), l(g) = l'(g), l(z) = l'(z)$

Consider the vertex b of T and $l(b)$ is the lowest index with respect to P. Now,

$$P' = P \cup \{b\} = \{a, c\} \cup \{b\} = \{a, c, d\} \text{ and}$$
$$T' = T - \{b\} = \{b, d, e, f, g, z\} - \{b\} = \{d, e, f, g, z\}.$$

Then, we compute

$$l'(d) = \min [l(d), l(b) + W(b, d)] = \min [7, 4 + 2] = \min [7, 6] = 6$$
$$l'(e) = \min [l(e), l(b) + W(b, e)] = \min [8, 4 + \infty] = \min [8, \infty] = 8$$
$$l'(f) = \min [l(f), l(b) + W(b, f)] = \min [\infty, 4 + \infty] = \min [\infty, \infty] = \infty$$
$$l'(g) = \min [l(g), l(b) + W(b, g)] = \min [\infty, 4 + \infty] = \min [\infty, \infty] = \infty$$
$$l'(z) = \min [l(z), l(b) + W(b, z)] = \min [\infty, 4 + \infty] = \min [\infty, \infty] = \infty$$

Fig. 4.44 (d) shows the result after iteration 2 and the respective indices of the nodes of T.

Iteration 3: Now, consider

$P = P'$, $T = T'$ and the respective indices w.r.t. P as

$l(d) = l'(d)$, $l(e) = l'(e)$, $l(f) = l'(f)$, $l(g) = l'(g)$, $l(z) = l'(z)$

Consider the vertex d of T and $l(d)$ is the lowest index with respect to P. Now,

$P' = P \cup \{d\} = \{a, c, b\} \cup \{d\} = \{a, c, b, d\}$ and

$T' = T - \{d\} = \{d, e, f, g, z\} - \{d\} = \{e, f, g, z\}$.

Then, we compute

$l'(e) = \min [l(e), l(d) + W(d, e)] = \min [8, 6 + 1] = \min [8, 7] = 7$

$l'(f) = \min [l(f), l(d) + W(d, f)] = \min [\infty, 6 + 6] = \min [\infty, 12] = 12$

$l'(g) = \min [l(g), l(d) + W(d, g)] = \min [\infty, 6 + \infty] = \min [\infty, \infty] = \infty$

$l'(z) = \min [l(z), l(d) + W(d, z)] = \min [\infty, 6 + \infty] = \min [\infty, \infty] = \infty$

Fig. 4.44 (e) shows the result after iteration 3 and the respective indices of the nodes of T.

Iteration 4: Now, consider

$P = P'$, $T = T'$ and the respective indices w.r.t. P as

$l(e) = l'(e)$, $l(f) = l'(f)$, $l(g) = l'(g)$, $l(z) = l'(z)$

Consider the vertex e of T as $l(e)$ is the lowest index with respect to P. Now,

$P' = P \cup \{e\} = \{a, c, b, d\} \cup \{e\} = \{a, c, b, d, e\}$ and

$T' = T - \{e\} = \{e, f, g, z\} - \{e\} = \{f, g, z\}$.

Then, we compute

$l'(f) = \min [l(f), l(e) + W(e, f)] = \min [12, 7 + \infty] = \min [12, \infty] = 12$

$l'(g) = \min [l(g), l(e) + W(e, g)] = \min [\infty, 7 + 2] = \min [\infty, 9] = 9$

$l'(z) = \min [l(z), l(e) + W(e, z)] = \min [\infty, 7 + \infty] = \min [\infty, \infty] = \infty$

Fig. 4.44 (f) shows the result after iteration 4 and the respective indices of the nodes of T.

Iteration 5: Now, consider

$P = P'$, $T = T'$ and the respective indices w.r.t. P as

$l(f) = l'(f)$, $l(g) = l'(g)$, $l(z) = l'(z)$

Consider the vertex g of T and $l(g)$ is the lowest index with respect to P. Now,

$P' = P \cup \{g\} = \{a, c, b, d, e\} \cup \{g\} = \{a, c, b, d, e, g\}$ and

$T' = T - \{g\} = \{f, g, z\} - \{g\} = \{f, z\}$.

Then, we compute

$l'(g) = \min [l(f), l(g) + W(g, f)] = \min [12, 9 + 2] = \min [12, 11] = 11$

$l'(z) = \min [l(z), l(g) + W(g, z)] = \min [\infty, 9 + 7] = \min [\infty, 16] = 16$

Fig. 4.44 (g) shows the result after iteration 5 and the respective indices of the nodes of T.

Iteration 6: Now, consider

$P = P'$, $T = T'$ and the respective indices w.r.t. P as $l(f) = l'(f)$, $l(z) = l'(z)$

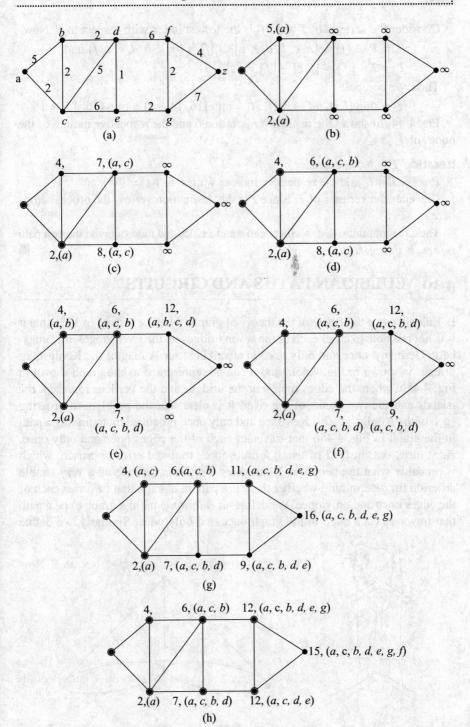

Fig. 4·44

Consider the vertex f of T and $l(f)$ is the lowest index with respect to P. Now,

$P' = P \cup \{f\} = \{a, c, b, d, e, g\} \cup \{f\} = \{a, c, b, d, e, g, f\}$ and
$T' = T - \{f\} = \{f, z\} - \{f\} = \{z\}$.

Then, we compute

$l'(z) = \min [l(z), l(f) + W(f, z)] = \min [16, 11 + 4] = \min [16, 15] = 15$

Fig. 4.44 (h) shows the result after iteration 6 and the respective indices of the nodes of T.

Iteration 7:   Now, consider

$P = P', T = T'$ and the respective indices w.r.t. P as $l(z) = l'(z)$.

Consider the vertex z of T. Since z is the destination vertex, the process stops here.

Thus, the minimum distance between a and z is 15, and moreover the shortest path is (a, c, b, d, e, g, f, z).   ■

4.10   EULERIAN PATHS AND CIRCUITS

L. Euler became the father of the theory of graphs when he proved in 1736 that it was not possible to cross each of the seven bridges on the river Pregel in Königsberg, Germany, once and only once in a walking tour. A map of the Königsberg bridges is shown in Fig. 4.45*a*, and it can be represented as the graph shown in Fig. 4.45*b*, where the edges represent the bridges and the vertices represent the islands and the two banks of the river. It is clear that the problem of crossing each of the Königsberg bridges once and only once is equivalent to finding a path in the graph in Fig. 4.45*b* that traverses each of the edges once and only once. As it turns out, instead of using a brute-force trial-and-error approach, which is probably what the people at Königsberg did, Euler discovered a very simple criterion for determining whether there is a path in a graph that traverses each of the edges once and only once. We define an *eulerian path* in a graph to be a path that traverses each edge in the graph once and only once. Similarly, we define

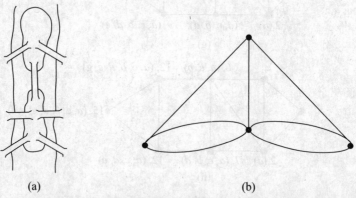

(a)   (b)

Fig. 4.45   (a) Map of the Königsberg bridges (b) Its graphical representation.

an *eulerian circuit* in a graph to be a circuit that traverses each edge in the graph once and only once. We restrict our discussion to undirected graphs for the time being. As will be seen later, extension to directed graphs is rather straightforward.

To establish a necessary and sufficient condition for the existence of eulerian paths or circuits in an arbitrary graph, we introduce the notion of the *degree* of a vertex. The degree of a vertex is the number of edges incident with it. (Note that a loop will contribute a count of 2.) We observe first that in any graph there is an even number of vertices of odd degree. Since each edge contributes a count of 1 to the degree of each of the two vertices with which it is incident, the sum of the degrees of the vertices is equal to twice the number of edges in a graph. It follows that there must be an even number of vertices of odd degree.

The existence of eulerian paths or eulerian circuits in a graph is related to the degrees of the vertices. We show now a result due to Euler:

Theorem 4.3   An undirected graph possesses an eulerian path if and only if it is connected and has either zero or two vertices of odd degree.*

Proof: Suppose that the graph possesses an eulerian path. That the graph must be connected is obvious. When the eulerian path is traced, we observe that every time the path meets a vertex, it goes through two edges which are incident with the vertex and have not been traced before. Thus, except for the two vertices at the two ends of the path, the degree of any vertex in the graph must be even. If the two vertices at the two ends of the eulerian path are distinct, they are the only two vertices with odd degree. If they coincide, all vertices have even degree, and the eulerian path becomes an eulerian circuit. Thus, the necessity of the stated condition is proved.

To prove the sufficiency of the stated condition, we construct an eulerian path by starting at one of the two vertices that are of odd degree† and going through the edges of the graph in such a way that no edge will be traced more than once. For a vertex of even degree, whenever the path "enters" the vertex through an edge, it can always "leave" the vertex through another edge that has not been traced before. Therefore, when the construction eventually comes to an end, we must have reached the other vertex of odd degree. If all the edges in the graph were traced this way, clearly, we would have an eulerian path. If not all of the edges in the graph were traced, we shall remove those edges that have been traced and obtain a subgraph formed by the remaining edges. The degrees of the vertices of this subgraph are all even. Moreover, this subgraph must touch the path that we have traced at one or more vertices since the original graph is connected. Starting from one of these vertices, we can again construct a path that passes through the edges. Because the degrees of the vertices are all even, this path must return eventually to the vertex at which it starts. We can combine this path with the path we have constructed to obtain one which starts and ends at the two vertices of odd

---

* We rule out the uninteresting case of graphs containing isolated vertices.

† We start at an arbitrary vertex if there is no vertex of odd degree.

degree. If necessary, the argument is repeated until we obtain a path that traverses all the edges in the graph. ■

Corollary 4.3.1:   An undirected graph possesses an eulerian circuit if and only if it is connected and its vertices are all of even degree.

We conclude from Theorem 4.3 and Corollary 4.3.1 that the graph in Fig. 4.46*a* has an eulerian path but not an eulerian circuit, because the graph is connected and there are exactly two vertices, *d* and *e*, of odd degree. Also, the graph in Fig. 4.46*b* has an eulerian circuit because the graph is connected and all the vertices are of even degree.

We show now some illustrative examples.

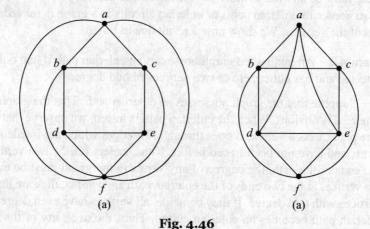

(a)   (a)

Fig. 4.46

Example 4.10   We often encounter the puzzle of determining the possibility of drawing a given figure in a continuous trace with no part of the figure being repeated. For example, the figure in Fig. 4.47*a* can be traced as shown in Fig. 4.40*b*. Imagine that the figure in Fig. 4.47*a* is a graph as shown in Fig. 4.47*c*. Then the problem of tracing the figure in Fig. 4.47*a* is that of determining the existence of an Euler path in the graph in Fig. 4.47*c*. Since the graph in Fig. 4.47*c* has only two vertices of odd degree, it has an eulerian path. Similarly, the two figures in Fig. 4.47*d* can also be drawn in a continuous trace with no portion of the figures being repeated. ■

Example 4.11   We want to know whether it is possible to arrange the 28 different dominoes* in a circle so that the adjacent halves of every two adjacent dominoes in the arrangement are the same. We construct a graph with seven vertices corresponding to blank, 1, 2, 3, 4, 5, and 6. There is an edge between every pair of vertices corresponding to a domino with its two halves being the two vertices the edge is incident with. It follows that an eulerian circuit in this graph

---

* See Example 2.17

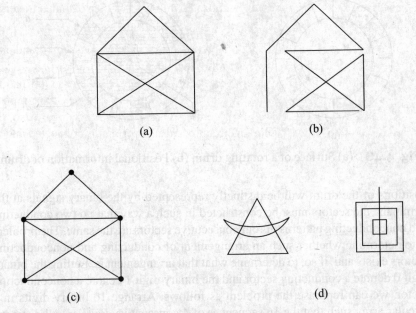

(a)   (b)

(c)   (d)

Fig. 4.47

will correspond to a circular arrangement, as specified in the foregoing. Since the degree of every vertex in this graph is 8, an eulerian circuit indeed exists.   ■

Our results can be extended immediately to directed graphs. In a directed graph, the *incoming degree* of a vertex is the number of edges that are incident *into* it, and the *outgoing degree* of a vertex is the number of edges that are incident *from* it. Similar to the results on undirected graphs, we have the following:

Theorem 4.4   A directed graph possesses an eulerian circuit if and only if it is connected and the incoming degree of every vertex is equal to its outgoing degree. A directed graph possesses an eulerian path if and only if it is connected and the incoming degree of every vertex is equal to its outgoing degree with the possible exception of two vertices. For these two vertices, the incoming degree of one is one larger than its outgoing degree, and the incoming degree of the other is one less than its outgoing degree.

Example 4.12   An interesting example is from an analog-to-digital conversion problem. The surface of a rotating drum is divided into 16 sectors and is shown in Fig. 4.48a. The positional information of the drum is to be represented by the digital binary signals, a, b, c, and d, as shown in Fig. 4.48b, where conducting (lined area) and nonconducting (white area) materials are used to make up the sectors. Depending on the position of the drum, the terminals a, b, c, and d will either be connected to ground or be insulated from it. For example, when the position of the drum is that shown in Fig. 4.48b, terminals a, c, and d are connected to ground, whereas terminal b is not. In order that the 16 different

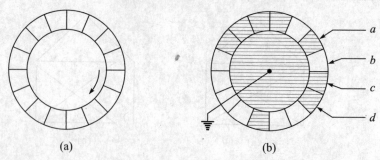

(a)   (b)

Fig. 4.48 (a) Surface of a rotating drum (b) Positional information of drum

positions of the drum will be distinctly represented by the binary signals at the terminals, the sectors must be constructed in such a way that no two conducting and nonconducting patterns of four consecutive sectors are the same. The problem is to determine whether such an arrangement of conducting and nonconducting sectors exists and, if so, to determine what that arrangement is. Letting the binary digit 0 denote a conducting sector and the binary digit 1 denote a nonconducting sector, we can rephrase the problem as follows: Arrange 16 binary digits in a circular array such that the 16 sequences of 4 consecutive digits are all distinct.

The answer to the question of the possibility of such an arrangement is affirmative, and it is actually quite obvious once the right point of view has been taken. We shall construct a directed graph with eight vertices, which are labeled with the eight distinct 3-digit binary numbers $\{000, 001, \ldots, 111\}$. From a vertex labeled $\alpha_1\alpha_2\alpha_3$, there is an edge to the vertex labeled $\alpha_2\alpha_3 0$ and an edge to the vertex labeled $\alpha_2\alpha_3 1$. The graph so constructed is shown in Fig. 4.49. Moreover, we shall label each edge of the graph with a 4-digit binary number. In particular, the edge from the vertex $\alpha_1\alpha_2\alpha_3$ to the vertex $\alpha_2\alpha_3 0$ is labeled $\alpha_1\alpha_2\alpha_3 0$, and the edge from the vertex $\alpha_1\alpha_2\alpha_3$ to the vertex $\alpha_2\alpha_3 1$ is labeled $\alpha_1\alpha_2\alpha_3 1$. Since the vertices are labeled with the eight distinct 3-digit binary numbers, the edges will be labeled with the 16 distinct 4-digit binary numbers. In a path of the graph, the labels for any two consecutive edges must be of the form $\alpha_1\alpha_2\alpha_3\alpha_4$ and $\alpha_2\alpha_3\alpha_4\alpha_5$; namely, the three trailing digits of the label of the first edge are identical to the three leading digits of the label of the second edge. Since the 16 edges in the graph are labeled with distinct binary numbers, it follows that corresponding to an eulerian circuit of the graph, there is a circular arrangement of 16 binary digits in which all sequences of 4 consecutive digits are distinct. For instance, corresponding to the eulerian circuit $(e_0, e_1, e_2, e_5, e_{10}, e_4, e_9, e_3, e_6, e_{13}, e_{11}, e_7, e_{15}, e_{14}, e_{12}, e_8)$, the sequence of 16 binary digits is 0000101001101111. (The circular arrangement is obtained by closing the two ends of the sequence.) According to our result in the foregoing, the existence of an eulerian circuit in the graph is obvious, because every one of the vertices has an incoming degree equal to 2 and an outgoing degree equal to 2. Moreover, we can find an eulerian circuit in the graph by following the construction procedure suggested in the proof of Theorem 4.3.

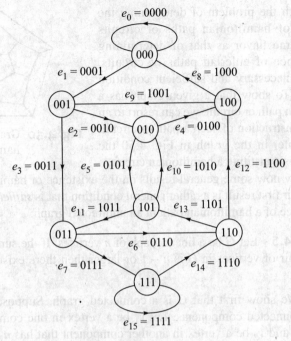

Fig. 4.49

Using a similar argument, we can show that it is possible to arrange 2^n binary digits in a circular array such that the 2^n sequences of n consecutive digits in the arrangement are all distinct. To show this, we construct a directed graph with 2^{n-1} vertices which are labeled with the 2^{n-1} $(n-1)$-digit binary numbers. From the vertex $\alpha_1\alpha_2\alpha_3 \ldots \alpha_{n-1}$, there is an edge to the vertex $\alpha_2\alpha_3 \ldots \alpha_{n-1}0$ which is labeled $\alpha_1\alpha_2\alpha_3 \ldots \alpha_{n-1}0$, and an edge to the vertex $\alpha_2\alpha_3 \ldots \alpha_{n-1}1$ which is labeled $\alpha_1\alpha_2\alpha_3 \ldots \alpha_{n-1}1$. Clearly, this graph has an eulerian circuit which corresponds to a circular arrangement of the 2^n binary digits. ∎

4.11 HAMILTONIAN PATHS AND CIRCUITS

A problem similar to the determination of an eulerian path or an eulerian circuit is to determine a path or a circuit that passes through each vertex in a graph once and only once. We define a *hamiltonian path* (circuit) to be a path (circuit) that passes through each of the vertices in a graph exactly once. (Sir William Hamilton invented the game "all around the world" in which the player is asked to determine a route along the dodecahedron that will pass through each angular point once and only once.)

As an example, consider the problem of seating a group of people at a round table. If we let the vertices of an undirected graph denote the people and the edges represent the relation that two people are friends, a hamiltonian circuit corresponds to a way of seating them so that everyone has a friend on each side.

Although the problem of determining the existence of hamiltonian paths or circuits has the same flavor as that of determining the existence of eulerian paths or circuits, no simple necessary and sufficient condition is known. To show that a given graph has a hamiltonian path or circuit, we can resort to an explicit construction of such a path or circuit. For example, in the graph in Fig. 4.50 the heavy edges constitute a hamiltonian circuit.

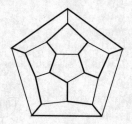

Fig. 4.50 Graph containing a hamiltonian circuit

We show now some general results on the existence of hamiltonian paths or circuits. Our first result is a rather general condition that is *sufficient* to guarantee the existence of a hamiltonian path in an undirected graph:

Theorem 4.5 Let G be a linear graph of n vertices. If the sum of the degrees for each pair of vertices in G is $n - 1$ or larger then there exists a hamiltonian path in G.*

Proof: We show first that G is a connected graph. Suppose G has two or more disconnected components. Let v_1 be a vertex in one component that has n_1 vertices and v_2 be a vertex in another component that has n_2 vertices. Since the degree of v_1 is at most $n_1 - 1$ and the degree of v_2 is at most $n_2 - 1$, the sum of their degrees is at most $n_1 + n_2 - 2$, which is less than $n - 1$, and we have a contradiction.

We show now how a hamiltonian path can be constructed in a step-by-step manner, starting with a path containing a single edge. Let there be a path of $p - 1$ edges, $p < n$, in G which meets the sequence of vertices $(v_1, v_2, ..., v_p)$. If either v_1 or v_p is adjacent to a vertex that is not in the path, we can immediately extend the path to include this vertex and obtain a path of p edges. Otherwise, both v_1 and v_p are adjacent only to the vertices that are in the path. We want to show that in that case there is a circuit containing exactly the vertices $v_1, v_2, ..., v_p$. If v_1 is adjacent to v_p, then the circuit $(v_1, v_2, ..., v_p, v_1)$ will suffice, so let us assume that v_1 is adjacent only to $v_{i1}, v_{i2}, ..., v_{ik}$, where $2 \leq i_j \leq p - 1$.† If v_p is adjacent to one of $v_{i1-1}, v_{i2-1}, ..., v_{ik-1}$, say v_{j-1}, then, as shown in Fig. 4.51, the circuit $(v_1, v_2,$

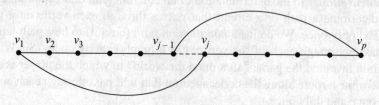

Fig. 4.51

$v_3, \ldots, v_{j-1}, v_p, v_{p-1}, \ldots, v_j, v_1)$ contains exactly the vertices $v_1, v_2, \ldots, v_p$. If v_p is not adjacent to any one of $v_{i1-1}, v_{i2-1}, \ldots, v_{ik-1}$, then v_p is adjacent to at most $p - k - 1$ vertices. Consequently, the sum of the degrees of v_1 and v_p is at most $n - 2$, which is a contradiction.

Now that we have a circuit containing all the vertices $v_1, v_2, \ldots, v_p$, let us pick a vertex v_x that is not in the circuit. Because G is connected, there is a vertex v_k that is not in the circuit with an edge between v_x and v_k for some v_k in $\{v_1, v_2, \ldots, v_p\}$, as shown in Fig. 4.52a. We now have the path $(v_x, v_k, v_{k+1}, \ldots, v_{j-1}, v_p, v_{p-1}, \ldots, v_j, v_1, v_2, \ldots, v_{k-1})$, which contains p edges, as shown in Fig. 4.52b.

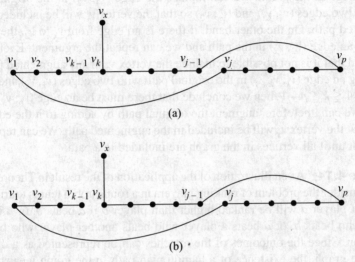

Fig. 4.52

We can repeat the foregoing construction until we obtain a path with $n - 1$ edges. ∎

It is easy to see that the condition in Theorem 4.5 is a sufficient but not a necessary condition for the existence of a hamiltonian path in a graph. Let G be an n-gon, $n > 5$. It is clear that G has a hamiltonian path although the sum of the degrees of any two vertices is 4.

Example 4.13 Consider the problem of scheduling seven examinations in seven days so that two examinations given by the same instructor are not scheduled on consecutive days. If no instructor gives more than four examinations, show that it is always possible to schedule the examinations. Let G be a graph with seven vertices corresponding to the seven examinations. There is an edge between any two vertices which correspond to two examinations given by different instructors. Since the degree of each vertex is at least 3, the sum of the degrees of any two vertices is at least 6. Consequently, G always contains a hamiltonian path, which corresponds to a suitable schedule for the seven examinations. ∎

Another interesting result is given in Theorem 4.6.

Theorem 4.6   There is always a hamiltonian path in a directed complete graph.

Proof: Let there be a path with $p - 1$ edges in a directed complete graph which meets the sequence of vertices $(v_1, v_2, ..., v_p)$. Let v_x be a vertex that is not included in this path. If there is an edge (v_x, v_1) in the graph, we can augment the original path by adding the edge (v_x, v_1) to the path so that the vertex v_x will be included in the augmented path. If, on the other hand, there is no edge from v_x to v_1 then there must be an edge (v_1, v_x) in the graph. Suppose that (v_x, v_2) is also an edge in the graph. We can replace the edge (v_1, v_2) in the original path with the two edges (v_1, v_x) and (v_x, v_2) so that the vertex v_x will be included in the augmented path. On the other hand, if there is no edge from v_x to v_2, then there must be an edge (v_2, v_x) in the path and we can repeat the argument. Eventually, if we find that it is not possible to include the vertex v_x in any augmented path by replacing an edge (v_k, v_{k+1}) in the original path with two edges (v_k, v_x) and (v_x, v_{k+1}) with $1 \leq k \leq p - 1$ then we conclude that there must be an edge (v_p, v_x) in the graph. We can, therefore, augment the original path by adding to it the edge (v_p, v_x) so that the vertex v_x will be included in the augmented path. We can repeat the argument until all vertices in the graph are included in a path.   ■

Example 4.14   As an illustration of the application of the result in Theorem 4.5, let us consider the problem of ranking players in a round-robin tennis tournament such that player a will be ranked higher than player b if a beats b, or a beats a player who beats b, or a beats a player who beats another player who beats b, and so on. Since the outcomes of the matches can be represented as a directed complete graph, the existence of a hamiltonian path in the graph means that it is always possible to rank the players linearly. (Note that such a ranking is not necessarily unique.)   ■

Example 4.15   As another illustrative example, we consider the problem of printing and then binding n books. There is one printing machine and one binding machine. Let p_i and b_i denote the printing time and binding time of book i, respectively. If it is known for any two books i and j that either $b_i \geq p_j$ or $b_j \geq p_i$, show that it is possible to specify an order in which the books are printed (and then bound) so that the binding machine will be kept busy until all books are bound, once the first book is printed. (Thus, the total time it takes for completing the whole task is $p_k + \sum_{i=1}^{n} b_i$ for some k.) Let us construct a directed graph of n vertices corresponding to the n books. There is an edge from vertex i to vertex j if and only if $b_i \geq p_j$. We note that this is a directed complete graph, and a hamiltonian path in the directed complete graph will be an ordering of the books satisfying the condition stated above.   ■

There is no general method of solution to the problem of proving the non-existence of a hamiltonian path or circuit in a graph. We present here, however, an illustrative example.

Example 4.16 We want to show that the graph in Fig. 4.53a has no hamiltonian path. We label the vertex a by A and label all the vertices that are adjacent to it by B. Continuing, we label all the vertices that are adjacent to a B vertex by A and label all the vertices that are adjacent to an A vertex by B, until all vertices are labeled. The labeled graph is shown in Fig. 4.53b. If there is a hamiltonian path in the graph then it must pass through the A vertices and the B vertices alternately. However, since there are nine A vertices and seven B vertices, the existence of a hamiltonian path is impossible. ∎

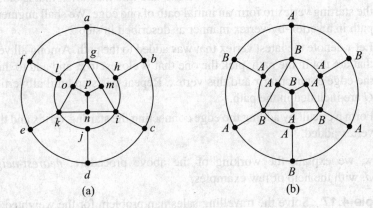

(a)　　　　　　　　　(b)

Fig. 4.53

*4.12　THE TRAVELING SALESPERSON PROBLEM

We discuss in this section a natural extension of the problem of finding a hamiltonian circuit in a graph. The *traveling salesperson problem* has long been of great interest. Let $G = (V, E, w)$ be a complete graph of n vertices, where w is a function from E to the set of positive real numbers such that for any three vertices i, j, k in V

$$w(i, j) + w(j, k) \geqq w(i, k)*$$

We shall refer to $w(i, j)$ as the length of edge $\{i, j\}$. The traveling salesperson problem asks for a hamiltonian circuit of minimum length, where, again, the length of a circuit is defined as the sum of the lengths of the edges in the circuit.

A physical interpretation of the abstract formulation is rather obvious: Consider the graph G as a map of n cities where $w(i, j)$ is the distance between cities i and j. A salesperson wants to have a tour of the n cities which starts and ends at the same city and includes visiting each of the remaining $n - 1$ cities once and only once. Moreover, an itinerary that has a minimum total distance is desired.

---

* This condition, known as the *triangle inequality,* is needed to prove the result in (4.2). On the other hand, one might be able to argue that the triangular inequality is satisfied in most real-life cases anyway.

The traveling salesperson problem turns out to be a difficult one in that we know of no "efficient"* procedure for solving the problem. Recalling our discussion in Sec. 3.9 on the job-scheduling problem, one might wish to look for simple procedures that will give good results to the traveling salesperson problem. To illustrate such a possibility, we present a procedure, known as the *nearest-neighbor method,* which gives reasonably good results for the traveling salesperson problem:

1. Start with an arbitrarily chosen vertex, and find the vertex that is closest to the starting vertex to form an initial path of one edge. We shall augment this path in a vertex-by-vertex manner as described in step 2.

2. Let x denote the latest vertex that was added to the path. Among all vertices that are not in the path, pick the one that is closest to x, and add to the path the edge connecting x and this vertex. Repeat this step until all vertices in G are included in the path.

3. Form a circuit by adding the edge connecting the starting vertex and the last vertex added.

Now, we explain the working of the above procedure, *nearest-neighbor method*, with the help of few examples.

Example 4.17　Solve the travelling salesman problem for the weighted graph given in Fig. 4.54 using nearest-neighbor method.

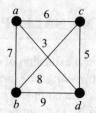

Fig. 4.54　An example of weighted graph

Solution:　Let the starting vertex be a. The nearest-neighbor of vertex a is vertex d as d is reachable with lowest cost than all other adjacent vertices. The corresponding graph is shown in Fig. 4.55(a).

Now, the current vertex is d and the nearest vertex adjacent to d is vertex c as it has the smallest distance from d. The corresponding graph is shown in Fig. 455(b).

---

* As the reader would immediately respond, it entirely depends on what we mean by an "efficient procedure." The efficiency of computation procedures is an important subject in theory of computation, which we shall study in Chap. 7. At this moment, let us just say that there is no known procedure that can solve the traveling salesperson problem with more than several hundred cities with the use of a large-scale digital computer for a reasonable amount of time.

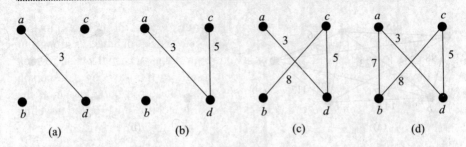

Fig. 4.55

Then, the current vertex is c and the nearest vertex adjacent to c is vertex a. But, vertex a is already included in the path. So, by considering the other available adjacent vertices of vertex c which are not there in the path, we get the nearest vertex adjacent to c is the vertex b. The corresponding graph is shown in Fig. 4.55(c).

Now, the current vertex is vertex b and there are no other vertices available which have to be included in the path to get the closed path from vertex b to vertex a. We add the vertex a to the current path to get a closed path (circuit). Finally, we obtain the closed path (circuit) $\{a\,d\,c\,b\,a\}$ which is shown in Fig. 4.55(d). This closed path (circuit) which is obtained by using the nearest-neighbor method has a total distance 23. ∎

Example 4.18 Solve the travelling salesman problem for the weighted graph whose corresponding adjacency matrix is shown below, using nearest-neighbor method.

	a	b	c	d	e
a	0	58	98	147	135
b	58	0	142	167	133
c	98	142	0	113	137
d	147	167	113	0	56
e	135	133	137	56	0

Solution: The weighted graph corresponding to the above adjacency matrix is shown in Fig. 4.56(a).

Let the starting vertex be d. The nearest-neighbor of d is vertex e as e is reachable from d with lowest cost than all other adjacent vertices. So, by adding the vertex e to the initial path we obtain the corresponding graph as shown in Fig. 4.56(b).

Now, the current vertex is e and the nearest vertex adjacent to vertex e is vertex b as it has the smallest distance from e comparing all other adjacent vertices

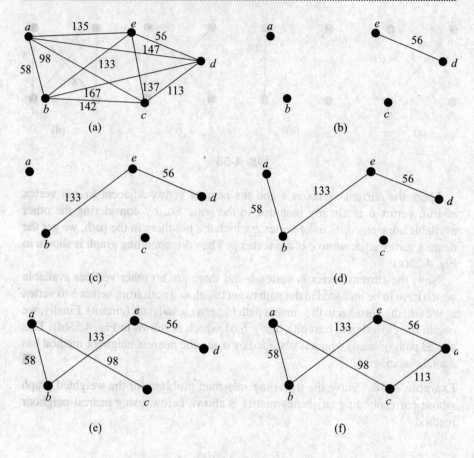

Fig. 4.56

of e. So, by adding the vertex b to the path, we obtain the corresponding graph as shown in Fig. 4.56(c).

Now, the current vertex is b and the nearest vertex adjacent to vertex b is vertex a as it has the smallest distance from b comparing all other adjacent vertices of b. So, by adding vertex a to the path, we get the corresponding graph as shown in Fig. 4.56(d).

Here, the current vertex is a and the nearest vertex adjacent to a is vertex c as it has the smallest distance from a. So, by adding vertex c to the path, we obtain the corresponding graph as shown in Fig. 4.56(e).

Now, the current vertex is vertex c and there are no other vertices available which have to be included in the path to get the closed path from vertex c to vertex d. We add the vertex d to the current path to get a closed path (circuit). Finally, we obtain the closed path (circuit) $\{d\ e\ b\ a\ c\ d\}$ which is shown in Fig. 4.56(f). This closed path (circuit) which is obtained by using the nearest-neighbor method has a total distance 458. ∎

Example 4.19 Solve the travelling salesman problem for the weighted graph given in Fig. 4.57 using nearest-neighbor method.

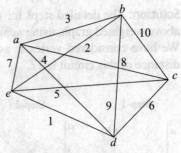

Fig. 4.57 An example weighted graph

Solution: The detailed steps for solving the travelling salesman problem for the above weighted graph, using nearest-neighbor method, are presented in Fig. 4.58. We have considered vertex d as the starting vertex. It may be noted that the distance of this circuit is 20. ■

Example 4.20 Solve the travelling salesman problem for the weighted graph given in Fig. 4.59 using nearest-neighbor method.

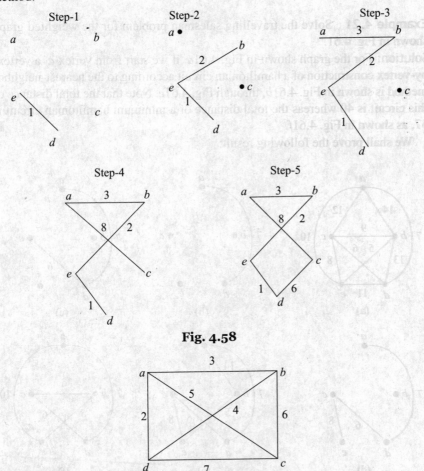

Fig. 4.58

Fig. 4.59 An example weighted graph

Solution: The detailed steps for solving the travelling salesman problem for the above weighted graph, using nearest-neighbor method, are presented in Fig 4.60. We have considered vertex *a* as the starting vertex. It may be noted that the distance of this circuit is 17. ∎

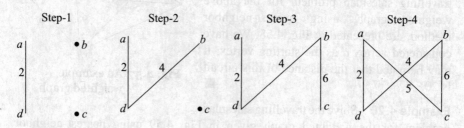

Fig. 4.60

Example 4.21   Solve the travelling salesman problem for the weighted graph shown in Fig. 4.61.

Solution: For the graph shown in Fig. 4.61*a*, if we start from vertex *a*, a vertex-by-vertex construction of a hamiltonian circuit according to the nearest-neighbor method is shown in Fig. 4.61*b*, through Fig. 4.61*e*. Note that the total distance of this circuit is 40 whereas the total distance of a minimum hamiltonian circuit is 37, as shown in Fig. 4.61*f*. ∎

We shall prove the following result:

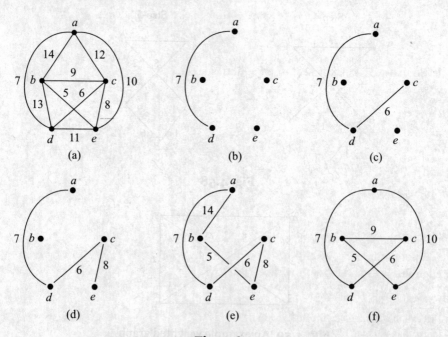

Fig. 4.61

Theorem 4.7 For a graph with n vertices, let d be the total distance of a hamiltonian circuit obtained according to the nearest-neighbor method and d_0 be the total distance of a minimum hamiltonian circuit. Then,

$$\frac{d}{d_0} \leq \frac{1}{2} \lceil \lg n \rceil + \frac{1}{2} \tag{4.2}$$

Proof: Before proceeding with the proof, let us illustrate the general idea of the proof by considering a specific case. Let D denote the hamiltonian circuit obtained according to the nearest-neighbor method. Let l_1 denote the length of the longest edge in D, l_2 be the length of the next longest edge in D, and, in general, l_i be the length of the ith longest edge in D. Thus,

$$d = \sum_{i=1}^{n} l_i$$

For the sake of illustration, let us assume $n = 14$. *Suppose* we can prove that

$$
\begin{aligned}
d_0 &\geq 2l_1 \\
d_0 &\geq 2l_2 \\
d_0 &\geq 2(l_3 + l_4) \\
d_0 &\geq 2(l_5 + l_6 + l_7 + l_8) \\
d_0 &\geq 2(l_9 + l_{10} + l_{11} + l_{12} + l_{13} + l_{14})
\end{aligned} \tag{4.3}
$$

then we shall have

$$5d_0 \geq 2 \sum_{i=1}^{14} l_i = 2d$$

or

$$\frac{d}{d_0} \leq \frac{5}{2} = \frac{1}{2} \lceil \lg 14 \rceil + \frac{1}{2}$$

So that we can have a set of inequalities similar to that in eq. (4.3) for general n, we shall prove

$$d_0 \geq 2l_1 \tag{4.4}$$

$$d_0 \geq 2 \sum_{i=k+1}^{2k} l_i \qquad 1 \leq k \leq \left\lfloor \frac{n}{2} \right\rfloor \tag{4.5}$$

and

$$d_0 \geq 2 \sum_{i=\lceil n/2 \rceil + 1}^{n} l_i \tag{4.6}$$

Note that if n is even, eq. (4.6) is included in eq. (4.5).

First of all, eq. (4.4) follows from the triangle inequality. Suppose the longest edge in D is incident with vertices x and y. Then the triangle inequality implies

---

[†] Recall that we adopted the notation $\lg n$ for $\log_2 n$. We use $\lceil x \rceil$ to denote the smallest integer larger than or equal to x.

that the length of any path between x and y is larger than or equal to l_1. Since any hamiltonian circuit of G can be broken up as two paths between x and y, eq. (4.4) follows immediately.

Let a_i denote the vertex *to which* the ith longest edge in D was added in our construction according to the nearest-neighbor method. (For example, according to this convention, the vertices in the graph in Fig. 4.61a are so named in Fig. 4.62a.) For a fixed k, $1 \leq k \leq \lfloor n/2 \rfloor$, let H be the complete subgraph of G containing the vertices a_i, $1 \leq i \leq 2k$. Let T denote the hamiltonian circuit in H that visits the vertices in H in the same circular order as a minimum hamiltonian circuit visits the vertices in G.* Let t denote the length of T. (In the illustrative example in Fig. 4.61, consider the case $k = 2$. The subgraph H is that shown in Fig. 4.62b. In the minimum hamiltonian circuit in Fig. 4.61f, the vertices are visited in the circular order a_2, a_1, a_5, a_3, a_4, so the circuit T is that shown in Fig. 4.62c, and $t = 36$.) Because of the triangle inequality, we have

$$d_0 \geq t \tag{4.7}$$

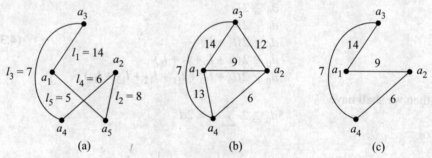

Fig. 4.62

Let $\{a_i, a_j\}$ be an edge in T. If in our construction according to the nearest-neighbor method, vertex a_i was added before a_j, we have $w(a_i, a_j) \geq l_i$. If a_j was added before a_i, we have $w(a_j, a_i) \geq l_j$, which is the same as $w(a_i, a_j) \geq l_j$. Thus, we have

$$w(a_i, a_j) \geq \min(l_i, l_j) \tag{4.8}$$

Summing eq. (4.8) for all the edges in T, we obtain

$$t \geq \sum_{(a_i, a_j) \in T} \min(l_i, l_j) \tag{4.9}$$

Note that the smallest possible value of $\min(l_i, l_j)$ in the sum in eq. (4.9) is l_{2k}, the next smallest possible value is l_{2k-1}, and so on. Furthermore, for any $1 \leq i \leq 2k$, l_i can appear in the sum at most two times. Since there are $2k$ edges in T, the sum in eq. (4.9) is larger than or equal to two times the sum of the lengths of the k shortest edges.

---

* All vertices in G but not in H are ignored in the circular order.

Consequently, we have

$$t \geq \sum_{(a_i, a_j) \in T} \min(l_i, l_j) \geq 2(l_{2k} + l_{2k-1} + \dots + l_{k+1})$$

$$= 2\sum_{i=k+1}^{2k} l_i \qquad (4.10)$$

Combining eq. (4.7) and eq. (4.10), we obtain eq. (4.5).

Inequality (4.6) can be proved in a similar manner:* Let D_0 denote a minimum hamiltonian circuit. Using the same argument as that of deriving eq. (4.9), we obtain

$$d_0 \geq \sum_{(a_i, a_j) \in D_0} \min(l_i, l_j)$$

Using the same argument as that for deriving eq. (4.10), we obtain

$$d_0 \geq \sum_{(a_i, a_j) \in D_0} \min(l_i, l_j) \geq 2(l_n + l_{n-1} + \dots + l_{\lceil n/2 \rceil + 1}) + l_{\lceil n/2 \rceil}$$

$$\geq 2(l_n + l_{n-1} + \dots + l_{\lceil n/2 \rceil + 1})$$

$$= 2\sum_{i=\lceil n/2 \rceil + 1}^{n} l_i$$

Now, for $k = 1, 2^1, 2^2, \dots, 2^{\lceil \lg n \rceil - 2}$, eq. (4.5) yields $\lceil \lg n \rceil - 1$ inequalities:

$$d_0 \geq 2l_2$$
$$d_0 \geq 2(l_3 + l_4)$$
$$d_0 \geq 2(l_5 + l_6 + l_7 + l_8)$$
$$\dots\dots\dots\dots\dots\dots\dots\dots\dots\dots\dots\dots$$
$$d_0 \geq 2(l_{2^{\lceil \lg n \rceil - 2} + 1} + l_{2^{\lceil \lg n \rceil - 2} + 2} + \dots + l_{2^{\lceil \lg n \rceil - 1}})^\dagger$$

Summing these inequalities, we obtain

$$(\lceil \lg n \rceil - 1)d_0 \geq 2\left(\sum_{i=2}^{2^{\lceil \lg n \rceil - 1}} l_i\right) \qquad (4.11)$$

Since

$$\left\lceil \frac{n}{2} \right\rceil + 1 \leq 2^{\lceil \lg n \rceil - 1} + 1 \qquad \text{for } n > 1$$

eq. (4.6) yields

$$d_0 \geq 2\sum_{i=2^{\lceil \lg n \rceil - 1} + 1}^{n} l_j \qquad (4.12)$$

Adding eq. (4.4), (4.11), and (4.12), we obtain

$$(\lceil \lg n \rceil + 1)d_0 \geq 2\sum_{i=1}^{n} l_i = 2d$$

---

* We only need to consider this case when n is odd.

$\dagger$ Note that $2^{\lceil \lg n \rceil - 1}$ is the largest power of 2 that is smaller than n.

or

$$\frac{d}{d_0} \le \frac{1}{2}\lceil \lg n \rceil + \frac{1}{2}$$

∎

*4.13 FACTORS OF A GRAPH

The notion of a hamiltonian circuit of a graph can be extended to that of a 2-factor of a graph. We first present, however, a more general definition: A *k-factor* of a graph is defined to be a spanning subgraph of the graph with the degree of each of its vertices being k. For example, for the graph in Fig. 4.63*a*, Fig. 4.63*b* shows a 1-factor and Fig. 4.63*c* shows a 2-factor of the graph. Note that a graph might have many different k-factors, or it might not have any k-factor at all for some k. For example, Fig. 4.64*a* and *b* shows two graphs that have no 1-factor and Fig. 4.64*c* shows a graph that has no 2-factor.

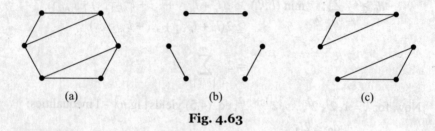

(a)   (b)   (c)

Fig. 4.63

Although we can show that the graph in Fig. 4.64*a* has no 1-factor and the graph in Fig. 4.64*c* has no 2-factor by exhaustion, it probably is not obvious that the graph in Fig. 4.64*b* does not have a 1-factor. We show now an interesting proof of this result. (For an alternative proof, see Prob. 4.40.) Suppose we are given a chessboard with its two diagonally opposite corners truncated, as shown in Fig. 4.65. Suppose we have some dominoes, each of which covers exactly two of the squares in the chessboard. We want to know whether it is possible to cover the truncated chessboard with 31 dominoes. We note that this is exactly the

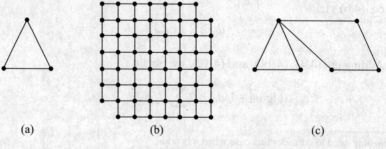

(a)   (b)   (c)

Fig. 4.64

problem of determining whether there is a 1-factor in the graph in Fig. 4.64*b*. We recall that the squares of a standard chessboard are alternately colored black and white. Since the two truncated squares are both white, as shown in Fig. 4.65, there are 30 white squares and 32 black squares in the truncated chessboard. Because a domino always covers a black square and a white square no matter how it is placed, the impossibility of covering the chessboard follows immediately.

Fig. 4.65

Consider the problem of scheduling meetings for a number of committees. There are two conference rooms, and it is possible to schedule two meetings concurrently. However, because of overlapping memberships of the committees, certain pairs of meetings cannot be scheduled in the same time slot. Let $G = (V, E)$ be a graph, where V is the set of meetings and an edge $\{a, b\}$ in E means that the two meetings a and b can be scheduled in the same time slot. As the reader will note, a 1-factor of G will be an acceptable pairing.

As was mentioned earlier, the notion of a 2-factor is a generalization of that of a hamiltonian circuit, since, according to Euler's theorem, a 2-factor is a set of vertex-disjoint circuits the union of which contains all the vertices of the graph. As an illustrative example, let us present the solution of a puzzle commonly known as "instant insanity." We are given four cubes, each of their faces being colored with one of the four colors blue, green, red, and yellow, as shown in Fig. 4.66*a*, where the cubes are numbered 1, 2, 3, 4, and the colors of the faces are abbreviated as b, g, r, y. We are asked to stack the four cubes in a column so that the four colors will show in each of the four sides of the column, as illustrated in Fig. 4.66*b*. Indeed, the name of this puzzle derives from the possibility of a player becoming insane when trying to sort out the large number of different ways to stack the cubes. We first note that the four cubes can be represented by the graph in Fig. 4.67*a*, where the four vertices correspond to the four colors. Corresponding to each cube there are three edges in the graph specifying the colors of the three pairs of opposite faces. One should note at this point that, as far as this problem is concerned, the only information we need on each cube is the colors of the three pairs of opposite faces. Indeed, a lesson to learn from this example is the importance of seeing the essentials and not being confused by irrelevant information when trying to solve a problem. If we look at a solution of this problem, we note that the colors of the cubes on two opposite sides of the column can be described by a 2-factor of the graph in Fig. 4.67*a* such that the 2-factor contains four edges, which are labeled 1, 2, 3, 4, respectively. Figure 4.67*b* shows a 2-factor that satisfies these conditions. Once such an observation is made, the puzzle can be rephrased as that of looking for two edge-disjoint 2-factors of the graph so that the four edges in each 2-factor are labeled distinctly with 1, 2, 3, 4. The 2-factors in Fig. 4.67*b* and *c* correspond to the solution in Fig.

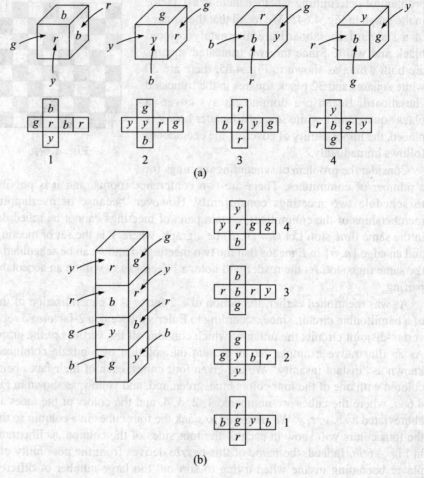

Fig. 4.66

4.66b. After extracting the two 2-factors from the graph in Fig. 4.67a, a pleasant surprise is to discover that the edges remaining as shown in Fig. 4.67d also form a 2-factor whose edges are labeled distinctly with 1, 2, 3, 4. What this means is that our solution may contain a bonus feature, namely, the cubes can be oriented with the four "bottoms" colored distinctly and the four "tops" colored distinctly at the same time.

*4.14 PLANAR GRAPHS

We study now a class of graphs called *planar graphs*. Not only is this class of graphs encountered very frequently, it also has many extremely interesting properties, some of which we shall discuss here.

A graph is said to be *planar* if it can be drawn on a plane in such a way that

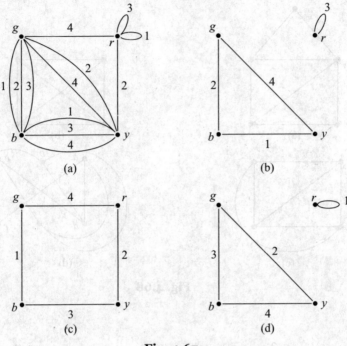

Fig. 4.67

no edges cross one another, except, of course, at common vertices. Figure 4.68*a* shows a planar graph. Notice that the graph in Fig. 4.68*b* is also planar because it can be redrawn as that shown in Fig. 4.68*c*. Figure 4.68*d* shows a nonplanar graph. As a matter of fact, the graph in Fig. 4.68*d* corresponds to the well-known problem of determining whether it is possible to connect three houses *a, b*, and *c* to three utilities *d, e*, and *f* in such a way that no two connecting pipelines cross one another. Experience shows that this cannot be done. In other words, the graph representing the pipeline connections is indeed a nonplanar graph. (The reader may feel a little bit uncomfortable when we say that a graph is nonplanar simply because, after a certain number of attempts, we find that we cannot draw the graph on a plane so that there will be no crossing edges. This issue will be settled rigorously later.)

Suppose we draw a planar graph on the plane and take a sharp knife to cut along the edges; then the plane will be divided into pieces that are called the *regions* of the graph. To be more formal, a region of a planar graph is defined to be an area of the plane that is bounded by edges and is not further divided into subareas. For example, the graph in Fig. 4.69*a* has five regions, as shown in Fig. 4.69*b*. Notice that cutting along the edge *a* does not further divide region 1, and cutting along the edges *b, c*, and *d* does not further divide region 5. A region is said to be *finite* if its area is finite, and is said to be *infinite* if its area is infinite. Clearly, a planar graph has exactly one infinite region.

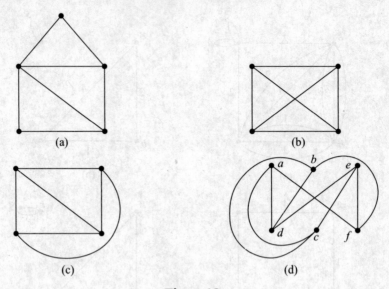

Fig. 4.68

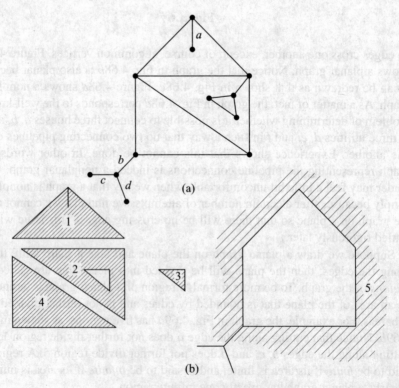

Fig. 4.69

We have the following result:

Theorem 4.8 For any connected planar graph,

$$v - e + r = 2 \qquad (4.13)$$

where **v**, **e**, and **r** are the number of vertices, edges, and regions of the graph, respectively.

Proof: The proof proceeds by induction on the number of edges. As the basis of induction, we observe that for the two graphs with a single edge shown in Fig. 4.70, eq. (4.13) is satisfied. As the induction step, we assume that eq. (4.13) is satisfied in all graphs with $n - 1$ edges. Let G be a connected graph with n edges. If G has a vertex of degree 1, the removal of this vertex together with the edge incident with it will yield a connected graph G', as illustrated in Fig. 4.71a. Since eq. (4.13) is satisfied in G', it is also satisfied in G, because putting the removed edge and vertex

Fig. 4.70

back into G will increase the count of vertices by 1 and the count of edges by 1, but will not change the count of regions. If G has no vertex of degree 1, the removal of any edge in the boundary of a finite region* will yield a connected graph G', as illustrated in Fig. 4.71b. Since eq. (4.13) is satisfied in G', it is also satisfied in G, because putting the removed edge back into G' will increase the count of edges by one and the count of regions by one, but will not change the count of vertices.[†]   ∎

Equation (4.13) is known as *Euler's formula* for planar graphs. It is truly remarkable that, with no exception, all connected planar graphs must satisfy such a simple formula. Let us consider now some applications of Euler's formula. First we want to show that in any connected linear planar graph that has no loops and has two or more edges,

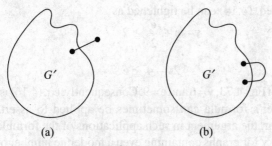

(a)   (b)

Fig. 4.71

---

* It is not difficult to see that, if G has no finite region, G must contain a vertex of degree 1.

[†] Equation (4.13) is not satisfied by disconnected planar graphs. Why is our proof not valid for disconnected planar graphs?

$$e \leq 3v - 6$$

Let us count the edges in the boundary of a region and then compute the total count for all the regions.* Because the graph is linear, each region is bounded by three or more edges. Therefore, the total count is larger than or equal to $3r$. On the other hand, since an edge is in the boundaries of at most two regions, the total count is less than or equal to $2e$. Thus,

$$2e \geq 3r$$

or

$$\frac{2e}{3} \geq r$$

According to Euler's formula, we have

$$v - e + \frac{2e}{3} \geq 2 \tag{4.14}$$

or

$$3v - 6 \geq e \tag{4.15}$$

We show now that the graph in Fig. 4.72 is not a planar graph. Since for this graph $v = 5$ and $e = 10$, the inequality in eq. (4.15) is not satisfied.

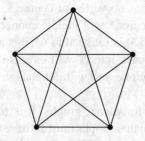

Fig. 4.72

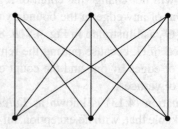

Fig. 4.73

We shall show that the graph in Fig. 4.73 is not a planar graph either. If the graph were planar, every region would be bounded by four or more edges. Thus, the inequality in eq. (4.14) can be tightened as

$$v - e + \frac{e}{2} \geq 2$$

or

$$2v - 4 \geq e \tag{4.16}$$

For the graph in Fig. 4.73, $v = 6$ and $e = 9$. Consequently, eq. (4.16) is contradicted.

Although Euler's formula can sometimes be applied to assert that a given graph is nonplanar, the argument in such applications of the formula can become involved and tricky for graphs containing even a moderate number of vertices and edges. Moreover, except by actually mapping a graph on the plane, we have seen no way of asserting that a given graph is planar. We shall state a theorem due to Kuratowski that enables us to determine unequivocally the planarity of a graph.

---

* Edges such as a, b, c, d in Fig. 4.69a are considered to be not in the boundary of any region.

The planarity of a graph is clearly not affected if an edge is divided into two edges by the insertion of a new vertex of degree 2, as illustrated in Fig. 4.74a, or if two edges that are incident with a vertex of degree 2 are combined as a single edge by the removal of that vertex, as illustrated in Fig. 4.74b. This suggests the following definition: Two graphs G_1 and G_2 are said to be *isomorphic to within vertices of degree* 2 if they are isomorphic or if they can be transformed into isomorphic graphs by repeated insertions and/or removals of vertices of degree 2, as illustrated in Fig. 4.74a and b. For example, the two graphs in Fig. 4.74c are isomorphic to within vertices of degree 2.

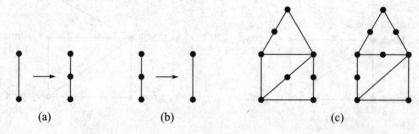

(a)   (b)   (c)

Fig. 4.74

Theorem 4.9 (Kuratowski)   A graph is planar if and only if it does not contain any subgraph that is isomorphic to within vertices of degree 2 to either the graph in Fig. 4.72 or Fig. 4.73.

The graphs in Figs. 4.72 and 4.73 are also called *Kuratowski graphs*. We note that Kuratowski's theorem is indeed a very strong characterization result in the sense that, although there are numerous nonplanar graphs, they all must contain a subgraph that is isomorphic to within vertices of degree 2 to one of the Kuratowski graphs. The proof of this theorem is lengthy although it is elementary. We shall not include the proof here, which can be found in Berge [3] or Liu [12].

4.15   GRAPH COLORING

Suppose a graph G with n nodes is given. It is required to paint its nodes such that no two adjacent nodes will be of the same color. What is the minimum number of colors required? This constitutes a coloring problem. After painting the nodes, one can group them into different sets such as one set consisting of all red nodes, another of green, another of yellow and so forth. This is a partitioning problem. The coloring and partitioning can also be performed on the edges of a graph. In case of planar graphs the coloring can be done for the regions of the graphs. We discuss the coloring problem in the following sections. In the remaining part of the book, we use the terms nodes and vertices interchangeably.

Assigning all the nodes of a graph with colors such that no two adjacent nodes are assigned the same color is called the *proper coloring* (or simply *coloring*) of a graph. A graph in which every vertex has been assigned a color according to a proper coloring is called a *properly colored graph*. A given graph can be properly colored in many different ways. In many situations, we need a *proper coloring* that requires the minimum number of colors. A graph G that requires minimum k different colors for its *proper coloring* is known as *k-chromatic* or *k-colorable* and the number k is called the *chromatic number* of G. Symbolically, we denote chromatic number of graph G as $k(G)$. It may be noted that the graph in Fig. 4.75(c) is 3-chromatic, because it requires minimum 3 different colors for its proper coloring.

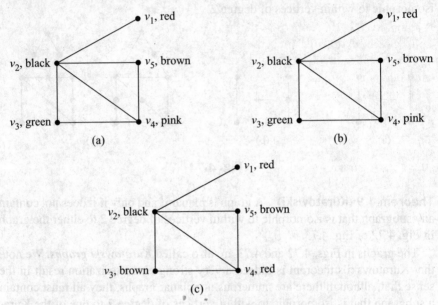

Fig. 4.75 Proper coloring of a graph

Minimal coloring of graphs and chromatic numbers for some commonly used graphs are illustrated in the following examples.

Example 4.22 A **complete graph** is a graph where each vertex is connected to every other vertex in the graph by an edge. We require at least 6 colors to color the vertices of a complete graph of six vertices so that no two adjacent vertices have the same color. So, the chromatic number of a complete graph with six vertices is 6, i.e. $k(K_6) = 6$. A coloring of K_6 using six colors is shown in Fig. 4.76. ∎

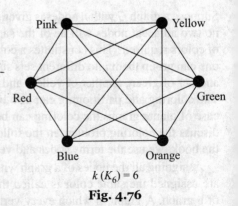

$k(K_6) = 6$

Fig. 4.76

Example 4.23 A **cycle graph** is a graph that consists of a single cycle, or in other words, some number of vertices connected in a closed chain. The cycle graph with n vertices is denoted as C_n. The number of vertices in C_n equals the number of edges, and every vertex has degree 2; that is, every vertex has exactly two edges incident upon it. Let us consider a cycle graph with 5 vertices, i.e. $n = 5$. It may be observed that minimum 3 colors are required to color the vertices so that no two adjacent vertices have the same color. So, the chromatic number of a cycle graph with five vertices is 3, i.e. $k(C_5) = 3$. This is shown in Fig. 4.77a. Now let us consider a cycle graph with 6 vertices, i.e. $n = 6$. Here, we need only 2 colors to color the vertices so that no two adjacent vertices will have the same color. So, the chromatic number of a cycle graph with six vertices is 2, i.e. $k(C_6) = 2$. This is shown in Fig. 4.77b. In general, the chromatic number of a cycle graph with odd number of vertices (for $n > 1$) is 3 and with even number of vertices is 2. ∎

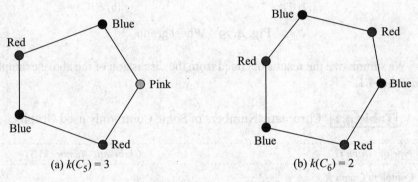

(a) $k(C_5) = 3$ (b) $k(C_6) = 2$

Fig. 4.77 Cycle graph

Example 4.24 The **n-star graph** (S_n) is a graph consisting of n nodes with one node having degree $n - 1$ and the other $n - 1$ nodes having degree 1. We need at least 2 colors to color the vertices of the n-star graph with six vertices so that no two adjacent vertices will have the same color. So, the chromatic number of an n-star graph with six vertices is 2, i.e. $k(S_6) = 2$. This is shown in Fig. 4.78. ∎

Example 4.25 A **wheel graph** (W_n) is a graph with n vertices, formed by connecting a single vertex to all vertices of a cycle having $(n - 1)$ vertices. Let us consider a wheel graph with 5 vertices, i.e. $n = 5$. It may be observed that minimum 3 colors are required to color the vertices so that no two adjacent vertices have the same color. So, the chromatic number of a wheel graph with five vertices is 3, i.e. $k(W_5) = 3$. This is shown in Fig. 4.79a. Now let us consider a wheel graph with 6 vertices, i.e. $n = 6$. Here, we

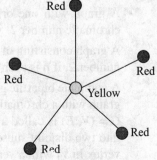

Fig. 4.78 Star graph

need 4 colors to color the vertices so that no two adjacent vertices will have the same color. So, the chromatic number of a wheel graph with six vertices is 4, i.e. $k(W_6) = 4$. This is shown in Fig. 4.79b. In general, the chromatic number of a wheel graph with odd number of vertices (for $n > 1$) is 3 and with even number of vertices is 4.   ■

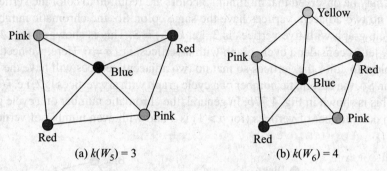

(a) $k(W_5) = 3$ (b) $k(W_6) = 4$

Fig. 4.79   Wheel graph

We summarize the results obtained from the discussion of the above examples in Table 4.1.

Table 4.1   Chromatic Numbers of Some Commonly used Graphs

Type of Graph G	Chromatic Number k(G)
Complete Graph K_n	n
Star Graph C_n, $n > 1$	2
Cycle Graph C_n, $n > 1$	3 for n odd
	2 for n even
Wheel Graph W_n, $n > 2$	3 for n odd
	4 for n even

Some observations which follow from the above discussions are given below.

- A graph which consists of only isolated vertices has chromatic number 1.

- A graph with one or more edges (without a self loop) has a minimum chromatic number 2.

- A graph consisting of simply one circuit with $n \geq 3$ vertices has chromatic number 2, if n is even and 3, if n is odd.

- A complete bipartite graph $K_{m,n}$ has chromatic number 2. Conversely, every graph with a chromatic number 2 is bipartite. It may be noted that a graph $G = (V, E)$ is called a bipartite graph if its vertex set V can be partitioned into two disjoint subsets V_1 and V_2 such that every edge $E \in G$ connects a vertex in V_1 with a vertex in V_2.

- Every tree with two or more vertices has chromatic number 2.

- A graph has chromatic number 2 if and only if it has no circuits of odd length.
- If d is the maximum degree of the vertices in a graph G, then

  Chromatic number of $G \le d + 1$.

The problem that can also be viewed as a graph coloring problem is the map coloring problem. A coloring of a map is a way to color each region (e.g. country, state, district, etc.) so that no two adjacent regions will have the same color. The map coloring problem is to find the smallest number of colors that can be used. We can view this problem as the proper graph coloring problem as follows. If a map M is given, construct a graph G_M with one vertex for each region and an edge joining any two vertices whose corresponding regions share a common boundary. Then, the proper colorings of G_M will be exactly the colorings of Map M.

4.15.1 Applications of Graph Coloring

Graph coloring has many applications to problems related to scheduling and assignments. Below, we illustrate some examples explaining the applications of graph coloring.

Example 4.26 This example illustrates an application of the assignment of radio channels. Ministry of Broadcasting, Government of India, requires to assign radio channels 2 through 10 to different stations, so that no 2 stations within 200 km can operate on the same channel. This problem can be solved by using graph coloring as follows:

Construct a graph by assigning a vertex to each station. Two vertices are joined by an edge if they are located within 200 km of each other. An assignment of channels will correspond to a proper coloring of the graph where each color represents a different channel. ∎

Example 4.27 This example illustrates an application related to the scheduling of examinations in a University. The examination controller of a University needs to schedule the graduate examination. This problem can be solved by using graph coloring as follows:

Construct a graph where the vertices represent the courses. Connect an edge between two vertices if there is a common student they represent. Each time slot for an examination is represented by a different color. A scheduling of the examination will correspond to a coloring of the associated graph.

For example, suppose there are 5 examinations to be scheduled. Suppose the courses are numbered 1 through 5. Let the following pairs of courses have common students: 1 and 2, 1 and 3, 2 and 3, 2 and 4, 2 and 5, 3 and 4, 4 and 5, 5 and 1. A scheduling consists of a coloring of the associated graph. A coloring of the associated graph can be made using 3 colors as the chromatic number of the associated graph is 3. A coloring of the graph using 3 colors and the associated scheduling are shown in Fig. 4.80. ∎

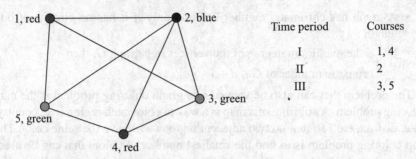

Time period	Courses
I	1, 4
II	2
III	3, 5

Fig. 4.80   Scheduling of examinations using graph coloring

4.15.2   Chromatic Partitioning

A proper coloring of a graph induces a partitioning of the vertices into different subsets. For example, the coloring in Fig. 4.75c results in the partitioning $\{v_1, v_4\}$, $\{v_2\}$ and $\{v_3, v_5\}$.

It may be observed that no two vertices in any of these 3 subsets are adjacent. Such a subset of vertices is called an *independent set*. In other words, we can state that:

A set of vertices in a graph is said to be an *independent set of vertices* (or simply an *independent set*) if no two vertices in the set are adjacent. For example in Fig. 4.75c, $\{v_1, v_4\}$ is an independent set. It may be noted that, a single vertex in any graph constitutes an independent set.

A maximal independent set is an independent set to which no other vertex can be added without affecting its independence property. The set $\{v_1, v_4\}$ in Fig. 4.75c is a maximal independent set. It may be observed that a graph has many maximal independent sets which are of different sizes. Out of all the maximal independent sets, one with the largest number of vertices is often particular interest.

4.15.3   Chromatic Polynomial

The problem of computing the total number of different proper colorings of a graph G using a set $S = \{c_1, c_2, \ldots, c_n\}$ of colors is closely associated with the problem of computing $k(G)$, the chromatic number of G. Suppose G is a graph and $n \geq 0$ is an integer. Let $P(n)$ be the number of edge to properly color G using n or fewer colors. As $P(n)$ is a definite number for each n, so P can be considered as a function. It can be shown that P is a polynomial in n. Generally P is known as the chromatic polynomial of G.

Example 4.28   Consider the linear graph G given in Fig. 4.81.

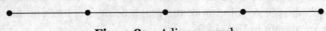

Fig. 4.81   A linear graph

Suppose we have n colors. The first vertex can be colored with any color. The second vertex can be colored with any color that was not selected for vertex 1. Hence there are $n-1$ choices for second vertex. The third vertex can be colored with any color that was not selected for second vertex. So, there are $n-1$ choices for third vertex. A similar result may be obtained for fourth and fifth vertices. By applying the multiplication principle of counting, we obtain the total number of proper colorings as $n(n-1)^4$. Hence, for the above graph G, $P(n) = n(n-1)^4$. ∎

From example 4.28 we observe that $P(0) = 0$, $P(1) = 0$, and $P(2) = 2$. So, there are no proper colorings of the above graph using zero color or one color. There are two proper colorings using two colors. From this we observe that $k(G) = 2$.

In general, it can be stated that if G is a graph with no multiple edges and P is the chromatic polynomial of G then $k(G)$ is equal to the smallest positive integer n for which $P(n) \neq 0$.

Making similar arguments as given in example 4.28, it can be shown that for a linear graph G with m vertices, $m \geq 1$, $P(n) = n(n-1)^{m-1}$. Hence, by the above principle, $k(G) = 2$, for every linear graph having m vertices.

Problems

4.1 A man is supposed to bring a dog, a sheep, and a bag of cabbage across a river on a rowboat. The boat is very small, and he can carry only one of these items on the boat at a time. Furthermore, he cannot leave the dog alone with the sheep nor the sheep alone with the cabbage. In order to determine how he should proceed, we shall describe the possible steps he can take by an undirected graph. Let the vertices of a graph represent all the allowable configurations. For example, the man, the dog, the sheep, and the cabbage are all on one side of the river is the initial configuration; the man, the dog, the sheep, and the cabbage are all on the other side of the river is the final configuration. The man, the dog, and the sheep are on one side of the river while the cabbage is on the other side of the river is one allowable intermediate configuration. Let there be an edge between two vertices if the man can make a trip across the river so that the configuration corresponding to one of the vertices can be transformed into that corresponding to the other vertex, and conversely. Construct the graph and determine all possible ways for the man to transport the items across the river.

4.2 (a) Three married couples on a journey come to a river where they find a boat which cannot carry more than two persons at a time. The crossing of the river is complicated by the fact that the husbands are all very jealous and will not permit their wives to be left without them in a company where there are other men present. Construct a graph to show how the transfer can be made.

   (b) Prove that the puzzle in part (a) cannot be solved if there are four couples.

   (c) Prove that the puzzle in part (a) can be solved if there are four couples and the boat holds three persons.

4.3 An electronic circuit is built to recognize sequences of 0s and 1s. In particular it shall accept sequences of the form 010*10, where 0* means any number (including none) of 0s. For example, 0110, 01010, and 010000010 are all acceptable sequences. Construct a directed graph in which every vertex has two outgoing edges labeled 0 and 1, and in which there are two vertices v_i (the initial vertex) and v_f (the final vertex) such that every path from v_i to v_f is a sequence of the form 010*10. (For each sequence the circuit will start at v_i and trace the edges according to the 0s and 1s in the sequence. The circuit will accept the sequence if the path terminates at v_f.)

4.4 Repeat Prob. 4.3 for sequences of the form 01*(10)*10*, where (10)* means any number (including none) of 10 patterns, using each of the following modifications:

(a) For each vertex there is no restriction on the number of outgoing edges labeled 0 or 1. The sequence of labels on every path from v_i to v_f is a sequence of the form described above. Furthermore, for every sequence of the form described above there is a corresponding path from v_i to v_f.

(b) There may be several final vertices, $v_{f1}, v_{f2}, \ldots$. The sequence of labels on every path from v_i to some final v_{fj} is a sequence of the form described above. Furthermore, for every sequence of the form described above there is a corresponding path from v_i to some final vertex v_{fj}.

Meeting	Starting time	Meeting	Estimated length of meeting
1st	8:00 a.m.	1st	90 min.
2nd	9:00 a.m.	2nd	60 min.
3rd	11:00 a.m.	3rd	120 min.
4th	2:00 p.m.	4th	120 min.
5th	3:30 p.m.	5th	90 min.
6th	4:00 p.m.	6th	30 min.
(a)		(b)	

Fig. 4P.1

4.5 The head of the department of computer science wanted to call six committee meetings on a certain day. After sending out notices on the starting times of the meetings, as shown in Fig. 4P.1a, his secretary, Mrs. Mason, discovered that the agendas of these meetings had been revised. She subsequently made a new estimation on the lengths of these meetings, as shown in Fig. 4P.1b. Since these meetings must be held in the order they were originally scheduled, changes in the starting times of some of these meetings became necessary. Hoping to make as few changes as possible, Mrs. Mason constructed the following undirected graph: Let $v_1, v_2, \ldots, v_6$ be six vertices representing the six meetings. Let there be an edge between v_i and v_j for $i < j$ if the sum of the lengths of the ith, the $(i + 1)$st, the $(i + 2)$nd, ..., and the $(j - 1)$st meetings is less than or equal to the difference between the originally chosen starting times of the jth and the ith meeting.

(a) What is the physical significance of an edge between v_i and v_j? Of a complete subgraph containing $v_{i1}, v_{i2}, \ldots, v_{ik}$? Of a largest possible complete subgraph?

(b) Suppose in rescheduling the meetings, Mrs. Mason wanted to make sure that the first meeting cannot begin prior to 8 : 00 a.m., and the last meeting cannot run beyond 5 : 00 p.m. How can she make use of a computer program that determines a largest possible complete subgraph in a given graph? Determine a new set of starting times for the meetings with as few changes from the original ones as possible.

4.6 Let $G = (V, E)$ be an undirected graph with k components and $|V| = n$, $|E| = m$. Prove that $m \geq n - k$.

4.7 n cities are connected by a network of k highways. (A highway is defined to be a road between two cities that does not go through any intermediate cities.) Show that if $k > \frac{1}{2}(n-1)(n-2)$, then one can always travel between any two cities through connecting highways.

4.8 An ordered n-tuple $(d_1, d_2, ..., d_n)$ of non-negative integers is said to be *graphical* if there exists a linear graph with no self-loops that has n vertices with the degrees of the vertices being $d_1, d_2, ..., d_n$.

(a) Show that $(4, 3, 2, 2, 1)$ is graphical.

(b) Show that $(3, 3, 3, 1)$ is not graphical.

(c) Without loss of generality, suppose $d_1 \geq d_2 \geq d_3 \geq ... \geq d_n$. Show that $(d_1, d_2, ..., d_n)$ is graphical if and only if $(d_2 - 1, d_3 - 1, ..., d_{d1} - 1, d_{d1+1} - 1, d_{d1+2}, ..., d_n)$ is graphical.

(d) Use the result in part (c) to determine whether $(5, 5, 3, 3, 2, 2, 2)$ is graphical.

4.9 (a) Show that the sum of the in-degrees over all vertices is equal to the sum of the out-degrees over all vertices in any directed graph.

(b) Show that the sum of the squares of the in-degrees over all vertices is equal to the sum of the squares of the out-degrees over all vertices in any directed complete graph.

4.10 A graph is said to be *self-complementary* if it is isomorphic to its complement.

(a) Show a self-complementary graph with four vertices.

(b) Show a self-complementary graph with five vertices.

(c) Is there a self-complementary graph with three vertices? Six vertices?

(d) Show that a self-complementary graph must have either $4k$ or $4k + 1$ vertices.

4.11 A set of vertices in an undirected graph is said to be a *dominating set* if every vertex not in the set is adjacent to one or more vertices in the set. A *minimal dominating set* is a dominating set such that no proper subset of it is also a dominating set.

(a) For the graph in Fig. 4P.2 find two minimal dominating sets of different sizes.

(b) Let the vertices of a graph represent cities and the edges represent communication links between cities. Give a physical interpretation of the notion of a dominating set in this case.

(c) Let the 64 squares of a chessboard be represented by 64 vertices. Let there be an edge between two vertices if their corresponding squares are in the same row, same column, or same (backward or forward) diagonal. It is known that five queens can be placed on the chessboard so that they will dominate all 64 squares. Moreover, five is the minimum number of queens that is needed. Restate this statement in graph theoretic terms.

4.12 A set of vertices in an undirected graph is said to be an *independent set* if no two vertices in it are adjacent. A *maximal independent set* is an independent set which will no longer be one when any vertex is added to the set.

(a) For the graph in Fig. 4P.2 find two maximal independent sets of different sizes.

(b) How can the problem of placing eight queens on a chessboard so that no one captures another be stated in graph theoretic terms?

4.13 (a) The edges of a K_6 are to be painted either red or blue. Show that for any arbitrary way of painting the edges there is either a red K_3 (a K_3 with all its edges painted red) or a blue K_3.

(b) Use the result in part (a) to show that among a group of six people there are either three who are mutual friends or three who are strangers to each other.

(c) The edges of K_n are painted either red or blue in some arbitrary way. Show that if there are six or more red edges incident with one vertex, then there is either a red K_4 or a blue K_3. Show that if there are four or more blue edges incident with one vertex, then there is either a red K_4 or a blue K_3.

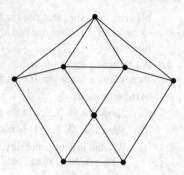

(d) Show that for any arbitrary way of painting the edges of K_9 either red or blue there is either a red K_4 or a blue K_3.

4.14 By *properly coloring* a graph we mean to paint the vertices of the graph with one or more distinct colors in such a way that no two adjacent vertices are painted with the same color.

Fig. 4P.2

(a) What is the minimum number of colors that is needed to properly color the graph in Fig. 4P.3a? The graph in Fig. 4P.3b? The graph in Fig. 4P.3c?

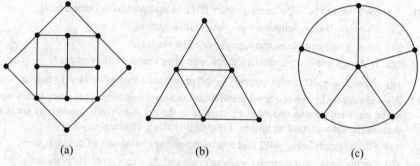

(a)   (b)   (c)

Fig. 4P.3

(b) Let G be a linear graph with no self-loops. Let the vertices of G represent examinations to be given during the final examination period. Let the edges of G represent constraints such that an edge between two vertices means the corresponding examinations cannot be scheduled in the same time slot. What interpretation can be given to a way of properly coloring G? to the minimum number of colors needed to properly color G?

4.15 (a) Let $G = (V, E)$ be a linear directed graph where V represents a set of people and E represents a parent-child relationship such that an edge (a, b) in E means a is a parent of b. G is called a *genetic graph*. We note that G has the following properties:

1. The incoming degree of every vertex is at most 2.

2. There is no circuit in G.

3. The vertices of G can be colored with two colors so that for any two edges (a, c) and (b, c) in E, a and b are colored with different colors.

What genetic interpretation can we give to these conditions?

(b) Let $\hat{G} = (V, \hat{E})$ be an undirected graph such that there is an edge $\{a, b\}$ in $\hat{E}$ if and only if there are two edges (a, c) and (b, c) in E for some c. Show that condition

(3) can be satisfied if and only if $\hat{G}$ can be properly colored with two colors. (See Prob. 4.14 for the definition of proper coloring.)

(c) Show that an undirected graph can be properly colored with two colors if and only if it contains no circuit of odd length.

(d) We define an alternating circuit in a directed graph as a sequence of edges (v_1, v_2) (v_3, v_2) (v_3, v_4) (v_5, v_4) ... (v_{k-1}, v_k) (v_1, v_k) such that reversing the direction of alternating edges in the sequence will yield a (directed) circuit. Show that condition (3) can be satisfied if and only if the length of every alternating circuit in G is divisible by 4.

4.16 The *distance* between two vertices in an undirected graph is defined to be the minimum number of edges in a path between them. The *diameter* of an undirected graph is defined to be the maximum of the distances between all pairs of vertices.

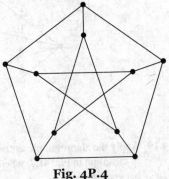

Fig. 4P.4

(a) What is the diameter of the graph in Fig. 4P.4?

(b) Let the vertices of a graph represent computers and the edges represent data communication links between computers. In this case, what is the physical significance of the diameter of the graph?

(c) Let d denote the diameter of a graph with n vertices. Let δ denote the maximum of the degrees of the vertices. Show that

$$1 + \delta + \delta(\delta - 1) + \delta(\delta - 1)^2 + ... + \delta(\delta - 1)^{d-1} \geq n$$

[Thus, if we want to design a computer communication network with the constraints: (1) a computer can communicate with any other computer without going through more than $d - 1$ intermediate computers; (2) a computer can communicate directly with at most δ computers, then we cannot have a network containing "too many" computers.]

4.17 The graph in Fig. 4P.5 shows the communication channels and the communication time delays in the channels among eight communication centers. The centers are represented by vertices, the channels are represented by edges, and the communication time delay (in minutes) in each channel is represented by the weight of the edge. Suppose that at 3 : 00 p.m. communication center a broadcasts through all its channels the news that

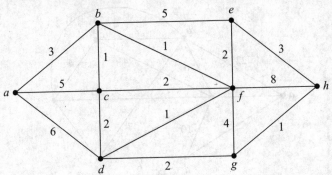

Fig. 4P.5

someone has found a way to build a better mousetrap. Other communication centers will then broadcast this news through all their channels as soon as they receive it. For the communication centers b, c, d, e, f, g, and h, determine the earliest time each receives the news.

4.18 Apply the algorithm presented in Sec. 4.9 to determine a shortest path between a and z in the graph in Fig. 4P.6, where the numbers associated with the edges are the distances between vertices.

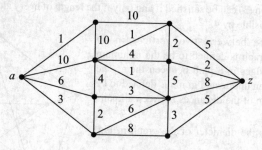

Fig. 4P.6

4.19 Apply the algorithm presented in Sec. 4.9 to determine a shortest path between a and z in the graph in Fig. 4P.7, where the numbers associated with the edges are the distances between vertices.

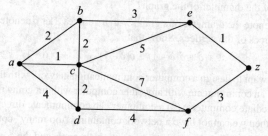

Fig. 4P.7

4.20 Apply the algorithm presented in Sec. 4.9 to determine a shortest path between a and z in the graph in Fig. 4P.8, where the numbers associated with the edges are the distances between vertices.

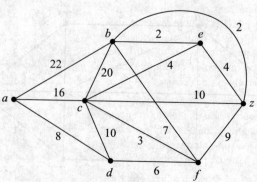

Fig. 4P.8

4.21 Apply the algorithm presented in Sec. 4.9 to determine a shortest path between a and z in the graph in Fig. 4P.9, where the numbers associated with the edges are the distances between vertices.

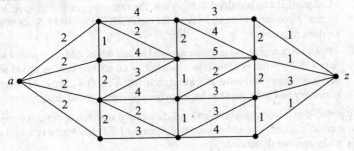

Fig. 4P.9

4.22 Apply the algorithm presented in Sec. 4.9 to determine a shortest path between a and z in the graph in Fig. 4P.10, where the numbers associated with the edges are the distances between vertices.

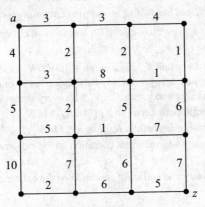

Fig. 4P.10

4.23 Let G be a connected graph with no self-loops where the edges represent the streets in a city. A police officer want to make a round trip to patrol each side of each street exactly once. Furthermore, the officer wants to patrol the two sides of a street in opposite directions. Show that such a trip can always be designed.

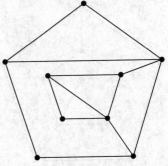

4.24 Among the many rooms in an old mansion, there is a ghost in each room that has an even number of doors. If the mansion has only one entrance, prove that a person entering from outside can always reach a room in which there is no ghost.

4.25 (a) The edges in the graph in Fig. 4P.11 can be partitioned into two (edge-disjoint) paths. Show one such partition.

Fig. 4P.11

(b) Let G be a connected graph with k vertices of odd degree ($k > 0$). Show that the edges in G can be partitioned into $k/2$ (edge-disjoint) paths.

(c) Let G be a graph with k vertices of odd degree ($k > 0$). What is a minimum number of edges that can be added to G so that the resultant graph will have an eulerian circuit? Show how this can be done for the graph in Fig. 4P.11. State how this can be done in general.

(d) In part (c), suppose we are only allowed to add edges that are parallel to existing edges in G. What is a minimum number of edges that can be added so that the resultant graph will have an eulerian circuit? Can this always be done? State a necessary and sufficient condition under which this can be done.

4.26 Is it possible to move a knight on an 8×8 chessboard so that it completes every possible move exactly once? A move between two squares of the chessboard is completed when it is made in either direction.

4.27 Find a circular arrangement of nine a's, nine b's, and nine c's such that each of the 27 words of length 3 from the alphabet $\{a, b, c\}$ appears exactly once.

4.28 (a) Show a graph that has both an eulerian circuit and a hamiltonian circuit.

(b) Show a graph that has an eulerian circuit but has no hamiltonian circuit.

(c) Show a graph that has no eulerian circuit but has a hamiltonian circuit.

(d) Show a graph that has neither an eulerian circuit nor a hamiltonian circuit.

4.29 (a) Does K_{13} have an eulerian circuit? A hamiltonian circuit?

(b) Repeat part (a) for K_{14}.

4.30 A *complete bipartite* graph $K_{m,n}$ is a graph with $V = V_1 \cup V_2$ being the set of vertices such that there are no edges joining any two vertices in V_1 or any two vertices in V_2, but there is an edge joining every vertex in V_1 with every vertex in V_2.

(a) Is there a hamiltonian circuit in $K_{4,4}$? In $K_{4,5}$? In $K_{4,6}$?

(b) Is there a hamiltonian path in $K_{4,4}$? In $K_{4,5}$? In $K_{4,6}$?

(c) State a necessary and sufficient condition on the existence of a hamiltonian circuit in $K_{m,n}$.

(d) State a necessary and sufficient condition on the existence of a hamiltonian path in $K_{m,n}$.

4.31 Show that the graph in Fig. 4P.12 has no hamiltonian circuit.

4.32 Show that any hamiltonian circuit in the graph shown in Fig. 4P.13 that contains the edge x must also contain the edge y.

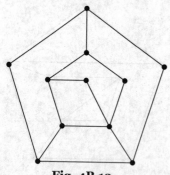

Fig. 4P.12

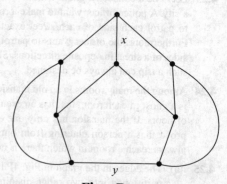

Fig. 4P.13

4.33 Let G be an undirected linear graph with n vertices, $n \geq 3$. Let the vertices of G represent n people and the edges of G represent a friendship relationship among them such that two vertices are connected by an edge if and only if the corresponding persons are friends.

   (a) What interpretation can be given to the degree of a vertex?

   (b) What interpretation can be given to the fact that G is a connected graph?

   (c) What interpretation can be given to a subgraph of G that is a complete graph with m vertices?

   (d) What interpretation can be given to a 1-factor of G?

   (e) Suppose that between any two people they know all the remaining $n - 2$ people. Show that the n people can be stood in line so that everyone stands next to two of his friends, except the two persons at the two ends of the line, each of them stands next to only one of his friends.

     Hint: Apply Theorem 4.6.

   (f) Extend Theorem 4.6 to show that if the sum of the degrees for each pair of vertices of a linear graph with n vertices is n or larger then there exists a hamiltonian circuit in G.

   (g) Use the result in part (*f*) to show that the condition in part (*e*) guarantees that the n people can be stood around a circle so that everyone stands next to two of his friends for $n \geq 4$.

4.34 Let G be a complete directed graph. A nonempty subset of the vertices of G is said to be an *outclassed group* if any edge joining a vertex in the subset and a vertex not in the subset is always directed from the latter to the former. Show that G has a directed circuit containing all the vertices if there is no outclassed group of vertices.

4.35 Eleven students plan to have dinner together for several days. They will be seated at a round table, and the plan calls for each student to have different neighbors at every dinner. For how many days can this be done?

4.36 An n-cube is an undirected graph with 2^n vertices which are labeled with the 2^n n-digit binary numbers. There is an edge between two vertices if their binary labels differ exactly at one digit. Show that an n-cube has a hamiltonian circuit for any $n \geq 1$. (A sequential arrangement of the 2^n n-digit binary numbers such that every two adjacent numbers differ in exactly one digit is known as a *Gray code*.)

4.37 An undirected graph is said to be *orientable* if direction can be assigned to each of the edges of the graph so that the resultant directed graph is strongly connected.

   (a) Show that the graph in Fig. 4P.14 is orientable.

   (b) Show that any graph with an eulerian circuit is orientable.

   (c) Show that any graph with a hamiltonian circuit is orientable.

   (d) Show that a connected undirected graph is orientable if and only if each edge of the graph is contained in at least one circuit.

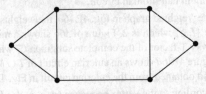

Fig. 4P.14

4.38 (a) Use the nearest-neighbor method to determine a hamiltonian circuit for the graph in Fig. 4P.15, starting at vertex a.

(b) Repeat part (a), except starting at vertex d instead.

(c) Determine a minimum hamiltonian circuit for the graph in Fig. 4P.15.

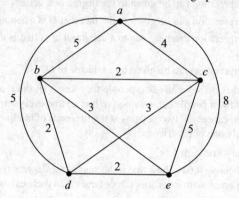

Fig. 4P.15

4.39 We present in this problem a procedure that produces a good, but not necessarily best possible, result for the traveling salesperson problem discussed in Sec. 4.12. Again, let $G = (V, E, w)$ be a complete graph of n vertices, where w is a function from E to the set of positive real numbers satisfying the triangle inequality. Let T be a minimum spanning tree of G. (See Sec. 4.7 for the definition of a minimum spanning tree.)

(a) Let V' denote the subset of vertices that have odd degrees in the subgraph T. We claim that there must be an even number of vertices in V'. Why?

(b) Let G' be the complete subgraph of G that contains all the vertices in V'. Let M denote a 1-factor of G' that has minimum weight. (The weight of a 1-factor is defined to be the sum of the weights of the edges in the 1-factor.) Let $T \cup M$ denote the graph obtained by superimposing the graph T and M. (If an edge appears in both T and M, it will appear twice in $T \cup M$.) Show that $T \cup M$ has an eulerian circuit.

(c) Show that the weight of T is less than that of a minimum hamiltonian circuit.

(d) Show that the weight of M is less than or equal to half of that of a minimum hamiltonian circuit.

(e) Show how we can obtain a hamiltonian circuit of G from the eulerian circuit of $T \cup M$ by avoiding to visit vertices that have already been visited such that the weight of the former is less than or equal to that of the latter. Consequently, we conclude that the weight of the hamiltonian circuit obtained is less than 1.5 times that of a minimum hamiltonian circuit.

For example, for the weighted graph in Fig. 4P.16a, the weights of all edges are 1 except the weight of edge $\{f, g\}$ which is 2. Figure 4P.16b shows a minimum spanning tree T. Figure 4P.16c shows a 1-factor of the complete subgraph G' which contains the vertices $\{a, b, c, e, f, g\}$. Figure 4P.16d shows an eulerian circuit of $T \cup M$, and Fig. 4P.16e shows a hamiltonian circuit obtained from the eulerian circuit in Fig. 4P.16d, where the eulerian circuit is traced according to the vertex sequence $(a, b, c, d, e, f, d, a, g, a)$.

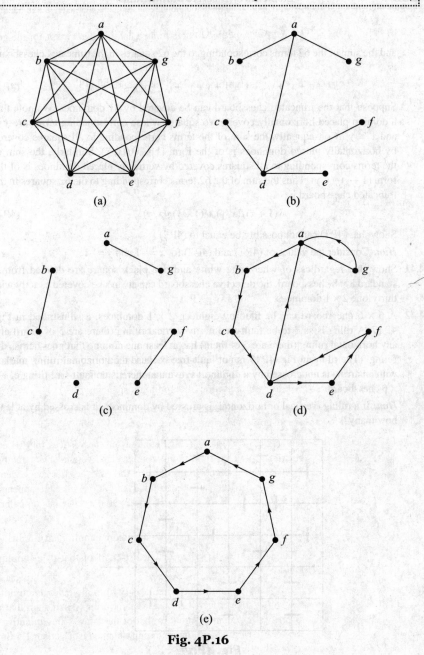

Fig. 4P.16

4.40 We show in this problem an alternative proof of the result on the impossibility of covering a truncated chessboard with dominoes presented in Sec. 4.13. Let us identify each square of the chessboard by a term $x^i y^j$, $0 \leq i \leq 7$ and $0 \leq j \leq 7$, where i is the x coordinate of the square and j is the y coordinate of the square. Thus the sum of the 64 terms corresponding to the 64 squares in a chessboard is

$$(1 + x + x^2 + \ldots + x^7)(1 + y + y^2 + \ldots + y^7)$$

and the sum of the 62 terms corresponding to the 62 squares in the truncated chessboard is

$$(1 + x + x^2 + \ldots + x^7)(1 + y + y^2 + \ldots + y^7) - 1 - x^7 y^7 \qquad (4\text{P}.1)$$

Suppose that the truncated chessboard can be covered by 31 dominoes. We note that a domino placed horizontally covers two squares whose corresponding terms are $x^i y^j$ and $x^{i+1} y^j$. Consequently, the sum of the terms corresponding to all squares covered by horizontally placed dominoes is of the form $(1 + x)f(x, y)$. Similarly, the sum of the terms corresponding to all squares covered by vertically placed dominoes is of the form $(1 + y)g(x, y)$. Thus the sum of the 62 terms corresponding to the 62 squares in the truncated chessboard is

$$(1 + x)f(x, y) + (1 + y)g(x, y) \qquad (4\text{P}.2)$$

Show that (4P.1) cannot possibly be equal to (4P.2).

Hint: Consider the values of (4P.1) and (4P.2) for $x = -1$ and $y = -1$.

4.41 Show that regardless of where one white and one black square are deleted from a standard 8×8 chessboard, the defective chessboard can always be covered exactly with thirty-one 2×1 dominoes.

4.42 A 6×6 chessboard can be tiled by eighteen 2×1 dominoes, as illustrated in Fig. 4P.17. A tiling is said to be fault-free if any vertical ruling (there are 5 of them) and any horizontal ruling (there are 5 of them) has at least one domino that goes across the ruling. (The tiling in Fig. 4P.17 is not fault-free because the horizontal ruling marked with an arrow is not crossed by a domino.) Prove that there is no fault-free tiling of a 6 $\times$ 6 chessboard.

Hint: If a ruling (vertical or horizontal) is crossed by dominoes, it is crossed by at least how many?

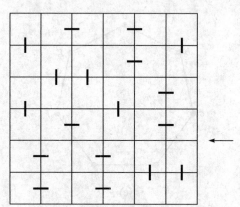

Fig. 4P.17

4.43 A graph $G = (V, E)$ is called a *bipartite* graph if the set of vertices V can be partitioned into two nonempty subsets X and Y such that there is no edge in E joining two vertices in X or two vertices in Y.

(a) Let $G = (V, E)$ be a bipartite graph. Let X represent a set of workmen and Y represent a set of jobs. Let an edge $\{v_x, v_y\}$ in E denote the fact that workman v_x is qualified to perform job v_y. What interpretation can be given to a 1-factor of G?

(b) Let X represent a set of committees and Y represent a set of senators. Let an edge $\{v_x, v_y\}$ in E denote the fact that senator v_y is a member of committee v_x. What interpretation can be given to a 1-factor of G?

(c) Let X represent a set of boys and Y represent a set of girls. Let an edge $\{v_x, v_y\}$ in E denote the fact that boy v_x knows girl v_y. What interpretation can be given to a 1-factor of G? a hamiltonian circuit in G?

4.44 (a) Show that a linear planar graph has a vertex of degree 5 or less.

   (b) Show that a linear planar graph with less than 30 edges has a vertex of degree 4 or less.

4.45 Show that in a connected planar linear graph with 6 vertices and 12 edges, each of the regions is bounded by 3 edges.

4.46 Let G be a graph with 11 or more vertices. Show that either G or $\overline{G}$ is nonplanar.

4.47 The *thickness* of a graph G is defined to be the minimum number of (edge-disjoint) planar subgraphs into which G can be decomposed. We shall denote the thickness of G by $\theta(G)$.

   (a) What is the thickness of a planar graph?

   (b) What is $\theta(K_5)$? $\theta(K_8)$?

   (c) Show that for any linear graph with no self-loops G

$$\theta(G) \geq \left\lceil \frac{e}{3v-6} \right\rceil$$

   (d) Show that

$$\theta(K_n) \geq \left\lceil \frac{n+7}{6} \right\rceil$$

Hint: Show that $\lceil p/q \rceil = \lfloor (p+q-1)/q \rfloor$ for any positive integers p and q.

4.48 Define chromatic number of a graph.

4.49 Prove that the chromatic number of a graph will not exceed by more than one from the maximum degree of the vertices in a graph.

4.50 Find the minimum number of colors needed to color the maps given below so that no two adjacent regions have the same color.

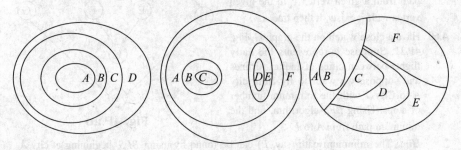

Fig. 4P.18

4.51 Find the chromatic number of the given graph.

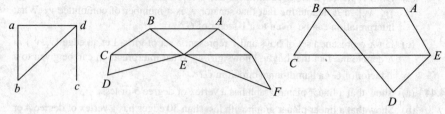

Fig 4P.19

4.52 Which graphs have a chromatic number of 1?

4.53 What is the least number of colors needed to color the map of India?

4.54 Show that a simple graph which has a circuit with an odd number of vertices in it, cannot be colored using two colors.

4.55 The computer science department has six committees, each meeting holds once in a month. How many different meeting times must be used to ensure that no member is scheduled to attend two meetings at the same time, if the committees are A_1 = {Niel, Anu, Jay}, A_2 = {Anu, Lee, Lalita},

A_3 = {Niel, Lalita, Jay}, A_4 = {Lee, Lalita, Jay}, A_5 = {Niel, Anu}, A_6 = {Anu, Lalita, Jay}?

4.56 A zoo wants to set up natural habitats to exhibit its animals. Unfortunately, some animals will eat some of the others if given the opportunity. How can a graph model and coloring be used to determine the number of different habitats needed and the replacement of the animals in these habitats?

4.57 Explain how graph coloring can be used in modeling. Use at least two different examples.

4.58 A graph G is said to be complete if each vertex v_i is adjacent to every other vertex v_j in G. Apply *DFS* and *BFS* to a complete graph of '4' vertices. List the vertices in the order they would be visited.

4.59 For the graph given in Fig. 4P.20, check whether there is a path from vertex labeled 'A' to vertex at level 'G'.

Hint: Both the traversal methods are employed to decide whether there is a path from a given vertex v_i to the given vertex v_j. If it exists, it then traces.

4.60 Have a close watch on the graph G, Fig. 4P.21. Suppose it represents the daily flights between cities of Indian Airlines and suppose we want to fly from city A to City J with the minimum number of stops. Using *BFS* algorithm, find the minimum path from A to J.

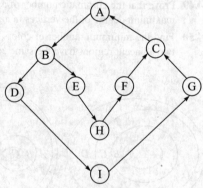

Fig. 4P.20

Hint: The minimum path (say, P) can be found by using *BFS*, beginning at city A. Whenever J is faced, we stop traversing further.

4.61 Consider the graph in Question No. 4.60. Find out the stops that are reachable from J (including J itself).

Hint: One way to do this is to use *DFS* on graph G getting started at node J.

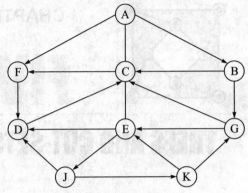

Fig. 4P.21

Programming Exercises

1. Write a program to implement all set operations on a given graph G, such as union, intersection, and ring sum operations.

2. Write a program to determine whether two vertices of a given graph are adjacent or not.

3. Write a program to compute the degree of a vertex v of a given graph G.

4. Write a program to describe a variation of breadth-first search that assigns the integer n to the nth vertex visited in the search.

5. Write a program to describe a variation of depth-first search that assigns the integer m to the mth vertex visited in the search.

6. A graph is said to be connected if for every two vertices v_i to v_j there is either a path from v_i to v_j or v_j to v_i. Write an algorithm to decide whether a given graph is connected or not. Hint: Modify the BFS algorithm.

7. Find the adjacency matrix and adjacency lists of the graph in Fig. 4P.22. If a depth-first search is initiated from vertex v_1, then find the list of visited vertices.

   Implement through program, and then, modify the same program to find out the list of visited nodes (vertices) in BFS traversal method.

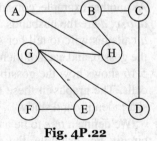

Fig. 4P.22

Objective
....

*To present the
concepts associated
with trees and
cut-sets.*

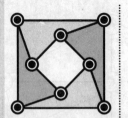

CHAPTER

FIVE

TREES AND CUT-SETS

5.1   TREES

We study in this chapter a class of graphs called *trees*. Consider a group of boxers contending for the title of heavyweight champion of the world. Suppose that each boxer has one chance to challenge the reigning champion, and the loser of any match will be eliminated from contention. Let $G = (V, E)$ be an undirected graph where the vertices in V represent the boxers and the edges in E represent the matches. That is, for x and y in V, $\{x, y\}$ is in E if there was a match between x and y. For example, let $V = \{a, b, c. d, e, f, g, h, i\}$. Suppose a was the reigning champion at the beginning. In the subsequent challenge matches, a beat b, c, and d, and then lost the title to e; e beat f and g, and then lost the title to h; and finally, h lost the title to i. The graph in Fig. 5.1a shows all the matches that took place. As another example, consider four gossipy couples $\{a, A, b, B, c, C, d, D\}$, where a, b, c, d are the husbands and A, B, C, D are, respectively, their wives. Suppose a calls his wife to tell her some gossip, she then calls the other wives to spread the gossip, and each of them, in turn, calls her husband about it. The graph in Fig. 5.1b shows how the gossip was spread where the edges represent the telephone calls. The graphs in these examples share some common properties, which we shall identify and study.

We define a *tree* to be a connected (undirected) graph that contains no simple circuit. For example, the graphs in Fig. 5.1a and b are trees. A collection of

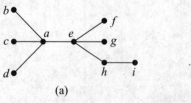

(a)

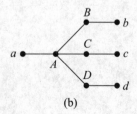

(b)

Fig. 5.1

disjoint trees is called, quite appropriately, a *forest*. A vertex of degree 1 in a tree is called a *leaf* or a *terminal node*, and a vertex of degree larger than 1 is called a *branch node* or *an internal node*. For example, the vertices b, c, d, f, g, and i in Fig. 5.1a are leaves and the vertices a, e, and h are branch nodes. We note first some properties of trees:

1. There is a unique path between every two vertices in a tree.*
2. The number of vertices is one more than the number of edges in a tree.
3. A tree with two or more vertices has at least two leaves.

Property 1 follows almost directly from the definition of a tree. Because a tree is a connected graph, there is at least one path between every two vertices. However, if there were two or more paths between a pair of vertices, there would be a circuit in the tree. We have thus proved property 1. For the examples in Fig. 5.1a and b we can check this property immediately.

We shall prove property 2 by induction on the number of vertices in the tree. As the basis of induction, we see that a tree with one vertex contains no edge, and a tree with two vertices contains one edge. Let there be a tree T with $\mathbf{v}$ vertices and $\mathbf{e}$ edges.[†] Let $\{a, b\}$ be an edge in T. Suppose we remove the edge $\{a, b\}$ from T. We claim that the remaining edges form a forest of two trees. Let c be a vertex such that the path between a and c in T does not include the edge $\{a, b\}$. Then the path between b and c in T must include the edge $\{a, b\}$ because, otherwise, there is a circuit in T. Thus, after the removal of the edge $\{a, b\}$, there is a path between a and c but no path between b and c. Similarly, let d be a vertex such that the path between a and d in T includes the edge $\{a, b\}$. Then the path between b and d does not include the edge $\{a, b\}$. Thus, after the removal of the edge $\{a, b\}$, there is a path between b and d but no path between a and d. Consequently, the removal of the edge $\{a, b\}$ divides T into two disjoint trees T' and T'', where T' contains a and all the vertices whose paths to a in T do not contain the edge $\{a, b\}$ and T'' contains b and all the vertices whose paths to b in T do not contain the edge $\{a, b\}$. Since both T' and T'' have at most $\mathbf{v} - 1$ vertices, it follows from the induction hypothesis that

$$\mathbf{e}' = \mathbf{v}' - 1$$
$$\mathbf{e}'' = \mathbf{v}'' - 1$$

where $\mathbf{e}'$ and $\mathbf{e}''$ are the numbers of edges and $\mathbf{v}'$ and $\mathbf{v}''$ are the numbers of vertices in T' and T''. Thus,

$$\mathbf{e}' + \mathbf{e}'' = \mathbf{v}' + \mathbf{v}'' - 2$$

Since

$$\mathbf{e} = \mathbf{e}' + \mathbf{e}'' + 1$$
$$\mathbf{v} = \mathbf{v}' + \mathbf{v}''$$

We have

$$\mathbf{e} = \mathbf{v} - 1$$

---

* Throughout this chapter, we shall use the term *path* to mean *elementary path* unless specified otherwise.

[†] We shall use $\mathbf{v}$ to denote the number of vertices and $\mathbf{e}$ the number of edges in a graph.

We note that the tree in Fig. 5.1a has nine vertices and eight edges, the tree in Fig. 5.1b has eight vertices and seven edges.

Property 3 follows from Property 2. We recall that the sum of the degrees of the vertices in any graph is equal to $2e$, which is also equal to $2v - 2$ in a tree. Since a tree with more than one vertex cannot have any isolated vertex, there must be at least two vertices of degree 1 in the tree. Both the examples in Fig. 5.1 have more than two leaves. As an exercise, we ask the reader to characterize all trees that have exactly two leaves. (See Prob. 5.1.)

We show now some results on the characterization of trees. All of these characterizations can be considered as equivalent definitions of trees:

1. A graph in which there is a unique path between every pair of vertices is a tree.

2. A connected graph with $e = v - 1$ is a tree.

3. A graph with $e = v - 1$ that has no circuit is a tree.

To show characterization 1, we note first that a graph in which there is a path between every pair of vertices is connected. Moreover, the graph cannot contain a circuit if these paths are unique, since the existence of a circuit implies the existence of two distinct paths between a certain pair of vertices. Thus, we can conclude that a graph in which there is a unique path between every pair of vertices is a tree.

As an example, consider the spies in a spy ring that is organized so that every two spies can communicate with each other either directly or through a unique chain of their colleagues. Let V be the set of spies and E be a set of edges such that the edge $\{a, b\}$ in E means spies a and b can communicate with each other directly. According to characterization 1, $G = (V, E)$ is a tree.

We now show characterization 2. Let G be a connected graph with $e = v - 1$. Suppose G contains a simple circuit C.* Let c denote the number of vertices in C. Clearly, the number of edges in C is equal to c. Since G is connected, every vertex of G that is not in C must be connected to the vertices in C. Now each edge of G that is not in C can connect only one additional vertex to the vertices in C. There are $v - c$ vertices that are not in C, so G must contain at least $v - c$ edges that are not in C. Thus, we must have $e \geq c + (v - c) = v$, which is a contradiction. It follows that G does not contain any circuit and is, therefore, a tree.

Consider an example in which someone sends a batch of chain letters to her friends. Her friends, in turn, send chain letters to their friends who have not received one before, and so on. Let $G = (V, E)$ be a graph where V is the set of people who received a chain letter, together with the originator, and E is a set of edges representing the letters. Since each letter adds one person to the group of people who received chain letters we have $e = v - 1$. Furthermore, G is a connected graph because there is only one originator of the letters. Thus, according to characterization 2, G is a tree.

Let us now show characterization 3. Let G be a graph with $e = v - 1$ that has no circuit. Suppose G is not connected. Let G', G'', ... denote the connected

---

* If G contains a circuit, G contains a simple circuit.

components of G. Since each of G', G'', ... is connected and has no circuits, they are all trees. According to Property 2 of trees shown in the foregoing, we have

$$e' = v' - 1$$
$$e'' = v'' - 1$$

where e', e'', ... are the numbers of edges and v', v'', ... are the numbers of vertices in G', G'', ... We have

$$e' + e'' + ... = v' - 1 + v'' - 1 + ... \tag{5.1}$$

Since

$$e = e' + e'' + ...$$
$$v = v' + v'' + ...$$

(5:1) implies

$$e < v - 1$$

which is a contradiction. Thus, G must be connected and is, therefore, a tree.

Consider the example presented earlier of a group of boxers contending for the heavyweight championship. We want to show that the graph describing the challenge matches, G, is always a tree for any group of boxers and for any possible outcomes of the matches. Since each match eliminates exactly one of the boxers from contention, we have $e = v - 1$. Suppose we have a circuit in G. Let $(c_1, c_2, c_3, ..., c_k)$ denote the sequence of vertices in the circuit. *Without loss of generality*, we can assume c_2 is the loser in the match between c_1 and c_2. In that case, c_2 must be the winner and c_3 the loser in an earlier match. Similarly, c_3 must be the winner and c_4 must be the loser in a match before the match between c_1 and c_2. Finally, c_k must be the winner and c_1 must be the loser in a match before the match between c_1 and c_2, which clearly is an impossibility. Thus, according to characterization 3, G is a tree.

5.2 ROOTED TREES

A directed graph is said to be a *directed tree* if it becomes a tree when the directions of the edges are ignored. For example, Fig. 5.2*a* shows a directed tree. A directed tree is called a *rooted tree* if there is exactly one vertex whose incoming degree is 0 and the incoming degrees of all other vertices are 1. The vertex with incoming degree 0 is called the *root* of the rooted tree. For example, Fig. 5.2*b* shows a rooted tree. In a rooted tree, a vertex whose outgoing degree is 0 is called a *leaf* or a *terminal node*, and a vertex whose outgoing degree is nonzero is called a *branch node* or an *internal node*. There are many occasions when we encounter structures that can be represented as rooted trees. For example, the organization chart of a corporation in Fig. 5.3 can be represented immediately by a rooted tree.

Let a be a branch node in a rooted tree. A vertex b is said to be a *son** of a if there is an edge from a to b. Also, a is said to be the *father* of b. Two vertices are said to be *brothers* if they are sons of the same vertex. A vertex c is said to be

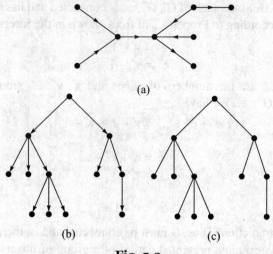

(a)

(b) (c)

Fig. 5.2

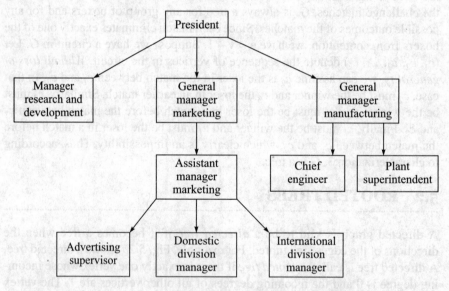

President

Manager research and development

General manager marketing

General manager manufacturing

Assistant manager marketing

Chief engineer

Plant superintendent

Advertising supervisor

Domestic division manager

International division manager

Fig. 5.3 A rooted tree representing the organization chart of a corporation

a *descendant* of *a* if there is a directed path from *a* to *c*. Also, *a* is said to be an *ancestor* of *c*. These terms indeed remind us that what we commonly call family trees are indeed rooted trees.

Let *a* be a branch node in the tree *T*. By the *subtree with a as the root* we mean the subgraph $T' = (V', E')$ of *T* such that V' contains *a* and all of its descendants

---

† In the literature, the terms *daughter* and *child* were also used. We shall not constantly worry about the question of sex discrimination.

and E' contains the edges in all directed paths emanating from a. By a *subtree of a* we mean a subtree that has a son of a as root.

When we draw a rooted tree, if we consistently follow the convention of placing the sons of a branch node below it, the arrowheads of the edges may be omitted, because they will be understood to be pointing downward. Figure 5.2c shows an example.

Consider the rooted tree in Fig. 5.4a which is the family tree of a man who has two sons, with the older son having no children and the younger son having three. Although the rooted tree in Fig. 5.4b is isomorphic to that in Fig. 5.4a, it could be the family tree of another man whose older son has three children and whose younger son has none. This example motivates the definition of an ordered tree, which allows us to refer to each subtree of a branch node in an unambiguous way. An *ordered tree* is a rooted tree with the edges incident from each branch node labeled with integers 1, 2, …, i, ….* Consequently, the subtrees of a branch node can be referred to as the first, second, …, and ith subtrees of the branch node corresponding to the labels of the edges incident from it. (Note that we do not insist that the labels be consecutive integers. Thus, for example, if the three edges incident from a branch node are labeled 1, 2, 5, we shall say that the node

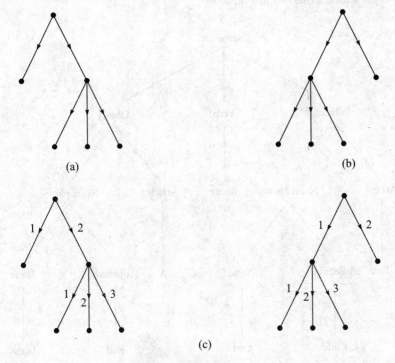

(a)   (b)

(c)

Fig. 5.4

---

* Such labels can be implicit when they are obvious from the way the tree was defined or the way the tree was drawn.

has no third or fourth subtree.) For example, the rooted trees in Fig. 5.4a and b are labeled as shown in Fig. 5.4c. Two ordered trees are said to be isomorphic if there is one-to-one correspondence between their vertices and edges that preserves the incidence relation and if the labels of corresponding edges match. Thus, the two ordered trees in Fig. 5.4c are not isomorphic. An ordered tree in which every branch node has at most *m* sons is called an *m-ary tree.** An *m*-ary tree is said to be *regular* if everyone of its branch nodes has exactly *m* sons. An important class of *m*-ary trees is *binary trees*. For binary trees, instead of referring to the first subtree or the second subtree of a branch node, we often refer to the *left subtree* or the *right subtree* of the node.

The reader probably has seen how the structure of a sentence can be diagrammed as an ordered tree. Figure 5.5 shows an example. As another example, we note how an arithmetic expression can be represented as a binary tree. It is clear that simple expressions such as $a + b$ and $c * d * e$ can be represented as shown in Fig. 5.6a and b, where the operands appear in the leaves and the operators appear in the branch nodes of the ordered trees. Note that parentheses are no longer needed when an arithmetic expression is represented as a binary tree. For example, the arithmetic expression $(((a + b * c) * d - e)/(f + g)) + h * i * j$ is represented as shown in Fig. 5.6c.

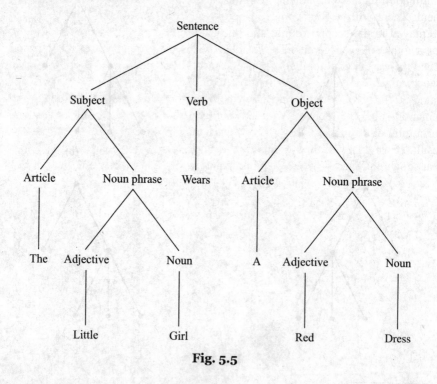

Fig. 5.5

---

* Clearly, a corresponding notion can be defined for all rooted trees.

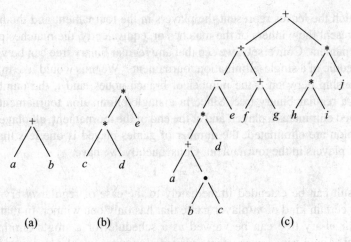

(a)   (b)   (c)

Fig. 5.6

5.3   PATH LENGTHS IN ROOTED TREES

Consider the problem of determining the number of games played in a single-elimination tennis tournament.* Suppose there are eight players in the tournament. There will be four games to be played in the first round, two games to be played in the second round, and one game to be played in the final round, for a total of seven games. The problem seems to become more complicated when there is an odd number of players, say 11, in the tournament. In this case, there will be five games in the first round (one of the players draws a bye), three games in the second round, one game in the third round (one of the three players remaining after the second round draws *a* bye), and one game in the final round for a total of 10 games. There is, however, a more direct way to determine the result. If we examine the schedule of a single-elimination tournament such as that shown in Fig. 5.7, we realize immediately that it is exactly a regular binary

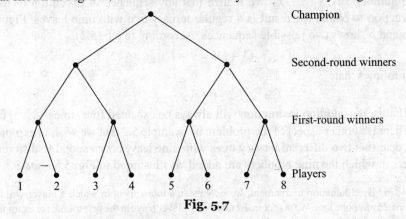

Champion

Second-round winners

First-round winners

Players

Fig. 5.7

---

* A single-elimination tournament is one in which a player will be eliminated after one loss.

tree in which the leaves represent the players in the tournament and the branch nodes represent the winners of the matches or, equivalently, the matches played in the tournament. Conversely, we see that any regular binary tree can be viewed as the schedule of a single-elimination tournament.* We thus would like to know the relationship between i, the number of branch nodes, and t, the number of leaves, of a regular binary tree. Since in a single-elimination tournament each game played eliminates a player, and at the end of the tournament, all players but the champion are eliminated, the number of games played is one less than the number of players in the tournament. Consequently, we have

$$i = t - 1$$

The result can be extended immediately to the case of regular m-ary trees. Imagine a certain kind of m-player game that has only one winner. In that case, any regular m-ary tree can be viewed as a schedule for a single-elimination tournament. Again, since every game played eliminates $m - 1$ players and only the champion remains at the end of the tournament, we have[†]

$$(m - 1)i = t - 1 \tag{5.2}$$

We consider some examples:

Example 5.1 Consider the problem of connecting 19 lamps to a single electric outlet by using extension cords each of which has four outlets. Since any such connection is a quaternary tree with the single outlet connected to the root of the tree, according to eq. (5.2),

$$(4 - 1)i = 19 - 1$$

That is, although there are many ways to connect the lights, six extension cords are always needed. ∎

Example 5.2 Let us consider a hypothetical computer that has an instruction which computes the sum of three numbers. Suppose we want to find the sum of nine numbers, $x_1, x_2, \ldots, x_9$. We realize that any sequence of execution of this instruction to obtain the result is a regular ternary tree with nine leaves. Figure 5.8a and b shows two possible sequences. According to eq. (5.2),

$$(3 - 1)i = 9 - 1$$

It follows that

$$i = 4$$

That is, the addition instruction will always be executed four times. ∎

There is another aspect of the problem in Example 5.2 that we wish to explore. It is clear that two different ternary trees with nine leaves correspond to different orders in which the nine numbers are added, as illustrated in Fig. 5.8a and b.

---

* By a single-elimination tournament, we *only* mean a tournament in which a player will be eliminated after one loss. We do not insist that every player plays in the first round, for example.

[†] As an alternative proof, we note that mi is the total number of sons of the branch nodes, which is equal to the number of branch nodes and terminal nodes minus one (the root).

Although it is always the case that it takes at least four addition operations to compute the sum $x_1 + x_2 + \ldots + x_9$, the possibility of computing some partial sums concurrently (such as in the case of a multiprocessor computing system) makes one sequence superior to another. For example, the sequence of additions shown in Fig. 5.8a can be carried out in two steps, where in each step we compute all partial sums that can be computed concurrently. On the other hand, it takes four steps to carry out the sequence of additions shown in Fig. 5.8b. The *path length* of a vertex in a rooted tree is defined to be the number of edges in the path from the root to the vertex. For example, the path length of vertex x_1 in Fig. 5.8b is 4, and that of vertex x_5 is 3. We define the *height* of a tree to be the maximum of the path lengths in the tree. It is clear that an m-ary tree of height h has at most m^h leaves corresponding to the case shown in Fig. 5.8a. On the other hand, a regular m-ary tree of height h has at least $m + (m-1)(h-1)$ leaves corresponding to the case shown in Fig. 5.8b.

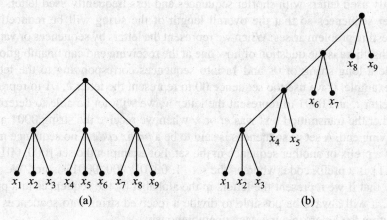

(a)   (b)

Fig. 5.8

Let I denote the sum of the path lengths of all the branch nodes and E denote the sum of the path lengths of the leaves in a rooted tree. We shall show that for a regular binary tree $E = I + 2i$, where i is the number of branch nodes. Consider an edge (x, y) in a regular binary tree T. The edge (x, y) is included in the computation of the path lengths of all the branch nodes and leaves of T in the subtree with y as its root. Since there is exactly one more leaf than branch node in the subtree this edge is counted one more time in the computation of E than in the computation of I. Repeating this argument for all edges in the binary tree, we obtain

$$E = 1 + \text{number of edges in the binary tree}$$
$$= 1 + 2i$$

We leave it to the reader to carry out the obvious extension to show that, for a regular m-ary tree,

$$E = (m-1)I + mi$$

5.4 PREFIX CODES

We present now more examples on the concept of path lengths in rooted trees. Consider a problem in telecommunication in which we want to represent the letters in the English alphabet by sequences of 0s and 1s (or equivalently by sequences of dashes and dots). Since the 26 letters in the alphabet must be represented by distinct sequences of 0s and 1s, they can be represented by sequences of length 5 ($2^4 < 26 < 2^5$). To send a message, we simply transmit a long string of 0s and 1s containing the sequences for the letters in the message. At the receiving end, this string of 0s and 1s will be divided into sequences of length 5 and the corresponding letters can be recognized.

It is well known, however, that the letters in the alphabet are not used with uniform frequencies. For example, the letters *e* and *t* are used more frequently than the letters *q* and *z*. Consequently, one might wish to represent more frequently used letters with shorter sequences and less frequently used letters with longer sequences so that the overall length of the string will be reduced. An interesting problem arises: When we represent the letters by sequences of various lengths, there is the question of how one at the receiving end can unambiguously divide a long string of 0s and 1s into sequences corresponding to the letters, For example, if we use the sequence 00 to represent the letter *e*, 01 to represent the letter *t*, and 0001 to represent the letter *w*, we will not be able to determine whether the transmitted text was *et* or *w* when we receive the string 0001 at the receiving end. A set of sequences is said to be a *prefix code* if no sequence in the set is a prefix of another sequence in the set. For example, the set {000, 001, 01, 10, 11} is a prefix code, whereas the set {1, 00, 01, 000, 0001} is not. We shall show that if we represent the letters in the alphabet by the sequences in a prefix code, it will always be possible to divide a received string into sequences representing the letters in a message unambiguously.

We note first that we can obtain a binary prefix code directly from a binary tree. For a given binary tree, we label the two edges incident from each branch node with 0 and 1. Let us assign to each leaf a sequence of 0s and 1s which is the sequence of labels of the edges in the path from the root to that leaf. For example, Fig. 5.9 shows a binary tree and the sequences assigned to its leaves, which we enclose in boxes for clarity. It is clear that the set of sequences assigned to the leaves in any binary tree is a prefix code.

Conversely, we want to show that corresponding to a prefix code there is a binary tree, with the two edges incident from each of the branch nodes labeled with 0 and 1, such that the sequences of 0s and 1s assigned to the leaves are the sequences

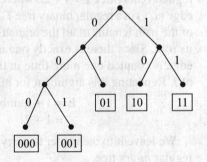

Fig. 5.9

in the code.* Let h denote the length of the longest sequence(s) in the prefix code. We construct a *full regular* binary tree of height $h^\dagger$ and label the two edges incident from each of the branch nodes with 0 and 1. Let us assign to each vertex a sequence of 0s and 1s that is the sequence of labels of the edges in the path from the root to the vertex. Clearly, each binary sequence of length less than or equal to h is assigned to exactly one vertex. Let us mark all the vertices that are assigned with sequences in the prefix code, and then prune the tree by removing every vertex, together with the edge incident to it, that does not have a marked descendant. Since no marked vertex is an ancestor of another marked vertex, the set of marked vertices will be exactly the set of leaves of the resultant tree. This is, indeed, the tree we are looking for. As an example, for the prefix code $\{1, 01, 000, 001\}$ we obtain the binary tree in Fig. 5.10b by pruning the full regular binary tree of height 3 in Fig. 5.10a, where the vertices that are assigned with sequences in the prefix code are boxed.

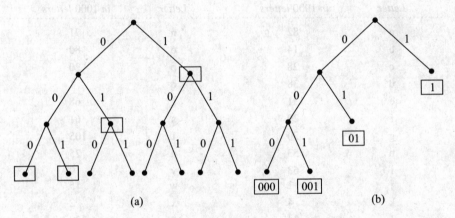

Fig. 5.10

Finally, we are ready to give a simple argument to show that it is always possible to divide a received string of 0s and 1s into sequences that are in a prefix code. Starting at the root of the binary tree, we shall trace a downward path in the tree according to the digits in the received string. That is, at a branch node, we shall follow the edge labeled with a 0 if we encounter a 0 in the received string, and we shall follow the edge labeled with a 1 if we encounter a 1 in the received string. When the downward path reaches a leaf, we know that a sequence in the prefix code has been detected, and we should return to the root of the tree to start looking for the next sequence. Clearly, this procedure guarantees that there will be no ambiguity in dividing the received string into sequences that are in the prefix code.

---

† A *full* regular binary tree is a regular tree in which all leaves have the same path length (equal to the height of the tree).

Another interesting problem is to be more precise about the idea of using short sequences to represent more frequently used letters. To this end, we need some information on the frequencies of usage of the letters. Indeed, such information is available, and Table 5.1 shows the average number of occurrences of the letters in the English alphabet. If we use a binary sequence of l_i digits to represent the ith letter in the alphabet, the average length of the binary string that represents an English text of 1000 letters will be $\sum_{i=1}^{26} w_i l_i$, where w_i is the average number of occurrences of the ith letter in 1000 letters.

Table 5.1 Average number of occurrences of the letters in the English alphabet

Letter	Number of occurrences in 1000 letters	Letter	Number of occurrences in 1000 letters
a	82	n	71
b	14	o	80
c	28	p	20
d	38	q	1
e	131	r	68
f	29	s	61
g	20	t	105
h	53	u	25
i	63	v	9
j	1	w	15
k	4	x	2
l	34	y	20
m	25	z	1

Our discussion leads us to the following problem: Suppose we are given a set of weights $w_1, w_2, \ldots, w_t$. Without loss of generality, let us assume $w_1 \leq w_2 \leq \ldots \leq w_t$. A binary tree that has t leaves with the weights $w_1, w_2, \ldots, w_t$ assigned to the leaves is said to be a *binary tree for the weights* $w_1, w_2, \ldots, w_t$. We define the *weight of a binary tree for the weights* $w_1, w_2, \ldots, w_t$ to be $\sum_{i=1}^{t} w_i l(w_i)$, where $l(w_i)$ is the path length of the leaf to which the weight w_i is assigned. The weight of a tree T shall be denoted $W(T)$. A binary tree for the weights $w_1, w_2, \ldots, w_t$ is said to be an optimal tree if its weight is minimum. For example, given the weights 5, 6, 7, 12, Fig. 5.11*a* shows an optimal tree. (We ask the reader to check that the tree in Fig. 5.11*b* is inferior.)

There is a very elegant procedure due to D. A. Huffman [6] for constructing an optimal tree for a given set of weights. The key observation that leads to the

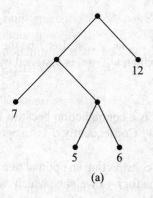

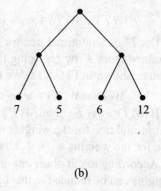

(a)   (b)

Fig. 5.11

construction procedure is that we can obtain an optimal tree for the weights $w_1, w_2, \ldots, w_t$, from an optimal tree T' for the weights $w_1 + w_2, w_3, w_4, \ldots, w_t$.*
Specifically, we claim that replacing the leaf in T' to which the weight $w_1 + w_2$ is assigned by the subtree shown in Fig. 5.12 will yield an optimal tree for the weights $w_1, w_2, \ldots, w_t$. For example, suppose we want to construct an optimal tree for the weights 3, 4, 5, 6, 12. Since we know the tree in Fig. 5.11a is an optimal tree for the weights 5, 6, 7, 12, we obtain the tree in Fig. 5.13 as an optimal tree for the weights 3, 4, 5, 6, 12. To prove our claim, we want to show first that there is an optimal tree for the weights $w_1, w_2, \ldots, w_t$ in which the leaves to which w_1 and w_2 are assigned are brothers. Suppose we have an optimal tree for the weights $w_1, w_2, \ldots, w_t$. Let a be a branch node of largest path length

Fig. 5.12

in the tree. Suppose the weights assigned to the sons of a are w_x and w_y. Thus, $l(w_x) \geq l(w_1)$ and $l(w_x) \geq l(w_2)$. On the other hand, since the tree is optimal we must have $l(w_x) \leq l(w_1)$ and $l(w_x) \leq l(w_2)$. [If $l(w_x) > l(w_1)$, interchanging the assignment of w_1 and w_x will yield a tree of similar weight, which is a contradiction. The same argument applies if $l(w_x) >$ $l(w_2)$.] Consequently, we have $l(w_x) = l(w_y) =$ $l(w_1) = l(w_2)$. Interchanging the assignment of w_x, w_y with that of w_1, w_2, we obtain an optimal tree in which the leaves to which w_1 and w_2 are assigned are brothers.

Let $\hat{T}$ denote an optimal tree for the weights $w_1, w_2, \ldots, w_t$ in which the leaves to which w_1 and w_2 are assigned are brothers. Replace the subtree in $\hat{T}$ that contains these two leaves and their father by a leaf, and assign to this

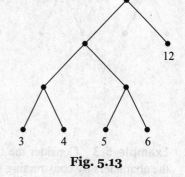

Fig. 5.13

new leaf the weight $w_1 + w_2$. Let $\hat{T}$ denote this resultant tree, which is a binary tree for the weights $w_1 + w_2, w_3, \ldots, w_t$. Clearly,

---

* Note that the weights $w_1 + w_2, w_3, w_4, \ldots, w_t$, might no longer be in increasing order.

$$W(\hat{T}) = W(\hat{\hat{T}}) + w_1 + w_2$$

Let T' be an optimal tree for the weights $w_1 + w_2, w_3, \ldots, w_t$. Let T be the tree obtained from T' by replacing the leaf in T' to which $w_1 + w_2$ is assigned by the subtree shown in Fig. 5.12. We have

$$W(T) = W(T') + w_1 + w_2$$

If $W(T) > W(\hat{T})$, then $W(T') > W(\hat{\hat{T}})$, which is a contradiction because T' is an optimal tree for the weights $w_1 + w_2, w_3, \ldots, w_t$. Consequently, T is an optimal tree for the weights $w_1, w_2, \ldots, w_t$.

According to our observation, the problem of constructing an optimal tree for t weights can be reduced to that of constructing one for $t - 1$ weights, which can be reduced to that of constructing one for $t - 2$ weights, and so on. Since the problem of constructing an optimal tree for two weights is a trivial one, the problem of constructing an optimal tree for t weights is solved. For example, for the weights 3, 4, 5, 6, and 12, Fig. 5.14 shows the step-by-step construction according to Huffman's procedure.

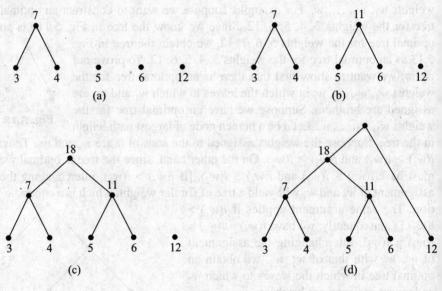

Fig. 5.14

Example 5.3 Consider the following statement and find the prefix codes for the characters by constructing the optimal binary prefix code.

"Merie eyes seen near lake."

Solution: The weight (frequency) of each of the letters in the above statement is given in Table 5.2.

	Table 5.2	Weights of the letters	
Letter	*Weight (Frequency)*	*Letter*	*Weight (Frequency)*
M	1	s	2
e	8	n	2
r	2	a	2
i	1	l	1
Space (b̷)	4	k	1
y	1	.	1

Step 1: Sort the weights (frequencies) of the above letters in increasing order in a queue. The resulting queue is shown in Fig 5.15 (a). Then, construct the subtrees from the queue.

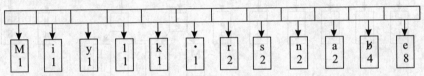

Fig. 5.15(a) The letters and their weights arranged in ascending order in a queue

The first subtree is constructed as shown in Fig 5.15 (b) by considering the first two lowest weights of the characters 'E' and 'i'. The root of the subtree has a value of 2 (by adding the weights of the leaf nodes of the sub-tree) and it cannot be placed at the beginning of the queue. So, it has to be placed in an appropriate position in the queue as shown in Fig. 5.15 (c).

Step 2: A new subtree is constructed as shown in Fig. 5.15(d) by considering the first two lowest weights of the characters 'y' and 'l' from the newly rearranged

Fig 5.15(b) The subtree constructed from letters 'E' and 'i'

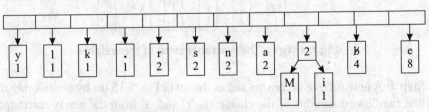

Fig 5.15(c) The rearrangement of the weights

queue of Fig 5.15 (c). The root of the subtree has a value of 2 and it cannot be placed at the beginning of the queue. So, it has to be placed in an appropriate position in the queue as shown in Fig. 5.15 (e).

Fig 5.15(d)   The subtree constructed from letters 'y' and 'l'

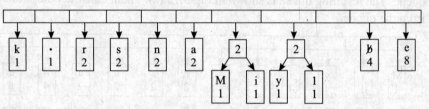

Fig 5.15(e)   The rearrangement of the weights

Step 3: A new subtree is constructed as shown in Fig. 5.15 (f) by considering the first two lowest weights of the characters 'k' and '.' from the newly rearranged queue of Fig 5.15 (e). The root of the subtree has a value of 2 and it has to be placed in an appropriate position in the queue as shown in Fig. 5.15 (g).

Fig 5.15(f)   The subtree constructed from letters 'k' and '·'

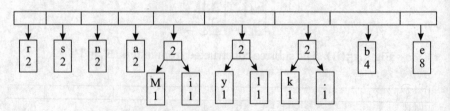

Fig 5.15(g)   The rearrangement of the weights

Step 4: A new subtree is constructed as shown in Fig. 5.15 (h) by considering the first two lowest weights of the characters 'r' and 's' from the newly rearranged queue of Fig. 5.15 (g). The root of the sub-tree has a value of 4 and placed in the appropriate position in the queue as shown in Fig. 5.15 (i).

Fig 5.15(h) The subtree constructed from letter 'r' and 's'

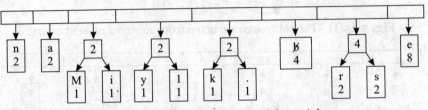

Fig 5.15(i) The rearrangement of the weights

Step 5: A new subtree is constructed as shown in Fig. 5.15 (j) by considering the first two lowest weights of the characters 'n' and 'a' from the newly rearranged queue of Fig. 5.15 (i). The root of the subtree has a value of 4 and placed in the appropriate position in the queue as shown in Fig. 5.15 (k).

Fig. 5.15(j) The subtree constructed from letters 'n' and 'a'

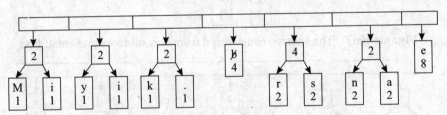

Fig. 5.15(k) The rearrangement of the weights

Step 6: A new subtree is constructed as shown in Fig. 5.15 (l) by considering the first two lowest weights of the first two subtrees present in the newly rearranged queue of Fig.5.15(k). The root of the new subtree has a value of 4 and placed in the appropriate position in the queue as shown in Fig. 5.15 (m).

Step 7: A new subtree is constructed as shown in Fig. 5.15 (n) by considering the first two lowest weights of the first two subtrees present in the newly rearranged queue of Fig. 5.15(m). The root of the new subtree has a value of 6 and placed in the appropriate position in the queue as shown in Fig. 5.15 (o).

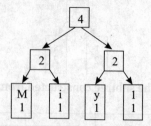

Fig. 5.15(l)   The subtree constructed from subtrees present at first

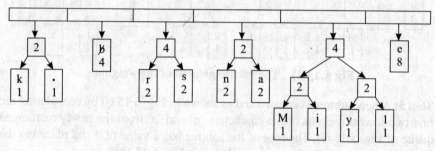

Fig. 5.15(m)   The rearrangement of the weights

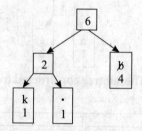

Fig. 5.15(n)   The subtree constructed from two subtrees present at first

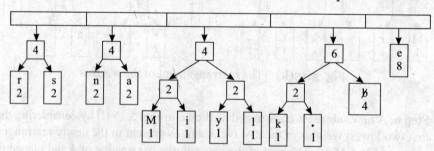

Fig. 5.15(o)   The rearrangement of the weights

Step 8: A new subtree is constructed as shown in Fig. 5.15 (p) by considering the first two lowest weights of the first two subtrees present in the newly rearranged queue of Fig. 5.15(o). The root of the new subtree has a value of 8 and placed in the appropriate position in the queue as shown in Fig. 5.15 (q).

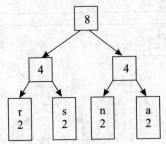

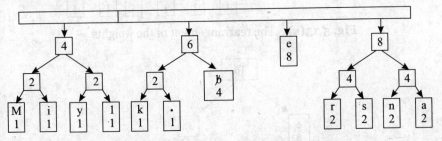

Fig 5.15(p) The subtree constructed from two subtrees present at first

Fig. 5.15(q) The rearrangement of the weights

Step 9: A new subtree is constructed as shown in Fig. 5.15 (r) by considering the first two lowest weights of the first two subtrees present in the newly rearranged queue of Fig. 5.15(q). The root of the new subtree has a value of 10 and placed in the appropriate position in the queue as shown in Fig. 5.15 (s).

Step 10: A new subtree is constructed as shown in Fig. 5.15 (t) by considering the first two lowest weights of the first two subtrees present in the newly rearranged queue of Fig. 5.15(s). The root of the new subtree has a value of 16 and placed in the appropriate position in the queue as shown in Fig. 5.15 (u).

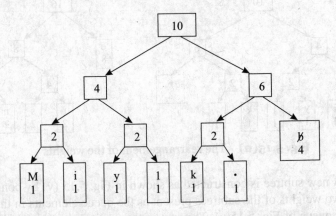

Fig. 5.15(r) The subtree constructed from two subtrees present at first

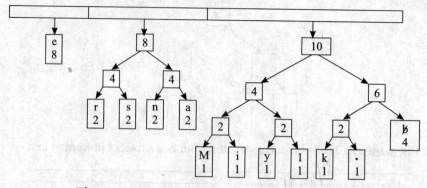

Fig. 5.15(s) The rearrangement of the weights

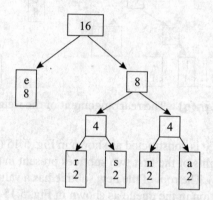

Fig. 5.15(t) The subtree constructed from two subtrees present at the beginning of the queue in Fig. 5.15(s)

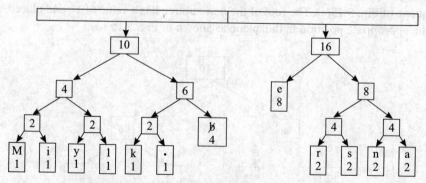

Fig. 5.15(u) The rearrangement of the weights

Step 11: A new subtree is constructed as shown in Fig. 5.15 (v) by considering the only two weights of the subtrees present as the queue elements in the newly rearranged queue of Fig. 5.15(u). The root of the new subtree has a value of 26 and placed in the appropriate position in the queue. This results in the same figure

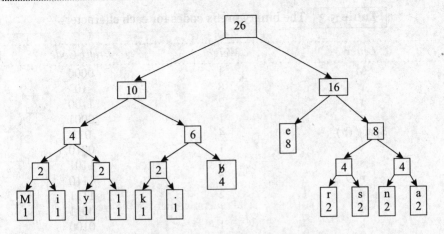

Fig. 5.15(v) The final optimal binary tree

as Fig. 5.15(v). As there are no more elements present in the queue, Fig. 5.15 (v) represents the final optimal binary tree for the given statement.

Now, we would like to get the binary prefix codes of each individual character present in the given statement depending on their frequencies of appearance in the statement.

We allocate '0' to the left edge of any root or subroot of the tree and '1' to the right edge of any root or subroot of the tree. We get the result as shown in Fig. 5.15 (w).

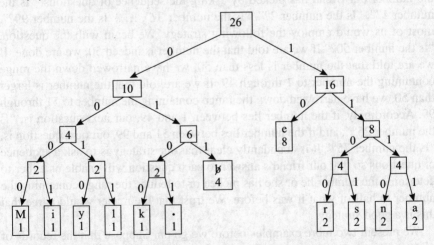

Fig. 5.15(w) The final optimal binary tree with binary prefix code

Now, we can find the binary prefix code for each letter present in the leaf nodes of the tree by traversing through the edges of the tree from the root node to each of the leaf nodes in Fig. 5.15(w). By the traversal process, we get the binary prefix codes as given in Table 5.3.

| Table 5.3 | The binary prefix codes for each character | |

Letter	Weight	Prefix Code
M	1	0000
e	8	10
r	2	1100
i	1	0001
Space (♭)	4	011
y	1	0010
s	2	1101
n	2	1110
a	2	1111
l	1	0011
k	1	0100
.	1	0101

5.5   BINARY SEARCH TREES

Suppose a friend of ours has picked a number between 1 and 99 and we want to determine what this number is by asking questions of the form, "Is the number 37?" Our friend will respond by telling us the number is indeed 37, or the number is smaller than 37, or the number is larger than 37. Although we can determine the number our friend has picked by asking the sequence of questions, "Is the number 1?", "Is the number 2?", "Is the number 3?", ...,. "Is the number 99?", most of us would employ the following strategy. We begin with the question, "Is the number 50?" If we are told that the number is indeed 50, we are done. If we are told that the number is less than 50, we have narrowed down the range containing the number to 1 through 49. If we are told that the number is larger than 50, we have narrowed down the range containing the number to 51 through 99. Accordingly, if the number lies between 1 and 49, our next question is, "Is the number 25?"; and if the number lies between 51 and 99, our next question is, "Is the number 75?" It is abundantly clear that our strategy is to ask a sequence of questions so that our friend's answer to each question will enable us either to determine the number he or she has picked or to reduce the range containing the number to half of what it was before. We trust that the reader would agree that this is a good strategy.

We present two more examples before we go on. Suppose that the records of the employees of a company are arranged according to social security numbers. An important problem is to design a procedure to search for the record of an employee, given her social security number. A similar problem is to find a person's telephone number in a telephone directory or to determine that the number is not listed. Clearly, the strategy in the example in the preceding paragraph can be readily applied to these cases.

Let us now formulate precisely the problem of searching for an item in an ordered list. We assume that we are dealing with items over which there is a linear ordering, <. In practical examples, the linear ordering can be numerical alphabetical, alphanumeric, and so on. Let $K_1, K_2, ..., K_n$ be the n items in an ordered list which are known as the *keys*. Assume that $K_1 < K_2 < ... < K$. Given an item x, our problem is to search the keys and determine whether x is equal to one of the keys or whether x falls between keys K_i and K_{i+1} for some. We note first that the search has $2n + 1$ possible outcomes, namely, x is less than K_1, x is equal to K_1, x is larger than K_1 but less than K_2, x is equal to K_2, and so on.

A search procedure consists of a sequence of comparisons between x and the keys where each comparison of x with a key tells us whether x is equal to, less than, or larger than that key.* We show now how we can describe a search procedure using a binary-tree representation. We define a *search tree* for the keys $K_1, K_2, ..., K_n$ to be a binary tree with n branch nodes and $n + 1$ leaves. The branch nodes are labeled $K_1, K_2, ..., K_n$, and the leaves are labeled $K_0, K_1, K_2, ..., K_n$,[†] such that, for the branch node with the label K_i, its left subtree contains only vertices with labels $K_j, j < i$, and its right subtree contains only vertices with labels $K_j, j \geq i$. For example, Fig. 5.16 shows a search tree for the keys K_1, K_2, K_3, K_4

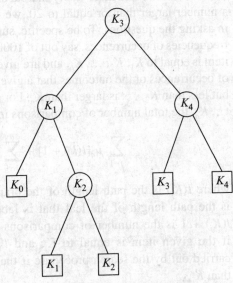

where, for clarity, we use circles to denote branch nodes and squares to denote leaves. We note immediately that a search tree corresponds to a search procedure: Starting with the root of the search tree, we compare a given item x with the label of the root K_i. If x is equal to K_i, the search is completed. If x is less than K_i we shall compare x with the left son of the root, and if x is larger than K_i we shall compare x with the right son of the root.[‡] Such comparison continues for successive branch nodes until either x matches a key or a leaf is reached. Clearly, if a leaf labeled K_j is reached, it means that x is larger than the key K_j but less than the key K_{j+1}. (If the leaf labeled K_n is reached, it means that x is less than K_1.

Fig. 5.16 A search tree

---

* Suppose we compare x with K_i and find out that x is less than K_i. A subsequent step compare x with K_j for $j > i$ would be totally wasteful. We assume the search procedures considered do not contain any such wasteful steps.

† The meaning of the label K_0 will become clear later on.

‡ In a binary tree, the left (right) son of a branch node is the root of the left (right) subtree of the node.

If the leaf labeled K_n is reached, it means that x is larger than K_n.) For example, let AB, CF, EG, PP be the keys K_1, K_2, K_3, K_4 in the search tree in Fig. 5.16. Given the item BB, the search steps according to Fig. 5.16 will be:

1. Compare BB with K_3, which is EG.
2. Since BB is less than EG, compare BB with K_1, which is AB.
3. Since BB is larger than AB, compare BB with K_2, which is CF.
4. Since BB is less than CF, the leaf labeled K_1 is reached.

Thus, we conclude that the item BB is larger than AB and less than CF.

One obvious criterion for measuring the effectiveness of a search procedure is the maximum number of comparisons the procedure carries out in the worst case, that is, the height of the corresponding search tree. Consequently, for a given set of n keys a search tree whose height is $\lceil \lg(n + 1) \rceil$ will correspond to a best-possible search procedure. On the other hand, since there always exists a binary search tree of height $\lceil \lg(n + 1) \rceil$ for any n,* the problem of designing a best-possible search procedure according to this criterion is not a difficult one.

In general, the outcomes of our searches might occur in different frequencies. For example, in the problem of guessing the number a friend of ours has picked, if we know that it is more likely that he or she picks a number less than 20 than a number larger than or equal to 20, we might want to reconsider our strategy in asking the questions. To be specific, suppose we are given $u_1, u_2, \ldots, u_n$ as the frequencies of occurrences, say out of 1000 searches, of the outcomes that a given item is equal to $K_1, K_2, \ldots, K_n$, and are given $w_0, w_1, w_2, \ldots, w_n$ as the frequencies of occurrences of the outcomes that a given item is less than K_1, is larger than K_1 but less than K_2, ..., is larger than K_n. For a given search tree for the keys $K_1, K_2, \ldots, K_n$, the total number of comparisons in 1000 searches will equal

$$\sum_{j=1}^{n} u_j[l(k_j) + 1] + \sum_{j=0}^{n} w_j l'(k_j) \tag{5.3}$$

where $l(K_j)$ is the path length of the branch node that is labeled K_j and $l'(K_j)$ is the path length of the leaf that is labeled K_j in the search tree. Note that $l(K_j) + 1$ is the number of comparisons carried out by the search procedure if the given item is equal to K_j, and $l'(K_j)$ is the number of comparisons carried out by the search procedure if the given item is larger than K_j and less than K_{j+1}.

5.6 SPANNING TREES AND CUT-SETS

Let G be a connected graph where the vertices represent the buildings in a factory, and the edges represent connecting tunnels between the buildings. One might wish to determine a subset of tunnels which should be kept open all the

---

* See Prob. 5.15.

time so that we can reach one building from another through these tunnels. One might also wish to determine the subsets of tunnels whose blockage will separate some of the buildings from the others. We study in this section the concepts of *subsets of connecting edges* and *subsets of disconnecting edges* in a graph.

A *tree of a graph* is a subgraph of the graph which is a tree. A *spanning tree of a connected graph* is a spanning subgraph of the graph which is a tree. For example, Fig. 5.17*b* shows a tree and Fig. 5.17*c* shows a spanning tree of the graph in Fig. 5.17*a*. A *branch* of a tree is an edge of the graph that is in the tree. A *chord*, or a *link*, of a tree is an edge of the graph that is not in the tree. The set of the chords of a tree is referred to as the *complement* of the tree.

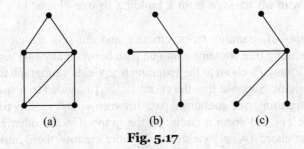

(a)   (b)   (c)

Fig. 5.17

We observe that a *connected graph always contains a spanning tree*. Suppose we are given a connected graph. If the graph does not contain any circuit, then it is a tree. If the graph contains one or more circuits, we can remove an edge from one of the circuits and still have a connected subgraph. Such removal of edges from circuits can be repeated until we have a spanning tree. It follows immediately from this argument that a spanning tree is a minimal connecting subgraph* of a connected graph in the sense that from a connecting subgraph which is not a spanning tree, one or more of its edges can be removed so that the resultant graph is still a connecting subgraph, and, on the other hand, no edge can be removed from a spanning tree so that the resultant subgraph is still a connecting subgraph. In the example of buildings connected by tunnels, if we keep the tunnels corresponding to the edges in a spanning tree open, we are assured that we can reach from one building to another through these tunnels. Moreover, this would be a minimal set of tunnels that must be kept open.

For a connected graph with **e** edges and **v** vertices, there are **v** – 1 branches in any spanning tree. It follows that, relative to any spanning tree, there are **e** – **v** + 1 chords.

A *cut-set* is a (minimal) set of edges in a graph such that the removal of the set will increase the number of connected components in the remaining subgraph, whereas the removal of any proper subset of it will not. It follows that in a connected graph, the removal of a cut-set will separate the graph into two

---

* A *connecting subgraph* of a graph is a spanning subgraph that is connected.

parts. This suggests an alternative way of defining a cut-set. Let the vertices in a connected component of a graph be divided into two subsets such that every two vertices in each subset are connected by a path that meets only vertices in that subset. Then, the set of edges joining the vertices in the two subsets is a cut-set. As an example, for the graph in Fig. 5.18a, the set of edges $\{e_1, e_5, e_6, e_7, e_4\}$ is a cut-set, since its removal will leave an unconnected subgraph as shown in Fig. 5.18b, while the removal of any of its proper subsets will not. Also, this is the set of edges that join the vertices in the two subsets $\{v_1, v_5\}$ and $\{v_2, v_3, v_4\}$. Figure 5.18a is redrawn as Fig. 5.18c to emphasize such a division of vertices. In the example of the buildings connected by tunnels, if the tunnels corresponding to the edges in a cut-set are blocked, then the buildings will be separated into two clusters with no passage from a building in one cluster to a building in another.

The concepts of spanning trees, circuits, and cut-sets are closely related. Because a spanning tree contains a unique path between any two vertices in the graph, the addition of a chord to the spanning tree yields a subgraph that contains exactly one circuit. Suppose that the chord $\{v_1, v_2\}$ is added to a spanning tree. Because the spanning tree contains a path between v_1 and v_2, this path together with the edge $\{v_1, v_2\}$ form a circuit in the graph. On the other hand, if the addition of the chord $\{v_1, v_2\}$ yields two or more circuits, there must be two or

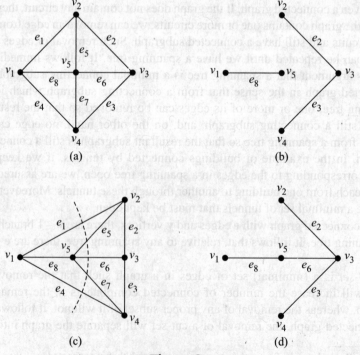

(a)   (b)

(c)   (d)

Fig. 5.18

more paths between v_1 and v_2 in the spanning tree, which is clearly impossible. For a given spanning tree, a unique circuit can be obtained by adding to the spanning tree each of the chords. The set of $\mathbf{e} - \mathbf{v} + 1$ circuits obtained in this way is called the *fundamental system of circuits* relative to the spanning tree. A circuit in the fundamental system is called a *fundamental circuit*. Since a fundamental circuit contains exactly one chord of the spanning tree, it is referred to as the fundamental circuit corresponding to the chord. For example, for the graph in Fig. 5.18a and the spanning tree in Fig. 5.18d, the fundamental circuit corresponding to the chord e_1 is the circuit $\{e_1, e_2, e_6, e_8\}$, and the other fundamental circuits are $\{e_5, e_2, e_6\}$, $\{e_4, e_8, e_6, e_3\}$, and $\{e_7, e_6, e_3\}$.

Since the removal of any branch from a spanning tree breaks the spanning tree up into two trees (either or both of which may consist of a single vertex), we say that corresponding to a branch in a spanning tree there is a division of the vertices in the graph into two subsets corresponding to the vertices in the two trees. It follows that for every branch in a spanning tree there is a corresponding cut-set. For example, for the graph in Fig. 5.18a, the removal of the branch e_3 from the spanning tree in Fig. 5.18d divides the vertices into the two subsets $\{v_1, v_2, v_3, v_5\}$ and $\{v_4\}$. The corresponding cut-set is $\{e_3, e_7, e_4\}$. For a given spanning tree, the set of the $\mathbf{v} - 1$ cut-sets corresponding to the $\mathbf{v} - 1$ branches of the spanning tree is called the *fundamental system of cut-sets* relative to the spanning tree. A cut-set in the fundamental system of cut-sets is called a *fundamental cut-set*. Since a fundamental cut-set contains exactly one tree branch, it is referred to as the fundamental cut-set corresponding to the branch. For the graph in Fig. 5.18a and the spanning tree in Fig. 5.18d the fundamental cut-sets are $\{e_1, e_5, e_2\}$, $\{e_1, e_8, e_4\}$, $\{e_1, e_5, e_6, e_7, e_4\}$, and $\{e_4, e_7, e_3\}$.

We now present some of the properties of circuits and cut-sets. Unless otherwise stated, our discussion will be limited to connected graphs, since its extension to unconnected graphs is straightforward.

Theorem 5.1 A circuit and the complement of any spanning tree must have at least one edge in common.

Proof: If there is a circuit that has no common edge with the complement of a spanning tree, the circuit is contained in the spanning tree. However, this is impossible as a tree cannot contain a circuit. ∎

Theorem 5.2 A cut-set and any spanning tree must have at least one edge in common.

Proof: If there is a cut-set that has no common edge with a spanning tree, the removal of the cut-set will leave the spanning tree intact. However, this means that the removal of the cut-set will not separate the graph into two components, which is in contradiction to the definition of a cut-set. ∎

Theorem 5.3 Every circuit has, an even number of edges in common with every cut-set.

Proof: Corresponding to a cut-set, there is a division of the vertices of the graph into two subsets, which are the two sets of vertices in the two components of the graph when the edges in the cut-set are removed. Therefore, a path connecting two vertices in one subset must traverse the edges in the cut-set an even number of times, as illustrated in Fig. 5.19. (The edges in the circuit are drawn in heavy lines.) Since a circuit is a path from some vertex to itself, the theorem follows. ■

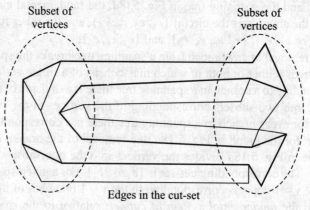

Subset of vertices

Subset of vertices

Edges in the cut-set

Fig. 5.19

The following results point out a close relationship between the fundamental system of circuits and the fundamental system of cut-sets relative to a spanning tree:

Theorem 5.4 For a given spanning tree, let $D = \{e_1, e_2, e_3, \ldots, e_k\}$ be a fundamental cut-set in which e_1 is a branch and $e_2, e_3, \ldots, e_k$ are chords of the spanning tree. Then, e_1 is contained in the fundamental circuits corresponding to e_i for $i = 2, 3, \ldots, k$. Moreover, e_1 is not contained in any other fundamental circuits.

Proof: Let C be the fundamental circuit corresponding to the chord e_2. Note that e_2 is in both C and D. Since C and D have an even number of edges in common and e_1 is the only other edge that can possibly be in both C and D,* e_1 must be contained in C. A similar argument can be applied to the fundamental circuits corresponding to the chords $e_3, e_4, \ldots, e_k$. On the other hand, let C' be the fundamental circuit corresponding to any chord not in D. C' cannot contain e_1 because otherwise, C' and D will have e_1 as the only common edge. ■

Similarly we have:

Theorem 5.5 For a given spanning tree, let $C = \{e_1, e_2, e_3, \ldots, e_k\}$ be a fundamental circuit in which e_1 is a chord and $e_2, e_3, \ldots, e_k$ are branches of the

---

* All the edges in C with the exception of e_2 are branches, and all the edges in D with the exception of e_1 are chords.

spanning tree. Then, e_1 is contained in the fundamental cut-sets corresponding to e_i for $i = 2, 3, ..., k$. Moreover, e_1 is not contained in any other fundamental cut-set.

We leave the proof of Theorem 5.5 as an exercise (Prob. 5.21), since it is quite similar to that of Theorem 5.4.

5.7 MINIMUM SPANNING TREES

For a given graph, one might want to determine a spanning tree of the graph. We consider here the more general problem of determining a minimum spanning tree of a weighted graph where real numbers are assigned to the edges as their weights. The weight of a spanning tree is defined to be the sum of the weights of the branches of the tree. A *minimum spanning tree* is one with minimum weight. "More specifically we can say that in a weighted graph G, a spanning tree T is a minimum spanning tree iff there exists no other spanning tree at a distance of one from T whose weight is smaller than that of T." An obvious physical interpretation of this problem is to consider the vertices of a graph as cities and the weights of the edges as the costs of setting up and maintaining communication links between the cities. Suppose we want to set up a communication network connecting all cities at minimum cost. The problem is then that of determining a minimum spanning tree. We present three simple algorithms that do so.

Our first procedure is based on the observation that among all edges in a circuit, the edge with the largest weight is not in a minimum spanning tree.* Let C be a circuit in a weighted graph, and e be the edge of the largest weight in C. Suppose that e is a branch of a spanning tree T. Let D denote the fundamental cut-set corresponding to the branch e. Since the circuit C and the cut-set D must have an even number of edges in common, besides the edge e there must be at least one more edge that is in both C and D. Let f be one such edge. Note that f is a chord of the spanning tree T because D is a fundamental cut-set. Let us add the edge f to the spanning tree T and denote the resultant subgraph U. Clearly, U is a spanning subgraph containing exactly one circuit, the fundamental circuit corresponding to f. According to Theorem 5.4, e is contained in the fundamental circuit corresponding to f. Removing e from U, we obtain a spanning tree whose weight is smaller than that of T.

Our observation suggests a procedure to determine a minimum spanning tree of a connected weighted graph. We shall construct a subgraph of the weighted graph in a step-by-step manner, examining the edges one at a time in increasing order of weights. An edge will be added to the partially constructed subgraph if its inclusion does not yield a circuit, and will be discarded otherwise. The

---

* To simplify the presentation, we assume that the weights of the edges are distinct. In the case that the weights of the edges are not all distinct, this result should be stated in a more general form: Among all edges in a circuit, an edge with largest weight is not contained in *some* minimum spanning tree.

construction terminates when all the edges have been examined. It is clear that our construction yields a subgraph that contains no circuit. We note that the subgraph is also connected since, for an edge $\{a, b\}$ in the original graph, either the edge $\{a, b\}$ is included in the subgraph or there is a path between a and b in the subgraph. Thus, the subgraph we have constructed is a tree. Moreover, it is a spanning tree because the original graph is connected. Finally, the spanning tree is minimum because in the construction procedure an edge was excluded in favour of edges of larger weights only if the excluded edge is known to be one that cannot be in a minimum spanning tree. In other words, the v-1 edges in the subgraph are indeed v-1 edges of the smallest weights that can be included in a minimum spanning tree. This technique was proposed by Joseph Kruskal in 1956. So this is known as *Kruskal's algorithm* for finding minimum spanning tree. Now we describe Kruskal's algorithm in a stepwise manner. The input to the algorithm is a graph $G = (V, E)$ in the form of an adjacency matrix.

5.8 KRUSKAL'S ALGORITHM

(1) List all the edges of graph G in the increasing order of weights.

(2) Select the smallest edge (having minimum weight) from the list and add it to the spanning tree, (which is initially empty), if the inclusion of the edge does not make a circuit. If the selected edge makes a circuit, then remove it from the list.

(3) Repeat steps 1 and 2 until the tree contains v-1 edges (where v is the number of vertices) or the list is empty.

(4) Now if the tree contains less than v-1 edges and the list happened to be empty then no spanning tree is possible, else it gives the minimum spanning tree.

Now we explain the working of Kruskal's algorithm by considering the following examples:

Example 5.4 Let us consider the weighted graph G shown in Fig. 5.20. First, we arrange all the edges of the graph 'G' in the increasing order of their weights as shown in Table 5.4. By applying Kruskal's algorithm to Fig. 5.20 the third column of Table 5.5 is updated with either one of the two values '**Yes**' or '**No**'. Here, '**Yes**' stands for the selection of the corresponding edges to be included in the spanning tree and '**No**' stands for the rejection of the corresponding edge.

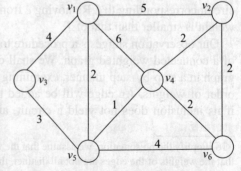

Fig. 5.20 A weighted graph 'G'

Table 5.4	Edges of the weighted graph of Fig. 5.20 in increasing order of their weights

Edges in increasing order of their weights.	*Weights of edges*
$v_4 - v_5$	1
$v_1 - v_5$	2
$v_2 - v_4$	2
$v_4 - v_6$	2
$v_2 - v_6$	2
$v_3 - v_5$	3
$v_1 - v_3$	4
$v_5 - v_6$	4
$v_1 - v_2$	5
$v_1 - v_4$	6

Iteration 1: Consider the edge (v_4, v_5) having smallest weight of '1' from the Table 5.4 and add it to the spanning tree by updating the third column of the first row representing the edge (v_4, v_5) to **'Yes'**.

Iteration 2: Consider the edge (v_1, v_5) having smallest weight of '2' from the remaining edges available in Table 5.4 and add it to the spanning tree by updating the third column of the second row representing the edge (v_1, v_5) to **'Yes'**.

Iteration 3: Consider the edge (v_2, v_4) having smallest weight of '2' from the remaining edges available in Table 5.4 and add it to the spanning tree by updating the third column of the third row representing the edge (v_2, v_4) to **'Yes'**.

Iteration 4: Consider the edge (v_4, v_6) having smallest weight of '2' from the remaining edges available in Table 5.4 and add it to the spanning tree by updating the third column of the forth row representing the edge (v_4, v_6) to **'Yes'**.

Iteration 5: Consider the edge (v_2, v_6) having smallest weight of '2' from the remaining edges available in Table 5.4. As the inclusion of this edge to the spanning tree will result in a loop, so this edge cannot be included into the spanning tree. So, update the third column of the fifth row representing the edge (v_2, v_6) to **'No'**.

Iteration 6: Consider the edge (v_3, v_5) having smallest weight of '3' from the remaining edges available in Table 5.4 and add it to the spanning tree by updating the third column of the sixth row representing the edge (v_3, v_5) to **'Yes'**.

Iteration 7: The algorithm stops as the tree already contains $v - 1$ number of edges, where v is the number of vertices i.e. the number of vertices in

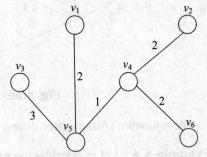

Fig. 5.21 Minimum spanning tree of the graph 'G' given in Fig. 5.20

the graph is 6 and we had already found 5 edges in the tree connecting all vertices without creating a loop.

The updated table is shown in Table 5.5.

Table 5.5 Edges selected in the spanning tree

Edges in increasing order of their weights	Weights of edges	Selection of the edge
$v_4 - v_5$	1	Yes
$v_1 - v_5$	2	Yes
$v_2 - v_4$	2	Yes
$v_4 - v_6$	2	Yes
$v_2 - v_6$	3	No
$v_3 - v_5$	3	Yes
$v_1 - v_3$	4	
$v_5 - v_6$	4	
$v_1 - v_2$	5	
$v_1 - v_4$	6	

The minimum spanning tree drawn from Table 5.5 is shown in Fig. 5.21. ∎

Example 5.5 Let us consider the weighted graph shown in Fig. 5.22. First, we arrange all the edges of the graph in the increasing order of their weights. Applying Kruskal's algorithm to Fig. 5.22, we construct Table 5.6, where **Yes** stands for the selection of the corresponding edge to be included in the spanning tree and **No** stands for the rejection of the corresponding edge.

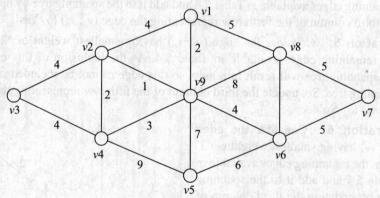

Fig. 5.22 A weighted graph

The minimum spanning tree drawn from Table 5.6 is shown in Fig. 5.23. ∎

Example 5.6 Let us consider the weighted graph shown in Fig 5.24.

First, we arrange all the edges of the weighted graph in increasing order of their weights. Then, by applying Kruskal's algorithm, we construct Table 5.7.

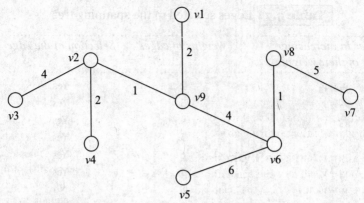

Fig. 5.23 Minimum spanning tree of the graph given in Fig. 5.22.

Table 5.6 Edges selected in the spanning tree

Edges in increasing order of their weights	Weights of edges	Selection of the edge
$v_2 - v_9$	1	Yes
$v_6 - v_8$	1	Yes
$v_1 - v_9$	2	Yes
$v_2 - v_4$	2	Yes
$v_4 - v_9$	3	No
$v_2 - v_3$	4	Yes
$v_3 - v_4$	4	No
$v_1 - v_2$	4	No
$v_6 - v_9$	4	Yes
$v_1 - v_8$	5	No
$v_7 - v_8$	5	Yes
$v_6 - v_7$	5	No
$v_5 - v_6$	6	Yes
$v_5 - v_9$	7	
$v_8 - v_9$	8	
$v_4 - v_5$	9	

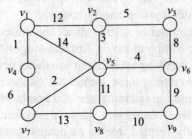

Fig. 5.24 A weighted graph

Table 5.7 Edges selected in the spanning tree

Edges in increasing order of their weights	Weights of edges	Selection of the edge
$v_5 - v_7$	2	Yes
$v_2 - v_5$	3	Yes
$v_5 - v_6$	4	Yes
$v_2 - v_3$	5	Yes
$v_4 - v_7$	6	Yes
$v_1 - v_4$	7	Yes
$v_3 - v_6$	8	No
$v_6 - v_9$	9	Yes
$v_8 - v_9$	10	Yes
$v_5 - v_8$	11	
$v_1 - v_2$	12	
$v_1 - v_8$	13	
$v_1 - v_5$	14	

The minimum spanning tree drawn from Table 5.7 is shown in Fig. 5.25.

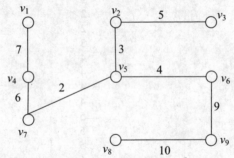

Fig. 5.25 Minimum spanning tree of the graph given in Fig.5.25 using Kruskal's algorithm

As another example, a minimum spanning tree for the weighted graph in Fig. 5.26a is shown in Fig. 5.26b. Note how the edges with weight 4 and weight 7 are excluded in the step-by-step construction.

Kruskal's algorithm requires sorting of all the edges in order of increasing weight. Because of the sorting involved, Kruskal's algorithm is not efficient. Also the algorithm requires verifying at each step whether a newly selected edge forms a circuit or not. To overcome these limitations, Robert Prim has proposed an algorithm to find a minimum spanning tree of a graph. Prim's algorithm requires no sorting of edges but constructs a minimal spanning tree by successively connecting the partially formed tree to its nearest neighbor. Now we present Prim's algorithm in a stepwise manner. The input to this algorithm is a graph $G = (V, E)$ in the form of an adjacency matrix.

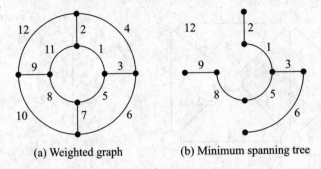

(a) Weighted graph   (b) Minimum spanning tree

Fig. 5.26 A weighted graph and minimum spanning tree

5.9 PRIM'S ALGORITHM

(1) Draw n isolated vertices and label them as $v_1, v_2, ..., v_n$, where n is the number of vertices.

(2) Represent the given weights of the edges of graph G in an $n \times n$ matrix.

(3) Assign the weights of nonexistent edges (e.g. corresponding to pairs of towns between which no direct root can be constructed) as very high.

(4) Start from vertex v_1 and connect it to its nearest neighbours (i.e. to the vertex which has the smallest entry in row 1 of the matrix), say v_k. If more than one smallest entry is there, then arbitrarily select one of them.

(5) Consider v_1 and v_k as one subgraph and connect the subgraph to its closest neighbours (i.e. to a vertex other than v_1 and v_k which has the smallest entry in rows 1 and k). Suppose this new vertex be v_i.

(6) Consider the tree with vertices v_1, v_k and v_i as one subgraph and continue the process until all the n vertices have been connected by $n-1$ edges.

(7) Exit.

Now we explain the working of Prim's algorithm by taking the following example.

Example 5.7 Let us consider the weighted graph shown in Figure 5.27. First, we represent the given weights of the edges of the graph in a 6×6 adjacency matrix.

Now, we explain the different stages involved in constructing the minimal spanning tree of the above graph using Prim's algorithm.

Initial Stage: Draw 6 isolated vertices as shown in Fig 5.28 (a).

Stage 1: Start from vertex v_1 and connect it to the nearest neighbor v_5 as it has the smallest entry in row 1. This is shown in Fig. 5.28 (b).

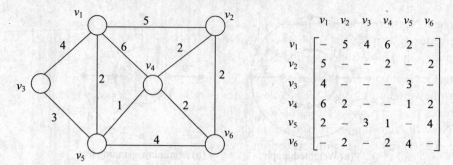

Fig. 5.27 A weighted graph and its associated adjacency matrix

Stage 2: Now, consider the vertices v_1 and v_5 as one subgraph and connect it to the vertex v_4 as it has the smallest entry in rows 1 and 5 other than vertices v_1 and v_5. This is shown in Fig. 5.28 (c).

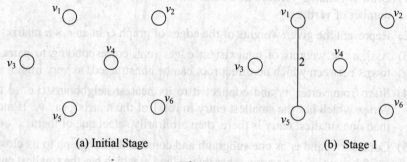

(a) Initial Stage   (b) Stage 1

Fig. 5.28

Stage 3: Then, consider the vertices v_1, v_5, v_4 as one subgraph and connect it to the vertex v_2 as it has the smallest entry in rows 1, 5 and 4 other than vertices v_1, v_5, v_4. This is shown in Fig. 5.28 (d).

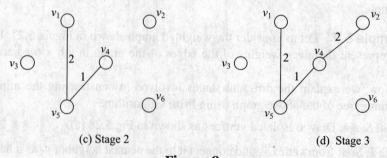

(c) Stage 2   (d) Stage 3

Fig. 5.28

Stage 4: Next, consider the vertices v_1, v_5, v_4, v_2 as one subgraph and connect it to the vertex v_6 as it has the smallest entry in rows 1, 5, 4 and 2 other than vertices v_1, v_5, v_4, v_2. This is shown in Fig. 5.28 (e).

Stage 5: Now, consider the vertices v_1, v_5, v_4, v_2, v_6 as one subgraph and connect it to the vertex v_2 as it has the smallest entry in rows 1, 2, 4, 5 and 6 other than vertices v_1, v_5, v_4, v_2, v_6. This is shown in Fig. 5.28(f).

Now, the algorithm exits as there are already 5 edges connecting the 6 vertices. Fig. 5.28(f) shows the minimal spanning tree of the given graph.

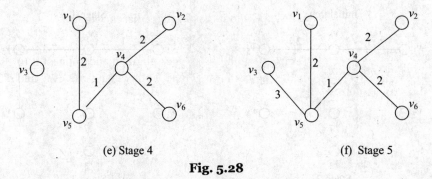

(e) Stage 4   (f) Stage 5

Fig. 5.28

Example 5.8 Let us consider the weighted graph in Fig. 5.29. First we represented the given weights of the edges of the given graph G in an $n \times n$ matrix.

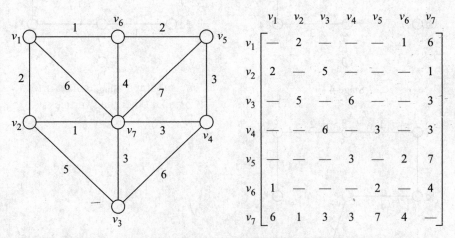

	v_1	v_2	v_3	v_4	v_5	v_6	v_7
v_1	—	2	—	—	—	1	6
v_2	2	—	5	—	—	—	1
v_3	—	5	—	6	—	—	3
v_4	—	—	6	—	3	—	3
v_5	—	—	—	3	—	2	7
v_6	1	—	—	—	2	—	4
v_7	6	1	3	3	7	4	—

Fig. 5.29 A weighted graph and its associated adjacency matrix

Then, applying Prim's algorithm, we obtained the minimal spanning tree. The different stages involved in constructing the minimal spanning tree of the above graph are shown in Fig. 5.30. ∎

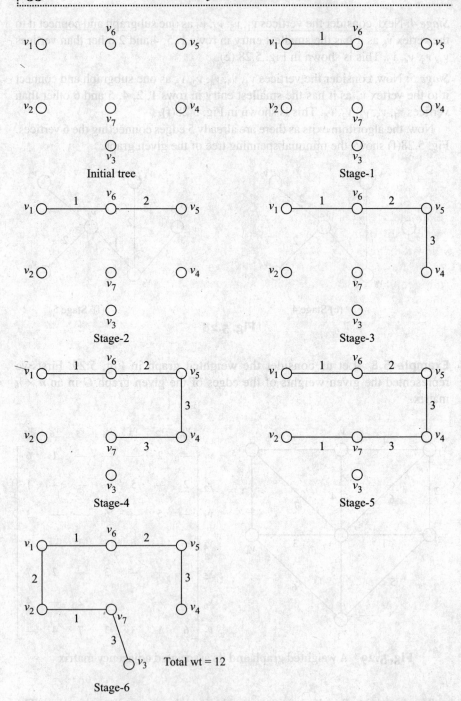

Fig. 5.30 Stages involved in constructing minimal spanning tree using Prim's algorithm

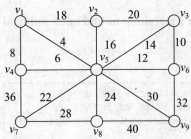

$$\begin{array}{c c c c c c c c c c}
 & v_1 & v_2 & v_3 & v_4 & v_5 & v_6 & v_7 & v_8 & v_9 \\
v_1 & - & 18 & - & 8 & 4 & - & - & - & - \\
v_2 & 18 & - & 20 & - & 16 & - & - & - & - \\
v_3 & - & 20 & - & - & 14 & 10 & - & - & - \\
v_4 & 8 & - & - & - & 6 & - & 36 & - & - \\
v_5 & 4 & 16 & 14 & 6 & - & 12 & 22 & 24 & 30 \\
v_6 & - & - & 10 & - & 12 & - & - & - & 32 \\
v_7 & - & - & - & 36 & 22 & - & - & 28 & - \\
v_8 & - & - & - & - & 24 & - & 28 & - & 40 \\
v_9 & - & - & - & - & 30 & 32 & - & 40 & -
\end{array}$$

Fig. 5.31 The weighted graph

Fig. 5.32 The associated adjacency matrix of the graph given in Fig. 5.31

Example 5.9 Let us consider another weighted graph given in Fig. 5.31. First, we construct the adjacency matrix for the above graph given in Fig. 5.31 and show it in Fig. 5.32.

Then, by applying Prim's algorithm, we get the minimal spanning tree. The different stages involved in constructing the minimal spanning tree are shown in Fig 5.33.

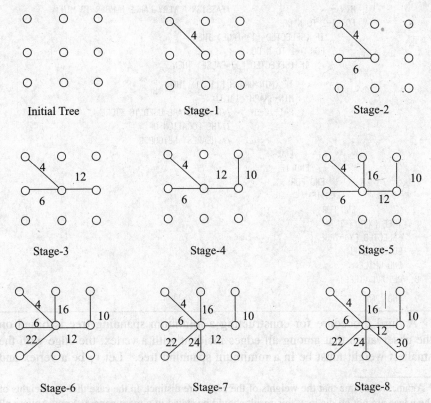

Fig. 5.33 Stages involved in constructing the minimum spanning tree of Fig. 5.31 using Prim's algorithm

Now, we present the pseudo code for Prim's algorithm to find out a minimal spanning tree of a given graph.

Pseudo Code for Prim's Algorithm

```
1. Input GRAPH in the form of an adjacency matrix with vertex labelled as 1, 2, ..., N.
   Use an array SELECTED [1 ... N] of Boolean values, either TRUE or FALSE.
   Use an empty adjacency matrix named TREE of order same as that of the input graph,
   to store the resulting spanning tree R.
2. FOR I=1 TO N DO
     1. SELECTED [I] = FALSE        //INITIALLY NO VERTEX IS SELECTED
3. END FOR

4. FOR I=1 TO N DO
     1. FOR J=1 TO N DO
          1. TREE [I][J]=0
          2. END FOR
5. END FOR

6. SELECTED [1]=TRUE, EDGE=1       //INITIALIZE VERTEX 1 AND EDGE COUNTER
                                   //EDGE COUNTS THE NUMBER OF EDGES

7. WHILE (EDGE<N) DO
           MIN = ∞                 //ASSIGN A VERY LARGE NUMBER TO MIN
           FOR I=1 TO N DO
               IF (SELECTED [I]=TRUE) THEN
               FOR J=1 TO N DO
                   IF (SELECTED [J]=FALSE) THEN

                   IF (MIN>GRAPH [I][J]) THEN
                   MIN=GRAPH [I][J]
                   R=I, C=J        //R AND C ARE USED TO STORE
                                   //THE LOCATION OF
                                   // NEAREST NEIGHBOR
                   END IF
                 END IF
               END FOR
             END IF
           END FOR
   TREE [X][Y]=1
   SELECTED [Y]=TRUE
   EDGE=EDGE+1
   END WHILE
8. RETURN (TREE)

9. END
```

A third procedure for constructing a minimum spanning tree is based on the observation that among all edges incident with a vertex, the edge with the smallest weight must be in a minimum spanning tree.* Let v_1 be a vertex and

---

* Again, we assume that the weights of the edges are distinct. In the case that the weights of the edges are not all distinct, this result should be stated in a more general form: Among all edges incident with a vertex, an edge with smallest weight is contained in *some* minimum spanning tree.

$\{v_1, v_2\}$ be the edge with the smallest weight among all edges incident with v_1. Let T be a spanning tree not containing the edge $\{v_1, v_2\}$. Let us add the edge $\{v_1, v_2\}$ to T and denote the resultant subgraph U. Note that U contains exactly one circuit, the fundamental circuit corresponding to the chord $\{v_1, v_2\}$. This circuit is made up of the edge $\{v_1, v_2\}$ and the path from v_1 to v_2 in T. Let $(v_1, v_{i1}, v_{i2}, \dots, v_{ik}, v_2)$ denote the sequence of vertices in that path. We observe that removing the edge $\{v_1, v_{i1}\}$ from U yields a spanning tree whose weight is smaller than that of T.

Let $G = (V, E)$ be a graph, and v_1 and v_2 be two vertices in V. We introduce the notion of obtaining a graph G' from G by *coalescing* the vertices v_1 and v_2. Intuitively, G' is a graph obtained from G by combining the vertices v_1 and v_2 into one "supervertex" and retaining all the edges in G. For example, Fig. 5.34b shows a graph obtained from the graph in Fig. 5.34a by coalescing the vertices v_1 and v_2. Because G and G' are, in general, multigraphs, we shall identify the edges in E by edge names, such as e_1 and e_2, instead of the vertices with which they are incident. Let $G' = (V', E')$ such that V' contains all the vertices in V except that the vertices v_1 and v_2 are removed and a new vertex v^* is introduced, and E' contains all the edges in E except that, if an edge was incident with v_1 or v_2 in G, it is incident with v^* in G'.* We have the following observation: Let e be an edge with smallest weight that is not a self-loop in G. Let G' be the graph obtained from G be coalescing the vertices v_1 and v_2 with which the edge e is incident in G, and T' be a minimum spanning tree of G'. Let T denote a subgraph of G consisting of all the edges in T' together with the edge e. We want to show that T is a minimum spanning tree of G. First of all, we note that T is indeed a spanning tree of G. Secondly, we have

$$W(T) = W(T') + w(e)$$

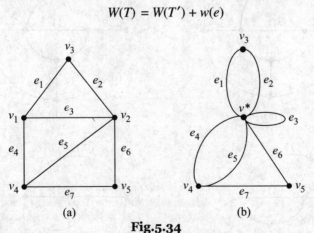

(a)   (b)

Fig. 5.34

---

* An edge between v_1 and v_2 becomes a self-loop at v^* (For the purpose of constructing a minimum spanning tree, we could choose to remove all self-loops in G'. However, we do not do so because we do not wish to deviate from the standard definition of coalescing two vertices in a graph.)

where $w(e)$ denotes the weight of edge e, and $W(T)$ and $W(T')$ denote the sum of the weights of the edges in T and T', respectively. Finally, if T were not a minimum spanning tree of G, there exists a minimum spanning tree of G, $\hat{T}$, which contains the edge e such that

$$W(\hat{T}) < W(T)$$

Let $\hat{T}$ denote the tree obtained from $\hat{T}$ by coalescing the vertices v_1 and v_2 and removing the edge e. Clearly, $\hat{T}$ is a spanning tree of G'. Since

$$W(\hat{T}) = W(\hat{T}) + w(e)$$

we obtain

$$W(\hat{T}) < W(T')$$

which is a contradiction of the assumption that T is a minimum spanning tree of the graph G'.

Our observations suggest immediately another procedure for determining a minimum spanning tree in a connected weighted graph. Let $\{v_1, v_2\}$ be the edge of the smallest weight in a graph G. Since $\{v_1, v_2\}$ must be included in a minimum spanning tree of G, we can coalesce the two vertices v_1 and v_2 to obtain the graph G', and then try to determine a minimum spanning tree of G'. The step can then be repeated until we terminate with a graph that has a single vertex.

As an example, for the weighted graph in Fig. 5.24a, several steps of the construction are shown in Fig. 5.35a through d. Note how the edges with weights 4 and 7 are excluded in the step-by-step construction.

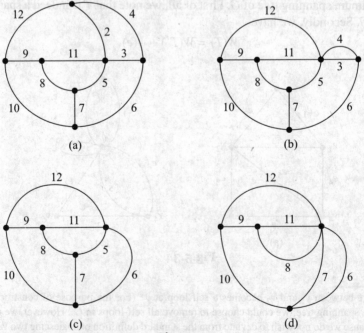

(a)   (b)

(c)   (d)

Fig.5.35

5.10   TRANSPORT NETWORKS

A weighted directed graph is said to be a *transport network* if the following conditions are satisfied:

1. It is connected and contains no loops.
2. There is one and only one vertex in the graph that has no incoming edge.
3. There is one and only one vertex in the graph that has no outgoing edge.
4. The weight of each edge is a nonnegative real number.

In a transport network, the vertex that has no incoming edge is called the *source* and is denoted by a; the vertex that has no outgoing edge is called the *sink* and is denoted by z. The weight of an edge is called the *capacity* of the edge. The capacity of the edge (i, j) is denoted by $w(i, j)$.

Clearly, a transport network represents a general model for the transportation of material from the origin of supply to the destination through shipping routes, where there are upper limits on the amount of material that can be shipped through the routes. Figure 5.36a shows an example of a transport network.

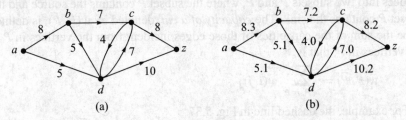

Fig. 5.36

A *flow* in a transport network, ϕ, is an assignment of a nonnegative number $\phi(i, j)$ to each edge (i, j) such that the following conditions are satisfied:

1. $\phi(i, j) \leq w(i, j)$ for each edge (i, j).

2. $\sum_{\text{all } i} \phi(i, j) = \sum_{\text{all } k} \phi(j, k)$ for each vertex j except the source a and the sink z.*

In terms of the transportation of material, $\phi(i, j)$ is the amount of material to be shipped through the route (i, j). Condition 1 means that the amount of material to be shipped through a route cannot exceed the capacity of the route. Condition 2 means that, except at the source and at the sink, the amount of material flowing into a vertex must equal the amount of material flowing out of the vertex. For example, Fig. 5.36b shows a flow in the transport network in Fig. 5.36a. The first number associated with an edge is the capacity of the edge, and the second number associated with an edge is the flow in the edge. The quantity $\sum_{\text{all } i} \phi(a, i)$ is said to be the *value of the flow* ϕ and is denoted by ϕ_v. Intuitively, it is clear that

---

* We define $\phi(x, y)$ to be zero if there is no edge from x to y.

$$\phi_v = \sum_{\text{all}\, i} \phi(a, i) = \sum_{\text{all}\, k} \phi(k, z)$$

that is, the total outgoing flow at the source is equal to the total incoming flow at the sink. This result is proved rigorously in the proof of Theorem 5.6. For a given flow, an edge (i, j) is said to be *saturated* if $\phi(i, j) = w(i, j)$, and is said to be *unsaturated* if $f(i, j) < w(i, j)$. A *maximum flow* in a transport network is a flow that achieves the largest possible value. It is conceivable that there might be more than one maximum flow in a transport network. In other words, there might be a number of different flows, all of which attain the largest possible value.

One frequently wants to determine the largest amount of material that can be shipped from the source to the sink of a given transport network. Moreover, it is desirable to have an algorithm for constructing a flow in the network that achieves the largest possible value. We shall present an algorithm for doing so. To this end, let us introduce first some useful concepts and results.

A *cut* in a transport network is a cut-set of the undirected graph, obtained from the transport network by ignoring the direction of the edges, that separates the source from the sink. The notation $(P, \overline{P})$ is used to denote a cut that divides the vertices into two subsets P and $\overline{P}$, where the subset P contains the source and the subset $\overline{P}$ contains the sink. The *capacity of a cut*, denoted by $w(P, \overline{P})$, is defined to be the sum of the capacities of those edges incident from the vertices in P to the vertices in $\overline{P}$; that is,

$$w(P, \overline{P}) = \sum_{i \in P,\, j \in \overline{P}} w(i, j)$$

For example, the dashed line in Fig. 5.37 identifies a cut that separates the subset of vertices $P = \{a, d\}$ from the subset of vertices $\overline{P} = \{b, c, z\}$. The capacity of this cut is equal to $8 + 7 + 10 = 25$.

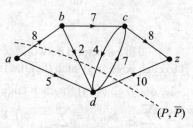

$(P, \overline{P})$

Fig.5.37

The following result gives an upper bound on the values of flows in a transport network.

Theorem 5.6   The value of any flow in a given transport network is less than or equal to the capacity of any cut in the network.

Proof: Let ϕ be a flow and $(P, \overline{P})$ be a cut in a transport network. For the source a,

$$\sum_{\text{all}\, i} \phi(a, i) - \sum_{\text{all}\, j} \phi(j, a) = \sum_{\text{all}\, i} \phi(a, i) = \phi_v \qquad (5.3)$$

since $\phi(j, a) = 0$ for any j. For a vertex p other than a in P,

$$\sum_{\text{all}\, i} \phi(p, i) - \sum_{\text{all}\, j} \phi(j, p) = 0 \qquad (5.4)$$

Combining eqs. (5.3) and (5.4), we have

$$\phi_v = \sum_{p \in P} \left[\sum_{\text{all } i} \phi(p, i) - \sum_{\text{all } j} \phi(j, p) \right]$$

$$= \sum_{p \in P; \text{all } i} \phi(p, i) - \sum_{p \in P; \text{all } j} \phi(j, p)$$

$$= \sum_{p \in P; i \in P} \phi(p, i) + \sum_{p \in P; i \in \bar{P}} \phi(p, i)$$

$$- \left[\sum_{p \in P; i \in P} \phi(j, p) + \sum_{p \in P; j \in \bar{P}} \phi(j, p) \right] \quad (5.5)$$

Note that

$$\sum_{p \in P; i \in P} \phi(p, i) = \sum_{p \in P; j \in P} \phi(j, p)$$

because both sums run through all the vertices in P. Thus, (5.5) becomes

$$\phi_v = \sum_{p \in P; i \in \bar{P}} \phi(p, i) - \sum_{p \in P; j \in \bar{P}} \phi(j, p) \quad (5.6)$$

But, since $\sum_{p \in P; j \in \bar{P}} \phi(j, p)$ is always a nonnegative quantity, we have

$$\phi_v \leq \sum_{p \in P; i \in \bar{P}} \phi(p, i) \sum_{p \in P; i \in \bar{P}} w(p, i) = w(P, \bar{P}) \quad \blacksquare$$

Equation (5.6) is a useful result which can be stated as: For any cut $(P, \bar{P})$, the values of a flow in a transport network equal the sum of flows in the edges from the vertices in P to the vertices in $\bar{P}$ minus the sum of flows in the edges from the vertices in $\bar{P}$ to the vertices in P.

We are now ready to present an algorithm for constructing a maximum flow in a transport network. In view of the result that the value of any flow in a transport network is less than or equal to the capacity of any cut, whenever we can construct a flow ϕ the value of which is equal to the capacity of some cut $(P, \bar{P})$, we can be certain that ϕ is a maximum flow. Because if there were a larger flow, its value would exceed the capacity of the cut $(P, \bar{P})$. As it turns out, we can always construct a flow the value of which is equal to the capacity of a cut using the following procedure, which is known as the *labeling procedure*. To start this procedure, we must construct an initial flow ϕ in the network. However, such construction poses no problem as we can always start, trivially, with zero flow in every edge.

At first, the source a is labeled $(-, \infty)$. (The significance of such a label will become clear later.) Next, all the vertices that are adjacent from a are scanned. A vertex b that is adjacent from a is labeled $(a^+, \Delta b)$, where Δb is equal to $w(a, b) - \phi(a, b)$, if $w(a, b) > \phi(a, b)$; it is not labeled if $w(a, b) = \phi(a, b)$. After all the vertices that are adjacent from the source a are scanned and labeled (if possible), those vertices that are adjacent to or from the labeled vertices are scanned. Let b be a labeled vertex, and let q be a vertex that is adjacent *from* b. The vertex q is labeled $(b^+, \Delta q)$, where Δq is equal to the smaller of the two quantities Δb and

$[w(b, q) - \phi(b, q)]$ if $w(b, q) > \phi(b, q)$. The vertex q is not labeled if $w(b, q) = \phi(b, q)$. Let b be a labeled vertex, and let q be a vertex that is adjacent to b. The vertex q is labeled $(b^-, \Delta q)$, where Δq is equal to the smaller of the two quantities Δb and $\phi(q, b)$ if $\phi(q, b) > 0$. The vertex q is not labeled if $\phi(q, b) = 0$. Such a labeling procedure is not necessarily unique. The vertex q might be adjacent to or from more than one labeled vertex. Also, there might even be an edge incident from b to q as well as an edge incident from q to b. In any case, when a vertex can be labeled in more than one way, an arbitrary choice of these ways is made.

Let us examine the meanings of these labels before proceeding with the presentation of the remaining steps in the procedure. For a vertex that is adjacent from the source (like vertex b), the label $(a^+, \Delta b)$ means that the flow into b can be increased by an amount equal to Δb. Moreover, such an increment can be drawn from the source a. Similarly, for a vertex q that is adjacent from a labeled vertex b, the label $(b^+, \Delta q)$ means that, by drawing the increment from the vertex b, the total incoming flow into q from the labeled vertices can be increased by Δq. For a vertex q that is adjacent to a labeled vertex b, the label $(b^-, \Delta q)$ means that, by decreasing the flow from q to b, the total outgoing flow from q to the labeled vertices can be decreased by Δq. In either of these cases, an increase in the flow equal to Δq from the vertex q to the unlabeled vertices is assured. The meaning of the label of the source, $(-, \infty)$ should also become clear now. It means that (out from nowhere) the source can supply an infinite amount of material to the other vertices.

If we repeat the procedure of labeling the vertices that are adjacent to or from the labeled vertices, one of the following two cases shall arise:

Case 1   Sink z is labeled, say, with a label $(y^+, \Delta z)$. [Of course, z will never have a label like $(y^-, \Delta z)$.] We can increase the flow in the edge (y, z) from $\phi(y, z)$ to $\phi(y, z) + \Delta z$, as the increment is guaranteed by the vertex y. Note that vertex y must be labeled either $(q^+, \Delta y)$ or $(q^-, \Delta y)$, with $\Delta y \geq \Delta z$, for some vertex q. If y is labeled $(q^+, \Delta y)$, we shall, in turn, draw the increment from vertex q by increasing the flow in the edge (q, y) from $\phi(q, y)$ to $\phi(q, y) + \Delta z$. On the other hand, if y is labeled $(q^-, \Delta y)$, we shall decrease the flow in the edge (y, q) from $\phi(y, q)$ to $\phi(y, q) - \Delta z$ so that increment Δz from y to z is compensated. The process is continued back to the source a, and the value of the flow in the transport network will be increased by amount Δz. The labeling procedure can now be started all over again to further increase the value of the flow in the network.

Case 2   Sink z is not labeled. Let us denote all the labeled vertices by P and all the unlabeled vertices by $\overline{P}$. The fact that sink z is not labeled means that the flow in each of the edges incident from the vertices in P to the vertices in $\overline{P}$ is equal to the capacity of that edge, and that the flow in each of the edges incident from the vertices in $\overline{P}$ to the vertices in P is equal to zero. We have thus obtained a flow, the value of which is equal to the capacity of the cut $(P, \overline{P})$. The flow, therefore, is a maximum flow.

Consider the following illustrative example. For the transport network in Fig. 5.38*a*, we start with zero flow in every edge. (The first number associated with an edge is its capacity, and the second number is the flow in the edge.) Figure 5.38*b* shows the first pass of the labeling procedure. Notice that the sink *z* can be labeled either with $(d^+, 3)$ or with $(b^+, 2)$. We choose arbitrarily the label $(d^+, 3)$. Figure 5.38*c* shows the second pass, and Fig. 5.38*d* shows the third pass.

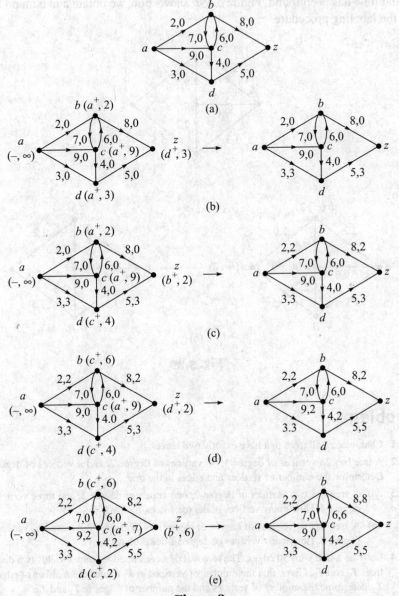

Fig.5.38

Notice that in Fig. 5.38d vertex b is labeled $(c^+, 6)$ and vertex d is labeled $(c^+, 4)$; that is, vertex c has guaranteed a total flow of 10 to vertices b and d although Δc is only equal to 9. However, since vertex c would have to supply either the increment of flow at b or the increment of flow at d, but not at both, in the augmentation step no difficulty will arise. Figure 5.38e shows the last pass of the labeling procedure, which yields a maximum flow of 13.

As another example, consider the transport network in Fig. 5.39a where an initial flow has been found. Figure 5.39b shows how we obtain a maximum flow by the labeling procedure.

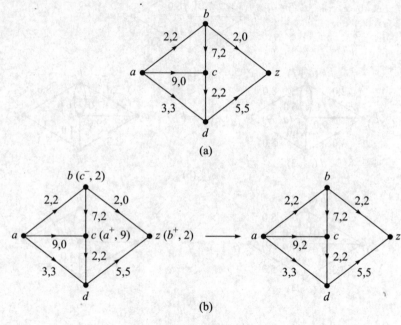

(a)

(b)

Fig. 5.39

Problems

5.1 Characterize all trees that have exactly two leaves.

5.2 A tree has $2n$ vertices of degree 1, $3n$ vertices of degree 2, and n vertices of degree 3. Determine the number of vertices and edges in the tree.

5.3 (a) A tree has two vertices of degree 2, one vertex of degree 3, and three vertices of degree 4. How many vertices of degree 1 does it have?

   (b) A tree has n_2 vertices of degree 2, n_3 vertices of degree 3, ..., and n_k vertices of degree k. How many vertices of degree 1 does it have?

5.4 Let T be a tree with 50 edges. The removal of a certain edge from T yields two disjoint trees T_1 and T_2. Given that the number of vertices in T_1 equals the number of edges in T_2, determine the number of vertices and the number of edges in T_1 and T_2.

5.5 (a) Show that the sum of the degrees of the vertices of a tree with n vertices is $2n - 2$.

(b) For $n \geq 2$, let $d_1, d_2, ..., d_n$ be n positive integers such that $\sum_{i=1}^{n} d_i = 2n - 2$. Show that there exists a tree whose vertices have degrees $d_1, d_2, ..., d_n$.

5.6 The center of a (connected) graph is defined to be a vertex v with the property that the maximum distance between v and any other vertex is as small as possible. (See Prob. 4.16 for the definition of the distance between two vertices in a graph.)

(a) Show an example of a graph that has one center.

(b) Show an example of a graph that has two or more centers.

(c) Show that a tree has either one or two centers. Moreover, if there are two centers they must be adjacent. Show an example of a tree that has two centers.

5.7 Let v be a vertex in a tree T. Clearly, direction can be assigned to the edges in T to obtain a rooted tree with v being the root. Let $v_1, v_2, ..., v_k$ denote the sons of v, and $s_1, s_2, ..., s_k$ denote the numbers of vertices in the subtrees with $v_1, v_2, ..., v_k$ as the roots. The weight of v is defined to be the maximum of $s_1, s_2, ..., s_k$.

(a) For the tree In Fig. 5P.1, compute the weights of all the vertices.

(b) A vertex that has minimum weight is said to be a *centroid* of the tree. Show an example of a tree that has one centroid. Show an example of a tree that has two centroids.

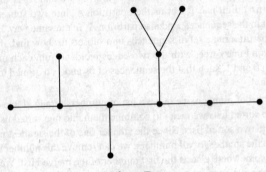

Fig. 5P.1

(c) Show that a tree has either one or two centroids. Moreover, if there are two centroids, they must be adjacent.

(d) Show that v is the only centroid of a tree if

$$s_j \leq s_1 + s_2 + ... + s_k - s_j \qquad \text{for all } j, 1 \leq j \leq k$$

(e) Show that a tree with two centroids has an even number of vertices. Moreover, the weight of each centroid is equal to half the number of vertices in the tree.

5.8 Show that a regular binary tree has an odd number of vertices.

5.9 Prove the result in Eq. (5.2) by induction on i.

5.10 By traversing a tree, we mean to visit each of the vertices of the tree exactly once in some sequential order. We describe here three principal ways that may be used to traverse a binary tree.

1. *Preorder traversal*: Visit the root, traverse the left subtree, then traverse the right subtree.

2. *Inorder (symmetric order) traversal*: Traverse the left subtree, visit the root, then traverse the right subtree.

3. *Postorder traversal*: Traverse the left subtree, traverse the right subtree, then visit the root.

Show the sequential orders in which the vertices of the tree in Fig. 5P.2 are visited in a preorder traversal, an in order traversal, and a postorder traversal.

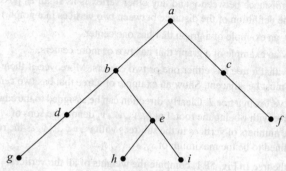

Fig. 5P.2

5.11 Let A be a set of binary sequences. Let us partition A into two subsets A_0 and A_1, where A_0 is the set of sequences in A whose first digit is a 0 and A_1 is the set of sequences in A whose first digit is a 1. Let us then partition A_0 into two subsets according to the second digit in the sequences, and also partition A_1 in the same way. Employ this idea of repeatedly partitioning a set of sequences into subsets to show that, if A is a prefix code, then there is a binary tree, with the two edges incident from each of the branch nodes labeled with 0 and 1, such that the sequences of 0s and 1s assigned to the leaves are the sequences in A.

5.12 By a *sorted list* of numbers we mean a list of numbers arranged in ascending order. By *merging* two sorted lists we mean to combine them into one sorted list. We describe one way to merge two sorted lists: Since the smaller one of the smallest numbers of the two lists must be the smallest of all numbers, we can remove this number from the list it is in and place it somewhere else as the first number of the merged list. We can now compare the smallest numbers of the two lists of remaining numbers and place the smaller one of the two as the second number of the merged list. This step can be repeated until the merged list is completely built up. Clearly, it takes $n_1 + n_2 - 1$ comparisons to merge two sorted lists with n_1 and n_2 numbers, respectively. Given m sorted lists, we can select two of them and merge these two lists into one. We can then select two lists from the $m - 1$ sorted lists and merge them into one. By repeating this step, we shall eventually end up with one merged list.

Let A_1, A_2, A_3, A_4 be four lists with 73, 44, 100, 55 numbers, respectively.

(a) Determine the total number of comparisons it takes to merge the four lists by merging A_1 and A_2, merging the resultant list with A_3, and then merging the resultant list with A_4.

(b) Determine the total number of comparisons it takes to merge the four lists by merging A_1 and A_2, merging A_3 and A_4, and then merging the two resultant lists.

(c) Determine an order to merge the four lists so that the total number of comparisons is minimum.

(d) Describe a general procedure for determining the order in which m sorted lists $A_1, A_2, ..., A_m$ are to be merged so that the total number of comparisons is minimum. (*Hint:* What is a convenient way to describe a certain order in which the lists are merged?)

5.13 For each of the following sets of weights, construct an optimal binary prefix code. For each weight in the set, give the corresponding code word.

(a) 8, 9, 12, 14, 16, 19

(b) 1, 2, 4, 5, 6, 9, 10, 12

(c) 5, 7, 8, 15, 35, 40

5.14 (a) How can the procedure in Sec. 5.4 for constructing an optimal binary tree be extended to that for constructing an optimal m-ary tree?

(b) Construct an optimal ternary tree for the weights 1, 2, 3, 4, 5, 6, 7, 8, 9.

(c) Construct an optimal ternary tree for the weights 1, 2, 3, 4, 5, 6, 7, 8. In general, when $t - 1$, where t is the number of weights, is not a multiple of $m - 1$ [see Eq. (5.2)] how should we proceed to construct an optimal m-ary tree?

5.15 Show how a binary search tree of height $\lceil \lg(n + 1) \rceil$ can be constructed for n keys, K_1, $K_2, \ldots, K_n$.

5.16 We define a *3-2 tree* to be a rooted tree in which the out-degree of a branch node is either 3 or 2. Furthermore, the path lengths of all leaves must be the same. For example, Fig. 5P.3a shows a 3-2 tree. A 3-2 tree can be used to describe a class of search procedures in which we compare an item either with one key or with two keys in each step of search. Using the 3-2 tree in Fig. 5P.3b as an example, explain in detail how such a search procedure works. How can we be sure that the number of leaves in a 3-2 tree is always equal to the number of keys plus one?

5.17 Prove that the complement of a spanning tree does not contain a cut-set and that the complement of a-cut-set does not contain a spanning tree.

5.18 Let L be a circuit in a graph G. Let a and b be any two edges in L. Prove that there exists a cut-set C such that $L \cap C = \{a, b\}$.

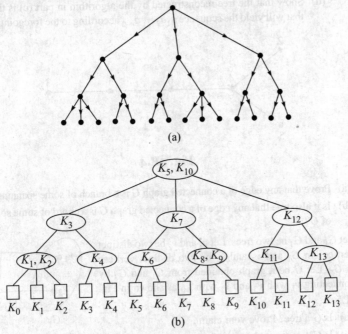

(a)

(b)

Fig. 5P.3

5.19 Let T_1 and T_2 be two spanning trees of a connected graph G. Let a be an edge that is in T_1 but not T_2. Prove that there is an edge b in T_2 but not T_1 such that both $(T_1 - \{a\}) \cup \{b\}$ and $(T_2 - \{b\}) \cup \{a\}$ are spanning trees of G.

5.20 (a) Let L_1 and L_2 be two circuits in a graph G. Let a be an edge that is in both L_1 and L_2, and let b be an edge that is in L_1 but not L_2. Prove that there exists a circuit L_3 which is such that $L_3 \subseteq (L_1 \cup L_2) - \{a\}$ and $b \in L_3$.

   (b) Repeat part (a) when the term *circuit* is replaced by the term *cut-set*.

5.21 Prove Theorem 5.5.

5.22 We show in this problem that there are n^{n-2} spanning trees in a complete graph with n distinctly labeled vertices. Without loss of generality, let the labels of the vertices be $1, 2, \ldots, n$. We shall demonstrate a one-to-one correspondence between the spanning trees and the n^{n-2} $n - 2$ digit sequences over the alphabet $\{1, 2, \ldots, n\}$. Let T denote a spanning tree whose vertices are labeled $1, 2, \ldots, n$. We construct a sequence $a_1 a_2 \ldots a_{n-2}$ as follows:

1. Let $i = 1$. Let T be the tree currently under examination.

2. Among all vertices of degree 1 in the tree currently under examination, select the one with the smallest label. Remove the edge that is incident with this vertex and let a_i equal the label of the *other* vertex with which this edge is incident.

3. The resultant tree in (2) becomes now the tree currently under examination. Increase i by 1, repeat (2) until a sequence of $n - 2$ digits is formed.

   (a) Determine the 4-digit sequence corresponding to the tree in Fig. 5P.4.

   (b) Show that the degree of the vertex with label i in T is equal to the number of times the letter i appears in $a_1 a_2 \ldots a_{n-2}$ plus one.

   (c) Determine an algorithm for reconstructing a tree from a sequence $a_1 a_2 \ldots a_{n-2}$.

   (d) Show that the tree reconstructed by the algorithm in part (c) is the only tree that will yield the sequence $a_1 a_2 \ldots a_{n-2}$ according to the foregoing procedure.

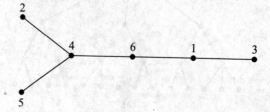

Fig. 5P.4

5.23 (a) Prove that any edge of a connected graph G is a branch of some spanning tree of G.

   (b) Is it also true that any edge of a connected graph G is a chord of some spanning tree of G?

5.24 Let G_1 and G_1 be two trees. Let v_1 and v_2 be two distinct vertices in G_1 and v_3 and v_4 be two distinct vertices in G_2. Let G be a graph obtained from G_1 and G_2 by connecting v_1 with v_3 and v_2 with v_4, as shown in Fig. 5P.5.

   (a) Is G a tree? Prove your claim.

   (b) Is G a connected graph? Prove your claim.

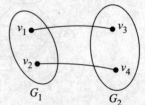

Fig. 5P.4

(c) What can you say about G_1 and G_2 if it is given that G has an eulerian circuit?

5.25 How many different spanning trees are there in each graph in Fig. 5P.6? (Note that the vertices are distinct.)

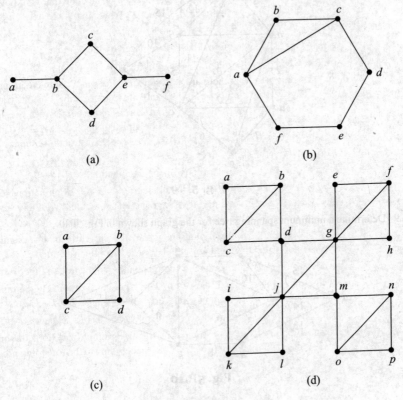

(a)　　　　　　　(b)

(c)　　　　　　　(d)

Fig. 5P.6

5.26 Determine a minimum spanning tree for the graph shown in Fig. 5P.7.

5.27 Determine a minimum spanning tree for the graph shown in Fig. 5P.8.

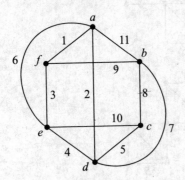

Fig. 5P.7

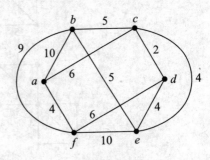

Fig. 5P.8

5.28 Determine a minimum spanning tree for the graph shown in Fig. 5P.9.

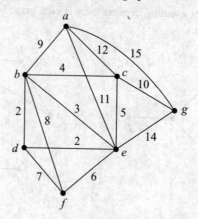

Fig. 5P.9

5.29 Determine a minimum spanning tree for the graph shown in Fig. 5P.10.

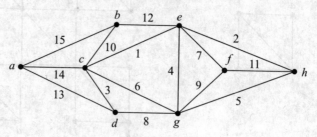

Fig. 5P.10

5.30 Determine a minimum spanning tree for the graph shown in Fig. 5P.11.

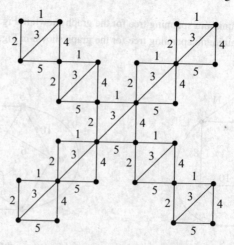

Fig. 5P.11

5.31 The telephone company made a mistake and built too many telephone lines between a group of houses. In the graph shown in Fig. 5P.12, the vertices are the houses and the edges are the telephone lines. The lengths of the edges are the lengths of the lines. To alleviate the problem, the telephone company wants to remove extra telephone lines so that the sum of the lengths of the remaining lines will be as small as possible, subject to the condition that every house is connected to every other house by a path of telephone lines. Cross out the lines that should be removed and determine the total length of the remaining lines.

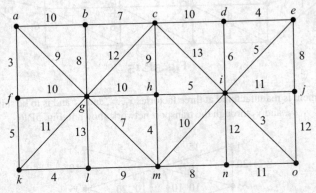

Fig. 5P.12

5.32 Use the labeling procedure to find a maximum flow in the transport network in Fig. 5P.13. Determine the corresponding minimum cut.

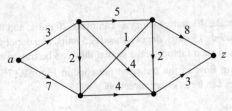

Fig. 5P.13

5.33 Use the labeling procedure to find a maximum flow in the transport network in Fig. 5P.14. Determine the corresponding minimum cut.

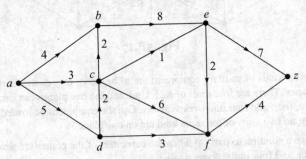

Fig. 5P.14

5.34 Use the labeling procedure to find a maximum flow in the transport network in Fig. 5P.15. Determine the corresponding minimum cut.

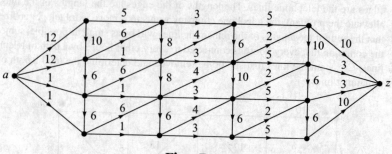

Fig. 5P.15

5.35 Equipment is manufactured at three factories x_1, x_2, and x_3, and is to be shipped to three depots y_1, y_2, and y_3 through the transport network shown in Fig. 5P.16.

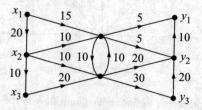

Fig. 5P.16

Factory x_1 can make 40 units, factory x_2 can make 20 units, and factory x_3 can make 10 units. Depot y_1 needs 15 units, depot y_2 needs 25 units, and depot y_3 needs 10 units. How many units should each factory make so that they can be transported to the depots?

5.36 Find a maximum flow in the transport network in Fig. 5P.17 in which flows in the unoriented edges can be in either direction.

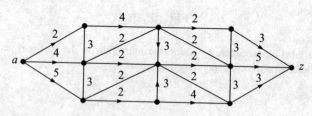

Fig. 5P.17

5.37 (a) Seven kinds of military equipment are to be flown to a destination by five cargo planes. There are four units of each kind, and the five planes can carry eight, eight, five, four, and four units, respectively. Can the equipment be loaded in such a way that no two units of the same kind are on one plane?

(b) Give a solution to part (a) when the capacities of the planes are seven, seven, six, four, and four units, respectively.

5.38 Construct a directed graph with four vertices and with no more than two edges from one vertex to another such that the outgoing and incoming degrees of the vertices are (5, 4), (3, 3), (1, 2), and (2, 2), respectively, by solving the corresponding network flow problem.

5.39 Given a transport network, we wish to find a flow such that the flow in each edge is larger than or equal to the capacity of the edge and the value of the flow is minimum.

    (a) Define the "capacity of a cut," and state the minimum-flow maximum-cut condition which is analogous to the maximum-flow minimum-cut condition presented in Sec. 5.10.

    (b) Prove the minimum-flow maximum-cut condition by designing an algorithm to find a minimum-flow.

5.40 Engineers and technicians are to be hired by a company to participate in three projects. The personnel requirements of these three projects are listed in the following table.

	Minimum number of people needed in each project	Minimum number in each category			
		Mechanical engineers	Mechanical technicians	Electrical engineers	Electrical technicians
Project I	40	5	10	10	5
Project II	40	10	5	15	5
Project III	20	5	0	10	5

Moreover, to prepare for later expansion, the company wants to hire at least 30 mechanical engineers, 20 mechanical technicians, 20 electrical engineers, and 20 electrical technicians. What is a minimum number of persons in each category that the company should hire, and how should they be allocated to the three projects?

5.41 In the graph in Fig. 5P.18, a minimum set of edges is to be selected such that every vertex is incident with at least one of the edges in the set. Solve this problem as a minimum-flow problem associated with a transport network.

5.42 Three candidates x_1, x_2, and x_3 have been promised minimum amounts of campaign money of $40,000, $23,000, and $50,000, respectively. Each candidate, in turn, has promised three campaign areas at least the amounts of money shown in the table below. In addition, each candidate will need at least $5,000 for his own expenses.

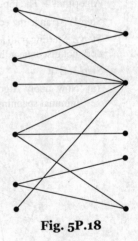

Fig. 5P.18

	Campaign area		
Candidate	C_1	C_2	C_3
x_1	$20,000	$10,000	$10,000
x_2	10,000	5,000	2,000
x_3	5,000	10,000	20,000

If the three campaign areas C_1, C_2, and C_3 require a minimum of $30,000, $25,000, and $50,000, respectively, to conduct a thorough campaign, what is a minimum amount of campaign money each candidate must obtain and how should it be distributed?

5.43 The labelled graph G in Fig. 5P.19 has three spanning trees.

(a) Find the spanning trees of G and their lengths.

(b) Which is the minimal spanning tree of G?

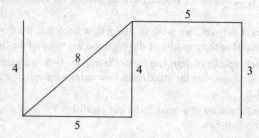

Fig. 5P.19

5.44 Following are two algorithms to find a minimal spanning tree of a graph G:

Algorithm 1: The input is a graph G with n vertices.

Step 1: Arrange the edges of G in increasing order of their weights.

Step 2: Starting with a vertex of G and proceeding sequentially, add each edge, which does not result in a cycle until $n - 1$ edges are added.

Step 3: Exit

Algorithm 2: The input is a graph G with n vertices.

Step 1: Arrange the edges of G in decreasing order of their weights.

Step 2: Starting with a vertex of G and proceeding sequentially, delete each edge, which does not disconnect the graph until $n - 1$ edges remain.

Step 3: Exit

(a) Now, apply Algorithm 1 to the labeled connected graph in Fig. 5P.20 to find a minimal spanning tree.

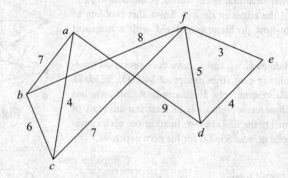

Fig. 5P.20

(b) Again, apply Algorithm 2 to the above graph to find a minimal spanning tree.

5.45 Prove that a pendant edge (an edge whose one end vertex is of degree one) in a connected graph G is contained in every spanning tree of G.

5.46 Can you construct a graph if you are given all its spanning trees? How?

5.47 Use the Kruskal's algorithm to find a shortest spanning tree in the following graph (See Fig. 5P.21).

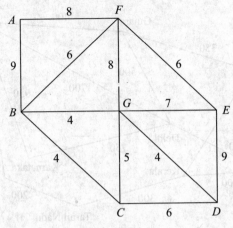

Fig. 5P.21

5.48 Using Prim's algorithm to find the minimum spanning tree for the weighted graph in Fig. 5P.22.

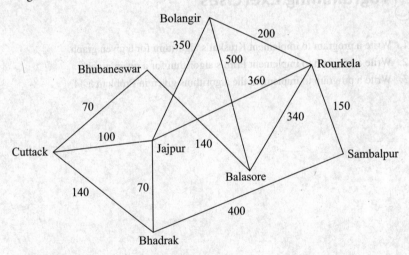

Fig. 5P.22

5.49 Work out an algorithm similar to Prim's algorithm for constructing a maximum spanning tree of a connected weighted graph.

5.50 Work out an algorithm similar to Kruskal's algorithm for constructing a maximum spanning tree of a connected weighted graph.

5.51 Find the adjacency matrix of the connected weighted graph in Fig. 5P.23.

   (a) Given the set of edges and their corresponding weights of a weighted connected graph, use Prim's algorithm to find a minimum spanning tree of this graph.

   (b) Given the set of edges and their corresponding weights of a weighted connected graph, use Kruskal's algorithm to find a minimum spanning tree of this graph.

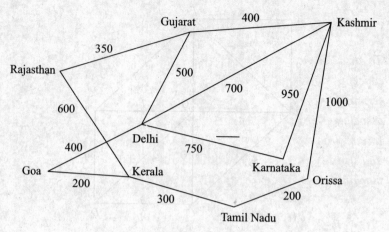

Fig. 5P.23

 Programming Exercises

1. Write a program to implement Kruskal's algorithm for a given graph.
2. Write a program to implement Prim's algorithm for a given graph.
3. Write a program to implement the algorithms given in Problem 5.44.

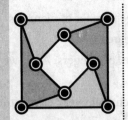
Objective

To discuss the
concepts and
terminologies
associated with
formal languages
and finite state
machines.

MODELING
COMPUTATION

6.1 INTRODUCTION

We shall examine in this chapter a seemingly simple question, namely, " How do we specify the elements of a set?" In Sec. 1.1 we suggested two simple ways to specify the elements of a set: to exhaustively list all elements in the set (provided, of course, that the set is finite), and to specify the properties that uniquely characterize the elements in the set. For example,

$$\{9, 16, 25, 36, 49\}$$
$$\{x \mid x \text{ is a perfect square}, 5 \leq x \leq 50\}$$

are two ways to describe the same set. So far, we have taken all of these for granted. On the one hand, we have not examined closely whether there is any pitfall when we specify the elements of a set in these ways. On the other hand, we have not looked into other possible ways that might also be effective and useful. As it turns out, some of the issues we shall discuss in this chapter not only are extremely interesting but also are of significant importance in theoretical computer science.

6.2 RUSSELL'S PARADOX AND
NONCOMPUTABILITY

When we want to specify the elements of a set that contains only a few elements, the most direct and obvious way is to exhaustively list all elements in the set. However, when a set contains a large number or an infinite number of elements, exhaustively listing all elements in the set becomes impractical or impossible. For example, we may have

$$P = \{x \mid x \text{ is a high school student in Illinois}\}$$

where P is a finite set with a large number of elements. We may have

$$Q = \{x \mid x \text{ is a perfect square}\}$$

where Q is a countably infinite set of integers. Also, we may have

$$R = \{x \mid \{a, b\} \subseteq x\}$$

Note that R is a set of sets such that every element in R has the set $\{a, b\}$ as a subset.

We want to show that there is a possible pitfall when we specify the elements of a set by specifying the properties that uniquely characterize these elements. Consider the set

$$S = \{x \mid x \notin x\}$$

It seems that we have followed the "recipe" and have defined a set S such that a set x is an element of S if $x \notin x$. Thus, for example, $\{a, b\}$ is an element of S because $\{a, b\} \notin \{a, b\}$. $\{\{a\}\}$ is also an element of S because $\{\{a\}\} \notin \{\{a\}\}$. However, suppose someone wants to know whether S is an element of S. In other words, she wants to know whether $S \in S$. Following the specification, we say that for S to be an element of S it must be the case that $S \notin S$, which is a self-contradictory statement. Let us turn around and assume that S is not an element of S; that is, $S \notin S$. Then, according to the specification, S should be an element of S. That is, if $S \notin S$ then $S \in S$—again, a self-contradictory statement. We hasten to point out that what we have said is not just a pun and have by no means attempted to confuse the reader with entangled and complicated syntax. Rather, contrary to our intuition, it is not always the case that we can precisely specify the elements of a set by specifying the properties of the elements in the set. Such an observation was first made by B. Russell in 1911, and is referred to as *Russell's paradox*.

So that the reader will have a deeper appreciation of the argument above, we mention here a few more examples.

Example 6.1 There is a barber in a small village. He will shave everybody who does not shave himself. It seems that we have here a precise description of a certain barber in the village. However, suppose the question whether the barber shaves himself is raised. If the barber shaves himself then he should not shave himself (because he only shaves those who do not shave themselves). On the other hand, if the barber does not shave himself then he should shave himself (because he shaves all of those who do not shave themselves). In both cases, we have a self-contradictory statement. Again, what is wrong is our way of specifying the barber. Consequently, we conclude that no such barber can exist.   ■

Example 6.2 We define a property that an adjective might or might not possess. An adjective is said to be *heterological* if it does not possess the property it describes. For example, the adjective "monosyllabic" is heterological (because it has more than one syllable), while the adjective "polysyllabic" is not heterological (because it has more than one syllable). Also, the adjective "long" is heterological if we agree that a word with five or more letters is a long word. Similarly, the adjective "short" is heterological. We now ask the question, "Is the adjective 'heterological' heterological?" If the adjective "heterological" is heterological then it is not heterological. On the other hand, if the adjective "heterological" is not heterological then it is heterological. Consequently, we conclude that heterological is not a well-defined property. ∎

Example 6.3 There were two craftsmen, Bellini and Cellini, from Florence. Whatever Bellini made, he always put a true inscription on it. On the other hand, whatever Cellini made, he always put a false inscription on it. If they were the only craftsmen around, what would you say if it was reported that the following sign was discovered?

> This sign
> was made by
> Cellini

∎

We give now a final illustration of the argument we just went through. While we all have been impressed by the power and versatility of the computer, we are going to show that there are tasks no computer can perform. Indeed, this is one of the most important concepts in theoretical computer science. (Again, we ask the reader to think about the question, "How do we prove that no computer is capable of performing a certain task?" before going on. To prove a computer is capable of performing a certain task, we can simply demonstrate how the task can be performed. On the other hand, when we say a certain task is beyond the capability of all computers, how do we know that it is not due to our ineptness as a user of the computer? Perhaps someone else will devise a way to use the computer to perform the task for us. How do we know for sure that it is not due to the fact that our computer is not "powerful" enough for the task? Perhaps someone else has a computer that is powerful enough to perform the task.) One of the nightmares of any computer science student is that a program enters an "infinite loop" and never stops. Thus, students frequently seek the help of a friendly consultant and ask him/her to look at a program and the data it works on to determine whether the program will ever stop. Instead of imposing such an unpleasant chore upon the consultant, one wonders about the possibility of writing a program that will examine any student's program together with the data it works on and report whether the program, working on the given data, will ever stop. Let us *assume* that someone has written such a program, which we shall refer to as T. The behavior of program T can be described in Fig. 6.1a, namely, program T will examine a program P and the data P works on, D, make the right diagnosis, print out a corresponding message, and then stop. When we were given program T, we can make a slight modification to obtain a program T'. The only difference between the two programs T and T' is that after diagnosing that a program working on a given set of data will stop, program T' will enter

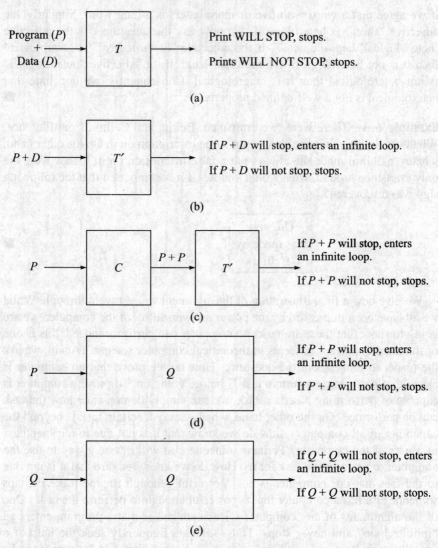

Program (P)
+ ——→ T ——→ Print WILL STOP, stops.
Data (D)
Prints WILL NOT STOP, stops.

(a)

$P + D$ ——→ T' ——→ If $P + D$ will stop, enters an infinite loop.
If $P + D$ will not stop, stops.

(b)

P ——→ C ——$P + P$——→ T' ——→ If $P + P$ will stop, enters an infinite loop.
If $P + P$ will not stop, stops.

(c)

P ——→ Q ——→ If $P + P$ will stop, enters an infinite loop.
If $P + P$ will not stop, stops.

(d)

Q ——→ Q ——→ If $Q + Q$ will not stop, enters an infinite loop.
If $Q + Q$ will not stop, stops.

(e)

Fig. 6.1

an infinite loop itself. Figure 6.1*b* describes the behavior of program T'. (Such a modification is easy as we all know how to add an infinite loop to a program.)

Since a program is composed of strings of letters and digits, and so is a set of data, it is possible that a program uses itself as the set of data it works on. (Whether the results will be meaningful or not is another question, which we are not concerned with here.) Thus, by constructing a small program C that copies a program for the program to use as data, we have what is shown in Fig. 6.1*c*. Let us simply put programs C and T' together and refer to it as program Q, as shown in Fig. 6.1*d*. We can summarize the behavior of program Q as follows:

1. Program Q accepts program P as input.
2. If program P, when using program P as input data, will eventually stop, then program Q will enter an infinite loop.
3. If program P, when using program P as input data, will enter an infinite loop, then program Q will stop.

Since program Q is a program itself, we can let program Q be the input to program Q. Thus, we have the situation depicted in Fig. 6.1e. Now, according to statements 2 and 3 above, we have:

2′. If program Q, when using program Q as input data, will eventually stop, then program Q will enter an infinite loop.
3′. If program Q, when using program Q as input data, will enter an infinite loop, then program Q will stop.

It is clear that both statements 2′ and 3′ are self-contradictory. Again, what leads to such contradictory statements is the assumption that program T exists. Consequently, we conclude that it is not possible to write a program that examines any given program and data set and determines whether the program will eventually stop.

We must conclude this section by reestablishing the reader's confidence. As it turns out (it is beyond the scope of this book to discuss the subject in detail), there will be no confusion in specifying a set by using characterizing properties of the elements of the set as long as we are confined to a certain *universe* of elements. For example, let A denote the set of all students. Then, the following sets are clearly well-defined:

$$F = \{x \mid x \in A, x \text{ is a freshman}\}$$
$$G = \{x \mid x \in \mathscr{P}(A), x \text{ is a set of students in one living group}\}$$

In the first example, A is the universe. In the second example, $\mathscr{P}(A)$ is the universe. At this point, a keen observer will point out that Russell's paradox will arise again, if we use as our universe a set that contains all the sets in the world. However, it can be shown that there does not exist a set that contains all the sets in the world. (Does that set contain itself as an element?) Indeed, Russell's paradox is equivalent to the assumption of the existence of such a set.

6.3 ORDERED SETS

As we mentioned in Chapter 1, a set is an *unordered* collection of objects. In this section, we shall introduce the notion of ordered sets of objects. To this end, we define first the notion of an ordered pair of objects. An *ordered pair* of objects is a pair of objects arranged in a fixed order. Thus, these two objects can be referred to as the first object and the second object of the ordered pair. We use the notation (a, b) to denote the ordered pair in which the first object (component) is a and the second object (component) is b. Note that an ordered pair differs from a set of two objects in two ways: First, the order of the two objects in an ordered pair is important. Thus, (a, b) and (b, a) are two different ordered pairs. Second, the two objects in an ordered pair do not have to be distinct. Thus, (a, a) is a well-defined ordered pair. We often encounter the notion of ordered pairs of objects. For example, among all players in a tennis tournament, an ordered pair (a, b) might denote the champion and the runner-up of the tournament. Thus, the ordered pair (a, b) does not mean the same as the ordered pair (b, a). As another example, among all students in a class, an ordered pair (a, b) might denote the students who obtained the highest score in two examinations. Thus, the pair (a, a) means that student a obtained the highest score in both examinations.

The notion of ordered pairs can be extended immediately. Although it is intuitively obvious that we might wish to define an ordered triple of objects, such as (a, b, c), to mean a triple of objects in which the first one is a, the second one is b, and the third one is c, we define, instead, an *ordered triple* formally as an ordered pair $((a, b), c)$, where the first component of the ordered pair is, in turn, an ordered pair.* Similarly, we define an *ordered quadruple* as an ordered pair $(((a, b), c), d)$, where the first component of the ordered pair is an ordered triple. We also define an *ordered n-tuple* as an ordered pair where the first component is an ordered $(n - 1)$-tuple.

An ordered n-tuple is indeed an "ordered set" with n elements. Specifically, the 1st, 2nd, ..., $(n - 1)$st elements of the ordered set are the $n - 1$ elements in the first component of the ordered n-tuple which, we repeat, is an ordered $(n - 1)$-tuple, and the nth element of the ordered set is the second component of the ordered n-tuple. Thus, for an ordered n-tuple, we can refer to the first, second, and nth element (component) of the ordered n-tuple. As a matter of fact, we frequently relax our notations, using (a, b, c) or abc to represent the ordered triple $((a, b), c)$, using (a, b, c, d) or $abcd$ to represent the ordered quadruple $(((a, b), c), d)$, and so on.

6.4 LANGUAGES

Let $A = \{a, b, c, d, ..., x, y, z\}$ denote the 26-letter English alphabet. Clearly, an n-letter word is an ordered n-tuple of the letters in the alphabet. Indeed, the ordered quintuple $((((o, r), d), e), r)$ corresponds to the word *order*. (This is exactly the reason we introduce the simpler notation for ordered n-tuples in Sec. 2.3.) In the context of languages, we often use the terms *sequences, strings,* or *sentences* (of letters) interchangeably with the term ordered n-tuples (of letters). We use the notation A^n or $\{a, b, c, d, ..., x, y, z\}^n$ to denote the *set* of all sequences of n letters from set A or set $\{a, b, c, d, ..., x, y, z\}$. We also use the notation $A^\star$ or $\{a, b, c, d, ..., x, y, z\}^\star$ to denote the set of all sequences of letters from set A, that is, all sequences of one letter, two letters, and n letters.† Thus, for example,

---

* The reason such a formal definition is used is that no *new* concept needs to be introduced.
† In the literature, the notation A^+ or $\{a, b, c, d, ..., x, y, z\}^+$ is often used. We use $\star$ to avoid possible confusion with the notation for the successor set of a set introduced in Chapter 1.

the set of all the names in a telephone directory is a subset of $A^\star$. Also, the set of all names with 5 letters in the directory is a subset of A^5. As another example, let B be a set consisting of both the upper case and lower case of the 26 letters in the English alphabet as well as 7 punctuation marks: the period, comma, colon, semicolon, exclamation point, question mark, and dash (which denotes a blank). That is,

$$B = \{a, b, \ldots, y, z, A, B, \ldots, Y, Z, ., ,, :, ;, !, ?, \_\}$$

Clearly, a sentence in the English language, such as *Where_is_John?* is a sequence in $B^\star$. Similarly, a statement in any programming language is a sequence in $C^\star$, where C is the character set of that particular programming language such as

$$C = \{A, B, \ldots, Y, Z, 0, 1, 2, \ldots, 8, 9, +, -, *, /, ;, ., =\}$$

We define formally the notion of a language: Let A be a finite set which is the *alphabet* of the language. A *language* (over the alphabet A) is a subset of the set $A^\star$.* Thus, for example, let $A = \{a, b, c\}$. The following sets are all languages over the alphabet A.

$$L_1 = \{a, aa, ab, ac, abc, cab\}$$
$$L_2 = \{aba, aabaa\}$$
$$L_3 = \{ \ \}$$
$$L_4 = \{a^i c b^i \mid i \geq 1\}$$

In the specification of L_4, note that we use the notation a^i to mean a sequence of i a's. Thus, $a^i c b^i$ means a sequence of i a's, followed by c, followed by i b's.

Since languages are defined as sets of strings, all set operations can be applied to languages. For example, let L_1, and L_2 be two languages. $L_1 \cup L_2$ is also a language that contains the sentences in either L_1 or L_2. Thus, if L_1 is the English language, and L_2 is the French language, $L_1 \cup L_2$ will be the set of all sentences someone who speaks both English and French can recognize. Similarly, $L_1 \cap L_2$ is a language that contains all the sentences that are in both L_1 and L_2. Thus, let L_1 be the programming language FORTRAN, and let L_2 be the programming language Pascal. Then $L_1 \cap L_2$ will be the set of all statements that are valid statements in both FORTRAN and Pascal. Also, as other examples, note that

$$\{a^i b^j \mid i > j \geq 1\} \cup \{a^i b^j \mid 1 \leq i < j\} = \{a^i b^j \mid i \neq j, i, j \geq 1\}$$
$$\{a^i b^i c^j \mid i, j \geq 1\} \cap \{a^i b^j c^i \mid i, j \geq 1\} = \{a^i b^i c^i \mid i \geq 1\}$$
$$\{a^i b^j \mid i \geq j \geq 1\} \oplus \{a^i b^j \mid 1 \leq i \leq j\} = \{a^i b^j \mid i \neq j, i, j \geq 1\}$$
$$\{a^i b^j \mid i, j \geq 1\} - \{a^i b^i \mid i \geq 1\} = \{a^i b^j \mid i \neq j, i, j \geq 1\}$$

6.5 PHRASE STRUCTURE GRAMMARS

Since a language is a set of strings, the problem of specifying a language is no longer a new one. However, the two ways of specifying the elements in a set

---

* Throughout our discussion we avoid the notion of a "null sequence," that is, a sequence that contains no letters. In general, a language may contain the null sequence as a sequence.

proposed in Chapter 1 are not quite suitable for the case of languages. Since most, if not all, languages have an infinite number of strings, an exhaustive listing of all strings is out of the question. Yet for any nontrivial language it is extremely complicated to describe the properties that uniquely characterize all strings in the language. Furthermore, for many applications, we are interested mostly in the following problems:

1. Given the specification of a language, automatically generate one or more strings in the language.

2. Given the specification of a language, determine whether a given string is in the language.

Consequently, it is desirable to have ways to describe languages that will facilitate us in solving these problems. To this end, we introduce the notion of specifying a language by a grammar, an idea originated from our study of natural languages. In particular, we shall study a class of grammars known as *phrase structure grammars*.

Let us present an example to motivate the formal definitions we are going to introduce later. Suppose we limit ourselves to a very restrictive subset of the sentences in English. We may begin by asking what a sentence in the language is. Suppose a sentence can be in one of two forms:

1. A **sentence** is a **noun-phrase** followed by a **transitive-verb-phrase** and another **noun-phrase**.

2. A **sentence** is a **noun-phrase** followed by an **intransitive-verb-phrase**.

We then ask what is a noun-phrase, transitive-verb-phrase, and intransitive-verb-phrase. We may have:

3. A **noun-phrase** is an **article** followed by a **noun**.

4. A **noun-phrase** is a **noun**.

Also,

5. A **transitive-verb-phrase** is a **transitive-verb**.

Also,

6. An **intransitive-verb-phrase** is an **intransitive-verb** followed by an **adverb**.

7. An **intransitive-verb-phrase** is an **intransitive-verb**.

Now, we must specify what is an article, noun, transitive-verb, intransitive-verb, and adverb. We may have:

8. An **article** is *a*.

9. An **article** is *the*.

Also,

10. A **noun** is *dog*.

11. A **noun** is *cat*.

Also,

12. A **transitive-verb** is *chases*.

13. A **transitive-verb** is *meets*.

Also,

14. An **intransitive-verb** is *runs*.

Also,

15. An **adverb** is *slowly*.

16. An **adverb** is *rapidly*.

All of these motivate the following notation:

$$\begin{aligned}
\textbf{sentence} &\rightarrow \textbf{noun-phrase transitive-verb-phrase}\\
&\quad\textbf{noun-phrase}\\
\textbf{sentence} &\rightarrow \textbf{noun-phrase intransitive-verb-phrase}\\
\textbf{noun-phrase} &\rightarrow \textbf{article noun}\\
\textbf{noun-phrase} &\rightarrow \textbf{noun}\\
\textbf{transitive-verb-phrase} &\rightarrow \textbf{transitive-verb}\\
\textbf{intransitive-verb-phrase} &\rightarrow \textbf{intransitive-verb adverb}\\
\textbf{intransitive-verb-phrase} &\rightarrow \textbf{intransitive-verb}\\
\textbf{article} &\rightarrow a\\
\textbf{article} &\rightarrow the\\
\textbf{noun} &\rightarrow dog\\
\textbf{noun} &\rightarrow cat\\
\textbf{transitive-verb} &\rightarrow chases\\
\textbf{transitive-verb} &\rightarrow meets\\
\textbf{intransitive-verb} &\rightarrow runs\\
\textbf{adverb} &\rightarrow slowly\\
\textbf{adverb} &\rightarrow rapidly
\end{aligned} \tag{6.1}$$

The meaning of the arrow in the lines above should be obvious. It indicates the possibility of transforming what is on its left-hand side to what is on its right-hand side. Also, the reader can immediately see that some sentences in the language are:

> *the dog meets a cat*
> *dog chases cat*
> *the cat runs slowly*

We shall explain many additional details after we introduce some general notations.

As defined above, a language is a subset of the strings in $A^\star$. A *phrase structure grammar* can be used to specify a language. It consists of four items:

1. A set of *terminals T*.

2. A set of *nonterminals N*.

3. A set of *productions P*.

4. Among all the nonterminals in N, there is a special nonterminal that is referred to as the *starting symbol*.

Let us explain now what all of these mean:

1. The terminals in T are symbols used to make up sentences in the language. For the example above, the set $\{a, the, dog, cat, chases, meets, runs, slowly, rapidly\}$ is the set of terminals.

2. The nonterminals in N are intermediate symbols used to describe the structure of the sentences. In the example above, the set {**sentence, noun-phrase, noun, article, transitive-verb-phrase, transitive-verb, intransitive-verb-phrase, intransitive-verb, adverb**} is the set of nonterminals.

3. The productions are grammatical rules that specify how sentences in the language can be made up. A production is of the form $\alpha \to \beta$, where α and β are strings of terminals and nonterminals. A production specifies that string α can be transformed into string β. In the example above, (2.1) is the set of productions.

4. The *starting symbol* is a special nonterminal that begins the generation of any sentence in the language. In the example above, **sentence** is the starting symbol.

Once we are given a grammar, we can generate the sentences in the language as follows:

1. Begin with the starting symbol as the current string of terminals and nonterminals.

2. If any portion of the current string of terminals and nonterminals matches the left-hand side of a production, replace that portion of the string by the right-hand side of the production. To be specific, let α denote the current string of terminals and nonterminals. Furthermore, suppose that α can be divided into three substrings $\alpha_1, \alpha_2,$ and α_3, that is, $\alpha = \alpha_1 \, \alpha_2 \, \alpha_3$. If there exists a production $\alpha_2 \to \beta$, then we can replace the substring α_2 in α by β to obtain the string $\alpha_1 \beta \alpha_3$. We use the notation $\alpha \Rightarrow \alpha_1 \beta \alpha_3$ to mean that the string α can be transformed into the string $\alpha_1 \beta \alpha_3$ by replacing a *portion* of the string α according to one of the productions in the grammar.

3. Any string of terminals obtained by repeating step 2 is a sentence in the language. Note that in step 2 the possibility exists that more than one production can be applied to transform the current string of terminals and nonterminals. In that case, any one of the productions can be chosen. On the other hand, if in step 2 we reach a string of terminals and nonterminals to which no production can be applied then we have reached a deadend and must begin with the starting symbol all over again to obtain a sentence in the language.

The process of generating a sentence as described above is also referred to as a *derivation*. In the above example, the sentence, "*a dog runs slowly*," is derived as follows:

$$\text{sentence} \Rightarrow \textbf{noun-phrase intransitive-verb-phrase}$$
$$\Rightarrow \textbf{noun-phrase intransitive-verb adverb}$$
$$\Rightarrow \textbf{noun-phrase intransitive-verb } rapidly$$
$$\Rightarrow \textbf{noun-phrase } runs\ rapidly$$
$$\Rightarrow \textbf{article noun } runs\ rapidly$$
$$\Rightarrow \textbf{article } dog\ runs\ rapidly$$
$$\Rightarrow a\ dog\ runs\ rapidly$$

We examine more examples:

Example 6.4 We want to construct a grammar for the language

$$L = \{aaaa, aabb, bbaa, bbbb\}$$

Since L has a finite number of strings, we can simply list all strings in the language. Thus, let $T = \{a, b\}$ be the set of terminals, $N = \{S\}$ be the set of nonterminals, and S be the starting symbol. We have as the set of productions

$$S \rightarrow aaaa$$
$$S \rightarrow aabb$$
$$S \rightarrow bbaa$$
$$S \rightarrow bbbb$$

We can, however, have a slightly simpler grammar. Let $N = \{S, A\}$ be the set of nonterminals with S being the starting symbol. The following set of productions will also specify the language L:

$$S \rightarrow AA$$
$$A \rightarrow aa$$
$$A \rightarrow bb$$
■

Example 6.5 We want to construct a grammar for the language

$$L = \{a^i b^{2i} | i \geq 1\}$$

Let $T = \{a, b\}$ and $N = \{S\}$, with S being the starting symbol. Let the set of productions be

$$S \rightarrow aSbb$$
$$S \rightarrow abb$$

Thus, for example, we obtain the string $aaabbbbbb$ as follows:

$$S \Rightarrow aSbb \Rightarrow aaSbbbb \Rightarrow aaabbbbbb$$
■

Example 6.6 We want to construct a grammar for the language

$$L = \{x | x \in \{a, b\}^\star, \text{ the number of } a\text{ s in } x \text{ is a multiple of } 3\}$$

Let $T = \{a, b\}$ and $N = \{S, A, B\}$, with S being the starting symbol. The set of productions is

$$S \rightarrow bS$$
$$S \rightarrow b$$
$$S \rightarrow aA$$

$$A \rightarrow bA$$
$$A \rightarrow aB$$
$$B \rightarrow bB$$
$$B \rightarrow aS$$
$$B \rightarrow a$$

For example, we have

$$S \Rightarrow bS \Rightarrow bbS \Rightarrow bbaA \Rightarrow bbabA \Rightarrow bbabaB \Rightarrow bbababB$$
$$\Rightarrow bbababbB \Rightarrow bbababbaS \Rightarrow bbababbab$$

We note that nonterminal A represents the set of all strings in which the number of a's is $3k + 2$, and nonterminal B represents the set of all strings in which the number of a's is $3k + 1$ for $k \geq 0$. ∎

Example 6.7 · Suppose we are given a grammar in which $T = \{a, b\}$ and $N = \{S, A, B\}$, with S being the starting symbol. Let the set of productions be

$$S \rightarrow aB$$
$$S \rightarrow bA$$
$$A \rightarrow a$$
$$A \rightarrow aS$$
$$A \rightarrow bAA$$
$$B \rightarrow b$$
$$B \rightarrow bS$$
$$B \rightarrow aBB$$

We observe that the sentences in the language are all strings of a's and b's in which the number of a's equals the number of b's. Such an observation becomes clear when we note that nonterminal A represents the set of strings in which the number of a's is one more than the number of b's, and nonterminal B represents the set of strings in which the number of b's is one more than the number of a's. ∎

Example 6.8 We want to construct a grammar for the language

$$L = \{a^i b^i \mid i, j \geq 1, i \neq j\}$$

We note that

$$L = L_1 \cup L_2$$

where

$$L_1 = \{a^i b^j \mid i > j\}$$
$$L_2 = \{a^i b^j \mid i < j\}$$

Note that

$$A \rightarrow aA$$
$$A \rightarrow aB$$
$$B \rightarrow aBb \quad\quad (6.2)$$
$$B \rightarrow ab$$

is a set of productions in a grammar for L_1, where $\{a, b\}$ is the set of terminals and $\{A, B\}$ is the set of nonterminals, with A being the starting symbol. Also,

Also,
$$C \to Cb$$
$$C \to Db$$
$$D \to aDb$$ (6.3)
$$D \to ab$$

is a set of productions in a grammar for L_2, where $\{a, b\}$ is the set of terminals and $\{C, D\}$ is the set of nonterminals, with C being the starting symbol.

We realize immediately that by adding the two productions
$$S \to A$$
$$S \to C$$

to the productions in (2.2) and (2.3), we have a grammar for L, with S being the starting symbol. However, we can simplify the grammar to

$$S \to A$$
$$S \to C$$
$$A \to aA$$
$$A \to aB$$
$$B \to aBb$$
$$B \to ab$$
$$C \to Cb$$
$$C \to Bb$$

∎

Example 6.9 Consider the following grammar which specifies assignment statements that involve identifiers, the arithmetic operators + and *, the equal sign, =, the left parenthesis, (, and the right parenthesis,). Let $T = \{A, B, C, D, +, *, (,), =\}$ and $N = \{$**asgn_stat, exp, term, factor, id**$\}$, with **asgn_stat** being the starting symbol. Let the following be the set of productions:

$$\textbf{asgn\_stat} \to \textbf{id = exp}$$
$$\textbf{exp} \to \textbf{exp + term}$$
$$\textbf{exp} \to \textbf{term}$$
$$\textbf{term} \to \textbf{term*factor}$$
$$\textbf{term} \to \textbf{factor}$$
$$\textbf{factor} \to \textbf{(exp)}$$
$$\textbf{factor} \to \textbf{id}$$
$$\textbf{id} \to A$$
$$\textbf{id} \to B$$
$$\textbf{id} \to C$$
$$\textbf{id} \to D$$

We note that
$$\textbf{asgn\_stat} \Rightarrow \textbf{id = exp}$$
$$\Rightarrow \textbf{id = exp + term}$$
$$\Rightarrow \textbf{id = exp + term*factor}$$
$$\Rightarrow \textbf{id = exp + term*(exp)}$$
$$\Rightarrow \textbf{id = exp + term*(exp + term)}$$
$$\Rightarrow \textbf{id = exp + term*(exp + factor)}$$

$$\Rightarrow \mathbf{id} = \mathbf{exp} + \mathbf{term}^*(\mathbf{exp} + \mathbf{id})$$
$$\Rightarrow \mathbf{id} = \mathbf{exp} + \mathbf{term}^*(\mathbf{exp} + B)$$
$$\Rightarrow \mathbf{id} = \mathbf{exp} + \mathbf{term}^*(\mathbf{term} + B)$$
$$\Rightarrow \mathbf{id} = \mathbf{exp} + \mathbf{term}^*(\mathbf{factor} + B)$$
$$\Rightarrow \mathbf{id} = \mathbf{exp} + \mathbf{term}^*(\mathbf{id} + B)$$
$$\Rightarrow \mathbf{id} = \mathbf{exp} + \mathbf{term}^*(D + B)$$
$$\Rightarrow \mathbf{id} = \mathbf{exp} + \mathbf{factor}^*(D + B)$$
$$\Rightarrow \mathbf{id} = \mathbf{exp} + \mathbf{id}^*(D + B)$$
$$\Rightarrow \mathbf{id} = \mathbf{exp} + D^*(D + B)$$
$$\Rightarrow \mathbf{id} = \mathbf{term} + D^*(D + B)$$
$$\Rightarrow \mathbf{id} = \mathbf{factor} + D^*(D + B)$$
$$\Rightarrow \mathbf{id} = \mathbf{id} + D^*(D + B)$$
$$\Rightarrow \mathbf{id} = A + D^*(D + B)$$
$$\Rightarrow C = A + D^*(D + B) \qquad\blacksquare$$

6.6 TYPES OF GRAMMARS AND LANGUAGES

In Sec. 6.5 we saw how grammars can be used to specify languages. As it turns out, using grammars to specify languages also leads us to a natural way of classifying languages. It is beyond the scope of this book to go into the details of this subject. However, we do want to state some of the results, without proof, so that the reader may appreciate more the subject matter.

Noam Chomsky had classified the grammars into four categories based on the types of productions. In this section, we briefly describe these four categories of grammars. In the following, we shall use A and B to denote arbitrary nonterminals, a and b to denote arbitrary terminals, and α and β to denote arbitrary strings of terminals and nonterminals. A grammar is said to be a *type-3 grammar* if all productions in the grammar are of the forms

$$A \to a$$
$$A \to aB \qquad (6.4)$$

or, equivalently,* of the forms

$$A \to a$$
$$A \to Ba \qquad (6.5)$$

---

* It is not obvious that the forms in (6.4) are equivalent to the forms in (6.5) in that languages that can be specified using productions of the forms in (6.4) can also be specified using productions of the forms in (6.5), and conversely. Furthermore, it can be shown that productions of the forms in (6.4) are equivalent to productions of the forms

$$A \to \gamma$$
$$A \to \gamma B$$

and productions of the forms in (6.5) are equivalent to productions of the forms

$$A \to \gamma$$
$$A \to B\gamma$$

where γ is an arbitrary string of terminals. See Probs. 6.45 and 6.46.

In other words, in any production the left-hand string is always a single non-terminal and the right-hand string is either a terminal or a terminal followed by a nonterminal. Thus, the grammar in Example 6.6 is a type-3 grammar.

In a *type-2 grammar*, every production is of the form

$$A \rightarrow \alpha$$

In other words, in any production the left-hand string is always a single non-terminal. Clearly, a type-3 grammar is trivially also a type-2 grammar. Thus, the grammar in Examples 6.5 and 6.7 are type-2 grammars.

In a *type-1 grammar*, for every production

$$\alpha \rightarrow \beta$$

the length of β is larger than or equal to the length of α. For example, the productions

$$A \rightarrow ab$$
$$A \rightarrow aA$$
$$aAb \rightarrow aBCb$$

all satisfy the condition, while the productions

$$aA \rightarrow a$$
$$ABc \rightarrow bc$$

do not. Again, clearly a type-3 or a type-2 grammar is also trivially a type-1 grammar.

A phrase structure grammar as defined above with no restriction is referred to as a *type-0 grammar*. Obviously, every type-1 grammar is a type-0 grammar.

Type-2 grammars are also called context-free grammar since a nonterminal symbol which is a left side of a production can always be replaced in a string, no matter what else is present in the string. If there is a production of the form $lAr \rightarrow l\,\alpha\,r$ (but not of the form $A \rightarrow \alpha$) then the grammar is called type-1 or context sensitive since A can be replaced by α only when it is surrounded by the Strings l and r, where l is the left context and r is the right context. Type-3 grammars are also called as regular grammars. Figure 6.2 shows the relationship among different types of grammars.

Corresponding to different types of grammar, there are different types of languages. Thus, a language is said to be a *type-i* ($i = 0, 1, 2, 3$) language if it can be specified by a type-i grammar, but cannot be specified by a type-$(i + 1)$ grammar. For example, the language

$$L = \{a^k\, b^k \,|\, k \geq 1\}$$

is a type-2 language because it can be specified by the type-2 grammar

$$A \rightarrow aAb$$
$$A \rightarrow ab$$

Yet, on the other hand, L cannot be specified by a type-3 grammar. Let us consider another example. The set $\{0^n\, 1^n\, 2^n \,|\, n = 0, 1, 2 \dots\}$ is a context sensitive language since it can be generated by a Type-1 grammar, but not by any Type-2

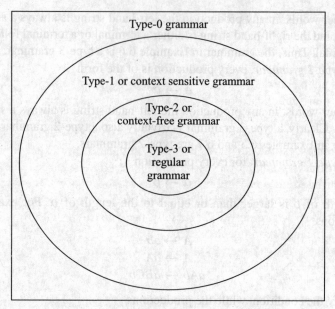

Fig. 6.2   Relationship among different types of grammars

grammar. Context-free and regular grammars have many important applications in programming languages. Context-free grammars are used in defining the syntax of almost all programming languages. Regular grammars can be used to search text for certain pattern and in lexical analysis. (Lexical analysis is the process of transforming input stream into a string of tokens for use by a parser.) Thus, corresponding to the four types of grammars, we also have four types of languages. Context-free and regular grammars have many important applications in programming languages. Context-free grammars are used in defining the syntax of almost all programming languages. Regular grammars can be used to search text for certain pattern and in lexical analysis. (Lexical analysis is the process of transforming input stream into a string of tokens for use by a parser.) There are some questions that arise naturally:

Are there languages that are not type-0 languages? The answer is affirmative. In other words, there are languages that cannot be specified by phrase structure grammars.

How about all the programming languages? They can be specified by phrase structure grammars. As a matter of fact, all of them are (almost) type-2 languages.*

---

* The word "almost" in parentheses deserves an explanation. Most features of high-level programming languages such as BASIC, FORTRAN, and Pascal can be specified by type-2 grammars. However, a few features cannot be described this way. Since there is a well-developed body of knowledge on type-2 grammars and languages, we usually apply many of the techniques developed for type-2 languages to handle most features and then make some special arrangements to take care of the "oddities."

Is each class of type-i languages non-empty? The answer is affirmative but is not as obvious as it seems. (Since we choose the definitions of the various types of grammars in a seemingly arbitrary manner, the possibility that any language that can be specified by a type-i grammar can also be specified by a type-$(i + 1)$ grammar is not precluded.)

From a more practical point of view, there is the important question of determining whether a given string indeed belongs to a language specified by a grammar, and if so, how that string is derived. In Sec. 6.5, we show how we can derive the sentences in a language. However, in practice, for example when we want to construct a compiler for a programming language we need to determine if a given string is indeed a legitimate sentence in the language. Then we need to discover how the sentence was derived so that we can translate it (into machine instruction codes) accordingly. Conceptually, these can all be done by exhaustive search, but efficient algorithms have been developed to perform the tasks.

Many of these questions are investigated in detail in the study of theory of formal languages and design and construction of compilers.

6.7 BASIC CONCEPTS OF INFORMATION PROCESSING MACHINE

By an *information-processing machine* we mean a device that receives a set of input signals and produces a corresponding set of output signals, as illustrated in Fig. 6.3. A table lamp can be considered an information-processing machine, with the input signal being either the *UP* or *DOWN* position of the switch and the output signal being either *LIGHT* or *DARK*. An adder is an information processing machine, with the input signals being two decimal numbers and the output signal being their sum. An automobile is an information-processing machine, with the input signals being the depression of the accelerator and the angular position of the steering wheel and with the output signals being the speed and direction of the vehicle. A vending machine is an information-processing machine, with the input signals being the coins deposited and the selection of merchandise and the output signals being the merchandise and, possibly, the change. Finally, a digital

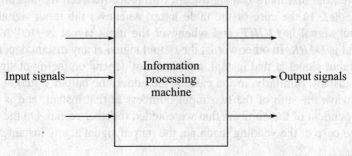

Input signals — Information processing machine — Output signals

Fig. 6.3

computer is an information-processing machine, with the user's program and data being the input signals and the results of the computation on the printout being the output signals.

In general, the input signals to an information-processing machine change with time. In that case, the output signals will also change with time accordingly. That is, in general, an information-processing machine receives a (time) sequence of input signals and produces a corresponding (time) sequence of output signals. Consider the example of a table lamp, where the input signal is one of the two possible switch positions, *UP* and *DOWN*, and the output signal is one of the two possible conditions, *LIGHT* and *DARK*. Thus, corresponding to the sequence of input signals

     UP   DOWN   DOWN   UP   DOWN   UP   UP   ...

there is the sequence of output signals

     LIGHT   DARK   DARK   LIGHT   DARK   LIGHT   LIGHT   ...

For the example of the adder, where the input signals are 2 one-digit numbers and the output signal is a two-digit number, corresponding to the sequences of input signals

     3   5   0   3   3   9   2   ...
     4   4   6   1   4   5   5   ...

the sequence of output signals is

     7   9   6   4   7   14   7   ...

Consider the example of a vending machine, where the input signal is a nickel, dime, or quarter, and the output signal is either a package of gum or nothing. Suppose a package of gum costs 30 cents. Then, corresponding to the sequence of input signals

     DIME   DIME   DIME   QUARTER   QUARTER
     NICKEL   QUARTER   NICKEL   ...

there is the sequence of output signals*

     NOTHING   NOTHING   GUM   NOTHING   GUM
     NOTHING   GUM   NOTHING   ...

We note that there is a significant difference between the machines in these examples. In the case of the table lamp, whenever the input signal is *UP* the output signal is *LIGHT*, and whenever the input signal is *DOWN* the output signal is *DARK*. In other words, the output signal at any instant depends only on the input signal at that instant, and does not depend on the input signals before that instant. Similarly, in the case of the adder, the output signal at any instant is always the sum of the two input numbers at that instant, and is completely independent of the numbers that were added together earlier. On the other hand, in the case of the vending machine, the output signal at any instant depends not

---

* We assume that the vending machine does not return any change.

only on the input signal at that instant but also on the preceding input signals. Thus, for the three successive input signals

DIME   DIME   DIME

the corresponding output signals are

NOTHING   NOTHING   GUM

Specifically, at the first instant, the input is *DIME* and the corresponding output is *NOTHING*; at the second instant, the input is *DIME* and the corresponding output is *NOTHING*; while at the third instant, the input is *DIME* and the corresponding output is *GUM*. Of course, such an observation does not surprise anyone because we are all aware that a vending machine is capable of remembering the total amount that has been deposited, while on the other hand, a table lamp is not capable (nor does it need to be capable) of remembering the previous input signals.

We divide machines into two classes—those with memory and those without memory. For a machine without memory, its output at any instant depends only on the input at that instant. Both the table lamp and the adder discussed above are examples of machines that have no memory. For a machine with memory, its output at any instant depends on the input at that instant as well as on inputs at previous instants because the machine can remember "what has happened in the past." Clearly, a vending machine can remember what has happened in the past. Yet, on the other hand, it does not (nor must it) remember *everything* that has happened in the past. At any instant, it remembers the total amount that has been deposited so far. However, as long as the total amount is, say, 25 cents, the machine makes no distinction about whether five nickels, two dimes and a nickel, a quarter, or other combinations of coins were deposited. To describe past events, we introduce the notion of a *state*. A state represents a summary of the past history of the machine. For the example of the vending machine, there are seven distinct states corresponding to the total deposit so far—namely, 0, 5, 10, 15, 20, 25, and 30 or more cents. Consequently, the state of the machine together with the input signals at a particular instant will determine the corresponding output signals at that instant. For the example of the vending machine, at any instant, the state that the machine is in together with the new deposit will enable the machine to determine whether it should have *NOTHING* or *GUM* as output. Furthermore, as additional input signals arrive, the machine will go from one state to another since it needs to update the summary of its history. In the case of the vending machine, it must update the total amount that has been deposited. Thus, for example, when the machine is in the 15 cents state, an input of 10 cents would bring the machine to the 25 cents state or an input of 25 cents would bring it to the 30 cents or more state, and so on. The behavior of the vending machine can be summarized as in Fig. 6.4. (The notations in Fig. 6.4, though obvious, are formally introduced in Sec. 6.8.)

As another example, consider a machine that accepts a sequence of positive integers between 1 and 100 and produces at any instant the largest integer the

Total deposit	New deposit			Total deposit	Merchandise delivered
	5¢	10¢	25¢		
0¢	5¢	10¢	25¢	0¢	Nothing
5¢	10¢	15¢	30¢ or more	5¢	Nothing
10¢	15¢	20¢	30¢ or more	10¢	Nothing
15¢	20¢	25¢	30¢ or more	15¢	Nothing
20¢	25¢	30¢ or more	30¢ or more	20¢	Nothing
25¢	30¢ or more	30¢ or more	30¢ or more	25¢	Nothing
30¢ or more	5¢	10¢	25¢	30¢ or more	Gum

New total deposit

(a)   (b)

Fig. 6.4

machine has so far received as output, as illustrated in Fig. 6.5. We note that as long as the machine can remember the largest integer it has received, when a new input comes in, the machine can compare the largest integer received so far against the new input and determine the corresponding output, which is the "new" largest integer it has received so far. Thus, for this machine, a summary of the past history can be represented by an integer equal to the largest integer it has received. Consequently, the machine may have 101 states corresponding to the integers 0, 1, ..., 100, representing the largest integer the machine has received. (Clearly, the state 0 means no integer has been received.) Of course, one could design a machine that remembers the largest and the second-largest integers received. The reader would agree immediately that although the machine would behave correctly, it maintains some redundant information (the second-largest integer received), which contributes nothing to the correct operation of the machine.

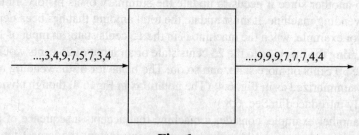

...,3,4,9,7,5,7,3,4   ...,9,9,9,7,7,7,4,4

Fig. 6.5

A machine may have a certain number of states corresponding to a certain number of distinct classes of past history. A machine with a finite number of states is called a *finite state machine*. On the other hand, a machine with an infinite number of states is called an *infinite state machine*. In this chapter, we shall restrict our discussion to finite state machines.

6.8 FINITE STATE MACHINES

We now introduce an abstract model of a finite state machine. A *finite state machine* is specified by:

1. A finite set of states $S = \{s_0, s_1, s_2, \ldots\}$.
2. A special element of the set S, s_0, referred to as the *initial state*.
3. A finite set of input letters $I = \{i_1, i_2, \ldots\}$.
4. A finite set of output letters $O = \{o_1, o_2, \ldots\}$.
5. A function f from $S \times I$ to S, referred to as the *transition function*.
6. A function g from S to O, referred to as the *output function*.

At any instant, a finite state machine is in one of its states. Upon the arrival of an input letter, the machine will go to another state according to the transition function. Furthermore, at each state the machine produces an output letter according to the output function. At the very beginning, the machine is in its initial state. A convenient way to describe a finite state machine is the tabular form used in Fig. 6.6. For the finite state machine shown in Fig. 6.6, the set of states is $\{s_0, s_1, s_2, s_3, s_4, s_5, s_6\}$, the set of input letters is $\{a, b, c\}$, and the set of output letters is $\{0, 1\}$. The double arrow pointing at s_0 indicates that s_0 is the initial state. The transition function f is specified in Fig. 6.6a, where the state in the intersection of a row (corresponding to state s_p) and a column (corresponding to input letter i_q) is the value $f(s_p, i_q)$.* The output function is specified in Fig. 6.6b. Usually, Fig. 6.6a and b can be combined as a single table, as in Fig. 6.7. As a matter of fact, the

State	Input			State	Output
	a	b	c		
$\Rightarrow s_0$	s_1	s_2	s_5	s_0	0
s_1	s_2	s_3	s_6	s_1	0
s_2	s_3	s_4	s_6	s_2	0
s_3	s_4	s_5	s_6	s_3	0
s_4	s_5	s_6	s_6	s_4	0
s_5	s_6	s_6	s_6	s_5	0
s_6	s_1	s_2	s_5	s_6	1
(a)				(b)	

Fig. 6.6

* To be exact, the notation should be $f((s_p, i_q))$. However, we follow a common practice in the literature to omit one pair of parentheses since there is no possible confusion as we pointed out once already in Chapter 3.

finite state machine in Fig. 6.6 is exactly the vending machine shown in Fig. 6.4. Specifically, the states $s_0, s_1, s_2, s_3, s_4, s_5,$ and s_6 correspond to the states 0, 5, 10, 15, 20, 25, and 30 or more cents. The input letters a, b, and c correspond to the coins *NICKEL*, *DIME*, and *QUARTER*. The output letters 0 and 1 correspond to what the vending machine will deliver—*NOTHING* or *GUM*.

State	Input a	Input b	Input c	Output
s_0	s_1	s_2	s_5	0
s_1	s_2	s_3	s_6	0
s_2	s_3	s_4	s_6	0
s_3	s_4	s_5	s_6	0
s_4	s_5	s_6	s_6	0
s_5	s_6	s_6	s_6	0
s_6	s_1	s_2	s_5	1

Fig. 6.7

We can describe a finite state machine graphically, as shown in Fig. 6.8. In the directed graph in Fig. 6.8, each vertex corresponds to a state of the machine. Again, the initial state is identified by a double arrow pointing at it. The output associated with a state is placed below the state name, separated from the state name by a horizontal bar. The transition from one state to another is indicated by a directed edge labeled with the corresponding input letter(s). Indeed, Figs. 6.7 and 6.8 describe the same finite state machine, as the reader can quickly confirm.

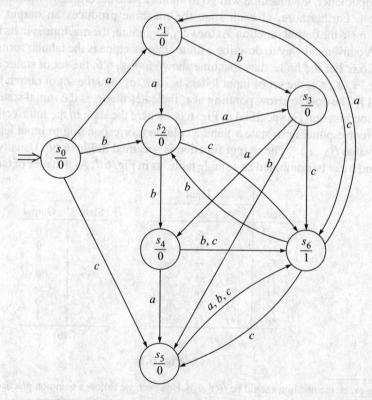

Fig. 6.8

6.9 FINITE STATE MACHINES AS MODELS OF PHYSICAL SYSTEMS

A finite state machine can be used to model a physical system. In Sec. 6.7 we saw how a vending machine could be modeled as a finite state machine. We show more examples in this section.

Consider the problem of designing a modulo 3 counter that receives a sequence of 0s, 1s, and 2s as input and produces a sequence of 0s, 1s, and 2s as output such that at any instant, the output is equal to the modulo 3 sum of the digits in the input sequence.* We note that the machine in Fig. 6.9 will generate the output sequence as specified. Note that A is a state corresponding to the situation that the modulo 3 sum of all input digits is 0, B is a state corresponding to the situation that the modulo 3 sum of all input digits is 1, and C is a state corresponding to the situation that the modulo 3 sum of all input digits is 2.

Consider another example in which we design a device that compares two binary numbers to determine whether they are equal, or which of the two is larger. We assume that the digits of the two numbers come in one by one, with the lower-order digits coming in first. Thus, the input alphabet is {00, 01, 10, 11}, where the two digits in each pair are the corresponding digits in the numbers being compared. The output alphabet is {*EQUAL, LARGER, SMALLER*}. Figure 6.10 shows the machine.

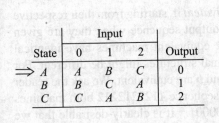

State	Input			Output
	0	1	2	
⟹ A	A	B	C	0
B	B	C	A	1
C	C	A	B	2

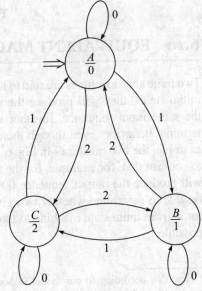

Fig. 6.9

---

* The modulo 3 sum of a set of integers is the remainder of the sum of the integers when it is divided by 3.

State	Input				Output
	00	01	10	11	
⟹ A	A	C	B	A	EQUAL
B	B	C	B	B	LARGE
C	C	C	B	C	SMALL

Fig. 6.10

Finally, Fig. 6.11 shows an example of a finite state machine that models the behavior of a student. The set of states is {*HAPPY, ANGRY, DEPRESSED*}, the set of inputs is {*HOMEWORK, PARTY, POOR_ EXAM*}, and the set of outputs is {*SING, CURSE, SLEEP*}. Although this is an oversimplified model, it does, in fact, capture a certain aspect of how a student reacts under various conditions. (We should point out that this is not simply a trite example included here to amuse the reader. Rather, psychologists, sociologists, economists, and scientists in many disciplines do use finite state machines to model systems they study.)

State	Input			Output
	HOMEWORK	PARTY	POOR EXAM	
⟹ A (HAPPY)	A	A	B	SING
B (ANGRY)	C	A	B	CURSE
C (DEPRESSED)	C	A	C	SLEEP

Fig. 6.11

6.10 EQUIVALENT MACHINES

Two finite state machines are said to be *equivalent* if, starting from their respective initial states, they will produce the same output sequence when they are given the same input sequence. In other words, equivalent machines have identical terminal behaviors even though their internal structures might be different. For example, the two machines in Fig. 6.12a and b are equivalent. We ask the reader to confirm that, for example, for the input sequence 1122212212 both machines will produce the output sequence 00010100001.* It is clearly desirable that we be able to determine whether two given finite state machines are equivalent, or for a given finite state machine to find an equivalent one that has fewer states, if possible.†

---

* Note that according to our model in Sec. 6.8, a finite state machine produces an output symbol (that of the initial state) before the arrival of the first input symbol. Consequently, there is always one more symbol in the output sequence than in the corresponding input sequence.
† Although we will not explore the issue of building finite state machines using electronic devices here, it is intuitively clear that it will be less expensive to build a finite state machine with fewer states.

	Input					Input		
State	1	2	Output		State	1	2	Output
⟹ A	B	C	0		⟹ A	B	C	0
B	F	D	0		B	C	D	0
C	G	E	0		C	D	E	0
D	H	B	0		D	E	B	0
E	B	F	1		E	B	C	1
F	D	H	0					
G	E	B	0					
H	B	C	1					
(a)					(b)			

Fig. 6.12

To identify equivalent machines, we introduce the notion of *equivalent states*. In a finite state machine, two states s_i and s_j are said to be *equivalent* if for any input sequence the machine will produce the same output sequence whether it starts in s_i or s_j. Clearly, two equivalent states can be combined into one without changing the terminal behavior of the machine. Specifically, if s_i and s_j are equivalent states, we can modify the transition function by eliminating state s_j and replacing all transitions into state s_j with state s_i. For example, for the finite state machine in Fig. 6.12a, given that C and F are equivalent states, D and G are equivalent states, and E and H are equivalent states, we can eliminate F, G, and H to obtain the machine in Fig. 6.12b.

Recall that a state of a machine represents a summary of the history of the machine. Thus, two states are equivalent if they represent summaries that are equivalent as far as the terminal behavior of the machine is concerned. For example, the machine in Fig. 6.12a accepts a sequence of 1 s and 2 s as inputs and will produce a 1 if the sum of all digits it has received is divisible by 4. Indeed, both states E and H represent that the sum of the digits the machine has received is a multiple of 4, both states C and F represent that the sum of the digits the machine has received is a multiple of 4 plus 2, and both states D and G represent that the sum of the digits the machine has received is a multiple of 4 plus 3. (State B represents that the sum of digits the machine has received is a multiple of 4 plus 1.) Consequently, equivalent states can be combined without changing the terminal behavior of the machine.

Our immediate question is how to determine whether two states are equivalent, since according to the definition, testing whether two states are equivalent would require an exhaustive examination of all possible input sequences of arbitrary length. We show now an effective procedure for such purpose. Two states are said to be 0-*equivalent* if they have the same output. Two states are said to be 1-*equivalent* if they have the same output and if, for every input letter, their successors are 0-equivalent. In general, two states are said to be *k-equivalent* if they have the same output and if, for every input letter, their successors are $(k-1)$-equivalent. For example, for the finite state machine in Fig. 6.13, states A and C are 0-equivalent, and states G and H are 1-equivalent. It follows immediately from the definition that if two states s_i and s_j are k-equivalent, then for any input sequence of length k or less the machine will produce identical output sequences no matter whether it is in state s_i or s_j. Clearly, two states are equivalent if they are k-equivalent for all k.

State	Input		Output
	0	1	
A	B	F	0
B	A	A	0
C	G	F	0
D	H	B	0
E	A	G	0
F	H	C	1
G	A	D	1
H	A	C	1

Fig. 6.13

Observing that if s_i and s_j are k-equivalent, and if s_i and s_h are k-equivalent, then s_j and s_h are also k-equivalent, we can define an *equivalence relation* on the set of all states such that two states are related if they are k-equivalent. Consequently, this relation induces a partition on the set of all states. We shall denote this partition π_k. For example, for the finite state machine in Fig. 6.13, we note that

$$\pi_0 = \{\overline{ABCDE}\ \overline{FGH}\}$$
$$\pi_1 = \{\overline{ABE}\ \overline{CD}\ \overline{F}\ \overline{GH}\}$$
$$\pi_2 = \{\overline{AB}\ \overline{CD}\ \overline{E}\ \overline{F}\ \overline{GH}\}$$

We shall show how to compute these partitions in the following theorem.

Theorem 6.1 Two states are in the same block in π_k if and only if they are in the same block in π_{k-1} and, for any input letter, their successors are in the same block in π_{k-1}.

Proof: Let s_i and s_j denote two states that are k-equivalent. According to the definition, they have the same output and, for any input letter, their successors are $(k-1)$-equivalent. Note that according to the definition, s_i and s_j are also $(k-1)$-equivalent. Thus, we conclude that two states are k-equivalent if and only if they are $(k-1)$-equivalent and, for any input letter, their successors are also $(k-1)$-equivalent. Thus, the theorem follows immediately. ∎

Theorem 6.1 immediately suggests a procedure for computing the partitions $\pi_0, \pi_1, \pi_2, \ldots, \pi_k$ successively. For example, for the finite state machine in Fig. 6.13, we note first that

$$\pi_0 = \{\overline{ABCDE}\ \overline{FGH}\}$$

because A, B, C, D, and E have the same output and F, G, and H have the same output. We observe that A and B are in the same block in π_0 and, moreover, for input 0 their successors are B and A, which are in the same block in π_0, and for input 1 their successors are both F, which, trivially, are in the same block of π_0. Thus, we can conclude that A and B will be in the same block in π_1. Similarly, because A and E are in the same block in π_0, and for input 0 their successors A and B are in the same block in π_0, and for input 1 their successors F and G are in the same block in π_0, we know that A and E will be in the same block in π_1. On the other hand, although A and C are in the same block in π_0, their successors B and G for input 0 are not in the same block in π_0, meaning that A and C will not be in the same block in π_1. We obtain

$$\pi_1 = \{\overline{ABE}\ \overline{CD}\ \overline{F}\ \overline{GH}\}$$

In a similar fashion, we obtain

$$\pi_2 = \{\overline{AB}\ \overline{CD}\ \overline{E}\ \overline{F}\ \overline{GH}\}$$

$$\pi_3 = \{\overline{AB}\ \overline{CD}\ \overline{E}\ \overline{F}\ \overline{GH}\}$$

We observe the following:

1. If π_k is equal to π_{k-1} then π_m is equal to π_{k-1} for all $m \geq k$ (because π_{k+1} is constructed from π_k in exactly the same way as π_k is constructed from π_{k-1}).

2. π_k is a refinement of π_{k-1} (because two states cannot possibly be k-equivalent unless they are $(k-1)$-equivalent).

Observation 1 enables us to terminate the construction procedure whenever we reach a point such that two successive partitions are identical. In that case, all the states that are k-equivalent are equivalent. Furthermore, observation 2 assures us that our construction procedure will not go beyond π_{n-2}, where n is the number of states in the machine, since π_0 has at least two blocks and π_{n-2} will have n blocks if the construction procedure was not terminated earlier. For the example in Fig. 6.13, since π_2 is equal to π_3, we can conclude that states A and B are equivalent, states C and D are equivalent, and states G and H are equivalent.

For a given finite state machine, we can employ the procedure presented above to determine the equivalent states and, consequently, to obtain an equivalent machine that might have fewer states. Finally, we note that once we know how to determine equivalent states in a machine, we are able to determine whether two given machines are equivalent. We refer the reader to Prob. 6.9.

6.11 FINITE STATE MACHINES AS LANGUAGE RECOGNIZERS

In Sec. 6.9 we saw several examples of how we can model physical systems by finite state machines. We see now that finite state machines can also be used naturally as devices to recognize (accept) sentences in a language. Here, the main objective of the machine is to recognize whether a string is a valid string or not, in the given language. In this case, the machine is specified by

(a) A finite set of states $S = \{s_0, s_1, s_2, \ldots\}$.

(b) A finite set of input letters $I = \{i_1, i_2, i_3, \ldots\}$.

(c) A Special element of the set S, s_0, referred to as initial state.

(d) A special set F representing the *final or accepting states*, where $F \subseteq S$.

(e) A function f from $S \times I$ to S, referred to as the transition function.

Let $O = \{0, 1\}$ be the output alphabet of a finite state machine. A state is said to be an *accepting* state if its output is 1. A state is said to be a *rejecting* state if its output is 0. Consequently, an input sequence is said to be *accepted* by the finite state machine if it leads the machine from the initial state to an accepting state final state.

On the other hand, an input sequence is said to be *rejected* by the finite state machine if it leads the machine from the initial state to a rejecting state (non-final state). We have the following examples.

Example 6.10   Figure 6.14 shows a finite state machine that accepts a language L = {automata}. ■

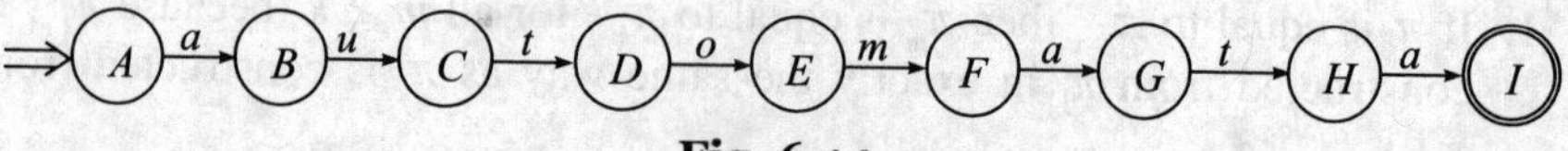

Fig. 6.14

In Fig. 6.14, we can specify all the elements of the above finite state machine as follows:

$S = \{A, B, C, D, E, F, G, H, I\}$

$I = \{a, u, t, o, m\}$

$S_0 = A$ (The initial state)

$F = \{I\}$ (The final or accepting state)

The transition function f is shown in Table 6.1, where an element in a row represents a state of S, and an element in a column represents an input from I. So, $f(A, a) = B$, $f(B, u) = C$, and so on. All blank entries in Table 6.1 are error entries. ■

Table 6.1   Transition function for Fig. 6.14

	a	u	t	o	m
A	B				
B		C			
C			D		
D				E	
E					F
F	G				
G			H		
H	I				
I					

Example 6.11   Figure 6.15 shows a finite state machine that accepts the language.

L = {all binary sequences that end with the digits 011}, i.e.

L = {011, 1011, 0011, 10011, 11011, ...}

In Fig. 6.15, we can specify all the elements of the above finite state machine as follows:

$S = \{A, B, C, D\}$

$I = \{0, 1\}$

$S_0 = A$ (The initial state)

$F = \{D\}$ (The final or accepting state)

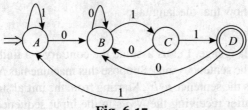

Fig. 6.15

The transition function f is shown in Table 6.2, where an element in a row represents a state of S, and an element in a column represents an input form I. So, $f(A, 0) = B, f(A, 1) = A, f(B, 0) = B, f(B, 1) = C$, and so on. ∎

Table 6.2 Transition function for Fig. 6.15

	0	1
A	B	A
B	B	C
C	B	D
D	B	A

Example 6.12 Figure 6.16 shows a finite state machine that accepts all binary sequences of the form any number of 0s, followed by one or more 1s, followed by one or more 0s, followed by a 1, followed by any number of 0s, followed by a 1, and then followed by anything. ∎

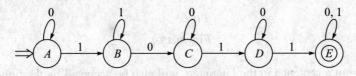

Fig. 6.16

A language is said to be a *finite state language* if there is a finite state machine that accepts exactly all sentences in the language. Thus, according to Example 6.11, the language consisting of all binary sequences that end with 011 is a finite state language. Example 6.12 shows another finite state language. Clearly, any given finite state machine defines a finite state language. On the other hand, a given language might or might not be a finite state language. We now show that there are languages that are not finite state languages.* In Sec. 6.12, we shall show how to construct a finite state machine to accept a given language that is known to be a finite state language.

---

* Once again, we have another example of how to demonstrate that some task (in this case, finding a finite state machine that accepts a given language) is impossible.

Example 6.13   Show that the language

$$L = \{a^k b^k | k \geq 1\}$$

is not a finite state language. Let us assume the contrary—a finite state machine exists that accepts the sentences in L. Suppose this machine has N states. Clearly, the machine accepts the sentence $a^N b^N$. Starting from the initial state, the machine will visit N states after receiving the N a's in the input sequence as depicted in Fig. 6.17a, where s_{j_0} is the initial state and $s_{j_1}, s_{j_2}, \ldots, s_{j_N}$ are the states the machine is in after receiving the sequence a^N. Also, $s_{j_{2N}}$ is the state the machine is in after receiving the sequence $a^N b^N$. Clearly, $s_{j_{2N}}$ is an accepting state. According to the "pigeonhole" principle, among the $N + 1$ states $s_{j_0}, s_{j_1}, s_{j_2}, \ldots, s_{j_N}$, there are two of them that are the same. Suppose the machine visits state s_k twice as shown in Fig. 6.17b, and there are x a's between the first and the second visit to state s_{jk}. Then the sequence

$$a^{N-x} b^N$$

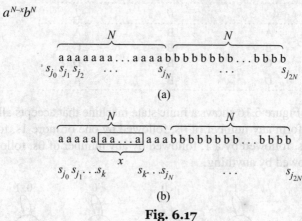

(a)

(b)

Fig. 6.17

which is not a sentence in the language, will also be accepted by the finite state machine. Consequently, we can conclude that language L is not a finite state language. ∎

Example 6.14   Show that the language

$$L = \{a^k | k = i^2, i \geq 1\}$$

is not a finite state language. Again, let us assume that there is a finite state machine that accepts language L. Let N denote the number of states in the machine. Let i be an integer that is sufficiently large such that

$$(i + 1)^2 - i^2 > N$$

Consider the situation depicted in Fig. 6.18. Since between the i^2th a and the $(i + 1)^2$th a, the finite state machine will visit a certain state s_k more than once, removal of the a's between these two visits will yield

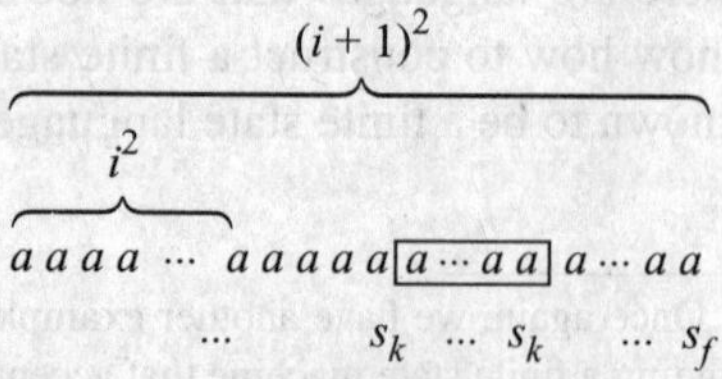

Fig. 6.18

a sequence that will also be accepted by the finite state machine. However, this sequence is not a sentence in the language because it contains more than i^2 but less than $(i + 1)^2$ a's. Thus, we conclude that L is not a finite state language. ∎

These two examples illustrate a general result, which is referred as the *pumping lemma* for finite state languages in the literature.

Theorem 6.2 Let L be a finite state language accepted by a finite state machine with N states. For any sequence α whose length is N or larger in the language, α can be written as uvw such that v is nonempty and uv^iw is also in the language for $i \geq 0$, where v^i denotes the concatenation of i copies of the sequence v. (In other words, uw, uvw, $uvvw$, $uvvvw$, ... are all in the language.)

Proof: Without loss of generality, let the length of α be N. Let $\alpha = a_1a_2a_3 \ldots a_N$. Let $s_{j0}, s_{j1}, s_{j2}, \ldots,$ s_{jN} denote the states the machine visits, where s_{j0} is the initial state and s_{jN} is an accepting state. Again, among the $N + 1$ states $s_{j0}, s_{j1}, s_{j2}, \ldots, s_{jN}$ there are two of them that are the same. Suppose that is state s_k, as shown in Fig. 6.19. If we divide α into three segments as shown in Fig. 6.19, we realize that the sequences uw, uvw, $uvvw$, $uvvvw$, ..., uv^iw, ..., will all lead the machine from the initial state s_{j0} to the accepting state s_{jN}. ∎

$$\overbrace{a_1\,a_2\,a_3 \ldots a_p}^{u} \overbrace{\ldots a_q}^{v} \overbrace{\ldots a_N}^{w}$$

$$s_{j_0}\,s_{j_1}\,s_{j_2}\,s_{j_3} \cdots s_k \cdots s_k \cdots s_{j_N}$$

Fig. 6.19

*6.12 FINITE STATE LANGUAGES AND TYPE-3 LANGUAGES

Somewhat surprisingly, there is a close relationship between finite state languages and type-3 languages. As a matter of fact, we shall show that a finite state language is a type-3 language and a type-3 language is a finite state language.* To this end, we introduce the notion of a *nondeterministic* finite state machine. A nondeterministic finite state machine differs from a deterministic finite state machine defined above in that the transition function for a nondeterministic machine is a function from $S \times I$ to $\mathscr{P}(S)$. Also, because nondeterministic finite state machines are used exclusively as language recognizers, the output letters are usually restricted to 0 and 1. Formally, a nondeterministic finite state machine is specified by the following:

1. A finite set of states $S = \{s_0, s_1, s_2, \ldots\}$.
2. A special element of the set S, s_0, referred to as the *initial state*.

---

* Let us make a small point here: If the initial state of a finite state machine is an accepting state, then according to the definition of acceptance, the *null sequence* (a sequence that contains no symbol) is a sentence in the language accepted by the finite state machine. However, according to our earlier discussion, we ignore the possibility of having the null sequence as a sentence in a type-3 language. We shall be consistent by ignoring the null sequence as a sequence that brings a finite state machine from the initial state to an accepting state when the initial state of the finite state machine is an accepting state.

3. A finite set of input letters $I = \{i_1, i_2, \ldots\}$.
4. A finite set of output letters $O = \{o_1, o_2, \ldots\}$.
5. A function F from $S \times I$ to $\mathscr{P}(S)$, referred to as the *transition function*.
6. A function g from S to O, referred to as the *output function*.

Example 6.15 Design an NFA to accept the set of strings over the alphabet set $\{0,1\}$ and ending with two consecutive zero's.

Solution: Fig. 6.20 shows the NFA which accepts the set of strings over the alphabet set $\{0, 1\}$ and ends with two consecutive zero's. ∎

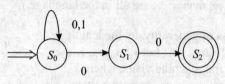

Fig. 6.20

Example 6.16 Degsing an NFA which accepts 1100 only.

Solution: Fig. 6.21 shows the NFA which accepts 1100 only. ∎

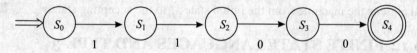

Fig. 6.21

Example 6.17 Construct an NFA which accepts the set of all binary strings containing 1000 1010 as substrings.

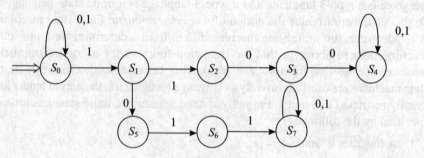

Fig. 6.22

Solution: Fig. 6.22 shows the NFA which accepts the set of all binary strings containing 1000 1010 as substrings. ∎

Example 6.18 Develop an NFA which accepts the set of all binary strings containing the third symbol from the left end as 1 and second symbol from left end as 0.

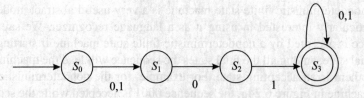

Fig. 6.23

Solution: Figure 6.23 shows the NFA which accepts the set of all binary strings containings the third symbol from the left end as 1 and second symbol from left end as 0. ∎

When a nondeterministic finite state machine is in a certain state and receives a certain input letter, it may have more than one next state. Indeed, the only distinction between a nondeterministic finite state machine and a deterministic one is that in a nondeterministic machine the transition function maps an ordered pair of state and input letter (the state of the machine and the input letter) to a subset of states (all possible next states) instead of to a single state. We can imagine that the machine will enter all these possible next states. (A useful way to visualize this is to imagine that the machine clones several copies of itself, and each copy is in one of the possible next states.) Starting from each next state and upon receiving another input letter, the machine will again enter all possible next states. Figure 6.24a shows a nondeterministic finite state machine, where a transition might have more than one next state. For example, when the machine is in state A and receives an input 1, the machine will enter both states B and C. Figure 6.24b shows the states of the machine corresponding to input sequence 000100001.

	Input		Output
State	0	1	
$\Rightarrow$ A	B	B, C	0
B	A, C	C	0
C	A	B, C	1

(a)

	0	0	0	1	0	0	0	0	1
A	B	A	A	B	A	A	A	A	B
		C	B	C	C	B	B	B	C
							C	C	

(b)

Fig. 6.24

One can point out immediately that a nondeterministic finite state machine is not a good model for any physical system since no physical system can clone itself into several copies for each transition indefinitely. However, we shall see that a nondeterministic finite state machine is a very useful abstract model, and are particularly interested in using it as a language recognizer. We say that a sequence is accepted by a nondeterministic finite state machine if starting from the initial state, among all the final states the sequence will lead the machine into, one of them is an accepting state. For example, for the nondeterministic finite state machine in Figure 6.24a, the sequence 0001 is accepted while the sequence 11100 is not.

One would naturally wonder, as a language recognizer, whether a nondeterministic finite state machine is more powerful than a deterministic finite state machine in the sense that there are languages that can be recognized by a nondeterministic machine but cannot be recognized by a deterministic one. (Because the model of a nondeterministic finite state machine includes the model of a deterministic finite state machine as a special case, a nondeterministic machine is at least as powerful as a deterministic one.) As it turns out, nondeterministic finite state machines are not more powerful than deterministic finite state machines. We show now that for any given nondeterministic finite state machine, there is a deterministic finite state machine that accepts exactly the same language. Let M be a nondeterministic finite state machine with

1. $\{s_0, s_1, s_2, \ldots\}$ being the set of states
2. s_0 being the initial state
3. $\{i_1, i_2, \ldots\}$ being the set of input letters
4. $\{0, 1\}$ being the set of output letters
5. F from $S \times I$ to $\mathcal{P}(S)$ being the transition function
6. g from S to $\{0, 1\}$ being the output function

We construct a corresponding deterministic finite state machine $\hat{M}$ as follows Let

1. $\mathcal{P}(S)$ be the set of states.
2. $\{s_0\}$ be the initial state.
3. $\{i_1, i_2, \ldots\}$ be the set of input letters.
4. $\{0, 1\}$ be the set of output letters.
5. $\hat{F}$ from $\mathcal{P}(S) \times I$ to $\mathcal{P}(S)$ be the transition function such that $\hat{F}(\{\ \}, i_a) = \{\}$ for any input letter i_q, and for any nonempty subset of S, S_p, $\hat{F}(S_p, i_q) = \bigcup_{s_r \in S_p} F(s_r, i_q)$.
6. $\hat{g}$ from $\mathcal{P}(S)$ to $\{0, 1\}$ be the output function such that for any $S_p \subseteq S$, $\hat{g}(S_p)$ is equal to 1 if there exists s_r in S_p such that $g(s_r)$ is equal to 1, and is equal to 0 otherwise.

Figure 6.25 shows an example. For the nondeterministic finite state machine —shown in Fig. 6.25a—the corresponding deterministic finite state *machine* $\hat{M}$ is shown in Fig. 6.25b. (In Fig. 6.25a, we follow a convention in the literature of using a—instead of the empty set symbol.) Once the reader understands the construction, he will be convinced that machines M and $\hat{M}$ accept exactly the same language, since an input sequence accepted by M will bring $\hat{M}$ to a state, which is a subset of states of M, in which there is at least one that is an accepting state in M. Therefore, we shall not include a formal proof here.

	Input		
State	0	1	Output
$\Rightarrow$ A	B	B, C	0
B	A, C	—	0
C	A	B, C	1

(a)

	Input		
State	0	1	Output
$\Rightarrow$ $\{A\}$	$\{B\}$	$\{B, C\}$	0
$\{B\}$	$\{A, C\}$	$\{\ \}$	0
$\{C\}$	$\{A\}$	$\{B, C\}$	1
$\{A, B\}$	$\{A, B, C\}$	$\{B, C\}$	0
$\{A, C\}$	$\{A, B\}$	$\{B, C\}$	1
$\{B, C\}$	$\{A, C\}$	$\{B, C\}$	1
$\{A, B, C\}$	$\{A, B, C\}$	$\{B, C\}$	1
$\{\ \}$	$\{\ \}$	$\{\ \}$	0

(b)

Fig. 6.25

Example 6.19 Convert the NFA given in Fig. 6.26 to a DFA.

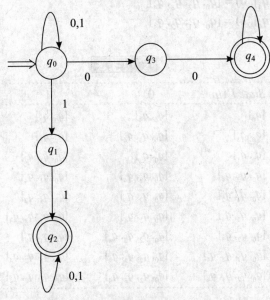

Fig. 6.26

Solution: First, we make the starting state of NFA as the starting state of DFA. Apply 0 and 1 as $1/p$ on state q_0. Now, we keep $1/p$ in 2nd and 3rd columns. Next, we take the new generated states which we place in 3rd and 4th columns. We keep them in first column and again apply 0's and 1's as $1/p$. Repeat the process until no new state is left.

Now,

$F(q_0, 0) = [q_0, q_3]$

$F(q_0, 0) = [q_0, q_1]$

$F([q_0, q_3], 0) = [q_0, q_3, q_4]$

$F([q_0, q_3], 1) = [q_0, q_1]$

$F([q_0, q_1], 0) = [q_0, q_3]$

$F([q_0, q_1], 1) = [q_0, q_1, q_2]$

$F([q_0, q_3, q_4], 0) = [q_0, q_3, q_4]$

$F([q_0, q_3, q_4], 1) = [q_0, q_1, q_4]$

$F([q_0, q_1, q_2], 0) = [q_0, q_2, q_3]$

$F([q_0, q_1, q_2], 1) = [q_0, q_1, q_2]$

$F([q_0, q_2, q_4], 0) = [q_0, q_3, q_4]$

$F([q_0, q_2, q_4], 1) = [q_0, q_1, q_2, q_4]$

$F([q_0, q_2, q_3], 0) = [q_0, q_2, q_3, q_4]$

$F([q_0, q_2, q_3], 1) = [q_0, q_1, q_2]$

$F([q_0, q_1, q_2, q_4], 0) = [q_0, q_2, q_3, q_4]$

$F([q_0, q_1, q_2, q_4], 1) = [q_0, q_1, q_2, q_4]$

$F([q_0, q_2, q_3, q_4], 0) = [q_0, q_2, q_3, q_4]$

$F([q_0, q_2, q_3, q_4], 1) = [q_0, q_1, q_2, q_4]$

Table 6.3

State $1/p$	0	1
q_0	$\{q_0, q_3\}$	$\{q_0, q_1\}$
q_1	ϕ	q_2
ⓠ2	q_2	q_2
q_3	q_4	ϕ
ⓠ4	q_4	q_4

Table 6.4

State / $1/p$	0	1
$[q_0]$	$[q_0, q_3]$	$[q_0, q_1]$
$[q_0, q_3]$	$[q_0, q_3, q_4]$	$[q_0, q_1]$
$[q_0, q_1]$	$[q_0, q_3]$	$[q_0, q_1, q_2]$
$[q_0, q_3, q_4]$	$[q_0, q_3, q_4]$	$[q_0, q_1, q_4]$
$[q_0, q_1, q_2]$	$[q_0, q_2, q_3]$	$[q_0, q_1, q_2]$
$[q_0, q_1, q_4]$	$[q_0, q_3, q_4]$	$[q_0, q_1, q_2, q_4]$
$[q_0, q_2, q_3]$	$[q_0, q_2, q_3, q_4]$	$[q_0, q_1, q_2]$
$[q_0, q_1, q_2, q_4]$	$[q_0, q_2, q_3, q_4]$	$[q_0, q_1, q_2, q_4]$
$[q_0, q_2, q_3, q_4]$	$[q_0, q_2, q_3, q_4]$	$[q_0, q_1, q_2, q_4]$

Now, we construct the corresponding DFA which is shown in Fig 6.27. ■

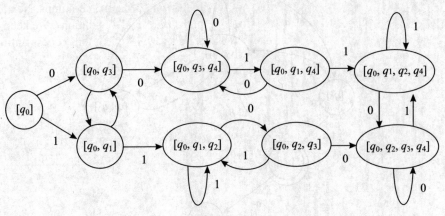

Fig. 6.27

Example 6.20   Convert the NFA given in Fig 6.28 to a DFA.

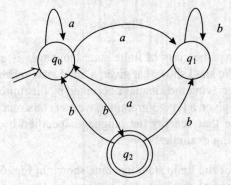

Fig. 6.28

Solution: From Fig. 6.28, it can be observed that

$F(q_0, a) = [q_0, q_1]$

$F(q_0, b) = [q_2]$

$F([q_0, q_1], a) = [q_0, q_1]$

$F([q_0, q_1], b) = [q_1, q_2]$

$F([q_2], a) = \phi$

$F([q_2], b) = [q_0, q_1]$

$F([q_1, q_2], a) = [q_0]$

$F([q_1, q_2], b) = [q_0, q_1]$

Using the similar procedure as followed in the above example, we construct the DFA and show it in Fig. 6.29. ■

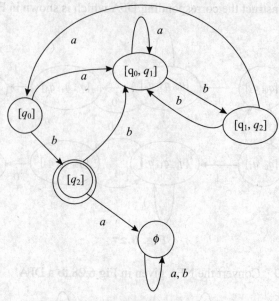

Fig. 6.29

We now show that the class of finite state languages is exactly the class of type-3 languages. We shall show that given a finite state machine, we can have a type-3 grammar specifying the language accepted by the finite state machine. We shall also show that given a type-3 grammar, we can construct a nondeterministic finite state machine that accepts the language specified by the grammar. We consider the following examples.

Example 6.21   For the finite state machine shown in Fig. 6.30*a*, we construct a grammar that specifies the language accepted by the finite state machine as follows.

1. Let $\{0, 1\}$, the set of input letters, be the set of terminals.

2. Let $\{A, B, C, D, E\}$, the set of states, be the set of nonterminals.

3. Let A, the initial state, be the starting symbol.

4. Corresponding to a transition $f(s_p, i_q) = s_k$, there is a production $s_p \to i_q s_k$ if s_k is not an accepting state, and there are two productions $s_p \to i_q s_k$ and $s_p \to i_q$ if s_k is an accepting state. For example, corresponding to the transition $f(A, 0) = B$, we have the production $A \to 0B$, and corresponding to the transition $f(C, 1) = D$, we have the productions $C \to 1D$ and $C \to 1$.

We obtain the grammar shown in Fig. 6.30*b*. Observing that every nonterminal in the grammar represent a set of sequences that bring the finite state machine from the corresponding state to an accepting state, one would agree that the grammar in Fig. 6.30*b* specifies the language accepted by the machine in Fig. 6.30*a*. ∎

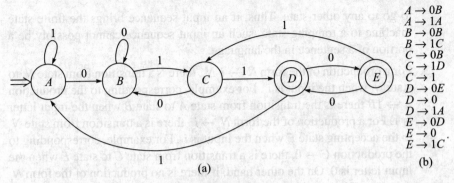

$$A \to 0B$$
$$A \to 1A$$
$$B \to 0B$$
$$B \to 1C$$
$$C \to 0B$$
$$C \to 1D$$
$$C \to 1$$
$$D \to 0E$$
$$D \to 0$$
$$D \to 1A$$
$$E \to 0D$$
$$E \to 0$$
$$E \to 1C$$

(a)   (b)

Fig. 6.30

Example 6.22 For the grammar in Fig. 6.31a, we construct a finite state machine that accepts the sentences in the language specified by the grammar as follows.

1. Let {0, 1}, the set of terminals, be the set of input letters.
2. Let there be a state corresponding to each nonterminal, with the state corresponding to the starting symbol being the starting state (state A in this case). Let there be an additional state E, which is an accepting state. Also, let there be an additional state T, which is called a *trapping* state. Whenever the machine enters a trapping state, it will stay there and will not be able

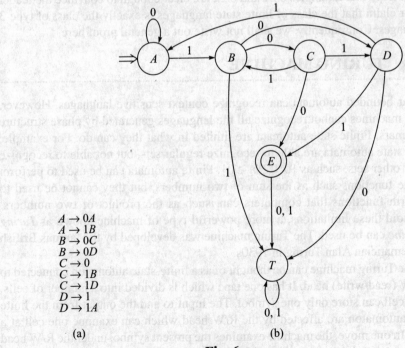

$$A \to 0A$$
$$A \to 1B$$
$$B \to 0C$$
$$B \to 0D$$
$$C \to 0$$
$$C \to 1B$$
$$C \to 1D$$
$$D \to 1$$
$$D \to 1A$$

(a)   (b)

Fig. 6.31

to go to any other state. Thus, if an input sequence brings the finite state machine to a trapping state, such an input sequence cannot possibly be a portion of a sentence in the language.

3. For a production of the form $N_p \rightarrow i_q N_k$, there is a transition from state N_p to state N_k when the input is i_q. For example, corresponding to the production $A \rightarrow 1B$ there is the transition from state A to state B when the input letter is 1. For a production of the form $N_p \rightarrow i_q$, there is a transition from state N_p to the accepting state E when the input is i_q. For example, corresponding to the production $C \rightarrow 0$, there is a transition from state C to state E when the input letter is 0. On the other hand, if there is no production of the form $N_p \rightarrow i_q N_k$ or $N_p \rightarrow i_q$ for state N_p and input i_q, there is a transition from N_p to trapping state T when the input is i_q. For example, there is a transition from state B to state T when the input letter is 1. Finally, for any input letter, there is a transition from accepting state E to trapping state T.

We thus obtain the nondeterministic finite state machine shown in Fig. 6.31*b*. Again, we trust that the construction is clear enough to convince the reader that the nondeterministic finite state machine we constructed accepts exactly the sentences in the language specified by the grammar in Fig. 6.31*a*. Since we have proved earlier that any language that can be accepted by a nondeterministic finite state machine can also be accepted by a deterministic one, the language specified by the grammar in Fig. 6.31*a* is indeed a finite state language. ∎

We hope that Examples 6.21 and 6.22 are clear enough to convince the reader of our claim that the class of finite state languages is exactly the class of type-3 languages. Consequently, we shall not write out a general proof here.

6.13 TURING MACHINE

Linear bounded automata can recognize context sensitive languages. However, these machines cannot recognize all the languages generated by phase structure grammars. Finite state automata are limited in what they can do. For example, finite state automata are able to recognize regular sets, but not able to recognize many other sets, such as $\{0^n 1^n 2^n | n \geq 0\}$. Finite automata can be used to perform simple functions such as the sum of two numbers, but they cannot be used to perform functions that computers can, such as the product of two numbers. To avoid these limitations, a more powerful type of machine known as *Turing machine* can be used. The Turing machine was developed by the famous British mathematician Alan Turing in 1930s.

The Turing machine can be thought of as a finite-state automaton connected to a R/W (read/write) head. It has one tape which is divided into a number of cells. Each cell can store only one symbol. The input to and the output from the finite state automaton are affected by the R/W head which can examine one cell at a time. In one move, the machine examines the present symbol under the R/W head on the tape and the present state of an automaton to determine:

(i) a new symbol to be written on the tape in the cell under the R/W head,

(ii) a motion of the R/W head along the tape: either the head moves one cell left (L), or one cell right (R),

(iii) the next state of the automaton, and

(iv) whether to halt or not.

The above model can be rigorously defined as follows:

Definition A Turing machine M is a 7-tuple, viz. $(Q, \Sigma, \Gamma, \delta, q_0, b, F)$, where the symbols have the following meanings:

Q : the finite nonempty set of states in the finite automaton.

Σ : the nonempty set of input symbols and is a subset of Γ and b does not belong to Σ.

Γ : the complete nonempty set of tape symbols. Σ is always a subset of Γ.

δ : the transition function that maps the states of finite automaton and tape symbols to states, tape symbols and movement of head, i.e. $Q \times \Gamma \perp Q \times \Gamma \times \{L, R\}$, where $\perp$ represents zero, one, or more moves of the Turing machine.

q_0 : the start state, a member of Q, in which the finite automaton is found initially.

b : the blank symbol which is in Γ but not in Σ.

F : the set of final or accepting states, a subset of Q.

Example 6.23 Design a Turing machine to recognize all strings consisting of even number of a's.

Solution: The construction is made by defining moves in the following manner:

(i) q_1 is the initial state. M enters state q_2 on scanning a and writes b.

(ii) If M is in state q_2 and scans a, it enters q_1 and writes b.

(iii) q_1 is the only accepting state.

Present state	Input symbol
q_1	bq_2R
q_2	bq_1R

Fig. 6.32 δ for Example 6.23

So, M accepts a string if it exhausts all input symbols in state q_1. Symbolically, $M = (\{q_1, q_2\}, \{a\}, \{a, b\}, \delta, q_1, b, \{q_1\})$ where δ is given in Fig. 6.32. ∎

Example 6.24 Design a Turing machine M to recognize the language $\{0^n1^n2^n | n \geq 1\}$.

Solution: Before designing the Turing machine M, let us develop a procedure for processing the input string 001122. After processing, we require a form like $bbbbbbq_7$. The processing is done using five steps:

Step 1 : q_1 is the initial state. The R/W head scans the leftmost 0, replaces 0 by b, and moves to the right. M enters q_2.

Step 2 : On scanning the leftmost 1, the R/W head replaces 1 by b and moves to the right. M enters q_3.

Step 3 : On scanning the leftmost 2, the R/W head replaces 2 by b, and moves to the right. M enters q_4.

Step 4 : After scanning the rightmost 2, the R/W head moves to the left until it finds the leftmost 0. As a result, the leftmost 0, 1, 2 are replaced by b.

Step 5 : Steps 1–4 are repeated until all 0's, 1s and 2s are replaced by b.

The change due to the processing of 001122 is given as $q_1 001122 \perp bq_2 01122$ $\perp b0q_2 1122 \perp b0bq_3 122 \perp b0b1q_3 122 \perp b0b1bq_4 2 \perp b0b1q_5 b2 \perp b0bq_5 1b2$ $\perp b0q_5 b1b2 \perp bq_5 0b1b2 \perp q_6 b0b1b2 \perp bq_1 0b1b2 \perp bbq_2 b1b2 \perp bbbq_2 1b2 \perp$ $bbbbq_3 b2 \perp bbbbbq_3 2 \perp bbbbbbq_4 b \perp bbbbbq_7 b.$

Thus, $q_1 001122 \perp q_7 bbbbbb$.

As q_7 is an accepting state, the string 001122 is accepted.

Here, $M = (\{q_1, q_2, q_3, q_4, q_5, q_6, q_7\}, \{0, 1, 2\}, \{0, 1, 2, b\}, \delta, q_1, b, \{q_7\})$, where δ is given in Fig. 6.33.

Present state	Input symbol			
	0	1	2	b
q_1	bRq_2	—	—	bRq_1
q_2	$0Rq_2$	bRq_3	—	bRq_2
q_3	—	$1Rq_3$	bRq_4	bRq_3
q_4	—	—	$2Lq_5$	bLq_7
q_5	$0Lq_6$	$1Lq_5$	—	bLq_5
q_6	$0Lq_6$	—	—	bRq_1
q_7	—	—	—	—

Fig. 6.33 δ for Example 6.24   ■

Problems

6.1 Professor Lai has just returned from a visit to an island where each inhabitant either always tells the truth or always lies. He told us that he heard the following statements made by two of the island's inhabitants A and B:

     A : B always lies.

     B : A always tells the truth.

What can you say about Professor Lai's vacation?

6.2 Let $A = \{a, b, c\}$, $B = (b, c, d)$ and

$$L_1 = \{a^i b^j \mid i \geq 1, j \geq 1\}$$
$$L_2 = \{b^i c^j \mid i \geq j \geq 1\}$$

$$L_3 = \{a^i b^j c^i d^j | i \geq 1, j \geq 1\}$$
$$L_4 = \{(ad)^i a^j d^j | i \geq 2, j \geq 1\}$$

Determine whether each of the following statements is true or false.

(a) L_1 is a language over A.

(b) L_1 is a language over B.

(c) L_2 is a language over $A \cup B$.

(d) L_2 is a language over $A \cap B$.

(e) L_3 is a language over $A. \cup B$.

(f) L_3 is a language over $A \cap B$.

(g) L_4 is a language over $A \oplus B$.

(h) L_1 is a language over $A - B$.

(i) L_1 is a language over $B - A$.

(j) $L_1 \cup L_2$ is a language over A.

(k) $L_1 \cup L_2$ is a language over $A \cup B$.

(l) $L_1 \cup L_2$ is a language over $A \cap B$.

(m) $L_1 \cap L_2$ is a language over B.

(n) $L_1 \cap L_2$ is a language over $A \cup B$.

(o) $L_1 \cap L_2$ is a language over $A \cap B$.

6.3 Let $A = \{a, b, c\}$ and $B = \{c, d\}$. Determine the following sets:

(a) $\{a^i b^j d | i \geq 1, j \geq 0\} \cap A^\star$

(b) $\{a^i b^j d | i \geq 1, j \geq 0\} \cap B^\star$

(c) $\{(cd)^i (bc)^j | i \geq 0, j \geq 0\} \cap A^\star$

(d) $\{(cd)^i (bc)^j | i \geq 0, j \geq 0\} \cap B^\star$

6.4 Obtain simpler expressions for the languages specified in the following:

(a) $\{xab | x \in \{a, b\}^i, i \geq 3\} \cup \{xbb | x \in \{a, b\}^i, i \geq 3\}$

(b) $\{a^i b^j | i, j = 1\} \cap \{a, b\}^\star$

(c) $\{(ab)^i c^i | i \geq 1\} \cap \{(a)^i (bc)^i | i \geq 1\}$

(d) $\{a\}^\star - \{a^i b^j a^i | i = 1, j \geq 0\}$

(e) $\{(ab)^i a (ba)^j | i, j = 1\} - \{a(ba)^i | i \geq 1\}$

(f) $\{a(ba)^i | i \geq 1\} \oplus \{(ab)^i a | i \geq 1\}$

6.5 Determine whether each of the following sentences is in the language generated by grammar specified by the productions in (6.1). If so, provide a step-by-step derivation.

(a) *cat chases the dog*

(b) *the dog meets rapidly*

(c) *the cat meets cat rapidly*

(d) *the cat meets slowly*

(e) *a dog chases rapidly*

(f) *cat runs rapidly*

(g) *a cat slowly chases the dog*

(h) *dog runs the cat*

(i) *dog slowly meets the cat*

(j) *cat runs*

6.6 Determine whether each of the following sentences is in the language generated by the grammar given in Example 6.9. If so, provide a step-by-step derivation.

(a) $B = C * D + A$

(b) $B = C + D * A$

(c) $C = D + (A + B)$

(d) $A = (C * D) + B$

(e) $B = (A + B * (C + D))$

6.7 Consider the language L specified by the grammar (T, N, S, P), where

$T = \{a, b, c\}$ is the set of terminals.

$N = \{S, A, B\}$ is the set of nonterminals.

S is the starting symbol.

$P = \{S \rightarrow AB, A \rightarrow ab, A \rightarrow aAb, B \rightarrow c, B \rightarrow Bc\}$ is the set of productions.

(a) Determine whether each of the following strings is a sentence in the language.

aabb

aaabbc

$$aaabbbccc$$
$$ababcc$$

(b) Describe the language L in set-theoretic notations.

6.8 Consider a grammar in which $N = \{$**signed_integer, sign, integer, digit**$\}$ and $T = \{+,$ $-, 0, 1\}$ with **signed_integer** being the starting symbol. Let the set of productions be

$$\text{signed\_integer} \to \text{sign integer}$$
$$\text{sign} \to +$$
$$\text{sign} \to -$$
$$\text{integer} \to \text{digit integer}$$
$$\text{integer} \to \text{digit}$$
$$\text{digit} \to 0$$
$$\text{digit} \to 1$$

Show a derivation of the string -010 in the language.

6.9 Design a grammar that will specify a language, including such sentences as the following:

Do you understand?

Do I like John?

Does he come?

Does she like Mary?

(We leave the details of the language to the reader's imagination.)

6.10 In the following, let $\{A, B, C, S\}$ be the set of nonterminals, with S being the starting symbol. Let $\{a, b, c\}$ be the set of terminals. Describe the language specified by each set of productions either verbally or in set-theoretic notations.

(a) $\{S \to aA, S \to aS, A \to ab\}$

(b) $\{S \to abS, S \to aA, A \to a\}$

(c) $\{S \to aAB, A \to aB, A \to a, B \to b, B \to c\}$

(d) $\{S \to aSA, S \to aB, A \to b, B \to c\}$

(e) $\{S \to Sa, S \to AB, A \to aA, A \to a, B \to b\}$

(f) $\{S \to aS, S \to b\}$

(g) $\{S \to AB, A \to aA, A \to a, B \to Bb, B \to b\}$

(h) $\{S \to AB, A \to ab, A \to aAb, B \to c, B \to Bc\}$

(i) $\{S \to aS, S \to bA, A \to aA, A \to a\}$

(j) $\{S \to aA, A \to bA, A \to bC, C \to cC, C \to c\}$

(k) $\{S \to aAb, S \to bBa, A \to aAb, A \to c, B \to bBa, B \to c\}$

(l) $\{S \to BA, A \to Aa, A \to a, B \to Bb, B \to c\}$

(m) $\{S \to AB, S \to c, A \to aC, C \to bS, B \to aD, D \to b\}$

(n) $\{S \to AB, A \to aA, A \to b, B \to bB, B \to a\}$

(o) $\{S \to aaA, A \to aa, A \to aaA, A \to B, B \to b, B \to bB\}$

6.11 Give a grammar that specifies each of the following languages:

(a) $L = \{a^{2i}b^{2j} | i \geq 1, j \geq 1\}$

(b) $L = \{(ab)^i c^{2j} | i \geq 1, j \geq 1\}$

(c) $L = \{a^i b^j | i < j, i \geq 1, j \geq 1\}$

(d) $L = \{a^i b^j | i \leq j \leq 2i, i \geq 1\}$

(e) $L = \{a^i b^j c^j | i \geq 1, j \geq 1\}$

(f) $L = \{a^i b^j c^q | i + j = q, i \geq 1, j \geq 1\}$

(g) $L = \{a^{2i} c b^{2j+1} | i \geq 1, j \geq 1\}$

(h) $L = \{a^i b^j c^j d^j e^k | i > 0, j > 0, k > 0\}$

6.12 Give a grammar that specifies each of the following languages:

(a) Every sentence in the language is a string of equal numbers of a's and b's.

(b) Every sentence in the language is a string of a's and b's with the number of a's being a multiple of 3.

6.13 Give a type-2 grammar generating the language L consisting of strings of 0s and 1s, with more 0s than 1s.

6.14 Suppose L_1 and L_2 are type-2 languages.

(a) Prove that $L_1 \cup L_2$ is also a type-2 language.

(b) Prove that $L_1 L_2$ is also a type-2 language where

$$L_1 L_2 = \{\alpha\beta \mid \alpha \in L_1, \beta \in L_2\}$$

6.15 Let $\{A, B, C, S\}$ be the set of nonterminals, with S being the starting symbol. Let $\{a, b\}$ be the set of terminals. For each set of productions in the following, determine the type of the corresponding grammar and the type of the corresponding language.

(a) $\{S \to ABC, A \to a, A \to b, aB \to b, bB \to a, bC \to a, aC \to b\}$

(b) $\{S \to AB, AB \to BA, A \to a, B \to b\}$

(c) $\{S \to AB, S \to BA, A \to a, B \to b\}$

(d) $\{S \to aB, S \to bA, A \to a, B \to b\}$

6.16 For each set of productions in the following, describe either verbally or in set-theoretic notations the language specified.

(a) $\{S \to aSBC, S \to aBC, CB \to BC, aB \to ab, bB \to bb, bC \to bc, cC \to cc\}$

(b) $\{S \to ABC, AB \to aAD, AB \to bAE, DC \to BaC, EC \to BbC, Da \to aD, Db \to bD,$

$Ea \to aE, Eb \to bE, aB \to Ba, bB \to Bb, AB \to aF, AB \to bG, F0 \to 0F, F1 \to 1F, G0 \to 0G, G1 \to 1G, FC \to a, GC \to b\}$

(c) $\{S \to aAB, Aa \to SBa, Ab \to SbB, B \to SA, B \to ba, aB \to b\}$

6.17 (a) Give a type-3 grammar that generates the language

$L = \{x \mid x \in \{a, b\}^\star$ and x does not contain two consecutive a's$\}$

(b) Give a type-2 grammar that generates the language

$L = \{x \mid x \in \{a, b\}^\star$ and x contains twice as many a's as b's$\}$

6.18 Design a finite state machine with $\{0, 1\}$ as its input alphabet and $\{0, 1, 2\}$ as its output alphabet such that for any input sequence the corresponding output sequence will consist of two 2s followed by the input sequence delayed by one time unit. For example, we might have:

Input sequence   10001011001

Output sequence   22100010110

Note that the first output symbol is the output of the initial state that occurs before the first input symbol.

6.19 Design a finite state machine with $\{0, 1\}$ as both its input and output alphabets such that output 1 will be produced beginning with the third 1 in any block of three or more 1s in the input sequence. For example, we might have:

Input sequence   0011110101100111111010

Output sequence   0000011000000000111000

6.20 A three-state finite state machine has $\{0, 1\}$ as its input and output alphabets. Given the following input sequence and its corresponding output sequence, determine the machine.

Input sequence   00010101

Output sequence   011001110

6.21 For the machine shown in Fig. 6P.1, applying the input symbol 0 requires 1 unit of energy and applying the input symbol 1 requires 2 units of energy. Determine a minimum-energy input sequence that takes the machine from state A to state H.

State	Input 0	1
A	B	C
B	E	D
C	B	C
D	E	F
E	E	C
F	H	G
G	E	D
H	G	G

Fig. 6P.1

6.22 A variation of the model of a finite state machine is as follows:

A finite set of states $S = \{s_0, s_1, s_2, \ldots\}$.

A special element of the set S, s_0, referred to as the *initial state*.

A finite set of input letters $I = \{i_1, i_2, \ldots\}$.

A finite set of output letters $O = \{o_1, o_2, \ldots\}$.

A function f from $S \times I$ to S, referred to as the *transition function*.

A function g from $S \times I$ to O, referred to as the *output function*.

Note that in this model output is associated with each state transition instead of with each state, as in the model introduced in Sec. 6.8.

(a) For the machine in Fig. 6P.2 where the state transition and the associated output are separated by a slash (/), determine the output sequence corresponding to the input sequence 110101.

(b) Determine an input sequence that will produce the output sequence 110101.

(c) Show a general procedure for determining an input sequence that will produce a given output sequence.

State	Input 0	1
$\Rightarrow$ A	B/1	C/0
B	B/1	C/0
C	D/1	C/1
D	B/0	D/0

Fig. 6P.2

6.23 For the model of finite state machines in Prob. 6.22, design a finite state machine with $\{0, 1\}$ as its input and output alphabets that produces an output sequence such that the 3rd, 6th, ..., $3k^{th}$ output symbols are the complement of the corresponding input symbols while the other output symbols are identical to the corresponding input symbols.

6.24 Let $\{s_0, s_1, \ldots, s_n\}$ be the set of states of a finite state machine with s_0 being the initial state. Let $A^\star$ be the set of all sequences over the input alphabet A. We define a binary relation R on $A^\star$ such that for α_1 and α_2 in $A^\star$, $(\alpha_1, \alpha_2) \in R$ if and only if both α_1 and α_2 will bring the finite state machine from s_0 to s_i for some s_i. Show that R is an equivalence relation.

6.25 For the finite state machine shown in Fig. 6P.3:

(a) List all 0-equivalent states.

(b) Find all equivalent states and obtain an equivalent finite state machine with the smallest number of states.

State	Input 0	1	Output
$\Rightarrow$ A	F	B	0
B	D	C	0
C	G	B	0
D	E	A	1
E	D	A	0
F	A	G	1
G	C	H	1
H	A	H	1

Fig. 6P.3

6.26 Show that the two finite state machines shown in Fig. 6P.4 are equivalent.

6.27 A partition on the set of states of a finite state machine π is called a *preserved* partition if for any two states s_j and s_k that are in the same block in π then the two states $f(s_j, i)$

State	Input 0	1	Output		State	Input 0	1	Output
$\Rightarrow A$	B	C	0		$\Rightarrow A$	H	C	0
B	B	D	0		B	G	B	0
C	A	E	0		C	A	B	0
D	B	E	0		D	D	C	0
E	F	E	0		E	H	B	0
F	A	D	1		F	D	E	1
G	B	C	1		G	H	C	1
					H	A	E	0

(a) (b)

Fig. 6P.4

and $f(s_k, i)$ are also in the same block in π for every input symbol i. For example, for the finite state machine shown in Fig. 6P.5(a), $\{\overline{AB}\ \overline{CD}\}$ is a preserved partition. Note that both $\{\overline{ABCD}\}$ and $\{\overline{A}\ \overline{B}\ \overline{C}\ \overline{D}\}$ are trivially preserved partitions.

(a) Can you find other preserved partitions on the set of states?

(b) For the finite state machine in Fig. 6P.5(b), find two preserved partitions π_1 and π_2 such that

$$\pi_1 \cdot \pi_2 = \{\overline{A}\ \overline{B}\ \overline{C}\ \overline{D}\ \overline{E}\ \overline{F}\}$$

(c) Show that if π_1 and π_2 are two preserved partitions, so are $\pi_1 \cdot \pi_2$ and $\pi_1 + \pi_2$.

State	Input 0	1		State	Input 0	1
A	B	C		A	F	B
B	A	D		B	B	A
C	D	A		C	C	E
D	C	B		D	E	F
				E	D	C
				F	A	D

(a) (b)

Fig. 6P.5

6.28 For each of the sets described below, find a deterministic finite state machine that recognizes the set:

(a) $L = \{(01)^i 1^{2j} | i \geq 1, j \geq 1\}$

(b) $L = \{0^i 10^j | i \geq 1, j \geq 1\}$

(c) $L = \{0^i 10^j | i \geq 1, j \geq 1\} \cup \{0^k | k \geq 3\}$

(d) $L = \{\text{all binary strings ending with } 001\} \cup \{1\}$

6.29 For each set described below, find a deterministic finite state machine that recognizes the set:

(a) The set of strings of 0s and 1s in each of which there is an even number of 0s

(b) The set of strings of 0s and 1s in each of which the number of 1s is not a multiple of 4

(c) The set of strings of 0s and 1s in each of which the number of 0s is even and the number of 1s is a multiple of 3

(d) The set of strings of 0s, 1s, and 2s in each of which every 1 is immediately followed by at least two 2s and every 0 is immediately preceded by at least two 2s

(e) The set of strings of 0s and 1s each of which is the binary representation of an integer of the form $4k + 3$, for $k \geq 1$

(f) The set of strings of 0s and 1s each of which is the binary representation of an integer of the form $8^k + 1$, for $k \geq 1$

(g) The set of strings of 0s and 1s each of which starts with a 1 and ends with 010

(h) The set of strings of 0s and 1s each of which ends with 01^k, $k \geq 1$

(i) The set of strings of 0s and 1s in each of which every 0 is followed by three or more 1s, with the first symbol being a 0

(j) The set of strings of 0s and 1s in each of which every block of 1s contains three or more 1s and is followed by exactly one 0, with the first three or more symbols being 1s

(k) The set of strings of 0s and 1s none of which contains the substring 010

6.30 Give a description (verbal or in set-theorectic notation) of the set of strings recognized by each of the finite state machines in Fig. 6P.6.

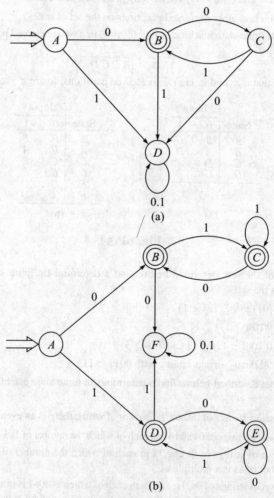

Fig. 6P.6(a,b)

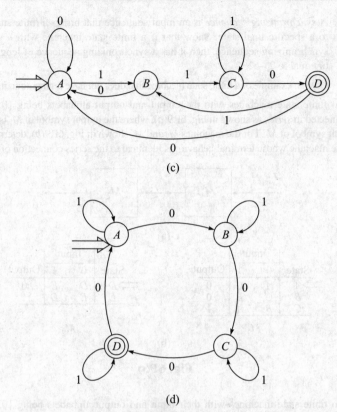

(c)

(d)

Fig. 6P.6(c,d)

6.31 Given a deterministic finite state machine with its initial state unspecified, an input sequence is said to be accepted by the finite state machine if one can choose an initial state so that the input sequence will bring the finite state machine from the chosen initial state to an accepting state.

    (a) Does the finite state machine shown in Fig. 6P.7 accept the input sequence 0110 according to this new definition of acceptance?

    (b) Are all languages accepted by finite state machines using this definition of acceptance regular languages? Prove your claim.

    (c) Repeat parts (a) and (b) if the definition of acceptance is changed to the following: An input sequence is said to be accepted by the finite state machine if, for any arbitrary choice of an initial state, the input sequence will bring the finite state machine from the chosen initial state to an accepting state.

State	Input 0	Input 1	Output
⟹ A	A	C	0
B	C	A	0
C	D	B	0
D	B	D	1

Fig. 6P.7

6.32 (a) The initial state of the finite state machine shown in Fig. 6P.8 is unknown. Design an input sequence that will bring the machine to state *B* regardless of the initial state.

State	Input 0	Input 1
A	B	A
B	A	D
C	C	A
D	B	C

Fig. 6P.8

(b) A *synchronizing sequence* is an input sequence that brings a finite state machine to a specific final state. Show that if a finite state machine with n states has a synchronizing sequence, then it has a synchronizing sequence of length less than or equal to $2^n - 2$.

(c) Give an example of a finite state machine that does not have a synchronizing sequence.

6.33 Two finite state machines with their input and output alphabets being $\{0, 1\}$ can be connected in *series* as shown in Fig. 6P.9(a), where the output symbol of M_1 is used as the input symbol of M_2. For the machines M_1 and M_2 shown in Fig. 6P.9(b), determine a finite state machine whose terminal behavior is identical to the series connection of M_1 and M_2.

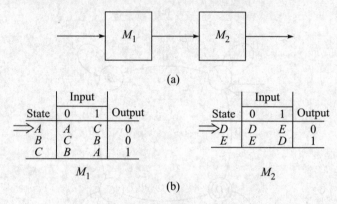

(a)

State	Input 0	Input 1	Output
$\Rightarrow A$	A	C	0
B	C	B	0
C	B	A	1

M_1

State	Input 0	Input 1	Output
$\Rightarrow D$	D	E	0
E	E	D	1

M_2

(b)

Fig. 6P.9

6.34 Two finite state machines with their input and output alphabets being $\{0, 1\}$ can be connected in *parallel* as shown in Fig. 6P.10(a), where each input symbol is sent to both machines simultaneously, and the overall output is the "logical or" of the output symbols from the two machines. For the machines M_1 and M_2 shown in Fig. 6P.10(b),

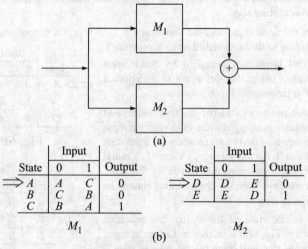

(a)

State	Input 0	Input 1	Output
$\Rightarrow A$	A	C	0
B	C	B	0
C	B	A	1

M_1

State	Input 0	Input 1	Output
$\Rightarrow D$	D	E	0
E	E	D	1

M_2

(b)

Fig. 6P.10

determine a finite state machine whose terminal behavior is identical to the parallel connection of M_1 and M_2.

6.35 Prove that if a finite state machine accepts a "sufficiently long" input sequence, then it accepts an infinite number of input sequences.

Hint: How do you define "sufficiently long" in a precise manner?

6.36 Show that each of the following languages is not a finite state language.

    (a) $L = \{0^i 1^j | i \geq j\}$ (b) $L = \{0^i 1^j | i \leq j\}$

    (c) $L = \{0^k | k = 2^i, i \geq 1\}$ (d) $L = \{1^i 0^j 1^{i+j} | i \geq 1, j \geq 1\}$

6.37 Show that the language

$$L = \{xx | x \text{ is a string of 0s and 1s}\}$$

is not a finite state language.

6.38 Construct a grammar for each of the languages accepted by the finite state machines in Probs. 6.30 and 6.40.

6.39 Convert each of the nondeterministic finite state machines in Fig. 6P.11 into deterministic form:

State	Input 0	Input 1	Output
⇒A	B	A, C	0
B	C	A	1
C	A	–	0

State	Input 0	Input 1	Output
⇒A	B, C	–	0
B	D	B	0
C	A	C	0
D	A	B, C	1

State	Input 0	Input 1	Output
⇒A	A, C	A, B	0
B	E	–	0
C	–	E	0
D	–	–	1
E	–	–	1

    (a)   (b)   (c)

Fig. 6P.11

6.40 Give a description (verbal or in set-theorectic notation) of the set of strings accepted by each nondeterministic finite state machine in Fig. 6P.12. (If a transition brings a state to the empty set, the corresponding edge is omitted.)

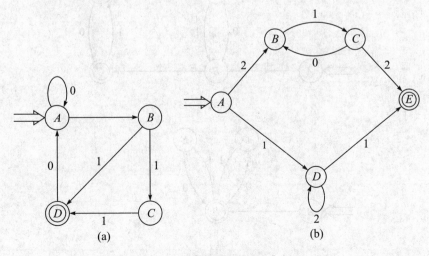

(a)   (b)

Fig. 6P.12

6.41 In this problem, we show that the notion of nondeterministic finite state machines is also very useful in helping us to design deterministic machines.

(a) Design a deterministic finite state machine with $\{0, 1\}$ as its input alphabet that accepts all sequences ending with either 1010 or 001.

(b) What is the set of sequences accepted by the nondeterministic finite state machine in Fig. 6P.13. Convert the nondeterministic machine into a deterministic one.

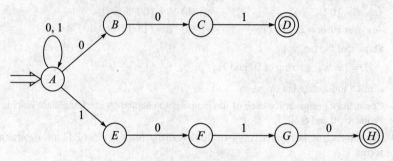

Fig. 6P.13

6.42 A sequence that contains no symbol is referred to as a *null sequence*, which is commonly denoted by λ. The notion of a null sequence can be understood easily by observing that (1) for an input sequence α, the concatenation of λ and α, $\lambda\alpha$, and the concatenation of α and λ, $\alpha\lambda$, will both bring the finite state machine to the same state as α does, and (2) if the initial state of a finite state machine is an accepting state, then λ is among the sequences accepted by the finite state machine.

The model of a finite state machine can be extended by allowing the inclusion of λ arrows, as shown in Fig. 6P.14(a). Note that the finite state machine can go from state B to state C "for free."

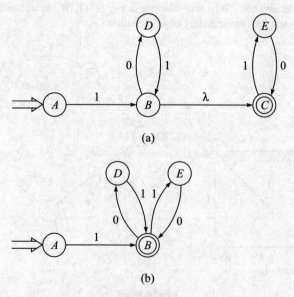

(a)

(b)

Fig. 6P.14

(a) For the finite state machine in Fig. 6P.14(*a*), which of the following sequences are accepted by the finite state machine: 101, 10101, 110, 11010, 10110, 11001? Describe in words the set of sequences accepted by the machine.

(b) The finite state machine in Fig. 6P.14(*b*) is obtained from the machine in Fig. 6P.14(*a*) by coalescing states *B* and *C*. Show that the two machines do not accept the same set of sequences by giving an example of sequences that are accepted by one but not by the other.

(c) How can the machine in Fig. 6P.14(*a*) be transformed into one that accepts the same set of sequences without using λ-arrows? State a general procedure for such transformation.

6.43 Let L_1 and L_2 be finite state languages. Show that $L_1 \cup L_2$ is also a finite state language.

6.44 Let *L* be a language. Let L^R be

$$L^R = \{x^R | x \in L\}$$

where x^R denotes the reversal of the sequence *x*. Show that if *L* is a finite state language, so is L^R.

6.45 Let *L* be a language that is specified by a grammar in which the productions are of the forms $A \to a$ and $A \to Ba$, where *A* and *B* are nonterminals and *a* is a terminal. Show that *L* is a finite state language.

Hint: Use the result in Prob. 6.44.

6.46 Let *L* be a language that is specified by a grammar in which the productions are of the forms $A \to \gamma$ and $A \to \gamma B$ where *A* and *B* are nonterminals and γ is a string of terminals. Show that *L* is a finite state language.

6.47 Find the Turing machine that recognizes the set of bit strings that have a 1 as their second bit, i.e. the regular set $(0 \cup 1) 1(0 \cup 1)^*$.

6.48 Design a Turing machine *M* to recognize the set $\{0^n 1^n | n \geq 1\}$.

6.49 Construct a Turing machine for adding two non negative integers *M* to recognize the language.

6.50 Construct a Turing machine which computes the function $f(n) = n + 2$, where $n \geq 0$.

6.51 Construct a Turing machine which computes the function $f(n) = 0$, for $n = 0, 1, 2$, and $f(n) = n - 3$, for $n = 3$.

6.52 Construct a Turing machine which computes the function $f(n) = n \bmod 4$.

6.53 Construct a Turing machine with tape symbols 0, 1 and *b* that replaces the first 0 with 1 and does not change any of the other symbols on the tape.

6.54 Construct a Turing machine with tape symbols 0, 1 and *b* that replaces all 0s on the tape with 1s and does not change any of the other symbols on the tape.

6.55 Construct a Turing machine that recognizes the set of all bit strings that contain at least two 0s.

6.56 Construct a Turing machine that recognizes the set of all bit strings that contain an odd number of 1s.

Objective
························

*To carry out
the analysis of
algorithms such
as finding the
complexity of
various algorithms.*

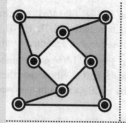

CHAPTER

SEVEN

ANALYSIS OF
ALGORITHMS

7.1 INTRODUCTION

An *algorithm* is a step-by-step specification on how to perform a certain task. Although it sounds a bit technical, a recipe is indeed an algorithm for preparing a meal. Also, the instruction sheet that comes with your new bicycle contains an algorithm for assembling the bicycle. There is an obvious reason for our interest in studying design and analysis of algorithms. To use a computer to perform any task, we must specify the steps it should carry out, that is, the algorithm for performing the task. As a matter of fact, the reader has already seen a number of algorithms. In Sec. 4.9, we presented an algorithm for determining a shortest path between two vertices in a weighted graph. In Sec. 4.12, we presented an algorithm for determining a traveling salesperson's tour in a weighted graph. In Sec. 5.7, we presented three different algorithms for determining a minimum spanning tree of a graph. In Sec. 5.8, we also presented an algorithm for determining a maximum flow in a transport network.

Whether we have designed an algorithm ourselves or are presented with an algorithm designed by someone else, there are several important considerations about the algorithm. First, the algorithm must be correct—it must perform its assigned task correctly. For example, an algorithm for determining a shortest path between two given vertices must indeed produce a path between these two vertices and, furthermore, a shortest path between the two vertices. Secondly, we would like to know how good the result produced by the algorithm is. This question is meaningful whenever the algorithm does not promise to produce the best possible result. In the case of finding a shortest path between two vertices, once the algorithm has been certified to be one that produces a shortest path between the two vertices, then, of course, the result is a best possible one. On the other hand, consider the nearest-neighbor algorithm for the traveling salesperson problem presented in Sec. 4.12. Since the algorithm does not always produce the best possible result, it is extremely desirable to be able to evaluate the worth of its result. We recall that the length of the tour produced by the nearest-neighbor algorithm can be measured against the shortest possible tour, as shown in Theorem 4.7. As another example, we recall the job-scheduling algorithm presented in Sec. 3.9. Again, the algorithm does not always produce a best possible schedule. However, we were guaranteed that the total execution time according to the schedule produced by our algorithm will never exceed two times the shortest possible execution time (Theorem 3.2). Thirdly, we want to determine the "cost" of executing the algorithm. Given that an algorithm indeed produces the desired result, we want to know the cost of obtaining the result. The most commonly used measure of the cost of executing an algorithm is the amount of time it takes. However, there are also other measures, such as the memory space required to execute the algorithm.

To study the various aspects of the design and analysis of computing algorithms is a natural topic for us to pursue at this point. On the other hand, we have already given the reader a glimpse of the subject matter. In particular, as was pointed out above, the reader has already been exposed to some considerations on the correctness and performance of algorithms on several occasions. In this chapter, we shall present some of the concepts in connection with the cost of executing an algorithm, not only as an introduction to the subject of analysis of algorithms but also as evidence that the mathematics we learned will indeed help us attack many problems.

7.2 TIME COMPLEXITY OF ALGORITHMS

As we pointed out above, we would like to determine the cost of executing a given algorithm. Obviously, the time it takes to execute the algorithm is one of the most important measures of the cost of execution. For the rest of this chapter, we shall restrict ourselves to measuring the time it takes to execute an algorithm, which is also referred to as the *time complexity* of the algorithm.

Let us begin with a simple example. Suppose we have n numbers that are stored in n registers $x_1, x_2, \ldots, x_n$. A number stored in a register will be referred to as the content of the register. Without loss of generality, we assume these numbers are distinct. We want to design an algorithm to determine the largest of these n numbers. We can use the following algorithm, which we shall refer to as algorithm **LARGEST1**.

Algorithm **LARGEST1**

1. Initially, place the number in register x_1 in a register called *max*.
2. For $i = 2, 3, \ldots, n$, do the following: Compare the number in register x_i with the number in register *max*. If the number in x_i is larger than the number in *max*, move the number in register x_i to register *max*. Otherwise, do nothing.

3. Finally, the number in register *max* is the largest of the n numbers in registers $x_1, x_2, ..., x_n$.

It is not difficult for the reader to convince herself that the algorithm indeed places the largest of the n numbers that are in registers $x_1, x_2, ..., x_n$ in register *max*. We shall, however, give a formal proof of the correctness of the algorithm.

Proof: We want to prove by induction the following statement: For any i, $2 \leq i \leq n$, after the execution of step 2 the number in *max* is the largest among the numbers in registers $x_1, x_2, ..., x_i$.

1. *Basis.* For $i = 2$, the number in *max* is the larger of x_1 and x_2.
2. *Induction step.* Assume that the statement is true for $i = k$; that is, the number in *max* after execution of step 2 for $i = k$ (but before execution of step 2 for $i = k + 1$) is the largest among the numbers in registers $x_1, x_2, ..., x_k$. The execution of step 2 for $i = k + 1$ compares the number in register x_{k+1} with the largest among the numbers in registers $x_1, x_2, ..., x_k$. Consequently, the larger of these two numbers will be the largest among the numbers in registers $x_1, x_2, ..., x_k, x_{k+1}$.

Thus, we can conclude that algorithm **LARGEST1** indeed places in register *max* the largest of the n numbers that are stored in registers $x_1, x_2, ..., x_n$. ■

As to how much time it takes to execute the algorithm, we note that each of the numbers in registers $x_2, x_3, ..., x_n$ is compared with the number in register *max* once. If we let c denote the time it takes to compare two numbers, the total time for the comparisons is $(n - 1)c$. Of course, if we are extremely meticulous, we should note that depending on the outcome of each comparison, we may or may not need to place a new number in register *max*, which may take a little additional time. However, taking into account such variation will involve a much more complicated analysis, since the number of times we need to place a new number in register *max* depends on the distribution of n numbers in the registers $x_1, x_2, ..., x_n$. Therefore, we assume that the time it takes to place a number in register *max* is either negligible or has been included in quantity c. Consequently, we say that the total time it takes to execute the algorithm is $(n - 1)c$. Since c is a quantity that depends on the particular computer we use, we frequently say that the time it takes to execute the algorithm is proportional to $n - 1$.

We present now another algorithm for determining the largest of n numbers in registers $x_1, x_2, ..., x_n$ which we shall refer to as algorithm **LARGEST2**.

Algorithm **LARGEST2**

1. Do the following for $i = 1, 2, ..., n - 1$: Compare the numbers in registers x_i and x_{i+1}. Place the larger of the two numbers in register x_{i+1} and the smaller in register x_i.
2. Finally, the number in register x_n is the largest of the n numbers.

We present first an illustrative example showing how the algorithm works. Figure 7.1 shows the steps.

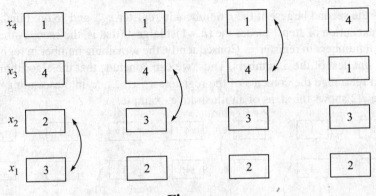

Fig. 7.1

To confirm that the algorithm is indeed correct, we ask the reader to supply a proof by induction that for any i, $1 \leq i \leq n - 1$, after the execution of step 1, the number in register x_{i+1} is the largest among the $i + 1$ numbers in registers x_1, x_2, ..., x_i, x_{i+1}. As to the time complexity of the algorithm, we note that it is also proportional to $n - 1$ since it makes $n - 1$ comparisons of numbers. (Step 1 is executed $n - 1$ times, and one comparison is made each time.)

At this time, we wish to point out a slight difference between the two algorithms. Algorithm **LARGEST1** does not disturb the contents of the n registers and always places the largest number in register *max*. On the other hand, algorithm **LARGEST2** not only places the largest number in register x_n but it also rearranges the contents of the other registers as the illustrative example above shows. One reason for introducing a second algorithm is to show the reader that generally many different algorithms can solve the same problem. In the present case, the two algorithms happen to have the same time complexity. As we shall see later on, different algorithms for solving the same problem might have vastly different time complexities. Also, different algorithms might have different "side effects" even though they produce the same result. In this case, algorithm **LARGEST1** does not rearrange the numbers in registers $x_1, x_2, ..., x_n$, while algorithm **LARGEST2** does.

Let us consider now another example. By sorting the n numbers stored in registers $x_1, x_2, ..., x_n$, we mean to rearrange them so that the rearranged contents of registers $x_1, x_2, ..., x_n$ are in ascending order. A sorting algorithm, known as *bubble sort*, works as follows.

Algorithm BUBBLESORT

1. Do the following for $i = n, n - 1, n - 2, ..., 4, 3, 2$: Use algorithm **LARGEST2** to place in register x_i the largest of the i numbers in registers $x_1, x_2, ..., x_i$.

2. Finally, the numbers in registers $x_1, x_2, ..., x_n$ are in ascending order.

To ascertain that algorithm **BUBBLESORT** indeed sorts the n numbers in registers $x_1, x_2, ..., x_n$, we note that for $i = n$, execution of step 1 places the largest of the n numbers in register x_n; for $i = n - 1$, execution of step 1 places the second largest of the n numbers in register x_{n-1}; and so on. Finally, for $i = 2$, execution of step 1 places the $(n-1)$st largest (that is, the *second* smallest) of the n numbers in register x_2. Consequently, the remaining number in register x_1 is the smallest of the n numbers. Thus, we can conclude that the algorithm does indeed rearrange the contents of the registers $x_1, x_2, \ldots, x_n$ into ascending order. Figure 7.2 shows the steps of an illustrative example.

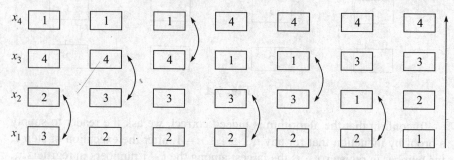

Fig. 7.2

Now let us consider the time complexity of the algorithm. We note that the first execution of step 1 uses $n - 1$ comparisons, the second execution of step 1 uses $n - 2$ comparisons, ..., and the $(n-1)$st execution of step 1 uses one comparison. Thus, the total number of comparisons used is

$$n(n-1) + (n-2) + \ldots + 2 + 1 = \frac{n(n-1)}{2}$$

Consequently, we conclude that the time complexity of the algorithm is proportional to $n(n-1)/2$.

7.3   A SHORTEST-PATH ALGORITHM

We now present another example to illustrate how to analyze an algorithm to determine its time complexity. Let us examine closely the algorithm that finds a shortest path from vertex a to vertex z in a weighted graph presented in Sec. 4.9. We repeat the algorithm here.

Algorithm **SHORTEST**

1. Initially, let $P = \{a\}$ and $T = V - \{a\}$. For every vertex t in T, let $l(t) = w(a, t)$.

2. Select the vertex in T that has the smallest index with respect to P. Let x denote such vertex.

3. If x is the vertex we wish to reach from a, stop. If not, let $P' = P \cup \{x\}$ and $T' = T - \{x\}$. For every vertex t in T', compute its index with respect to P' according to (5.1).

4. Repeat steps 2 and 3 using P' as P and T' as T.

Note that the algorithm begins with $P = \{a\}$, enlarges the set P one vertex at a time, and terminates when set P contains vertex z, Let n denote the number of vertices in the graph. Thus, the maximum number of iterations (the number of times steps 2 and 3 are repeated) the algorithm will go through is $n - 1$. During each iteration, we need to select the vertex in T that has the smallest index and to recompute the indices of the vertices in T'. Specifically, during the first iteration, we need to select a vertex out of $n - 1$ vertices and to recompute the indices of $n - 2$ vertices. During the second iteration, we need to select a vertex out of $n - 2$ vertices and to recompute the indices of $n - 3$ vertices, and so on. However, let us be generous and say that during each iteration we select a vertex out of (no more than) $n - 1$ vertices and recompute the indices of (no more than) $n - 1$ vertices. Note that using an algorithm similar to algorithm **LARGEST1**, we can select the smallest of $n - 1$ numbers in time proportional to $n - 1$. Also note that to compute the index of a vertex according to (4.1) requires a constant amount of time that is independent of the number of vertices in the graph. Thus, the time complexity for recomputing the indices of $n - 1$ vertices is also proportional to $n - 1$. Consequently, the time complexity of the computation carried out in each iteration is proportional to $(n - 1)$.*

Since there will be at most $n - 1$ iterations, we conclude that time complexity of algorithm **SHORTEST** is proportional to $(n - 1)^2$. When n is large, the difference between n and $n - 1$ becomes insignificant. (Do you really care whether you have one billion dollars or one billion and one dollars? Do you really care whether your computer program takes 10,000 seconds or 10,001 seconds to run to completion?) In fact, when n is large, the difference between n^2 and $(n - 1)^2$ also becomes insignificant. Thus, we often say that the time complexity of algorithm **SHORTEST** is proportional to n^2. (We shall discuss this point in greater detail in Sec. 8.3.)

7.4 COMPLEXITY OF PROBLEMS

Let us go back to the simple problem of finding the largest of n numbers that are stored in registers $x_1, x_2, ..., x_n$. In Sec. 7.2, we saw two algorithms that had time complexity proportional to $n - 1$. An immediate question one would raise is: Can we find another algorithm with lower time complexity? Two possibilities exist. Suppose after considerable effort we were not able to come up with an algorithm of lower time complexity. What can we conclude? Are we incompetent, or is there no algorithm with lower time complexity? On the other hand, suppose we discovered an algorithm with lower time complexity. We would naturally ask: Can we still do better than that? Consequently, it will be desirable to determine the *time complexity of a problem*, which is defined to be the time complexity of a "best" possible algorithm for solving the problem. In other words, given the time complexity of the problem, we know that there exists an algorithm which

---

* Of course, the reader should understand that if time complexity is proportional to $n - 1$, it is also proportional to $2(n - 1)$, with the latter being slightly redundant.

solves the problem in such time complexity, and that there is no algorithm with lower time complexity which also solves the problem. In practice, determining the time complexity of a problem is a rather difficult task. In many cases, we are only able to determine an upper bound and a lower bound on the time complexity of the problem. An upper bound on the time complexity of a problem means that a best possible algorithm for solving the problem will have a time complexity less than or equal to the bound. A common way to establish an upper bound of the time complexity of a problem is simply to design an algorithm for solving the problem. Clearly, the time complexity of any algorithm that solves the problem is an upper bound on the time complexity of the problem. On the other hand, to determine a lower bound on the complexity of the problem, we must establish that no algorithm for solving the problem will have complexity lower than that.* On the happy occasion that the upper bound equals the lower bound, we have determined the complexity of the problem. Furthermore, if indeed we have designed an algorithm to establish the upper bound, this algorithm is a best possible algorithm. We present two illustrative examples.

For the problem of determining the largest of n given numbers, we have established an upper bound on the complexity of the problem as $n - 1$ comparison steps by demonstrating an algorithm for solving the problem that uses $n - 1$ comparison steps. We want now to establish that $n - 1$ comparison steps is also a lower bound on the complexity of the problem. In other words, we want to show that it is impossible to design an algorithm to solve the problem that uses fewer than $n - 1$ comparison steps. Suppose that we were given an algorithm that purports to solve our problem using less than $n - 1$ comparison steps. Let us construct a graph with n vertices $v_1, v_2, \ldots, v_n$ corresponding to the n numbers. If the algorithm compares two numbers corresponding to two vertices v_i and v_j, there will be an edge joining vertices v_i and v_j. Consequently, if the algorithm uses less than $n - 1$ comparison steps, the graph will have less than $n - 1$ edges. According to our discussion in Sec. 5.1, the graph must be a disconnected graph. This means that there are two disjoint subsets of numbers among the n numbers such that no number in one subset is compared with any number in the other subset. If that is the case, no matter how the numbers in each subset are compared with one another, the algorithm cannot determine which of the two largest numbers of the two subsets is larger. Thus, the algorithm cannot possibly be a correct algorithm that determines the largest of n numbers.

Let us ask a trivial question on the complexity of the problem of determining the smallest of n numbers. Clearly, using an argument similar to that given above, we can conclude that the complexity of the problem is also proportional to $n - 1$.

We now ask the complexity of the problem of determining both the largest and smallest of n given numbers. First, let us try to establish an upper bound on the complexity of the problem by designing an algorithm to solve the problem. Consider the n numbers stored in registers $x_1, x_2, \ldots, x_n$. We can use

---

* Once again, how do we show that *no* algorithm will do better?

either algorithm **LARGEST1** or **LARGEST2** to determine the largest of the n numbers. Afterwards, use a "similar" algorithm to determine the smallest of the remaining $n - 1$ numbers. Clearly, such an algorithm has time complexity proportional to

$$(n - 1) + (n - 2) = 2n - 3$$

Consequently, $2n - 3$ is an upper bound on the complexity of the problem. As it turns out, there is a more efficient algorithm for this problem. In other words, there is a tighter upper bound on the complexity of the problem. For simplicity of presentation, we assume the n is an even number.* Let x_1, x_2, ..., x_n denote the n registers in which n numbers are stored. Consider the following algorithm.

Algorithm **LARGESMALL**

1. For $i = 1, 2, ..., n/2$, compare the two numbers in registers x_i and $x_{i+(n/2)}$, and place the smaller number in register x_i and the larger in register $x_{i+(n/2)}$.

2. Use algorithm **LARGEST1** to determine the largest of the $n/2$ numbers in registers $x_{(n/2)+1}$, $x_{(n/2)+2}$, ..., x_n. This is the largest of the n given numbers.

3. Use an algorithm similar to **LARGEST1** to determine the smallest of the $n/2$ numbers in registers x_1, x_2, ..., $x_{n/2}$. This is the smallest of the n given numbers.

We need to convince the reader first that the algorithm indeed determines the largest and smallest of the n given numbers. Note that after step 1 the largest of the n numbers is in one of the registers $x_{n/2}$, $x_{(n/2)+1}$, ..., x_n, and the smallest of the n numbers is in one of the registers x_1, x_2, ..., $x_{n/2}$. (A number in register x_i, $1 \leq i \leq n/2$, cannot possibly be the largest of the n numbers because it is smaller than (at least) one of the n numbers. Similarly, a number in register x_i, $n/2 + 1 \leq i \leq n$, cannot possibly be the smallest of the n numbers because it is larger than (at least) one of the n numbers.) Consequently, step 2 indeed determines the largest of the n numbers and step 3 determines the smallest.

As to the time complexity of the algorithm, we note that step 1 requires $n/2$ comparison steps, step 2 requires $(n/2) - 1$ comparison steps, and step 3 requires $(n/2) - 1$ comparison steps. Thus, the total number of comparison steps is $(3n/2) - 2$, which is an improvement over the more obvious algorithm suggested earlier.

We now conclude our discussion (and relieve our ambitious reader the burden of attempting to further improve the result in the preceding paragraph) by showing that $(3n/2) - 2$ is a lower bound on the complexity of the problem. We shall employ what is known as an *adversary argument* which counters the steps of an algorithm with unfavorable outcomes. It will be shown that regardless of the design of the algorithm, the adversary argument will force the algorithm to use at least $(3n/2) - 2$ comparison steps to determine the largest as well as the smallest of n given numbers. Suppose we were presented with an algorithm that solves our problem. Let a_1, a_2, ..., a_n denote the n given numbers. At any moment during

---

* We leave to the reader the case in which n is odd.

execution of the algorithm, we let A denote the set of numbers that so far have not been compared with any other number. We also let B denote the set of numbers that has already been confirmed not to be the largest, and let C denote the set of numbers that has been confirmed not to be the smallest. At the beginning of the execution of the algorithm, $A = \{a_1, a_2, \dots, a_n\}$, $B = \phi$, and $C = \phi$. At the end of execution, $|A| = 0$, $|B| = n - 1$, and $|C| = n - 1$. Note that a number may appear in both B and C. On the other hand, A and B are clearly disjoint, as are A and C. The general idea of the adversary argument is whenever the algorithm compares two numbers, the adversary argument will tell the outcome to the algorithm. The adversary argument selects the outcomes in such a way that the algorithm will be unable to determine the largest and smallest of the n numbers until conclusion of at least $(3n/2) - 2$ comparison steps. In other words, the algorithm will be unable to build up sets B and C such that $|B| = n - 1$ and $|C| = n - 1$ until conclusion of at least $(3n/2) - 2$ comparison steps. Of course, the response of the adversary argument should always be consistent. (That is, if the adversary argument tells the algorithm that $a_i < a_j$ and $a_j < a_k$, then it must respond with $a_i < a_k$ whenever the algorithm asks for the outcome of comparing a_i and a_k.) The adversary argument uses the following rules:

1. If the algorithm compares two numbers a_i and a_j such that a_i is in B but not in C, then $a_i < a_j$. (If both a_i and a_j are in B but not in C, the result is arbitrary as long as it is consistent.)

2. If the algorithm compares two numbers a_i and a_j such that a_i is in C but not in B, then $a_i > a_j$. (If both a_i and a_j are in C but not in B, the result is arbitrary as long as it is consistent.)

3. For any other comparison, the result is arbitrary as long as it is consistent.

We note first that the response of the adversary argument is always consistent. If number a_i is in B but not in C, it means a_i has never been compared with a number that is smaller than a_i. Consequently, rule 1 will never yield inconsistent answers. If number a_i is in C but not in B, it means a_i has never been compared with a number that is larger than a_i. Thus, rule 2 will never yield any inconsistent answer either.

Second, we note that if we compare two numbers in A, both numbers will be deleted from A with the smaller of the two added to B and the larger added to C. Thus, both $|B|$ and $|C|$ will be increased by 1. Any other comparison will at most cause *either* $|B|$ to increase by 1 *or* $|C|$ to increase by 1. Consequently, to increase $|B|$ from 0 to $n - 1$ and to increase $|C|$ from 0 to $n - 1$, the best any algorithm can do is to use $n/2$ comparisons to compare the n numbers that were initially in A and to use $2(n - 1) - n$ more comparisons so that sizes of $|B|$ and $|C|$ will reach $n - 1$ at the end. Thus, the total number of comparisons is at least

$$\frac{n}{2} + [2(n-1) - n] = \frac{3n}{2} - 2$$

We can conclude that $(3n/2) - 2$ is a lower bound on the time complexity of the problem of finding the largest and smallest of n numbers.

7.5   TRACTABLE AND INTRACTABLE PROBLEMS

Once we understand the notion of the time complexity of problems, we can have an intuitive feeling on the notion of computationally difficult or easy problems. When we were first introduced to digital computers, it was immediately impressed upon us that a computer can carry out arithmetic and logical operations at a tremendous speed, namely, millions or more operations per second. Since almost all problems we encounter in digital computation are finite in nature, it seems that there is no reason we cannot solve every problem by brute force. Consequently, there really seems to be no problem we cannot solve at all. Let us return to the traveling salesperson problem we discussed in Sec. 4.12. Since there are altogether $(n-1)!$ possible tours (why?), the following algorithm will certainly solve the problem for us: Compute the cost of each of $(n-1)!$ tours and pick the one with the lowest cost.

Thus, if our problem has 5 cities, we can simply examine all $4! = 24$ tours; if it has 10 cities, we can simply examine all $9! = 362,880$ tours; and if it has 70 cities, we can simply examine all $69!$ tours. The only flaw in this approach is that $n!$ becomes very large even for moderately large n. Take the instance of the problem with 70 cities, and assume that our computer can examine 10^{10} tours per second. Since

$$69! = 1.71122 \times 10^{98}$$

it will take the computer 1.71122×10^{88} seconds, which is approximately 5.42626×10^{78} centuries to examine all tours so that we can select the one with the lowest cost!

Let us examine another problem. Suppose we are given n integers $a_1, a_2, ..., a_n$ and constant K. We want to find a subset of integers $a_{i1}, a_{i2}, ...$ so that their sum is less than or equal to but is as close to K as possible. For example, given the 11 integers

$$4, 7, 8, 10, 12, 17, 25, 29, 31, 36$$

and $K = 63$, we ask the reader to select some of these integers so that their sum is less than or equal to 63 and is as close to 63 as possible. This problem, known as the *knapsack problem*, is motivated by the following situation: We have a knapsack of size K and n item of size $a_1, a_2, ..., a_n$. We want to pack some items into the knapsack so that they will all fit into the knapsack with as little remaining room as possible. There is an obvious algorithm for solving the problem: For each subset of $\{a_1, a_2, ..., a_n\}$, compute the difference between the sum of elements in the subset and K. Clearly, the subset that yields the smallest non-negative difference is the solution. Since the set $\{a_1, a_2, ..., a_n\}$ has 2^n subsets, examining all subsets allows us to select the subset that yields the smallest non-negative difference. It follows that the time complexity of such an algorithm is proportional to 2^n. For $n = 100$, $2^n = 1.26765 \times 10^{30}$. Again, even if we assume that our computer can examine 10^{10} subsets per second, it will still take 4.01969×10^{12} years to complete the computation.

We observe that n, n^2, n^3 and, for a fixed k, n^k grow slowly for increasing n while $n!$, 2^n, and 3^n grow rapidly for increasing n, as shown in Table 7.1. (In Sec. 8.3, we shall discuss the rate of growth of functions in detail.) Thus, we say that an algorithm with time complexity that does not grow faster than n^k is *efficient*, while an algorithm with time complexity that grows faster than n^k is *inefficient*.* Thus, the two algorithms presented here are both examples of inefficient algorithms. Yet, on the other hand, the algorithms presented in Sec. 7.2 for determining the largest of n numbers and the shortest-path algorithm presented in Sec. 7.3 are examples of efficient algorithms.

Table 7.1

	2	5	10	50	60	100
n	2	5	10	50	60	10^2
n^2	4	25	10^2	2.5×10^3	3.6×10^3	10^4
n^3	8	125	10^3	1.25×10^5	2.16×10^5	10^6
n^5	32	3125	10^5	3.12×10^8	7.78×10^8	10^{10}
2^n	4	32	10^3	1.13×10^{15}	1.15×10^{18}	1.27×10^{30}
3^n	9	243	5.9×10^4	7.18×10^{23}	4.24×10^{28}	5.15×10^{47}
$n!$	2	120	3.63×10^6	3.04×10^{64}	8.32×10^{81}	9.33×10^{177}

It follows naturally that a problem is considered *tractable* (computationally easy) if it can be solved by an efficient algorithm and *intractable* (computationally difficult) if there is no efficient algorithm for solving it. To show that a problem is tractable, we only need to demonstrate an efficient algorithm for solving the problem. Thus, we have already demonstrated that the problems of determining the largest of n numbers, sorting n numbers, and finding a shortest path between two given vertices in a graph are all tractable problems. To show that a problem is intractable, we must show that there cannot exist an efficient algorithm for solving the problem (in other words, to show a lower bound on the complexity of the problem that grows faster than n^k). Indeed, there are problems that have been shown to be intractable, but a detailed discussion of this topic is beyond the scope of this book. However, our discussion does bring up one of the most important unsolved problems in theoretical computer science. There is a class of problems, including the traveling salesperson problem and the knapsack problem, for which no efficient algorithm is currently known. Yet, on the other hand, we have not been able to prove that efficient algorithms cannot exist for their solution. In other words, we cannot confirm whether this class of problems is tractable or

---

* n is the size of the instance of the problem to be solved. For example, in the case of finding the largest number among a given set of numbers, n is the number of numbers in the set. In the case of sorting, n is the number of numbers to be sorted. In the case of finding a shortest path in a graph, n is the number of vertices in the graph.

not. What makes this class of problems so important is that it has been shown that these problems are either all tractable or all intractable. That is, if we can find an efficient algorithm to solve any problem in the class, we would then have efficient algorithms for solving all problems in the class. Or if we can prove that any problem in the class is intractable, we prove that all problems in the class are intractable. This class of problems is referred as the *class of N P-complete problems*. (*N P* stands for nondeterministic polynomial).

Problems

7.1 How can an algorithm be analyzed? What is profiling?

7.2 Write a recursive program for Fibonacci number series using recursion. Find out its time complexity.

7.3 Write an efficient algorithm for sorting an array which uses an auxiliary array. What is its time complexity?

7.4 Find an optimal solution to the knapsack instance $n = 7$, $m = 15$, $(p_1, p_2, ..., p_7) = (10, 5, 15, 7, 6, 18, 3)$ and $(w_1, w_2, ..., w_7) = (2, 3, 5, 7, 1, 4, 1)$.

7.5 Find an optimal placement for 13 programs on 3 tapes T_0, T_1 and T_2, where the programs are of length 12, 5, 8, 32, 7, 5, 18, 26, 4, 3, 11, 10 and 6.

7.6 Write the Bellman Ford algorithm to compute shortest paths.

7.7 What is Backtracking? Explain with respect to 8-queens problem.

7.8 What do you mean by N P-complete problems? Explain with 2 examples.

7.9 (a) Design an algorithm to determine whether n colored balls placed in n boxes are of the same color. The basic operation is to compare two balls in any two boxes and find out whether they are of the same color or not. Determine the complexity of your algorithm in terms of the number of basic operations used. Determine also the complexity of the problem.

   (b) Design an algorithm to determine whether n balls are of one or two colors. What is the complexity of your algorithm?

7.10 Given a row of n 0s and 1s, we wish to rearrange them so that the 0s will be grouped at the left and the 1s will be grouped at the right. The basic operation is to compare two *adjacent* digits and exchange their positions, if so desired. Design an algorithm and determine its complexity.

7.11 Design an algorithm to select the largest and second largest of n numbers. The basic operation is to compare two numbers and determine the larger and the smaller of the two. What is the complexity of your algorithm?

7.12 Given a complete m-ary tree of height h with a weight assigned to each edge (for example, the ternary tree in Fig. 7P.1), design an algorithm that finds a path of minimum weight from the root of the tree to any one of the leaves. What is the complexity of your algorithm?

7.13 What is the complexity of the nearest-neighbor algorithm for the traveling salesperson's problem in Sec. 4.12?

7.14 We examine here the problem of sorting n numbers, $x_1, x_2, ..., x_n$. Without loss of generality, we may assume the n numbers are distinct. Consider a class of sorting algorithms in which the basic operation is to compare two numbers and to branch according to the result of the comparison. That is, we may choose to compare any two

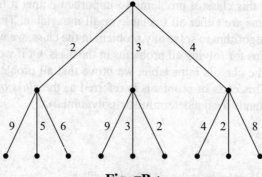

Fig. 7P.1

numbers x_i and x_j. If $x_i > x_j$, then one course of action will be followed. However, if $x_i < x_j$, then another course of action will be followed. Any such algorithm can be conveniently represented by a binary tree, where each internal node corresponds to a comparison operation and each leaf corresponds to a final outcome with the order of the n numbers completely determined.

(a) Figure 7P.2 shows part of a binary tree that describes an algorithm for sorting three numbers. Complete the description of the algorithm. What is the complexity of the algorithm, in terms of the number of comparisons made?

(b) Design an algorithm for sorting four numbers and determine its complexity.

(c) Determine a lower bound on the complexity of any algorithm for sorting n numbers in this class.

7.15 Among n given coins, one of them at most is a bad one. (A bad coin could be either heavier or lighter than a good coin.) There is also a supply of coins that are known to be good. We are given a scale balance that lets us compare the total weights of the coins placed on the two sides of the scale balance. We want to design algorithms that determine whether the coins are all good; and if they are not, we want to identify the bad coin and determine whether it is heavier or lighter than a good one. In particular,

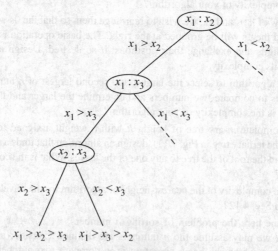

Fig. 7P.2

we will investigate a class of algorithms that allows a three-way branching after each use of the scale balance. That is, depending on whether the total weight of the coins in the left pan of the scale balance is larger than, equal to, or less than the total weight of the coins in the right pan, different courses of action will be followed. The complexity of such algorithms will be measured by the number of times the scale balance is used.

    (a) For $n = 1$, show an algorithm that solves the problem using the scale balance once, and thus conclude (trivially) that, within this class of algorithms, the complexity of the problem is indeed to use the scale balance once.

    (b) For $n = 4$, show an algorithm that solves the problem using the scale balance twice. Note that a convenient way to describe the algorithm would be to use a ternary tree in which every internal node represents one use of the scale balance. Determine a lower bound on the complexity of all algorithms in the class.

    (c) Show that a lower bound on the complexity of all algorithms in the class is to use the scale balance k times, where k is the smallest integer such that $n \leq (3^k - 1)/2$.

    (d) Can you find a nonbranching algorithm for $n = 4$ that also uses the scale balance only twice—that is, an algorithm in which the same comparison of weights will be made for the second use of the scale balance regardless of the outcome of the first use? Can you find a nonbranching algorithm for $n = 13$ that uses the scale balance three times? For $n = (3^k - 1)/2$ that uses the scale balance k times?

    Hint: This part is nontrivial.

7.16 Given the values of $a_0, a_1, a_2, \ldots, a_n$ and x, we want to evaluate the polynomial

$$p(x) = a_n x^n + a_{n-1} x^{n-1} + \ldots + a_1 x + a_0$$

In a most straightforward fashion, we can compute the value of each term $a_i x^i$ and add them together. Since the product $a_i x^i = a_i \cdot x \cdot x \ldots \cdot x$ can be computed in i multiplication operations, we need a total of $n(n-1)/2$ multiplication operations and n addition operations. Can you do better than that?

7.17 Consider the following algorithm that computes the sum of $x_1, x_2, \ldots, x_8$:

                                sum $:= x_1$
For $i = 2$ to 8
                          sum $:=$ sum $+ x_i$

Note that the execution of this algorithm requires seven units of time if we assume that it takes one unit of time to add two numbers. Now, assume that we have a large number of processors that can be used to do addition in parallel. We may employ the following algorithm where all addition operations in each "do in parallel" statement are assumed to be carried out simultaneously on different processors. Consequently, execution of this algorithm requires three units of time.

    1. Do in parallel

$$x_1 := x_1 + x_2$$
$$x_3 := x_3 + x_4$$
$$x_5 := x_5 + x_6$$
$$x_7 := x_7 + x_8$$

    2. Do in parallel

$$x_1 := x_1 + x_3$$
$$x_5 := x_5 + x_7+$$

    3. Sum $:- x_1 + x_5$

We assume a model of parallel computation in which there are infinitely many processors that operate simultaneously. In one unit of time, a processor can access a fixed number of registers, carry out one arithmetic, logical, or comparison operation, and store the results in a fixed number of registers.

(a) Using a model of parallel computation, design an algorithm similar to that presented above for finding the sum of 2^k numbers. What is the time complexity of your algorithm?

(b) Design a parallel algorithm that determines the maximum of 2^k numbers. What is the time complexity of your algorithm?

(c) Design a parallel algorithm that determines the number of positive numbers among 2^k numbers. What is the time complexity of your algorithm?

7.18 A *heap* is an arrangement of numbers at the nodes of a binary tree such that the following conditions are satisfied:
All the leaves are either at the lowest or the next to lowest level.
All the leaves at the lowest level are at the leftmost possible positions.
The number at any internal node is larger than the numbers at its two sons.

For example, the binary tree in Fig. 7P.3(*a*) is a heap, while that in Fig. 7P.3(*b*) is not.

(a) Given a binary tree with *n* numbers such that the first two conditions above are satisfied, design an algorithm to turn it into a heap. What is the complexity of your algorithm?

(b) Suppose we are given a heap with *n* numbers. If we replace the number at the root with the number in the rightmost leaf in the lowest level, we no longer have a heap. (For example, Fig. 7P.3(*c*) is obtained from Fig. 7P.3(*a*) this way.) Design an algorithm to restore the tree into a heap. What is the complexity of your algorithm?

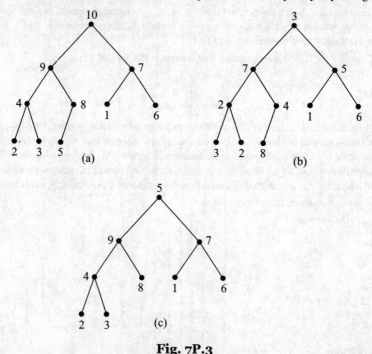

Fig. 7P.3

(c) Given a heap of n numbers, what can you say about the number at the root? The algorithms you designed in parts (a) and (b) can be put together to form a sorting algorithm. How? What is the complexity of your sorting algorithm?

7.19 We study the problem of computing x^n for given x and n, assuming that all intermediate results of computation are available to us.

(a) Given x, can you compute x^{16} in four multiplications?

(b) Given x, in how many multiplications can you compute x^{15}? x^{23}?

(c) For a given integer n, let $b_k b_{k-1} \ldots b_1 b_0$ denote its binary number representaion. For each b_i, we will replace b_i by SX if $b_i = 1$, and replace b_i by S if $b_i = 0$. For example, since the binary number representation for 29 is 11101. we obtain the sequence $SXSXSXSSX$. Removing the leading SX, we obtain the sequence $SXSXSSX$. If we substitute each S by *square*, and each X by *multiply by x*, we obtain a sequence of steps {*square, multiply by x, square, multiply by x, square, square, multiply by x*}, where *square* means to compute the square of the current result, and *multiply by x* means to multiply the current result by x. Show that starting with x as the current result, for $n = 29$, this sequence of steps indeed will compute x^{29}.

(d) Show how one can compute x^{59} using the algorithm presented in part (c)

(e) Prove that the algorithm presented in part (c) is indeed correct.

(f) Given an integer n, an addition chain for n is a sequence of integers

$$a_0 \, a_1 \, a_2 \ldots a_m$$

such that $a_0 = 1$, $a_m = n$, and $a_i = a_j + a_k$ for $k \le j < i$. For example,

1 2 3 5 7 14 28 29

and

1 2 3 6 7 14 28 29

are both addition chains for 29. What is the relationship between addition chains and evaluation of powers of x?

(g) Determine addition chains for 19, 33, 46, 79, and 87. In how many multiplications can you evaluate x^{19}, x^{33}, x^{46}, x^{79}, and x^{87}?

Objective

To describe the concepts of discrete numeric functions and generating functions and some combinatorial problems.

CHAPTER

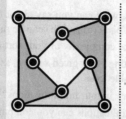

DISCRETE NUMERIC FUNCTIONS AND GENERATING FUNCTIONS

8.1 INTRODUCTION

We recall that a function is a binary relation that assigns to each element in the domain a unique value which is an element in the range. In this and the next chapter, we shall study the class of functions whose domain is the set of natural numbers and whose range is the set of real numbers. We shall refer to these functions as *discrete numeric functions* or, briefly, *numeric functions*. Numeric functions are of particular interest to us because we encounter them very often in digital computation.

We shall use boldface lower case letters to denote numeric functions. For a numeric function **a** we use $a_0, a_1, a_2, ..., a_r, ...$ to denote the values of the function at $0, 1, 2, ..., r, ...$*

Although, in principle, we can specify a numeric function by exhaustively listing its values $(a_0, a_1, a_2, ...)$, in practice we need to use a representation that is not infinitely long. Thus,

$$a_r = 7r^3 + 1 \quad r \geqq 0$$

$$b_r = \begin{cases} 2r & 0 \leq r \leq 11 \\ 3^r - 1 & r > 11 \end{cases}$$

$$c_r = \begin{cases} -4 & r = 3, 5, 7 \\ 0 & \text{otherwise} \end{cases}$$

---

* This is merely a simpler notation than what we introduced in Sec. 3.11 and Sec. 3.16, where we used $a(0), a(1), a(2), ..., a(r), ...$

$$d_r = \begin{cases} 2+r & 0 \le r \le 5 \\ 2-r & r > 5 \quad r \text{ is odd} \\ 2/r & r > 5 \quad r \text{ is even} \end{cases}$$

are examples of concise specification of numeric functions. When there is one simple expression for the value of the numeric function for every r such as a_r above, we shall also use the notation

$$\mathbf{a} = 7r^3 + 1$$

Let us consider the following examples:

Example 8.1 Suppose we deposit $100 in a savings account at an interest rate of 7 percent per year, compounded annually. At the end of the first year, the total amount in the account is $107; at the end of the second year, the total amount in the account is $114.49; at the end of the third year, the total amount in the account is $122.50, and so on. The amount in the account at the end of each year can be described by a numeric function $\mathbf{a}$, which can either be specified as (100, 107, 114.49, 122. 50, …) or as

$$a_r = 100(1.07)^r \qquad r \ge 0$$

or as

$$\mathbf{a} = 100(1.07)^r \qquad \blacksquare$$

Example 8.2 Let a_r denote the altitude of an aircraft, in thousands of feet, at the rth minute. Suppose the aircraft takes off after spending 10 minutes on the ground, climbs up at a uniform speed to a cruising altitude of 30,000 feet in 10 minutes, starts to descend uniformly after 110 minutes of flying time, and lands 10 minutes later. We have

$$a_r = \begin{cases} 0 & 0 \le r \le 10 \\ 3(r-10) & 11 \le r \le 20 \\ 30 & 21 \le r \le 120 \\ 3(130-r) & 121 \le r \le 130 \\ 0 & r \ge 131 \end{cases}$$

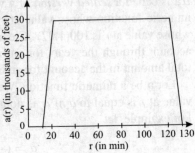

Fig. 8.1

This is represented as a graph as shown in Fig. 8.1

$\blacksquare$

8.2 MANIPULATION OF NUMERIC FUNCTIONS

The *sum* of two numeric functions is a numeric function whose value at r is equal to the sum of the values of the two numeric functions at r. The *product* of two numeric functions is a numeric function whose value at r is equal to the product of the values of the two numeric functions at r. For example, consider the two functions $\mathbf{a}$ and $\mathbf{b}$ where

and
$$a_r = \begin{cases} 0 & 0 \le r \le 2 \\ 2^{-r} + 5 & r \ge 3 \end{cases}$$

$$b_r = \begin{cases} 3 - 2^r & 0 \le r \le 1 \\ r + 2 & r \ge 2 \end{cases}$$

Let **c** be the sum of the two functions **a** and **b**, which we shall denote **a** + **b**. Then
$$c_r = a_r + b_r = \begin{cases} 3 - 2^r & 0 \le r \le 1 \\ 4 & r = 2 \\ 2^{-r} + r + 7 & r \ge 3 \end{cases}$$

Let **d** be the product of the two functions **a** and **b**, which we shall denote **ab**. Then
$$d_r = a_r b_r = \begin{cases} 0 & 0 \le r \le 2 \\ r \cdot 2^{-r} + 2^{-r+1} + 5r + 10 & r \ge 3 \end{cases}$$

For example, if **a** denotes the monthly income of a husband and **b** denotes the monthly income of his wife then **a** + **b** will be their joint monthly income. Let **a** denote the balance in a savings account in each month and **b** denote the monthly interest rate, which fluctuates from month to month. Then **ab** will be the interest earned in each month.

Let **a** be a numeric function and α be a real number. We use α**a** to denote a numeric function whose value at r is equal to α times a_r. The numeric function α**a** is called a *scaled version* of **a** with *scaling factor* α. For example, let **a** be a numeric function whose value at r is $(1.07)^r$. Then 100**a** is a numeric function whose value at r is $100(1.07)^r$. Clearly, if **a** describes the total amount in a savings account through the years for an initial deposit of $1, then 100**a** describes the total amount in the account for an initial deposit of $100.

Let **a** be a numeric function. We use |**a**| to denote a numeric function whose value at r is equal to a_r if a_r is nonnegative, and is equal to $-a_r$ if a_r is negative. For example, let
$$a_r = (-1)^r \left(\frac{2}{r^2} \right) \quad r \ge 0$$
Let **b** be |**a**|, then
$$b_r = \frac{2}{r^2} \quad r \ge 0$$

For example, let **a** be a numeric function where a_r is the difference between the output voltage of the electrical power supply after r hours of operation and a nominal reference voltage. Thus, positive a_r means that the voltage after r hours of operation is above the reference voltage, while negative a_r means that the voltage after r hours of operation is below the reference voltage. Thus, |**a**| gives the deviation of the output voltage from the reference voltage.

Let **a** be a numeric function and i a positive integer. We use $S^i\mathbf{a}$ to denote a numeric function such that its value at r is 0 for $r = 0, 1, 2, \ldots, i - 1$ and is a_{r-i} for $r \geq i$. For example, let

$$a_r = \begin{cases} 1 & 0 \leq r \leq 10 \\ 2 & r \geq 11 \end{cases}$$

Let **b** be $S^5\mathbf{a}$. Then

$$b_r = \begin{cases} 0 & 0 \leq r \leq 4 \\ 1 & 5 \leq r \leq 15 \\ 2 & r \geq 16 \end{cases}$$

As another example, let **a** describe the altitude of an aircraft as given in the foregoing. Then $S^{17}\mathbf{a}$ describes the altitude when takeoff is delayed by 17 minutes.

Let **a** be a numeric function and i a positive integer. We use $S^{-i}\mathbf{a}$ to denote a numeric function such that its value at r is a_{r+i} for $r \geq 0$. For example, let

$$a_r = \begin{cases} 1 & 0 \leq r \leq 10 \\ 2 & r \geq 11 \end{cases}$$

Let **b** be $S^{-7}\mathbf{a}$. Then

$$b_r = \begin{cases} 1 & 0 \leq r \leq 3 \\ 2 & r \geq 4 \end{cases}$$

As another example, let **a** be a numeric function where a_r is the number of applicants whose height is r inches above the minimum height requirement to join the Army. It follows that the numeric function $S^{-2}\mathbf{a}$ describes the numbers of applicants in the height groups if two inches have been added to the minimum height requirement.

The *accumulated sum* of a numeric function **a** is a numeric function whose value at r is equal to $\sum_{i=0}^{r} a_i$. For example, let **a** describe the monthly earnings of an employee. Let **b** be the accumulated sum of **a**. Then **b** gives her accumulated earnings by month. As another example, let

$$a_r = 100(1.07)^r \qquad r \geq 0$$

Let **b** be the accumulated sum of **a**. Then

$$b_r = \sum_{i=0}^{r} a_i = \sum_{i=0}^{r} 100(1.07)^r = \frac{10,000}{7}[(1.07)^{r+1} - 1] \qquad r \geq 0$$

Note that if we deposit \$100 each year in a savings account at an annual compounded interest rate of 7 percent, then b_r is the total amount we have in the account after r years.

The *forward difference* of a numeric function, **a** is a numeric function, denoted $\Delta\mathbf{a}$, whose value at r is equal to $a_{r+1} - a_r$. The *backward difference* of a numeric function **a** is a numeric function, denoted $\nabla\mathbf{a}$, whose value is equal to a_0 at 0 and is equal to $a_r - a_{r-1}$ at $r \geq 1$. Thus, if **a** describes the total business income of a company in each month, $\Delta\mathbf{a}$ will describe the increase of income from the rth month to the $(r + 1)$st month and $\nabla\mathbf{a}$ will describe the increase of income for the rth month over the $(r - 1)$st month. For example, let **a** be a numeric function such that

$$a_r = \begin{cases} 0 & 0 \le r \le 2 \\ 2^{-r} + 5 & r \ge 3 \end{cases}$$

Let **b** denote the forward difference of **a**, Δ**a**; then

$$b_r = \begin{cases} 0 & 0 \le r \le 1 \\ \dfrac{41}{8} & r = 2 \\ -2^{-(r+1)} & r \ge 3 \end{cases}$$

Let **c** denote the backward difference of **a**, ∇**a**; then

$$c_r = \begin{cases} 0 & 0 \le r \le 2 \\ \dfrac{41}{8} & r = 3 \\ -2^{-r} & r \ge 4 \end{cases}$$

We note that $S^{-1}(\nabla \mathbf{a}) = \Delta \mathbf{a}$.

Let **a** and **b** be two numeric functions. The *convolution* of **a** and **b**, denoted **a** * **b**, is a numeric function **c** such that

$$c_r = a_0 b_r + a_1 b_{r-1} + a_2 b_{r-2} + \ldots + a_i b_{r-i} + \ldots + a_{r-1} b_1 + a_r b_0 = \sum_{i=0}^{r} a_i b_{r-i}$$

For example, let **a** and **b** be the two numeric functions such that

$$a_r = 3^r \qquad r \ge 0$$

and

$$b_r = 2^r \qquad r \ge 0$$

Then, for **c** = **a** * **b**

$$c_r = \sum_{i=0}^{r} 3^i 2^{r-i} \qquad r \ge 0$$

Figure 8.2 shows the *C* code to compute the convolution of two numeric functions.

Example 8.3 Consider the problem of determining c_r, the number of sequences of length r that are made up of the letters $\{x, y, z, \alpha, \beta\}$, with the first portion of each sequence made up of English letters and the second portion made up of Greek letters. Since

$$a_r = 3^r$$

is the number of sequences of length r made up of the letters $\{x, y, z\}$ and

$$b_r = 2^r$$

is the number of sequences of length r made up of the letters $\{\alpha, \beta\}$,

$$c_r = \sum_{i=0}^{r} {}' 3^i 2^{r-i}$$

is the answer to our question. ∎

```
/* Program to find the convolution of two numeric functions */
#include<stdio.h>
int afn(int,int);
int bfn(int,int);
int main()
{
        system("clear");

        printf("\n Enter the two numeric functions");
        printf("a=3^r and b=2^r\n \n");
        int r, a, b, i, z = 0, c;
        printf("\n Enter the value of a:");
        scanf("%d",&a);
        printf("\nEnter the value of b:");
        scanf("%d", &b);
        printf("\n Enter the value of r:");
        scanf("%d". &r);
        for(i=0; i<=r; i++)
        {
                        c = afn(a,i) * bfn(b,r-i);
                        z+=c;
        }
        printf("\n\n The convolution of the above numeric functions is  given by
c= %d\n\n",z);
}


int afn(int l, int k)
{
        int i,r=1;
        for(i=0;i<k;i++)
                        r*=l;
        return r;
}


int bfn(int l,int k)
{
        int i,r = 1;
        for(i=0; i<k; i++)
                        r*=l;
        return r;
}
```

Fig. 8.2 C code to compute the convolution of two numeric functions

Example 8.4 Consider again the example of a savings account that receives annually compounded interest at a rate of 7 percent per year. Suppose we deposit $100 in the account at the beginning, $110 at the end of the first year, $120 at the end of the second year, $100(1 + 0.1r)$ at the end of the rth year, and so on. We want to know the total amount in the account at the end of the rth year. Let the numeric function **a** describe the yearly deposit, that is,

$$a_r = 100(1 + 0.1r) \qquad r \geq 0$$

Let **b** be a numeric function such that

$$b_r = (1.07)^r \qquad r \geq 0$$

Note that b_r is the amount in the savings account at the end of the rth year if $1 was deposited into the account at the beginning (or at the end of the 0th year). Thus, if a_i dollars was deposited in the savings account at the end of the ith year, it will become $a_i b_{r-i}$ dollars $r - i$ years later (or at the end of the rth year). It follows that

$$c_r = \sum_{i=0}^{r} a_i b_{r-i}$$

is the total amount in the savings account at the end of the rth year. ∎

Example 8.5 We consider the financial operation of a company. For every $100,000 of orders it receives, the company must borrow $70,000 as working capital for materials, machinery, wages, and so on. In particular, the company will need $30,000 immediately, $20,000 in the next month, and $5,000 in each of the subsequent four months. Thus, the needs for new working capital, in thousands of dollars, can be described by a numeric function **a** such that

$$a_r = \begin{cases} 30 & r = 0 \\ 20 & r = 1 \\ 5 & 2 \le r \le 5 \\ 0 & r \ge 6 \end{cases}$$

For every $1000 the company borrows, it must repay a total of $1100 in 11 installments of $100 each for 11 months starting with the month after the money was borrowed. Let **b** be a numeric function describing the repayment schedule, in thousands of dollars. We have

$$b_r = \begin{cases} 0 & r = 0 \\ 0.1 & r = 1, 2, \dots, 11 \\ 0 & r \ge 12 \end{cases}$$

Suppose the company has total orders of $200,000 in each of the first 10 months and total orders of $300,000 in subsequent months. We want to know the total repayment in the rth month. Let **c** be a numeric function such that

$$c_r = \begin{cases} 2 & 0 \le r \le 9 \\ 3 & r \ge 10 \end{cases}$$

represents the orders received in the rth month, in hundreds of thousands of dollars. We note that **a** * **b** will give the monthly repayment corresponding to a single order of $100,000 at the beginning. We ask the reader to check that **a** * **b** = (0, 3, 5, 5.5, 6, 6.5, 7, 7, 7, 7, 7, 7, 4, 2, 1.5, 1, .5, 0, 0, ...). Consequently, **c** * (**a** * **b**) will give the repayment schedule of all debts in thousands of dollars.* Again, we ask the reader to check that **c** * (**a** * **b**) = (0, 6, 16, 27, ...). ∎

---

* We ask the reader to ascertain that expressing a_r and b_r in thousands of dollars and c_r in hundreds of thousands of dollars will yield the repayment schedule in thousands of dollars.

8.3 ASYMPTOTIC BEHAVIOR OF NUMERIC FUNCTIONS

Let **a** be a numeric function describing the market value of a piece of farm land we purchased. In particular, let a_r be the value of the land after r years. If we purchased the farm land for long-term investment, we would be most interested in how a_r increases or decreases for large r. Let **b** be a numeric function in which b_r is the time it takes for a computer to process the payroll of r employees. To assess the efficiency of the data processing operation, we are mostly interested in knowing the amount of time it takes to process payrolls with large numbers of employees, since when there is only a small number of employees, the total processing time will not be prohibitively long under any circumstance and, consequently, is not a serious concern. Let **c** be a numeric function in which c_r is the time it takes for a certain sorting algorithm to sort r numbers. We are interested in how c_r increases when we want to use the algorithm to sort tens of thousands of names in the preparation of a telephone directory. By the *asymptotic behavior* of a numeric function, we mean how the value of the function varies for large r. For example, for

$$a_r = 5 \qquad r \geq 0$$

the value of the numeric function remains constant for increasing r. For

$$b_r = 5r^2 \qquad r \geq 0$$

the value of the function increases for increasing r and is proportional to r^2, while for

$$c_r = 5 \log r \qquad r \geq 0$$

the value of the function increases for increasing r and is proportional to $\log r$.

Finally, for

$$d_r = \frac{5}{r} \qquad r \geq 0$$

the value of the function decreases for increasing r, is proportional to $1/r$, and approaches 0 as a limit.

In many occasions, we are interested in comparing the asymptotic behavior of two numeric functions. To this end, we introduce the notion of *asymptotic dominance*. Let **a** and **b** be numeric functions. We say that **a** *asymptotically dominates* **b**, or **b** is *asymptotically dominated* by **a**, if there exist positive constants k and m such that*

$$|b_r| \leq ma_r \quad \text{for } r \geq k$$

For example, let **a** and **b** be two numeric functions such that

$$a_r = r + 1 \qquad r \geq 0$$

$$b_r = \frac{1}{r} + 7 \qquad r \geq 0$$

---

† Some authors use the condition $|b_r| \leq m|a_r|$ for $r \geq k$ instead. However, as the reader will see later on, it is meaningful to insist that a_r be positive.

Then **a** asymptotically dominates **b** because, for $k = 7$ and $m = 1$,

$$|b_r| \leq a_r \qquad \text{for } r \geq 7$$

On the other hand, **b** does not dominate **a** asymptotically, since for any choice of k and m, there exists r_0 such that $r_0 \geq k$ and $|a_{r_0}| > mb_{r_0}$. As another example, let **a** and **b** be two numeric functions such that

$$a_r = \frac{1}{100}r^2 - 1000$$

$$b_r = \begin{cases} -1,000,000 & 0 \leq r \leq 10 \\ -100,000r & r > 10 \end{cases}$$

Because for $k = 10^6 + 1$ and $m = 10$,

$$|b_r| \leq 10a_r \qquad \text{for } r \geq 10^6 + 1$$

we can conclude that **a** asymptotically dominates **b**.

Intuitively, that **a** asymptotically dominates **b** means that **a** grows faster than **b**. Thus, for sufficiently large r, the absolute value of b_r does not exceed a fixed proportion of a_r. For example, suppose we deposit \$1 in two separate bank accounts. After r years, our total deposit in account A becomes $1 + 0.2r$ dollars, and our total deposit in account B becomes $(1 + 0.03)^{4r}$ dollars.* Let

$$a_r = 1 + 0.2r \qquad r \geq 0$$
$$b_r = (1 + 0.03)^{4r} \qquad r \geq 0$$

We note that **b** asymptotically dominates **a** since, for $k = 9$ and $m = 1$,

$$|1 + 0.2r| \leq (1 + 0.03)^{4r} \qquad \text{for } r \geq 9$$

That is, the growth rate of our money in account B is higher than that in account A. Although in the first few years the total in account B is less than that in account A, the total in account B exceeds that in account A in the long run.

We leave the proofs of the following statements to the reader:

1. For any numeric function **a**, |**a**| asymptotically dominates **a**.

2. If **b** is asymptotically dominated by **a** then for any constant α, α**b** is also asymptotically dominated by **a**.

3. If **b** is asymptotically dominated by **a** then for any integer i, S^i**b** is asymptotically dominated by S^i**a**.

4. If both **b** and **c** are asymptotically dominated by **a** then for any constants α and β, α**b** + β**c** is also asymptotically dominated by **a**.

5. If **c** is asymptotically dominated by **b** and **b** is asymptotically dominated by **a**, then **c** is asymptotically dominated by **a**.

6. It is possible that **a** asymptotically dominates **b**, and **b** also asymptotically dominates **a**. For example, let

$$a_r = r^2 + r + 1 \qquad r \geq 0$$
$$b_r = 0.05r^2 - r^{1/3} - 9 \qquad r \geq 0$$

---

† That is, account A pays 20 percent simple annual interest (a somewhat outdated banking practice), and account B pays 12 percent annual interest that is compounded quarterly.

7. It is possible that **a** does not asymptotically dominate **b**, nor does **b** asymptotically dominate **a**. For example, let

$$a_r = \begin{cases} 1 & r \text{ is even} \\ 0 & r \text{ is odd} \end{cases}$$

$$b_r = \begin{cases} 0 & r \text{ is even} \\ 1 & r \text{ is odd} \end{cases}$$

8. It is possible that both **a** and **b** asymptotically dominate **c**, while **a** does not asymptotically dominate **b**, nor does **b** asymptotically dominate **a**. For example, let

$$a_r = \begin{cases} 1 & r = 3i \text{ or } 3i + 1 \\ 0 & r = 3i + 2 \end{cases}$$

$$b_r = \begin{cases} 1 & r = 3i \text{ or } 3i + 2 \\ 0 & r = 3i + 1 \end{cases}$$

$$c_r = \begin{cases} 1 & r = 3i \\ 0 & \text{otherwise} \end{cases}$$

For a given discrete numeric function **a**, let $O(\mathbf{a})$ denote the set of *all* numeric functions that are asymptotically dominated by **a**. $O(\mathbf{a})$ is read "order **a**" or "big-oh of **a**." Thus, if **b** is asymptotically dominated by **a** then **b** is in the set $O(\mathbf{a})$. Instead of saying **b** is in the set $O(\mathbf{a})$, we often simply say **b** is $O(\mathbf{a})$. For example, let

$$\mathbf{a} = r^2$$
$$\mathbf{b} = 10r^2 + 25$$
$$\mathbf{c} = 5 - r$$
$$\mathbf{d} = \frac{1}{2}r^2 \log r - r^2$$

We note that **b** is $O(\mathbf{a})$, **c** is $O(\mathbf{a})$, but **d** is not $O(\mathbf{a})$. Also, **a** is $O(\mathbf{d})$, as are **b** and **c**.

When numeric function **a** can be expressed in a simple closed form, such as **a** $= r^2$, we shall also write $O(\mathbf{a})$ as $O(r^2)$. Thus, when we say that a numeric function **b** is $O(r \log r)$, we mean that **b** is asymptotically dominated by the numeric function $\mathbf{a} = r \log r$. We want to remind the reader that **b** is $O(\mathbf{a})$ only means **b** does *not* grow faster than **a**; indeed, **b** could grow much slower than **a**. Thus, a statement such as "**b** grows too fast because **b** is $O(2^r)$" is not meaningful because we only know that **b** does not grow faster than 2^r. It is possible that **b** grows much slower than 2^r.

We note that the relations stated above in terms of asymptotic dominance can also be restated in terms of the "big-oh" notation as follows:

1. For any numeric function **a**, **a** is $O(|\mathbf{a}|)$.
2. If **b** is $O(\mathbf{a})$, then for any constant α, $\alpha\mathbf{b}$ is also $O(\mathbf{a})$.

3. If **b** is $O(\mathbf{a})$ then for any integer i, $S^i\mathbf{b}$ is $O(S^i\mathbf{a})$.

4. If both **b** and **c** are $O(\mathbf{a})$, then for any constants α and β, $\alpha\mathbf{b} + \beta\mathbf{c}$ is also $O(\mathbf{a})$.

5. If **c** is $O(\mathbf{b})$ and **b** is $O(\mathbf{a})$ then **c** is $O(\mathbf{a})$.

6. It is possible that **a** is $O(\mathbf{b})$ and **b** is also $O(\mathbf{a})$.

7. It is possible that **a** is not $O(\mathbf{b})$ and **b** is not $O(\mathbf{a})$.

8. It is possible that **c** is both $O(\mathbf{a})$ and $O(\mathbf{b})$, while **a** is not $O(\mathbf{b})$ and **b** is not $O(\mathbf{a})$.

Consider the following examples:

Example 8.6   Show that for $i \leq j$, αr^i is $O(r^j)$. Note that for $k = 1$ and $m = 1$,

$$|r^i| \leq r^j \qquad \text{for } r \geq 1$$

It follows that r^i is $O(r^j)$. Consequently, αr^j is $O(r^j)$.   ∎

Example 8.7   Let

$$\mathbf{a} = \alpha_0 + \alpha_1 r + \alpha_2 r^2 + \ldots + \alpha_n r^n$$

We want to show that **a** is $O(r^n)$. Note that

$$
\begin{aligned}
|\alpha_0 + \alpha_1 r + \alpha_2 r^2 + \ldots + \alpha_n r^n| &\leq |\alpha_0| + |\alpha_1|r + |\alpha_2|r^2 + \ldots + |\alpha_n|r^n \\
&\leq (|\alpha_0| + |\alpha_1| + |\alpha_2| + \ldots + |\alpha_n|)r^n
\end{aligned}
$$

Since for $k = 1$ and m $|\alpha_0| + |\alpha_1| + |\alpha_2| + \ldots + |\alpha_n|$

$$|\alpha_0 + \alpha_1 r + \alpha_2 r^2 + \ldots + \alpha_n r^n| \leq mr^n \qquad \text{for } r \geq 1$$

a is asymptotically dominated by r^n. Consequently, **a** is $O(r^n)$.

In fact, the result can also be derived more directly. According to Example 8.6, for $i \leq n$, $\alpha_i r^i$ is $O(r^n)$. Using the result in relation 4 above, we can conclude that **a** is $O(r^n)$.   ∎

Example 8.8   We note that $O(1) \subset O(\log r) \subset O(r) \subset O(r^i) \subset O(\alpha^r) \subset O(r!)$. We ask the reader to confirm the results.   ∎

Let **A** and **B** be two sets of numeric functions. We use the following notations to denote sets of numeric functions:

$$\mathbf{A} + \mathbf{B} = \{\mathbf{a} + \mathbf{b} \,|\, \mathbf{a} \in \mathbf{A}, \mathbf{b} \in \mathbf{B}\}$$

$$\alpha\mathbf{A} = \{\alpha\mathbf{a} \,|\, \mathbf{a} \in \mathbf{A}\}$$

$$\mathbf{A} \cdot \mathbf{B} = \{\mathbf{ab} \,|\, \mathbf{a} \in \mathbf{A}, \mathbf{b} \in \mathbf{B}\}$$

We state the following results and leave the proofs to the reader:

1. If **b** is $O(\mathbf{a})$ then $O(\mathbf{b})$ is a subset of $O(\mathbf{a})$. Consequently, if **b** is $O(\mathbf{a})$ and **a** is $O(\mathbf{b})$ then sets $O(\mathbf{a})$ and $O(\mathbf{b})$ are equal.

2. For any **a**, $O(\mathbf{a}) + O(\mathbf{a}) = O(\mathbf{a})$.

3. If $\mathbf{b} \in O(\mathbf{a})$ then $O(\mathbf{a}) + O(\mathbf{b}) = O(\mathbf{a})$.

4. For any constant α, $\alpha O(\mathbf{a}) = O(\alpha\mathbf{a}) = O(\mathbf{a})$.

5. For any **a** and **b**, $O(\mathbf{a})O(\mathbf{b}) = O(\mathbf{ab})$.

Let us consider the following examples:

Example 8.9 Let

$$\mathbf{a} = \frac{1}{3}r^3 + \frac{1}{2}r^2 + r$$

Clearly, $\mathbf{a}$ is $O(r^3)$. Also, $\mathbf{a}$ is in the set of numeric functions

$$\left\{\frac{1}{3}r^3\right\} + O(r^2)*$$

as well as the set of numeric functions

$$\left\{\frac{1}{3}r^3 + \frac{1}{2}r^2\right\} + O(r)$$

In the literature, we frequently write

$$\mathbf{a} = O(r^3) \tag{8.1}$$

$$\mathbf{a} = \frac{1}{3}r^3 + O(r^2) \tag{8.2}$$

$$\mathbf{a} = \frac{1}{3}r^3 + \frac{1}{2}r^2 + O(r) \tag{8.3}$$

or mean[†]

$$\mathbf{a} \in O(r^3)$$

$$\mathbf{a} \in \left\{\frac{1}{3}r^3\right\} + O(r^2)$$

$$\mathbf{a} \in \left\{\frac{1}{3}r^3 + \frac{1}{2}r^2\right\} + O(r)$$

Note that (8.1), (8.2), and (8.3) provide different information on the numeric function $\mathbf{a}$. Because

$$\left\{\frac{1}{3}r^3 + \frac{1}{2}r^2\right\} + O(r) \subset \left\{\frac{1}{3}r^3\right\} + O(r^2) \subset O(r^3)$$

Equation (8.3) is the strongest and (8.1) the weakest of the three relations concerning the behavior of numeric function $\mathbf{a}$. In other words, (8.3) implies (8.2) which, in turn, implies (8.1), but not conversely. ∎

---

* We remind the reader that this denotes the set of numeric functions $\mathbf{A} + \mathbf{B}$, where $\mathbf{A}$ is the set $\left\{\frac{1}{3}r^3\right\}$ and $\mathbf{B}$ is the set $O(r^2)$.

[†] Some authors prefer the interpretation:

$$\{\mathbf{a}\} \subseteq O(r^3)$$

$$\{\mathbf{a}\} \subseteq \left\{\frac{1}{3}r^3\right\} + O(r^2)$$

$$\{\mathbf{a}\} \subseteq \left\{\frac{1}{3}r^3 + \frac{1}{2}r^2\right\} + O(r)$$

Such slight difference in viewpoint is inconsequential.

Example 8.10 Let

$$\mathbf{a} = r + O\left(\frac{1}{r}\right)$$

$$\mathbf{b} = \sqrt{r} + O\left(\frac{1}{\sqrt{r}}\right)$$

We have

$$\mathbf{ab} = \left(r + O\left(\frac{1}{r}\right)\right)\left(\sqrt{r} + O\left(\frac{1}{\sqrt{r}}\right)\right)^{*}$$

$$= r^{3/2} + rO\left(\frac{1}{\sqrt{r}}\right) + \sqrt{r}\,O\left(\frac{1}{r}\right) + O\left(\frac{1}{r}\right)O\left(\frac{1}{\sqrt{r}}\right)$$

$$= r^{3/2} + O(\sqrt{r}) + O\left(\frac{1}{\sqrt{r}}\right) + O\left(\frac{1}{r^{2/3}}\right)$$

$$= r^{3/2} + O(\sqrt{r})$$ ∎

Similar to the "big-oh" notation, we also want to introduce the "big-omega" and "big-theta" notations. For a given numeric function **a**, let $\Omega(\mathbf{a})$ denote the set of all numeric functions **b** such that there exist positive constants k and m with[†]

$$|b_r| \geq ma_r \qquad \text{for } r \geq k$$

In other words, if **b** is in $\Omega(\mathbf{a})$ then **b** grows at least as fast as **a**. For example, let

$$a_r = 2r + 5 \qquad r \geq 0$$
$$b_r = r - 2 \qquad r \geq 0$$
$$c_r = r \log r \qquad r \geq 0$$
$$d_r = r^{3/2} \qquad r \geq 0$$

Both **b** and **c** are in $\Omega(\mathbf{a})$. However, neither **b** nor **c** is in $\Omega(\mathbf{d})$. In the literature, instead of saying **b** is in $\Omega(\mathbf{a})$, we often say **b** is $\Omega(\mathbf{a})$.

For a given numeric function **a**, let $\Theta(\mathbf{a})$ denote the set of all numeric functions **b** such that there exist positive constants m, m', and k with[‡]

$$ma_r \leq |b_r| \leq m'a_r \qquad \text{for } r \geq k$$

In other words, if **b** is in $\Theta(\mathbf{a})$ then **b** grows at the same rate as **a**. Again, instead of saying **b** is in $\Theta(\mathbf{a})$, we often say **b** is $\Theta(\mathbf{a})$. Thus, for example, according to our discussion in Sec. 7.2, the time complexity of the bubble sort algorithm is $\Theta(r^2)$. Consequently, the time complexity of the problem of sorting is $O(r^2)$. On the other hand, the time complexity of the problem of selecting the largest of r numbers, and the time complexity of the problem of selecting the largest and smallest of r numbers are both $\Theta(r)$.

---

* Again, we remind the reader that this denotes the set of numeric functions $\mathbf{A}\cdot\mathbf{B}$, where **A** is the set $r + O(1/r)$ and **B** is the set $\sqrt{r} + O(1/\sqrt{r})$.
† The notation is meaningful only if a_r is positive.
‡ The notation is meaningful only if a_r is positive.

8.4 GENERATING FUNCTIONS

As we pointed out in Sec. 8.1, a numeric function can be specified by an exhaustive listing of its values. In this section, we introduce an alternative way of representing numeric functions.

Suppose we have an iron rod and wish to make a horseshoe out of it. Since hammering a cold iron rod into a horseshoe is quite tedious, we first place the iron rod in a furnace. We can then hammer the hot iron rod into a (hot) horseshoe. When we dip the hot horseshoe in a water tank to cool it, we obtain the (cold) horseshoe we want. The moral of our example is rather obvious: Our goal is to turn a (cold) iron rod into a (cold) horseshoe. However, instead of trying to achieve this goal directly, we change the cold iron rod into a hot iron rod first. Once we make a hot horseshoe out of the hot iron rod, we can cool the hot horseshoe and obtain the cold horseshoe we want. The process is shown in Fig. 8.3a.

Recall that given a positive number x we can compute its logarithm $\ln x$. Indeed, the logarithm of a number can be viewed as an alternative representation of the number, since from x we can compute $\ln x$, and from $\ln x$ we can compute x. Thus, when we want to compute xy, instead of multiplying the two numbers x and y directly, we can represent x as $\ln x$ and y as $\ln y$, compute $\ln x + \ln y$, which is equal to $\ln xy$, and then obtain the product xy from its alternative representation $\ln xy$. Similarly, when we want to compute x/y instead of dividing x by y directly, we can compute $\ln (x/y)$, which is equal to $\ln x - \ln y$, and then obtain x/y from its alternative representation $\ln (x/y)$, The process is depicted in Fig. 8.3b.

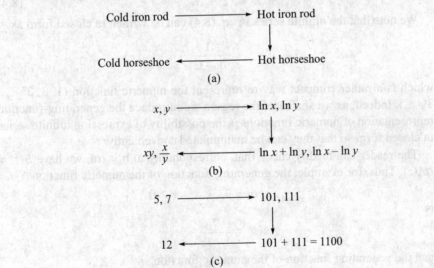

Cold iron rod ⟶ Hot iron rod

Cold horseshoe ⟵ Hot horseshoe

(a)

x, y ⟶ $\ln x, \ln y$

$xy, \dfrac{x}{y}$ ⟵ $\ln x + \ln y, \ln x - \ln y$

(b)

$5, 7$ ⟶ $101, 111$

12 ⟵ $101 + 111 = 1100$

(c)

Fig. 8.3

To a computer science student, the notion of alternative representation is a most familiar one. An alternative representation for a decimal number is its corresponding binary number. Thus, instead of adding, subtracting, multiplying, and dividing decimal numbers directly, we represent them as binary numbers, use a computer to carry out all arithmetic operations on binary numbers (which a computer can do effortlessly), and then obtain the results of our computation by converting the results in binary numbers into decimal numbers. Again, the process is shown in Fig. 8.3c.

These examples illustrate very well the notion of alternative representation for physical as well as mathematical entities. Furthermore, we saw that a *suitably chosen* alternative representation also leads to efficiency and easiness in some operations we wish to carry out.

We introduce now an alternative way to represent numeric functions. For a numeric function $(a_0, a_1, a_2, ..., a_r, ...)$, we define an infinite series

$$a_0 + a_1 z + a_2 z^2 + ... + a_r z^r + ...$$

which is called the *generating function* of the numeric function **a**. Indeed, we can take the viewpoint that we have introduced nothing more than a new notation at this moment. Instead of writing down the values of a numeric function one by one and using commas as "separators" as in $(a_0, a_1, a_2, ..., a_r, ...)$, we choose a formal variable z and use the powers of z as "indicators" in an infinite series such that the coefficient of z^r is the value of the numeric function at r. For a numeric function **a**, we shall use the corresponding upper case letter and write $A(z)$ to denote the generating function of **a**. Clearly, given a numeric function, we can easily obtain its generating function, and conversely. For example, the generating function of the numeric function $(3^0, 3^1, 3^2, ..., 3^r, ...)$ is

$$3^0 + 3z + 3^2 z^2 + 3^3 z^3 + ... + 3^r z^r + ... \tag{8.4}$$

We note that the infinite series in eq. (8.4) can be written in closed form as

$$\frac{1}{1 - 3z}$$

which is a rather compact way to represent the numeric function $(1, 3, 3^2, ..., 3^r, ...)$. Indeed, as we shall see, the reason we introduce the generating-function representation of numeric functions is the possibility of expressing infinite series in closed form so that they can be manipulated conveniently.

The reader can readily check that, corresponding to $\mathbf{b} = \alpha \mathbf{a}$, we have $B(z) = \alpha A(z)$. Thus, for example, the generating function of the numeric function

$$a_r = 7 \cdot 3^r \qquad r \geq 0$$

is

$$A(z) = \frac{7}{1 - 3z}$$

and the generating function of the numeric function

$$a_r = 3^{r+2} \qquad r \geq 0$$

is

$$A(z) = \frac{9}{1 - 3z}$$

It is also obvious that corresponding to $\mathbf{c} = \mathbf{a} + \mathbf{b}$, we have $C(z) = A(z) + B(z)$. Thus, the generating function of the numeric function

$$a_r = 2^r + 3^r \qquad r \geq 0$$

is

$$A(z) = \frac{1}{1 - 2z} + \frac{1}{1 - 3z}$$

Also, corresponding to the generating function

$$A(z) = \frac{2 + 3z - 6z^2}{1 - 2z}$$

which can be written as

$$A(z) = 3z + \frac{2}{1 - 2z}$$

we have

$$a_r = \begin{cases} 2 & r = 0 \\ 7 & r = 1 \\ 2^{r+1} & r \geq 2 \end{cases}$$

Let $\mathbf{a}$ be a numeric function and $A(z)$ its generating function. Let $\mathbf{b}$ be a numeric function such that

$$b_r = \alpha^r a_r$$

for some constant α. Since the generating function of $\mathbf{b}$ is

$$a_0 + \alpha a_1 z + \alpha^2 a_2 z^2 + \ldots + \alpha^r a_r z^r + \ldots$$
$$= a_0 + a_1(\alpha z) + a_2(\alpha z)^2 + \ldots + a_r(\alpha z)^r + \ldots$$

we have $B(z) = A(\alpha z)$. For example, since the generating function of the numeric function

$$a_r = 1 \qquad r \geq 0$$

is

$$A(z) = \frac{1}{1 - z}$$

the generating function of the numeric function

$$a_r = \alpha^r \qquad r \geq 0$$

is

$$A(z) = \frac{1}{1 - \alpha z}$$

As another example, corresponding to the generating function

$$A(z) = \frac{2}{1 - 4z^2}$$

which can be written as

$$A(z) = \frac{1}{1 - 2z} + \frac{1}{1 + 2z}$$

we have

$$a_r = 2^r + (-2)^r \qquad r \geq 0$$

or

$$a_r = \begin{cases} 0 & r \text{ odd} \\ 2^{r+1} & r \text{ even} \end{cases}$$

Unfortunately, for the case $\mathbf{c} = \mathbf{ab}$, there is no simple form in which we can express $C(z)$ in terms of $A(z)$ and $B(z)$.

Let $A(z)$ be the generating function of $\mathbf{a}$. It follows that $z^i A(z)$ is the generating function of $S^i \mathbf{a}$ for any positive integer i. For example, corresponding to

$$A(z) = \frac{z^4}{1 - 2z}$$

we have

$$a_r = \begin{cases} 0 & 0 \leq r \leq 3 \\ 2^{r-4} & r \geq 4 \end{cases}$$

Also, $z^{-i}[A(z) - a_0 - a_1 z - a_2 z^2 - \dots - a_{i-1} z^{i-1}]$ is the generating function of $S^{-i} \mathbf{a}$. Thus, the generating function of

$$a_r = 3^{r+2} \qquad r \geq 0$$

can be computed as

$$A(z) = z^{-2} \left(\frac{1}{1 - 3z} - 1 - 3z \right)$$

$$= z^{-2} \frac{9z^2}{1 - 3z}$$

$$= \frac{9}{1 - 3z}$$

For another example, let

$$a_r = \begin{cases} 0 & 0 \leq r \leq 8 \\ 2 & r = 9 \\ 3 & r = 10 \\ 3 & r = 11 \\ 2 & r = 12 \\ 0 & r = 13 \\ 1 & r = 14 \\ 3 & r = 15 \\ 2 & r = 16 \\ 2 & r = 17 \\ 0 & r \geq 18 \end{cases}$$

represent the hourly productivity of a machinist who comes to work at 8 a.m., where r indicates the hour of the day. Then

$$A(z) = z^9(2 + 3z + 3z^2 + 2z^3 + z^5 + 3z^6 + 2z^7 + 2z^8)$$

Suppose there are three machinists. One comes to work at 6 a.m., another at 8 a.m., and yet another at 9 a.m., and they simply shift their productivity according to their starting time. If we let **b** be a numeric function describing the total hourly productivity, we have

$$B(z) = (z^{-2} + 1 + z)A(z)$$

For **b** = Δ**a**, we have

$$B(z) = \frac{1}{z}[A(z) - a_0] - A(z)$$

and for **b** = ∇**a**, we have

$$B(z) = A(z) - zA(z)$$

The generating function representation of numeric functions is particularly useful in dealing with the convolution of numeric functions. Let **c** = **a** * **b**. Since

$$c_r = a_0 b_r + a_1 b_{r-1} + a_2 b_{r-2} + \ldots + a_{r-1}b_1 + a_r b_0$$

is the coefficient of z^r in the product

$$(a_0 + a_1 z + a_2 z^2 + \ldots + a_r z^r + \ldots)(b_0 + b_1 z + b_2 z^2 + \ldots b_r z^r + \ldots)$$

we conclude that the generating function $C(z)$ is equal to $A(z)B(z)$.

Example 8.11 Let **c** = **a** * **b** where

$$a_r = 3^r \qquad r \geq 0$$

and

$$b_r = 2^r \qquad r \geq 0$$

Since

$$A(z) = \frac{1}{1 - 3z}$$

and

$$B(z) = \frac{1}{1 - 2z}$$

we have

$$C(z) = A(z)B(z) = \frac{1}{1 - 3z}\frac{1}{1 - 2z} = \frac{3}{1 - 3z} - \frac{2}{1 - 2z}$$

or

$$c_r = 3(3)^r - 2(2)^r = 3^{r+1} - 2^{r+1} \qquad \blacksquare$$

Example 8.12 Let **a** be an arbitrary numeric function and **b** be the numeric function (1, 1, 1, ..., 1, ...). Let

$$\mathbf{c} = \mathbf{a} * \mathbf{b}$$

so that

$$c_r = \sum_{i=0}^{r} a_i b_{r-i} = \sum_{i=0}^{r} a_i$$

Thus **c** is the accumulated sum of **a**, and the generating function of **c** is

$$C(z) = \frac{1}{1-z}A(z)$$

For example, by letting $A(z)$ be $1/(1-z)$ we obtain the result that $1/(1-z)^2$ is the generating function of the numeric function $(1, 2, 3, ..., r, ...)$. ■

Example 8.13 We wish to evaluate the sum

$$1^2 + 2^2 + 3^2 + ... + r^2$$

Let us first determine the generating function of the numeric function $(0^2, 1^2, 2^2, 3^2, ..., r^2, ...)$. Differentiating both sides of the identity

$$\frac{1}{1-z} = 1 + z + z^2 + z^3 + z^4 + ... + z^r + ...$$

we obtain

$$\frac{1}{(1-z)^2} = 1 + 2z + 3z^2 + 4z^3 + ... + rz^{r-1} + ...$$

It follows that

$$\frac{d}{dz}\frac{z}{(1-z)^2} = 1^2 + 2^2 \cdot z + 3^2 \cdot z^2 + 4^2 \cdot z^3 + ... \, r^2 \cdot z^{r-1} + ...$$

and that

$$z\frac{d}{dz}\frac{z}{(1-z)^2} = 0^2 + 1^2 \cdot z + 2^2 \cdot z^2 + 3^2 \cdot z^3 + 4^2 \cdot z^4 + ... + r^2 \cdot z^r + ...$$

Thus, $z(d/dz)[z/(1-z)^2]$, which is equal to $[z(1+z)]/(1-z)^3$, is the generating function of the numeric function $(0^2, 1^2, 2^2, 3^2, ..., r^2, ...)$. Multiplying both the sides of the above resulting expression by $1/1-z$ and then replacing the term $1/1-z$ in the right hand side of the expression with the expression $(1 + z + z^2 + z^3 + ... + z^r + ...)$, we get

$$z(1+z)/(1-z)^4 = (0^2 + 1^2 \cdot z + 2^2 \cdot z^2 + 3^2 \cdot z^3 + ... + r^2 \cdot z^r + ...) \cdot (1 + z + z^2 + z^3 + ... + z^r + ...)$$

$$\Rightarrow z(1+z)/(1-z)^4 = 0^2 + (0^2 + 1^2)z + (0^2 + 1^2 + 2^2)z^2 + ... + (0^2 + 1^2 + 2^2 + ... + r^2)z^r + ...$$

It follows that $[z(1+z)]/(1-z)^4$ is the generating function of the numeric function $(0^2, 0^2 + 1^2, 0^2 + 1^2 + 2^2, 0^2 + 1^2 + 2^2 + 3^2, ..., 0^2 + 1^2 + 2^2 + 3^2 + ... + r^2, ...)$. According to the binomial theorem,* the coefficient of z^r in $1/(1-z)^4$ is

---

* The binomial theorem is

$$(1+z)^n = 1 + \sum_{r=1}^{} \frac{n(n-1)(n-2)...(n-r+1)}{r!}z^r$$

where the upper limit of the summation is n if n is a positive integer, and is ∞ otherwise.

$$\frac{(-4)(-4-1)(-4-2)\ldots(-4-r+1)}{r!}(-1)^r = \frac{4\times5\times6\times\ldots\times(r+3)}{r!}$$

$$= \frac{(r+1)(r+2)(r+3)}{1\cdot2\cdot3}$$

Therefore, the coefficient of z^r in the expansion of $[z(1+z)]/(1-z)^4$ is

$$\frac{r(r+1)(r+2)}{1\cdot2\cdot3} + \frac{(r-1)r(r+1)}{1\cdot2\cdot3} = \frac{r(r+1)(2r+1)}{6}$$

that is,

$$1^2 + 2^2 + 3^2 + \ldots + r^2 = \frac{r(r+1)(2r+1)}{6} \qquad \blacksquare$$

*8.5 COMBINATORIAL PROBLEMS

The generating-function representation of numeric functions is most useful in solving combinatorial problems. We shall present in this section some illustrative examples. Consider the numeric function **a** such that

$$a_r = C(n, r)$$

for a fixed n.* The generating function of **a** is

$$A(z) = C(n, 0) + C(n, 1)z + C(n, 2)z^2 + \ldots + C(n, r)z^r + \ldots C(n, n)z^n$$

Let us consider a roundabout way to select r objects from n objects. We can first divide the n objects into two piles, one with k objects and the other with $n - k$ objects, for some fixed k less than n. We can then select i objects from the first pile, where there are $C(k, i)$ ways, and $r - i$ objects from the second pile, where there are $C(n - k, r - i)$ ways, for $i = 0, 1, 2, \ldots, r$. Thus, we have the equation

$$C(n, r) = \sum_{i=0}^{r} C(k, i)C(n - k, r - i)$$

It follows that we can write $\mathbf{a} = \mathbf{d} * \mathbf{e}$ where

$$D(z) = C(k, 0) + C(k, 1)z + C(k, 2)z^2 + \ldots + C(k, k)z^k$$

and

$$E(z) = C(n - k, 0) + C(n - k, 1)z + C(n - k, 2)z^2 + \ldots + C(n - k, n - k)z^{n-k}$$

Repeating the argument a sufficient number of times, we obtain

$$A(z) = (1 + z)^n \qquad (8.5)$$

because the generating function of the numeric function $(C(1, 0), C(1, 1), 0, 0, \ldots)$ is $1 + z$. Let us also point out a very simple combinatorial argument that can also be used to derive eq. (8.5). Consider the coefficient of the term z^r in the expansion of $(1 + z)^n$. In computing the product of the n factors $1 + z$, each factor

---

* We recall that $C(n, r) = 1$ for $r = 0$ and $C(n, r) = 0$ for $r > n$.

will "contribute" either a 1 or a z. In particular, to make up the term z^r, r of the factors contribute a z each and $n - r$ of the factors contribute a 1 each. Consequently, the coefficient of z^r is the number of ways of selecting r of the n 1 + z factors to make up the term z^r, which, of course, is equal to $C(n, r)$. We show now some results that can be derived directly from eq. (8.5).

Example 8.14   Setting z to 1 in (8.5), we obtain

$$C(n, 0) + C(n, 1) + \ldots + C(n, r) + \ldots + C(n, n) = 2^n$$

That is, the number of ways to select none, one, two, $\ldots$, or n objects from n objects is 2^n.

Setting z to $- 1$ in (8.5), we obtain

$$C(n, 0) - C(n, 1) + C(n, 2) + \ldots + (-1)^r C(n, r) + \ldots + (-1)^n C(n, n) = 0$$

or

$$C(n, 0) + C(n, 2) + C(n, 4) + \ldots = C(n, 1) + C(n, 3) + C(n, 5) + \ldots$$

That is, the number of ways of selecting an even number of objects from n objects is equal to the number of ways of selecting an odd number of objects. ■

Example 8.15   The relation

$$C(n, r) = C(n - 1, r) + C(n - 1, r - 1) \qquad (8.6)$$

can be proved in several ways. By straightforward algebraic manipulation, we obtain

$$C(n, r) = \frac{n!}{r!(n - r)!}$$

$$= \frac{n!}{r!(n - r)!} \left(\frac{n - r}{n} + \frac{r}{n} \right)$$

$$= \frac{(n - 1)!}{r!(n - r - 1)!} + \frac{(n - 1)!}{(r - 1)!(n - r)!}$$

$$= C(n - 1, r) + C(n - 1, r - 1)$$

We can also prove eq. (8.6) using a combinatorial argument: If we are to select r objects from n objects, there are $C(n - 1, r)$ ways to select r objects so that a particular object is always excluded, and $C(n - 1, r - 1)$ ways so that this particular object is always included. Thus, eq. (8.6) follows. The use of generating functions provides a third proof of eq. (8.6). Note that $C(n, r)$ is the coefficient of z^r in $(1 + z)^n$, which can be written as $(1 + z)^{n-1} + z(1 + z)^{n-1}$. Since the coefficient of z^r in $(1 + z)^{n-1}$ is $C(n - 1, r)$, and the coefficient of z^r in $z(1 + z)^{n-1}$ is $C(n - 1, r - 1)$, (8.6) follows immediately. ■

We present now some further examples:

Example 8.16   Let $(a_0, a_1, a_2, \ldots)$ be a numeric function such that a_r is equal to the number of ways to select r objects from 10 objects among which one, which will be denoted X, can be selected at most twice, one, which will be denoted Y, can be selected at most thrice, and the others can be selected only once. We claim that the generating function of **a** is

$$A(z) = (1 + z + z^2)(1 + z + z^2 + z^3)(1 + z)^8$$

Note that the coefficient of z^r in $A(z)$ is the number of ways to make up the term z^r from the factors $1 + z + z^2$, $1 + z + z^2 + z^3$, and the eight factors $1 + z$. The contribution from the factor $1 + z + z^2$ can be 1, z, or z^2, corresponding to selecting the object X zero times, once, or twice. The contribution from the factor $1 + z + z^2 + z^3$ can be 1 or z or z^2 or z^3, corresponding to selecting the object Y zero times, once, twice, or thrice. The contribution of each of the eight factors $1 + z$ can be 1 or z, corresponding to selecting each of the eight remaining objects zero times or once. ∎

Example 8.17 Let a_r denote the number of ways of selecting r objects from n objects with unlimited repetitions. Since each object can be selected as many times as we wish, a_r is equal to the coefficient of z^r in

$$(1 + z + z^2 + \ldots)^n$$

Note that the contribution from each of the factors $1 + z + z^2 + \ldots$ will correspond to the number of times one of the objects is selected. Since

$$(1 + z + z^2 + \ldots)^n = \left(\frac{1}{1-z}\right)^n = (1 - z)^{-n}$$

we obtain

$$a_r = (-1)^r \frac{(-n)(-n-1)\ldots(-n-r+1)}{r!}$$

$$= \frac{(n+r-1)!}{r!(n-1)!}$$

$$= C(n + r - 1, r)$$

This result is a result we derived earlier in Chapter 2. ∎

Example 8.18 Suppose we want to determine the number of ways in which $2t + 1$ marbles can be distributed among three distinct boxes so that no box will contain more than t marbles. We claim that the coefficient of z^{2t+1} in

$$A(z) = (1 + z + z^2 + \ldots + z^t)^3$$

will be our answer. Note that the coefficient of z^{2t+1} in $A(z)$ is the number of ways to make up the term z^{2t+1} from the three factors $1 + z + z^2 + \ldots + z^t$. The contribution from each factor $1 + z + z^2 + \ldots + z^t$ can be 1, z, z^2, $\ldots$, or z^t corresponding to having none, one, two, $\ldots$, or t marbles in a box. Since

$$(1 + z + z^2 + \ldots + z^t)^3 = \left(\frac{1 - z^{t+1}}{1 - z}\right)^3$$

$$= (1 - 3z^{t+1} + 3z^{2t+2} - z^{3t+3})(1 - z)^{-3} \qquad (8.7)$$

the coefficient of z^{2t+1} in eq. (8.7) is the coefficient of z^{2t+1} in $(1-z)^{-3}$ minus three times the coefficient of z^t in $(1-z)^{-3}$. Thus, it is

$$C(3 + 2t + 1 - 1, 2t + 1) - 3C(3 + t - 1, t)$$

which is simplified as

$$C(2t + 3, 2t + 1) - 3C(t + 2, t) \qquad \blacksquare$$

Problems

8.1 A ping-pong ball is dropped to the floor from a height of 20 m. Suppose that the ball always rebounds to reach half of the height from which it falls.

(a) Let a_r denote the height it reaches in the rth rebound. Sketch the numeric function **a**.

(b) Let b_r denote the loss in height during the rth rebound. Express b_r in terms of a_r. Sketch the numeric function **b**.

(c) A second ping-pong ball is dropped from a height of 6 m. to the same floor at the same time as the first ball reaches the highest point of its third rebound. Let c_r denote the height the second ball reaches in its rth rebound. Express c_r in terms of a_r.

8.2 In a process control system, a monitoring device measures the temperature inside a chemical reaction chamber once every 30 s. Let a_r denote the rth reading in degrees in centigrade. Determine an expression for a_r if it is known that the temperature rises from 100 to 120° at a constant rate in the first 300 s and stays at 120° from then on.

8.3 Let **a** be a numeric function such that a_r is equal to the remainder when the integer r is divided by 17. Let **b** be a numeric function such that b_r is equal to 0 if the integer r is divisible by 3, and is equal to 1 otherwise.

(a) Let $c_r = a_r + b_r$. For what values of r is $c_r = 0$? For what values of r is $c_r = 1$?

(b) Let $d_r = a_r b_r$. For what values of r is $d_r = 0$? For what values of r is $d_r = 1$?

8.4 Let **a** be a numeric function such that

$$a_r = \begin{cases} 2 & 0 \le r \le 3 \\ 2^{-r} + 5 & r \ge 4 \end{cases}$$

(a) Determine $S^2\mathbf{a}$ and $S^{-2}\mathbf{a}$.

(b) Determine $\Delta\mathbf{a}$ and $\nabla\mathbf{a}$.

8.5 We introduce the notation

$$\Delta^2\mathbf{a} = \Delta(\Delta\mathbf{a})$$
$$\Delta^3\mathbf{a} = \Delta(\Delta^2\mathbf{a})$$
$$\dots\dots\dots\dots$$
$$\Delta^i\mathbf{a} = \Delta(\Delta^{i-1}\mathbf{a})$$

(a) Let **a** be a numeric function such that

$$a_r = r^3 - 2r^3 + 3r + 2$$

Determine $\Delta\mathbf{a}$, $\Delta^2\mathbf{a}$, $\Delta^3\mathbf{a}$, $\Delta^4\mathbf{a}$.

(b) Let **a** be a numeric function such that a_r is a polynomial of the form

$$\alpha_0 + \alpha_1 r + \alpha_2 r^2 + \dots + \alpha_k r^k$$

Show that $\Delta^{k+1}\mathbf{a}$ is equal to 0.

8.6 (a) Let $\mathbf{c} = \mathbf{ab}$. Show that

$$\Delta c_r = a_{r+1}(\Delta b_r) + b_r(\Delta a_r)$$

(b) Let **a** and **b** be two numeric functions such that $a_r = r + 1$ and $b_r = \alpha^r$ for all $r \geq 0$. Determine $\Delta(\mathbf{ab})$.

(c) Let **a** and **b** be two numeric functions. The quotient of **a** and **b** denoted **a/b** is a numeric function whose value at r is equal to a_r/b_r. Let $\mathbf{d} = \mathbf{a/b}$. Show that

$$\Delta d_r = \frac{b_r(\Delta a_r) - a_r(\Delta b_r)}{b_r b_{r+1}}$$

(c) Determine $\Delta(\mathbf{a/b})$ for the numeric functions **a** and **b** in part (b).

8.7 Let **a** be a numeric function. Let $\Delta^{-1}\mathbf{a}$ denote the accumulated sum of **a**. Are the two numeric functions $\Delta(\Delta^{-1}\mathbf{a})$ and $\Delta^{-1}(\Delta\mathbf{a})$ the same?

8.8 Interest for money deposited in a savings account is paid at a rate of 0.5 percent per month, with interest compounded monthly. Suppose \$50 is deposited into a savings account each month for a period of five years. What is the total amount in the account four years after the first deposit? Twenty years after the first deposit?

8.9 Determine **a** * **b** in the following. Give either a sketch or a closed-form expression of the resulting numeric function, whichever is more convenient.

(a)
$$a_r = \begin{cases} 1 & 0 \leq r \leq 2 \\ 0 & r \geq 3 \end{cases}$$

$$b_r = \begin{cases} 1 & 0 \leq r \leq 2 \\ 0 & r \geq 3 \end{cases}$$

(b)
$$a_r = 1 \qquad \text{for all } r$$

$$b_r = \begin{cases} 1 & r = 1 \\ 2 & r = 3 \\ 3 & r = 5 \\ -6 & r = 7 \\ 0 & \text{otherwise} \end{cases}$$

(c)
$$a_r = 2^r \qquad \text{for all } r$$

$$b_r = \begin{cases} 0 & 0 \leq r \leq 2 \\ 2^r & r \geq 3 \end{cases}$$

8.10 Let **a**, **b**, and **c** be numeric functions such that **a** * **b** = **c**. Given that

$$a_r = \begin{cases} 1 & r = 0 \\ 2 & r = 1 \\ 0 & r \geq 2 \end{cases}$$

$$c_r = \begin{cases} 1 & r = 0 \\ 0 & r \geq 1 \end{cases}$$

determine **b**.

8.11 Let

$$a_r = \begin{cases} 1 & r = 0 \\ 3 & r = 1 \\ 2 & r = 2 \\ 0 & r \geq 3 \end{cases}$$

$$c_r = 5^r \qquad \text{for all } r$$

Determine **b** so that **a** * **b** = **c**.

8.12 (a) Every particle inside a nuclear reactor splits into two particles in each second. Suppose one particle is injected into the reactor every second beginning at $t = 0$. How many particles are there in the reactor at the nth second?

(b) When a particle splits into two, one of them is actually the original particle and the other is a newly created particle. Suppose a particle has a lifetime of 10 seconds. That is, a particle created in the 0th second will vanish after the 10th second. Repeat part (a) and assume that all injected particles are newly created.

8.13 For a fee of $1000, a radio station will provide a store with 10 min of commercial time each day for five consecutive days and then 2 min of commercial time each day for the next five consecutive days. Suppose that every minute of commercial time on a particular day will produce a total sale of $500 on that day and a total sale of 500×2^{-n} on the nth day from that day.

(a) Suppose a fee of $1000 is paid to the radio station on the 0th day. Determine the numeric function **a**, where a_r is the total sale on the rth day.

(b) Suppose a fee of $2000 is paid to the radio station daily for 10 consecutive days starting on the 0th day. Determine the numeric function **b** where b_r is the total sale on the rth day.

8.14 Let **a**, **b**, and **c** be three numeric functions:

$$\mathbf{a} = 3r - 2$$
$$\mathbf{b} = \frac{2}{r} + 7$$
$$\mathbf{c} = r \ln r$$

(a) Does **a** dominate **b** asymptotically? Does **a** dominate **c** asymptotically? Does **b** dominate **a** asymptotically? Does **b** dominate **c** asymptotically? Does **c** dominate **a** asymptotically? Does **c** dominate **b** asymptotically?

(b) Does **a** + **b** dominate **a** asymptotically? Does **a** + **b** dominate **c** asymptotically?

(c) Does **ab** dominate **a** asymptotically? Does **a** dominate **ab** asymptotically? Does **ab** dominate **c** asymptotically? Does **c** dominate **ab** asymptotically?

(d) Does Δ**a** dominate **b** asymptotically?

(e) Does the accumulated sum of **a** dominate **c** asymptotically?

8.15 Let

$$\mathbf{a} = 3^r$$
$$\mathbf{b} = 2^r$$

(a) Does **a** dominate **b** asymptotically?

(b) Does **b** dominate **a** asymptotically?

(c) Does **a*****b** dominate **a** asymptotically?

(d) Does **a*****b** dominate **b** asymptotically?

8.16 Let

$$a_r = \sum_{i=0}^{r} i^2$$

(a) Show that **a** is $O(r^3)$.

(b) Show that **a** is $(r^3/3) + O(r^2)$.

(c) Let **b** be a numeric function such that **b** is $O(r^3)$. It is necessary that **b** is $(r^3/3) + O(r^2)$?

(d) Let **b** be a numeric function such that **b** is $(r^3/3) + O(r^2)$. Is it necessary that **b** is $O(r^3)$?

8.17 Simplify the expression $[\ln r + O(1/n)][n + O(\sqrt{n})]$.

8.18 Let

$$\mathbf{a} = \ln r$$

Show that for $\varepsilon > 0$, $\mathbf{a}$ is $O(r^i)$.

8.19 Given a numeric function $\mathbf{a}$, let

$$b_r = \begin{cases} a_r + a_{r/2} + a_{r/4} + \ldots + a_{r/2^i} & r = 2^i \\ 0 & r \neq 2^i \end{cases}$$

If $\mathbf{a}$ is $O(\sqrt{r})$, show that $\mathbf{b}$ is $O(\sqrt{r}\,\log r)$.

8.20 Let

$$a_r = \sum_{i=0}^{|\log_{3/2} r| - 1} \log_2 \left(\frac{2}{3} \right)^i r$$

$$= \log_2 r + \log_2 \left(\frac{2}{3} \right) r + \log_2 \left(\frac{4}{9} \right) r + \ldots$$

Show that a_r is $O(\log^2 r)$.

8.21 After careful analysis, a student concluded that a certain numeric function $\mathbf{a}$ is $0(r \log r)$. Upon hearing that, her roommate reminded her that she had forgotten to specify the base of the logarithm. Had she really forgotten something important?

8.22 (a) The time complexity of algorithm A is $O(r^2)$, and that of algorithm B is $O(r^2 \ln r)$. Can we conclude that algorithm A is superior to algorithm B?

   (b) The time complexity of algorithm A is $O(r^2)$, and that of algorithm B is $\Omega(r^2 \ln r)$. Can we conclude that algorithm A is superior to algorithm B?

   (c) The time complexity of algorithm A is $\Theta(r^2)$, and that of algorithm B is $\Theta(r^2 \ln r)$. Can we conclude that algorithm A is superior to algorithm B?

8.23 Two engineers were assigned the task of designing integrated circuit chips. Let a_r denote the total area of a chip that contains r transistors. For engineer A's design a_r is found to be $O(r^4)$. For engineer B's design, a_r is found to be $\Omega(\sqrt{r})$. Consequently, the manager concludes that when the number of transistors on a chip increases, A's design would occupy a large area and is therefore bad, while B's design would occupy a small area and is therefore good. Does he know what he is talking about?

8.24 A professor took his students out for beer on a Friday afternoon. After a couple of drinks, he declared: " The total amount of beer you are going to consume is big _____ of the size of my wallet, and is big _____ of your thirst." Granting the professor the privilege of abusing mathematical terminologies ever so slightly, can you fill in the blanks to make the statement meaningful?

8.25 Find a simple expression for the generating function of each of the following discrete numeric functions:

   (a) $1, -2, 3, -4, 5, -6, \ldots$ (b) $1, 2/3, 3/9, 4/77, \ldots, (r + 1)/3^r, \ldots$

   (c) $1, 1, 2, 2, 3, 3, 4, 4, \ldots$ (d) $0 \times 1, 1 \times 2, 2 \times 3, 3 \times 4, \ldots$

   (e) $0 \times 5^0, 1 \times 5^1, 2 \times 5^2, \ldots, r \times 5^r, \ldots$

8.26 Determine the generating function of the numeric function a_r, where

$$a_r = \begin{cases} 2^r & \text{if } r \text{ is even} \\ -2^r & \text{if } r \text{ is odd} \end{cases}$$

8.27 Determine the discrete numeric function corresponding to each of the following generating functions:

(a) $A(z) = \dfrac{1}{1 - z^3}$

(b) $A(z) = (1 + z)^n + (1 - z)^n$

(c) $A(z) = \dfrac{(1 + z)^2}{(1 - z)^4}$

(d) $A(z) = \dfrac{1}{5 - 6z - z^2}$

(e) $A(z) = \dfrac{z^5}{5 - 6z - z^2}$

(f) $A(z) = \dfrac{7z^2}{(1 - 2z)(1 + 3z)}$

(g) $A(z) = \dfrac{1 + z^2}{4 - 4z - z^2}$

(h) $A(z) = \dfrac{1}{(1 - z)(1 - z^2)(1 - z^3)}$

8.28 (a) Let a_r denote the number of ways a sum of r can be obtained when two indistinguishable dice are rolled. Determine $A(z)$.

    (b) Let b_r denote the number of ways a sum of r can be obtained when a single dice is rolled once and then two indistinguishable dice are rolled once. Determine $B(z)$.

8.29 Let a_r denote the number of ways to seat 10 students in a row of r chairs so that no two students will occupy adjacent seats. Determine the generating function of the discrete numeric function $(a_0, a_1, a_2, \ldots, a_r, \ldots)$.

8.30 The lifespan of a rabbit is exactly 10 years. Suppose that there are two newborn rabbits at the beginning, and the number of newborn rabbits in each year is two times that in the previous year. Determine the number of rabbits there are in the rth year.

8.31 Let a_r denote the number of ways to select r balls from an infinite supply of red, blue, and white balls with the constraint that the number of red balls selected is always an even number. Determine the generating function of the numeric function **a**.

8.32 In how many ways can $3r$ balls be selected from $2r$ red balls, $2r$ blue balls, and $2r$ white balls?

8.33 Let a_r denote the number of ways to select r balls from 100 red balls, 50 blue balls, and 50 white balls with the constraints that the number of red balls selected is not equal to two, the number of blue balls selected is not equal to three, and the number of white balls selected is not equal to four. Determine the generating function of the numeric function **a**.

8.34 A set of r balls is selected from an infinite supply of red, blue, white, and yellow balls. A selection must satisfy the condition that either the number of red balls is even and the number of blue balls is odd, or the number of white balls is even and the number of yellow balls is odd. Let a_r denote the total number of such selections.

    (a) Determine the generating function $A(z)$.

    (b) Find a closed-form expression for a_r. Evaluate the expression for $r = 23$.

8.35 Let a_r denote the number of ways to divide r identical marbles into four distinct piles so that each pile has an odd number of marbles that is larger than or equal to three.

    (a) Determine $A(z)$.

    (b) Determine a closed-form expression for a_r.

8.36 (a) Determine the sum

$$\binom{n}{1} + 2\binom{n}{2} + \ldots + i\binom{n}{i} + \ldots + n\binom{n}{n}$$

    (b) If we write down all the combinations of n letters $\{1, 2, \ldots, n\}$, that is, all 1-combinations, all 2-combinations, how many times does each letter occur?

8.37 Determine the sum

$$C(n, 0) + 2C(n, 1) + 2^2C(n, 2) + \ldots + 2^nC(n, n)$$

8.38 Determine the sum

$$\binom{n}{0}\binom{m}{k} + \binom{n}{1}\binom{m}{k-1} + \binom{n}{2}\binom{m}{k-2} + \ldots + \binom{n}{k}\binom{m}{0}$$

where $k \leq n$ and $k \leq m$.

8.39 (a) Let

$$A(z) = (1+z)^{2n} + z(1+z)^{2n-1} + \ldots + z^i(1+z)^{2n-i} + \ldots + z^n(1+z)^n$$

Show that

$$a_r = \begin{cases} \dbinom{2n+1}{r} & 0 \leq r \leq n \\ \dbinom{2n+1}{r} - \dbinom{n}{r-n-1} & n+1 \leq r \leq 2n+1 \\ 0 & \text{otherwise} \end{cases}$$

(b) Evaluate the sum

$$\binom{2n}{n} + \binom{2n-1}{n-1} + \ldots + \binom{2n-i}{n-i} + \ldots + \binom{n}{0}$$

8.40 (a) Show that

$$\binom{r}{0}^2 + \binom{r}{1}^2 + \binom{r}{2}^2 + \ldots + \binom{r}{i}^2 + \ldots + \binom{r}{r}^2 = \binom{2r}{r}$$

(b) Show that the generating function for **a**, where

$$a_r = \binom{2r}{r}$$

is $(1-4z)^{-1/2}$

Programming Exercises

1. Write a program to compute the sum of two given numeric functions.
2. Write a program to compute the product of two given numeric functions.
3. Write a program to compute the accumulated sum of a given numeric function.
4. Write a program to compute $S^i\mathbf{a}$, for any given numeric function **a** as described in Section 8.2.
5. Write a program to compute $S^{-i}\mathbf{a}$, for any given numeric function **a** as described in Section 8.2.

Objective

To present various
types of recurrence
relations and the
methods to find out
their solutions. We
also aim at discuss-
ing the divide and
conquer algorithms.

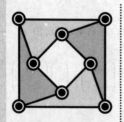

CHAPTER

NINE

RECURRENCE RELATIONS AND RECURSIVE ALGORITHMS

9.1 INTRODUCTION

Suppose we ask a friend the age of his oldest daughter. He could tell us directly that she is 19 years old or he could tell us that she is 6 years older than his second daughter. If we ask for the age of the second daughter, instead of telling us that she is 13 years old, he might tell us that she is 5 years older than his third daughter. In turn, he could tell us that his third daughter is 2 years older than his only son. When he tells us that his only son is 6 years old, we would have no difficulty in figuring out that his third daughter is 8 years old, his second daughter is 13 years old, and his oldest daughter is 19 years old.

Let us consider another example. Suppose we ask for instructions to get from our house to the railroad station. We are told, "Go on Prospect Avenue, then go east on Green Street. After passing the public library, go onto Springfield Avenue and then go north on Neil Street. At the bus depot, turn right at the traffic light onto University Avenue. At the second traffic light, turn left and you'll see the railroad station." This, of course, is a perfectly clear way to instruct someone to go from our house to the railroad station. However, there is an alternative way to give the instruction, which is simply, "*Go to the bus depot* and turn right at the traffic light onto University Avenue. At the second traffic light, turn left and you'll see the railroad station." We note that such an instruction consists of two parts: one part tells us how to go from the bus depot to the railroad station explicitly, and the other simple and concise part makes use of our knowledge of how to get from our house to the bus depot. Suppose we are not sure how to get from our house to the bus depot. In that case, we can be further instructed to "*Go to the public library* and onto Springfield Avenue. Then go north on Neil Street to the bus depot." Needless to say, either we know how to get from our house to the public library, or we should ask for further instruction.

The reader has undoubtedly realized what we are trying to say. In the first example, instead of telling us the age of his oldest daughter directly, our friend chose to tell us the age of his oldest daughter in terms of the age of his second-oldest daughter. Then, instead of telling us directly the age of his second-oldest daughter, he chose to tell us the age of his second-oldest daughter in terms of the age of his third-oldest daughter, and so on. In the second example, instead of spelling out explicitly all the details of some instruction, we specified the instruction partly in terms of knowledge we already have. We can make several observations about these two examples. First, using our prior knowledge can be a concise way to give information or instruction; for example, in directing someone to the railroad station, a great deal of information can be compressed into the simple statement, "Go to the bus depot." Secondly, we do need to do some work to make use of the knowledge we already have. In the first example, at a certain point, our friend must tell us directly the age of one of his children so that we can determine the ages of the other children. In the second example, we need to find out how to get to the public library before we can use the given instruction on how to get from there to the railroad station. Third, we might try to refer to some prior knowledge in successive steps (the age of our friend's son, that of his third-oldest daughter, and so on, or how to go to the public library, how to go to the bus depot, and so on). Such a chain of references can only be terminated when we reach a point where we know explicitly what to do without referring to other prior knowledge.* In this chapter, we shall apply what we have just learned first to the specification of discrete numeric functions, and then to the specification of algorithms.

9.2   RECURRENCE RELATIONS

Consider the numeric function $\mathbf{a} = (3^0, 3^1, 3^2, ..., 3^r, ...)$. Clearly, the function can be specified by a general expression for a_r, namely,

$$a_r = 3^r \quad r \geq 0$$

---

* An American professor has written a paper in English, his native language, and wishes to have it published in a French journal. Since he knows no French, he asked his French colleague, Professor Bestougeff, to translate the paper into French for him. After the translation was completed, the American professor felt that he should include a footnote in the paper to acknowledge his colleague's contribution. He wrote the footnote, "The author wishes to thank Professor Bestougeff for translating this paper into French for him," in English, and asked Professor Bestougeff to translate it into French for him, which the professor gladly did. It then occurred to the American professor that he should also acknowledge Professor Bestougeff for translating the footnote for him, So, he wrote another footnote, "The author wishes to thank Professor Bestougeff for translating the preceding footnote into French for him," he then asked Professor Bestougeff to translate that into French, and copied the French translation *twice* as two additional footnotes. His problem was completely solved!

As was pointed out in Chapter 8, the function can also be specified by its generating function, namely,

$$A(z) = \frac{1}{1-3z}$$

According to our discussion in Sec. 9.1, we note that there is still another way to specify the numeric function. Since the value of a_r is three times the value of a_{r-1}, for all r, once we know the value of a_{r-1} we can compute the value of a_r. The value of a_{r-1} can, in turn, be computed as three times the value of a_{r-2}, which, again, is equal to three times the value of a_{r-3}. Eventually, we need the value of a_0, which is known to be 1. Thus, we note that the relation

$$a_r = 3a_{r-1}$$

together with the information that $a_0 = 1$ also completely specifies the numeric function **a**.

As another example, consider the sequence of numbers* known as the *Fibonacci sequence of numbers*. The sequence starts with the two numbers 1, 1 and contains numbers that are equal to the sum of their two immediate predecessors. A portion of the sequence is

$$1, 1, 2, 3, 5, 8, 13, 21, 34, \ldots$$

It is quite difficult in this case to obtain a general expression for the rth number in the sequence by observation, which, incidentally, is

$$a_r = \frac{1}{\sqrt{5}}\left(\frac{1+\sqrt{5}}{2}\right)^{r+1} - \frac{1}{\sqrt{5}}\left(\frac{1-\sqrt{5}}{2}\right)^{r+1}$$

Nor is it obvious what the generating function for the numeric function is. Incidentally, it is

$$A(z) = \frac{1}{1-z-z^2}$$

On the other hand, the sequence can be described by the relation

$$a_r = a_{r-1} + a_{r-2}$$

together with the information $a_0 = 1$ and $a_1 = 1$.

For a numeric function $(a_0, a_1, a_2, \ldots, a_r, \ldots)$, an equation relating a_r, for any r, to one or more of the a_i's, $i < r$, is called a *recurrence relation*. A recurrence relation is also called a *difference equation*, and those two terms will be used interchangeably. In many discrete computation problems, it is sometimes easier to obtain a specification of a numeric function in terms of a recurrence relation than to obtain a general expression for the value of the numeric function at r or a closed-form expression for its generating function. It is clear that according to the recurrence relation, we can carry out a step-by-step computation to

---

* Clearly, a numeric function can be viewed simply as a sequence of real numbers, and conversely.

determine a_r from a_{r-1}, a_{r-2}, ..., to determine a_{r+1} from a_r, a_{r-1}, ..., and so on, provided that the value of the function at one or more points is given so that the computation can be initiated. These given values of the function are called *boundary conditions*. In the first example above, the boundary condition is $a_0 = 1$, and in the second example above, the boundary conditions are $a_0 = 1$ and $a_1 = 1$. We thus conclude that a numeric function can be described by a recurrence relation together with an appropriate set of boundary conditions. The numeric function is also referred to as the *solution of the recurrence relation*.

One step beyond determining the values of a numeric function in a step-by-step computation according to a given recurrence relation is to obtain from the recurrence relation either a general expression for the solution or a closed-form expression for its generating function. Unfortunately, no general method of solution for handling all recurrence relations is known. In the following, we shall study a class of recurrence relations known as *linear recurrence relations with constant coefficients*.

9.3 LINEAR RECURRENCE RELATIONS WITH CONSTANT COEFFICIENTS

A recurrence relation of the form

$$C_0 a_r + C_1 a_{r-1} + C_2 a_{r-2} + ... + C_k a_{r-k} = f(r) \tag{9.1}$$

where C_i's are constants, is called a *linear recurrence relation with constant coefficients*. The recurrence relation in eq. (9.1) is known as a *kth-order recurrence relation*, provided that both C_0 and C_k are nonzero. For example,

$$2a_r + 3a_{r-1} = 2^r$$

is a first-order linear recurrence relation with constant coefficients. Also, both

$$3a_r - 5a_{r-1} + 2a_{r-2} = r^2 + 5 \tag{9.2}$$

and

$$a_r + 7a_{r-2} = 0$$

are second-order linear recurrence relations with constant coefficients. In this chapter we shall restrict our discussion to linear recurrence relations with constant coefficients both because we frequently encounter this class of recurrence relations and know how to handle them quite well.

Consider the recurrence relation in eq. (9.2). Suppose we are given that $a_3 = 3$ and $a_4 = 6$, we can compute a_5 as

$$a_5 = \frac{-1}{3} [-5 \times 6 + 2 \times 3 - (5^2 + 5)] = 18$$

we can then compute a_6 as

$$a_6 = \frac{-1}{3} [-5 \times 18 + 2 \times 6 - (6^2 + 5)] = \frac{119}{3}$$

and so on. Also, we can compute

$$a_2 = \frac{-1}{2}[3 \times 6 - 5 \times 3 - (4^2 + 5)] = 9$$

$$a_1 = \frac{-1}{2}[3 \times 3 - 5 \times 9 - (3^2 + 5)] = 25$$

$$a_0 = \frac{-1}{2}[3 \times 9 - 5 \times 25 - (2^2 + 5)] = \frac{107}{2}$$

and so on. We conclude that eq. (9.2), together with the values $a_3 = 3$ and $a_4 = 6$, completely specifies the discrete numeric function **a**.

In general, for a kth-order linear recurrence relation with constant coefficients as shown in eq. (9.1), if k consecutive values of the numeric function **a**, a_{m-k}, a_{m-k+1}, ..., a_{m-1} are known for some m, the value of a_m can be calculated according to eq. (9.1), namely,

$$a_m = -\frac{1}{C_0}[C_1 a_{m-1} + C_2 a_{m-2} + \dots + C_k a_{m-k} - f(m)]$$

Furthermore, the value of a_{m+1} can be computed as

$$a_{m+1} = -\frac{1}{C_0}[C_1 a_m + C_2 a_{m-1} + \dots + C_k a_{m-k+1} - f(m+1)]$$

and the values of a_{m+2}, a_{m+3}, ... can be computed in a similar manner. Also, the value of a_{m-k-1} can be computed as

$$a_{m-k-1} = -\frac{1}{C_k}[C_0 a_{m-1} + C_1 a_{m-2} + \dots + C_{k-1} a_{m-k} - f(m-1)]$$

and the value of a_{m-k-2} can be computed as

$$a_{m-k-2} = -\frac{1}{C_k}[C_0 a_{m-2} + C_1 a_{m-3} + \dots + C_{k-1} a_{m-k-1} - f(m-2)]$$

The values of a_{m-k-3}, a_{m-k-4}, ... can be computed in a similar manner. Indeed, for a kth-order linear recurrence relation, the values of k consecutive a_i's are always sufficient to determine the numeric function **a** uniquely. In other words, the values of k consecutive a_i's constitute an appropriate set of boundary conditions.

Figure 9.1 shows the code for solving a kth-order recurrence relation.

```
/*solving kth-order recurrence relation */
#include<stdio.h>
#include<stdlib.h>
#include<math.h>

#define MAX 100

int main()
{
    int k,i,m,r;
    float a[MAX], b[MAX], c[MAX], sum1, sum2, temp;
    printf("\nThe general form of a kth-order Recurrence Relation (of polynomial type)
    is:\nc[0].a[r]+c[1].a[r-1]+c[2].a[r-2]+...+c[k].a[r-k]=b[0]+b[1].r+b[2].
    r^2+...+b[k].r^k");
    printf("\nEnter the order of Recurrence Relation:");
    scanf("%d",&k);
    if(k<1)
    {
```

```
                printf("\nOrder >= 1. Enter again:");
                scanf("%d",&k);
}
printf("Enter the value of the constant array-c :");
for (i=0;i<=k;i++)
{
                        printf("\nc[%d]=",i);
                        scanf("%f",&c[i]);
}
printf("\nEnter the value of coefficients of the equation on RHS:");
for (i=0;i<=k;i++)
{
                        printf("\nb[%d]=",i);
                        scanf("%f",&b[i]);
}
printf("Now, for calculating a[x], we need %d consecutive values of numeric
function - a:",k);
printf("\na[m]....a[m-%d]",k-1);
printf("\nEnter the maximum suffix of the boundary value-m :");
while(1){
        scanf("%d",&m);
        if(m < k-1)
                printf("\nUnacceptable value.m >= k-1.Enter again:");
        else
                break;
}
printf("\nNow, enter the array-a:");
for (i=0;i<k;i++)
{
                        printf("\na[%d]=",m-i);
                        scanf("%f",&a[i]);
}
printf("\nThe recurrence relation was entered successfully. It is:\n");
printf("\n%.1f.a[r]",c[0]);
for (i=1;i<=k;i++)
                printf("+ %.1f.a[r-%d]",c[i],i);
printf(" = %.1f",b[0]);
for (i=1;i<=k;i++)
                printf("+ %.1f.r^%d",b[i],i);
printf("\n\nAnd the boundary conditions are:");
for (i=0;i<k;i++)
                printf("\na[%d] = %.1f",m-i,a[i]);
printf("\n\nNow, enter the value of r for which you want to find a[r]:");
scanf("%d",&r);
if(r <= m-k)
{
        while(1)
        {
                sum1=0;sum2=0;
                for (i=0;i<=k;i++)
                {
                                temp=b[i]*pow(m,i);
                                sum1=sum1+temp;
                }
                for (i=0;i<k;i++)
                {
                                temp=c[i]*a[i];
                                sum2=sum2+temp;
                }
                a[k]=(sum1-sum2)/c[k];
                printf("\na[%d]=%f",m-k,a[k]);
                //shifitng array
                for (i=0;i<k;i++)
```

```
                                a[i]=a[i+1];
                if(r==(m-k))
                {
                        printf("\nFinal Answer:\na[%d]=%f",r,a[k-1]);
                        printf("\n\n\n\n\nEnter any number to exit...");
                        scanf("%d",&i);
                        exit(1);
                }
                m=m-1;
        }//end of while
    }//end of if
    else if(r > m)
    {
        while(1)
        {
                sum1=0;sum2=0;
                //shifitng array
                for(i=k;i>0;i--)
                        a[i]=a[i-1];
                for(i=0;i<=k;i++)
                {
                        temp=b[i]*pow(m+1,i);
                        sum1=sum1+temp;
                }
                for(i=1;i<=k;i++)
                {
                        temp=c[i]*a[i];
                        sum2=sum2+temp;
                }
                a[0]=(sum1-sum2)/c[0];
                printf("\na[%d]=%f",m+1,a[0]);
                m=m+1;
                if(r==m)
                {
                        printf("\nFinal Answer:\na[%d]=%f",r,a[0]);
                        printf("\n\n\n\n\nEnter any number to exit...");
                        scanf("%d",&i);
                        exit(1);
                }
        }/*end of while*/
    }/*end of else-if*/
    else
    {
        printf("\nFinal Answer:\na[%d]=%f",r,a[m-r]);
        printf("\n\n\n\n\nEnter any number to exit...");
        scanf("%d",&i);
    }
    return 0;
}
```

Output:

The general form of a kth-order Recurrence Relation (of polynomial type) is:
c[0].a[r]+c[1].a[r-1]+c[2].a[r-2]+...+c[k].a[r-k]=b[0]+b[1].r+b[2].
r^2+...+b[k].r^k
Enter the order of Recurrence Relation: 2
Enter the value of the constant array-c :
c[0]= 3
c[1]= -5
c[2]= 2

Enter the value of coefficients of the equation on RHS:
b[0]= 5
b[1]= 0
b[2]= 1

```
Now, for calculating a[x], we need 2 consecutive values of numeric function - a:
a[m]....a[m-1]
Enter the maximum suffix of the boundary value-m : 5

Now, enter the array-a:
a[4]= 6
a[3]= 3

The recurrence relation was entered successfully. It is:

3.0.a[r]+ -5.0.a[r-1]+ 2.0.a[r-2] = 5.0+ 0.0.r^1+ 1.0.r^2

And the boundary conditions are:
a[4] = 6.0
a[3] = 3.0

Now, enter the value of r for which you want to find a[r]: 6

a[5]=18.000000
a[6]=39.666667

Final Answer:
a[6]=39.666667

Enter any number to exit...
```

Fig. 9.1   C code for solving a kth-order recurrence relation.

On the other hand, for a kth-order linear recurrence relation with constant coefficients, fewer than k values of the numeric function will not be sufficient to determine the numeric function uniquely. For example, let

$$a_r + a_{r-1} + a_{r-2} = 4 \qquad (9.3)$$

If we are given that $a_0 = 2$, we can find many numeric functions that will satisfy the recurrence relation as well as the given boundary condition. Thus,

$$2, 0, 2, 2, 0, 2, 2, 0, 2, 2, 0, \ldots$$
$$2, 2, 0, 2, 2, 0, 2, 2, 0, 2, 2, \ldots$$
$$2, 5, -3, 2, 5, -3, 2, 5, -3, 2, \ldots$$

are all possibilities. Yet, more than k values of the numeric function might make it impossible for the existence of a numeric function that satisfies the recurrence relation and the given boundary conditions. For example, for the recurrence relation in eq. (9.3), if we were given that

$$a_0 = 2 \qquad a_1 = 2 \qquad a_2 = 2$$

then obviously a_0, a_1, and a_2 do not satisfy the recurrence relation. Consequently, no **a** can satisfy eq. (9.3) and the boundary conditions.

The values of k nonconsecutive a_i's might or might not constitute an appropriate set of boundary conditions, depending on the specific recurrence relation we have. We shall not study the problem of what constitutes an appropriate set of boundary conditions here, since it is not a significantly important one. See, however, Prob. 9.8.

We should point out that if a kth-order recurrence relation is not a linear recurrence relation with constant coefficients, k consecutive values of the numeric functions might not specify uniquely a solution. For example, consider the recurrence relation

$$a_r^2 + a_{r-1} = 5$$

Given that $a_0 = 1$, we note that

$$1, 2, \sqrt{3}, \dots$$
$$1, 2, -\sqrt{3}, \dots$$
$$1, -2, \sqrt{7}, \dots$$

are all solutions to the recurrence relation that satisfy the boundary condition.

We shall restrict our discussion to the solution of linear recurrence relations with constant coefficients. There is a significant advantage to restrict ourselves to this class of recurrence relations. Since we know that for a given set of boundary conditions the solution to a linear recurrence relation with constant coefficients is unique, as long as we are able to find a numeric function that satisfies the recurrence relation as well as the boundary conditions, it is *the* solution we are looking for. Such an argument should remove some of the "mystery" about the solution procedure we are going to present. We shall determine the solution by "guessing" what it will be. The justification for guessing is simply that it works: when the procedure yields a solution to the recurrence relation, it will be the correct solution.

9.4 HOMOGENEOUS SOLUTIONS

The (total) solution of a linear difference equation with constant coefficients is the sum of two parts, the *homogeneous solution*, which satisfies the difference equation when the right-hand side of the equation is set to 0, and the *particular solution*, which satisfies the difference equation with $f(r)$ on the right-hand side.* In other words, the discrete numeric function that is the solution of the difference equation is the sum of two discrete numeric functions—one is the homogeneous solution and the other is the particular solution. Let $\mathbf{a}^{(h)} = (a_0^{(h)}, a_1^{(h)}, \dots, a_r^{(h)}, \dots)$ denote the homogeneous solution and $\mathbf{a}^{(p)} = (a_0^{(p)}, a_1^{(p)}, \dots, a_r^{(p)}, \dots)$ denote the particular solution to the difference equation. Since

$$C_0 a_r^{(h)} + C_1 a_{r-1}^{(h)} + \dots + C_k a_{r-k}^{(h)} = 0 \tag{9.4}$$

and

$$C_0 a_r^{(p)} + C_1 a_{r-1}^{(p)} + \dots + C_k a_{r-k}^{(p)} = f(r)$$

---

* For a reader with previous exposure to the topic of differential equations, the analogy between the solution of linear difference equations with constant coefficients and that of linear difference equations with constant coefficients should be quite obvious. Indeed, that is the reason we begin to use the phrase *linear difference equations with constant coefficients* here instead of adhering to the phrase *linear recurrence relations with constant coefficients* all the time.

we have

$$C_0(a_r^{(h)} + a_r^{(p)}) + C_1(a_{r-1}^{(h)} + a_{r-1}^{(p)}) + \ldots + C_k(a_{r-k}^{(h)} + a_{r-k}^{(p)}) = f(r)$$

Clearly, the total solution, $\mathbf{a} = \mathbf{a}^{(h)} + \mathbf{a}^{(p)}$ satisfies the difference equation.

At this point, the reader is probably somewhat puzzled by the fact that we are interested in the homogeneous solution to the difference equation. In the first place, it seems that the particular solution would be the solution we seek. In the second place, the homogeneous solution does not even satisfy the given difference equation. [Note that the right-hand side of eq. (9.4) is set to 0.] However, we recall that many discrete numeric functions satisfy a given difference equation, but only one of them satisfies the given boundary conditions at the same time. As it will be seen later in Sec. 9.6, the particular solution alone will not, in general, satisfy the boundary conditions, while we can adjust the homogeneous solution so that the total solutions will satisfy the difference equation as well as the boundary conditions.

A homogeneous solution of a linear difference equation with constant coefficients is of the form $A\alpha_1^r$, where α_1 is called a *characteristic root* and A is a constant determined by the boundary conditions. Substituting $A\alpha^r$ for a_r in the difference equation with the right-hand side of the equation set to 0, we obtain

$$C_0 A\alpha^r + C_1 A\alpha^{r-1} + C_2 A\alpha^{r-2} + \ldots + C_k A\alpha^{r-k} = 0$$

This equation can be simplified to

$$C_0 \alpha^k + C_1 \alpha^{k-1} + C_2 \alpha^{k-2} + \ldots + C_k = 0$$

which is called the *characteristic equation* of the difference equation. Therefore, if α_1 is one of the roots of the characteristic equation (it is for this reason that α_1 is called a characteristic root), $A\alpha_1^r$ is a homogeneous solution to the difference equation.

A characteristic equation of kth degree has k characteristic roots. Suppose the roots of the characteristic equation are distinct. In this case it is easy to verify that

$$a_r^{(h)} = A_1\alpha_1^r + A_2\alpha_2^r + \ldots + A_k\alpha_k^r$$

is also a homogeneous solution to the difference equation, where $\alpha_1, \alpha_2, \ldots, \alpha_k$ are the distinct characteristic roots and $A_1, A_2, \ldots, A_k$ are constants which are to be determined by the boundary conditions.[*]

Example 9.1 Let us revisit the example of the Fibonacci sequence of numbers discussed in Sec. 9.2. The recurrence relation for the Fibonacci sequence of numbers is

$$a_r = a_{r-1} + a_{r-2}$$

The corresponding characteristic equation is

$$\alpha^2 - \alpha - 1 = 0$$

which has the two distinct roots

---

[*] The question of the uniqueness of the solution will be discussed later.

It follows that
$$\alpha_1 = \frac{1 + \sqrt{5}}{2} \qquad \alpha_2 = \frac{1 - \sqrt{5}}{2}$$

$$a_r^{(h)} = A_1 \left(\frac{1 + \sqrt{5}}{2}\right)^r + A_2 \left(\frac{1 - \sqrt{5}}{2}\right)^r$$

is a homogeneous solution where the two constants A_1 and A_2 are to be determined from the boundary conditions $a_0 = 1$ and $a_1 = 1$. ∎

Now suppose that some of the roots of the characteristic equation are multiple roots. Let α_1, be a root of multiplicity m. We shall show that the corresponding homogeneous solution is

$$(A_1 r^{m-1} + A_2 r^{m-2} + \ldots + A_{m-2} r^2 + A_{m-1} r + A_m) \alpha_1^r$$

where the A_i's are constants to be determined by the boundary conditions. It is clear that $A_m \alpha_1^r$ is a homogeneous solution of the difference equation in eq. (9.1). To show that $A_{m-1} r \alpha_1^r$ is also a homogeneous solution, we recall that α_1 not only is a root of the equation

$$C_0 \alpha^r + C_1 \alpha^{r-1} + C_2 \alpha^{r-2} + \ldots + C_k \alpha^{r-k} = 0 \qquad (9.5)$$

but also is a root of the derivative equation of eq. (9.5),

$$C_0 r \alpha^{r-1} + C_1 (r - 1) \alpha^{r-2} + C_2 (r - 2) \alpha^{r-3} + \ldots + C_k (r - k) \alpha^{r-k-1} = 0 \qquad (9.6)$$

because α_1 is a multiple root of eq. (9.5). Multiplying (9.6) by $A_{m-1} \alpha$ and replacing α by α_1, we obtain

$$C_0 A_{m-1} r \alpha_1^r + C_1 A_{m-1} (r - 1) \alpha_1^{r-1} +$$
$$C_2 A_{m-1} (r - 2) \alpha_1^{r-2} + \ldots + C_k A_{m-1} (r - k) \alpha_1^{r-k} = 0$$

which shows that $A_{m-1} r \alpha_1^r$ is indeed a homogeneous solution.

The fact that α_1 satisfies the second, third, ..., $(m - 1)$st derivative equations of eq. (9.5) enables us to prove that $A_{m-2} r^2 \alpha_1^r$, $A_{m-3} r^3 \alpha_1^r$, ..., $A_1 r^{m-1} \alpha_1^r$ are also homogeneous solutions in a similar manner.

Example 9.2 Consider the difference equation:
$$a_r + 6a_{r-1} + 12a_{r-2} + 8a_{r-3} = 0$$
The characteristic equation is
$$\alpha^3 + 6\alpha^2 + 12\alpha + 8 = 0$$
Thus,
$$a_r^{(h)} = (A_1 r^2 + A_2 r + A_3)(-2)^r$$
is a homogeneous solution since -2 is a triple characteristic root. ∎

Example 9.3 Consider the difference equation
$$4a_r - 20a_{r-1} + 17a_{r-2} - 4a_{r-3} = 0$$
The characteristic equation is
$$4\alpha^3 - 20\alpha^2 + 17\alpha - 4 = 0$$

and the characteristic roots are $\dfrac{1}{2}$, $\dfrac{1}{2}$, 4. Consequently, the homogeneous solution is

$$a_r^{(h)} = (A_1 r + A_2)\left(\frac{1}{2}\right)^r + A_3(4)^r \qquad\blacksquare$$

9.5 PARTICULAR SOLUTIONS

There is no general procedure for determining the particular solution of a difference equation. However, in simple cases, this solution can be obtained by the method of inspection. As will be demonstrated in the examples in this section, we first set up the general form of the particular solution according to the form of $f(r)$, and then determine the exact solution according to the given difference equation. Consider the difference equation

$$a_r + 5a_{r-1} + 6a_{r-2} = 3r^2 \qquad (9.7)$$

We assume that the general form of the particular solution is

$$P_1 r^2 + P_2 r + P_3 \qquad (9.8)$$

where P_1, P_2, and P_3 are constants to be determined. Substituting the expression in (9.8) into the left-hand side of eq. (9.7), we obtain

$$P_1 r^2 + P_2 r + P_3 + 5P_1(r-1)^2 + 5P_2(r-1)$$
$$+ 5P_3 + 6P_1(r-2)^2 + 6P_2(r-2) + 6P_3$$

which simplifies to

$$12P_1 r^2 - (34P_1 - 12P_2)r + (29P_1 - 17P_2 + 12P_3) \qquad (9.9)$$

Comparing eq. (9.9) with the right-hand side of eq. (9.7), we obtain the equations

$$12P_1 = 3$$
$$34P_1 - 12P_2 = 0$$
$$29P_1 - 17P_2 + 12P_3 = 0$$

which yield

$$P_1 = \frac{1}{4} \qquad P_2 = \frac{17}{24} \qquad P_3 = \frac{115}{288}$$

Therefore, the particular solution is

$$a_r^{(p)} = \frac{1}{4}r^2 + \frac{17}{24}r + \frac{115}{288}$$

In general, when $f(r)$ is of the form of a polynomial of degree t in r

$$F_1 r^t + F_2 r^{t-1} + \dots + F_t r + F_{t+1}$$

the corresponding particular solution will be of the form

$$P_1 r^t + P_2 r^{t-1} + \dots + P_t r + P_{t+1}$$

Example 9.4 Consider the difference equation

$$a_r + 5a_{r-1} + 6a_{r-2} = 3r^2 - 2r + 1 \tag{9.10}$$

The particular solution is of the form

$$P_1 r^2 + P_2 r + P_3 \tag{9.11}$$

Substituting (9.11) into (9.10), we obtain

$$P_1 r^2 + P_2 r + P_3 + 5P_1(r-1)^2 + 5P_2(r-1) + 5P_3$$
$$+ 6P_1(r-2)^2 + 6P_2(r-2) + 6P_3 = 3r^2 - 2r + 1$$

which simplifies to

$$12P_1 r^2 - (34P_1 - 12P_2)r + (29_1 - 17P_2 + 12P_3) = 3r^2 - 2r + 1 \tag{9.12}$$

Comparing the two sides of eq. (9.12), we obtain the equations

$$12P_1 = 3$$
$$34P_1 - 12P_2 = 2$$
$$29P_1 - 17P_2 + 12P_3 = 1$$

which yield

$$P_1 = \frac{1}{4} \qquad P_2 = \frac{13}{24} \qquad P_3 = \frac{71}{288}$$

Therefore, the particular solution is

$$a_r^{(p)} = \frac{1}{4} r^2 + \frac{13}{24} r + \frac{71}{288} \qquad \blacksquare$$

Example 9.5 Consider the difference equation

$$a_r - 5a_{r-1} + 6a_{r-2} = 1 \tag{9.13}$$

Since $f(r)$ is a constant, the particular solution will also be a constant P. Substituting P into (9.13), we obtain

$$P - 5P + 6P = 1$$

That is,

$$2P = 1$$

or

$$a_r^{(p)} = \frac{1}{2} \qquad \blacksquare$$

As another example, consider the difference equation

$$a_r + 5a_{r-1} + 6a_{r-2} = 42 \cdot 4^r \tag{9.14}$$

We assume that the general form of the particular solution is

$$P4^r \tag{9.15}$$

Substituting the expression in eq. (9.15) into the left-hand side of eq. (9.14), we obtain

$$P4^r + 5P4^{r-1} + 6P4^{r-2}$$

which simplifies to

$$\frac{21}{8} P4^r \tag{9.16}$$

Comparing eq. (9.16) with the right-hand side of eq. (9.14), we obtain

$$P = 16$$

Therefore, the particular solution is

$$a_r^{(p)} = 16 \cdot 4^r$$

In general, when $f(r)$ is of the form $\beta^r r$ the corresponding particular solution is of the form $P\beta^r$, if β is not a characteristic root of the difference equation. Furthermore, when $f(r)$ is of the form

$$(F_1 r^t + F_2 r^{t-1} + \dots + F_t r + F_{t+1})\beta^r$$

the corresponding particular solution is of the form

$$(P_1 r^t + P_2 r^{t-1} + \dots + P_t r + P_{t+1})\beta^r$$

if β is not a characteristic root of the difference equation. Consider the following example.

Example 9.6 Consider the difference equation

$$a_r + a_{r-1} = 3r2^r \tag{9.17}$$

The general form of the particular solution is

$$(P_1 r + P_2)2^r \tag{9.18}$$

Substituting eq. (9.18) into eq. (9.17), we obtain

$$(P_1 r + P_2)2^r + [P_1(r - 1) + P_2]2^{r-1} = 3r2^r$$

which simplifies to

$$\frac{3}{2} P_1 r2^r + \left(-\frac{1}{2} P_1 + \frac{3}{2} P_2\right) 2^r = 3r2^r \tag{9.19}$$

Comparing the two sides of eq. (9.19), we obtain the equations

$$\frac{3}{2} P_1 = 3$$

$$-\frac{1}{2} P_1 + \frac{3}{2} P_2 = 0$$

Thus,

$$P_1 = 2 \qquad P_2 = \frac{2}{3}$$

and the particular solution is

$$a_r^{(p)} = \left(2r + \frac{2}{3}\right)2^r \qquad \blacksquare$$

For the case that β is a characteristic root of multiplicity $m - 1$, when $f(r)$ is of the form

$$(F_1 r^t + F_2 r^{t-1} + \dots + F_t r + F_{t+1})\beta^r$$

the corresponding particular solution is of the form

$$r^{m-1}(P_1 r^t + P_2 r^{t-1} + \ldots + P_t r + P_{t+1})\beta^r$$

Let us examine the following examples.

Example 9.7 Consider the difference equation

$$a_r - 2a_{r-1} = 3 \cdot 2^r \tag{9.20}$$

Because 2 is a characteristic root (of multiplicity 1), the general form of the particular solution is

$$Pr2^r \tag{9.21}$$

Substituting (9.21) into (9.20), we obtain

$$Pr2^r - 2P(r-1)2^{r-1} = 3 \cdot 2^r$$

that is,

$$P2^r = 3 \cdot 2^r$$

or

$$P = 3$$

Thus, the particular solution is

$$a_r^{(p)} = 3r2^r \qquad \blacksquare$$

Example 9.8 For the difference equation

$$a_r - 4a_{r-1} + 4a_{r-2} = (r+1)2^r \tag{9.22}$$

since 2 is a double characteristic root, the general form of the particular solution is

$$r^2(P_1 r + P_2)2^r \tag{9.23}$$

Substituting (9.23) into (9.22), we obtain, after simplification:

$$6P_1 r2^r = r2^r$$

$$(-6P_1 + 2P_2)2^r = 2^r$$

which yield

$$P_1 = \frac{1}{6} \qquad P_2 = 1$$

Thus, the particular solution is

$$a_r^{(p)} = r^2\left(\frac{r}{6}+1\right)2^r \qquad \blacksquare$$

Example 9.9 Consider the difference equation

$$a_r = a_{r-1} + 7 \tag{9.24}$$

Since 1 is a characteristic root of the difference equation and 7 can be written as $7 \cdot 1^r$, the general form of the particular solution is Pr. (The reader should find out what happens if we assume the general form of the particular solution to be P instead.) Substituting $a_r^{(p)} = P_r$ into (9.24), we obtain

$$Pr = P(r-1) + 7$$

that is,

$$P = 7 \qquad \blacksquare$$

Example 9.10 For the difference equation

$$a_r - 2a_{r-1} + a_{r-2} = 7$$

we let $a_r^{(p)} = Pr^2$. We ask the reader to carry out the substitution to confirm that P
$= \frac{7}{2}$. ■

Example 9.11 Consider the difference equation

$$a_r - 5a_{r-1} + 6a_{r-2} = 2^r + r$$

The general form of the particular solution is

$$P_1 r 2^r + P_2 r + P_3$$

(Note that 2 is a characteristic root of the difference equation.) Substitution and comparison will yield

$$P_1 = -2 \qquad P_2 = \frac{1}{2} \qquad P_3 = \frac{7}{4}$$

and

$$a_r^{(p)} = -r2^{r+1} + \frac{1}{2}r + \frac{7}{4} \qquad ■$$

9.6 TOTAL SOLUTIONS

Finally, we must combine the homogeneous solution and the particular solution and determine the undetermined coefficients in the homogeneous solution. For a kth-order difference equation, the k undetermined coefficients $A_1, A_2, ..., A_k$ in the homogeneous solution can be determined by the boundary conditions, $a_{r_0}, a_{r_0+1},$ $..., a_{r_0+k-1}$, for any r_0. Suppose the characteristic roots of the difference equation are all distinct. The total solution is of the form

$$a_r = A_1 \alpha_1^r + A_2 \alpha_2^r + ... + A_k \alpha_k^r + p(r)$$

where $p(r)$ is the particular solution. Thus, for $r = r_0, r_0 + 1, ..., r_0 + k - 1$, we have the system of linear equations:

$$
\begin{aligned}
a_{r_0} &= A_1 \alpha_1^{r_0} + A_2 \alpha_2^{r_0} + ... + A_k \alpha_k^{r_0} + p(r_0) \\
a_{r_0+1} &= A_1 \alpha_1^{r_0+1} + A_2 \alpha_2^{r_0+1} + ... + A_k \alpha_k^{r_0+1} + p(r_0 + 1) \qquad (9.25) \\
&\qquad\qquad .... \\
a_{r_0+k-1} &= A_1 \alpha_1^{r_0+k-1} + A_2 \alpha_2^{r_0+k-1} + ... + A_k \alpha_k^{r_0+k-1} + p(r_0 + k - 1)
\end{aligned}
$$

These k linear equations can be solved for $A_1, A_2, ..., A_k$. For example, for the difference equation in (9.14), the total solution is

$$a_r = A_1(-2)^r + A_2(-3)^r + 16 \cdot 4^r$$

Suppose we are given the boundary conditions $a_2 = 278$ and $a_3 = 962$. Solving the equations

$$278 = 4A_1 + 9A_2 + 256$$
$$962 = -8A_1 - 27A_2 + 1024$$

we obtain

$$A_1 = 1 \qquad A_2 = 2$$

Thus,

$$a_r = (-2)^r + 2(-3)^r + 16 \cdot 4^r$$

is the total solution of the difference equation.

One might question how we can be sure that solutions of the k equations in (9.25) are always unique. It can be shown mathematically that this is indeed the case. However, in Sec. 9.2, recall that we demonstrated the uniqueness of the solution of a kth-order linear recurrence relation with constant coefficients for any given boundary conditions consisting of k consecutive values $a_{r0}, a_{r0+1}, \ldots,$ a_{r0+k-1}. Consequently, the uniqueness of the solution of the recurrence relation guarantees the uniqueness of the solutions of the k equations in (9.25). On the other hand, if we are given the value of the numeric function at k, not necessarily consecutive points, although we can set up k equations for the undetermined coefficients $A_1, A_2, \ldots, A_k$ similar to that in (9.25), since the solution of the recurrence relation might not be uniquely specified by such boundary conditions, it is not always the case that these equations can be solved uniquely.

When the characteristic roots of the difference equation are not all distinct, a derivation similar to the foregoing can be carried out. Again, the undetermined coefficients in the homogeneous solution can be determined uniquely by the value of the numeric function at k consecutive points.

9.7 SOLUTION BY THE METHOD OF GENERATING FUNCTIONS

Instead of solving a difference equation for an expression for the value of a numeric function as we did above, we can also determine the generating function of the numeric function from the difference equation. In many cases, once the generating function is determined, an expression for the value of the numeric function can easily be obtained.

Consider the recurrence relation

$$a_r = 3a_{r-1} + 2 \qquad r \geq 1 \tag{9.26}$$

with the boundary condition $a_0 = 1$. Let us point out that in (9.26) we write down explicitly (for the first time in this chapter) that the recurrence relation is valid only for $r \geq 1$, a fact we knew implicitly all along. Note that for $r = 0$, the recurrence relation becomes

$$a_0 = 3a_{-1} + 2$$

Since a_{-1} is not defined, we cannot assume that the recurrence relation is valid for $r = 0$. In general, for a given kth-order difference equation that specifies a numeric function, we should know for what values of r the equation is valid. First, we note that the equation is valid only if $r \geq k$ because, for $r < k$, the equation will involve a_{-i}'s, which are not defined. Furthermore, in many cases, a difference equation arises from a physical problem in which the value of a_i is meaningful only for $i \geq t$, for some t larger than or equal to 0. In that case, the difference equation is valid only for $r - k \geq t$.

Multiplying both sides of eq. (9.26) by z^r, we obtain

$$a_r z^r = 3a_{r-1} z^r + 2z^r \qquad r \geq 1 \qquad (9.27)$$

Summing (9.27) for all r, $r \geq 1$, we obtain

$$\sum_{r=1}^{\infty} a_r z^r = 3 \sum_{r=1}^{\infty} a_{r-1} z^r + 2 \sum_{r=1}^{\infty} z^r$$

Note that

$$\sum_{r=1}^{\infty} a_r z^r = A(z) - a_0$$

$$\sum_{r=1}^{\infty} a_{r-1} z^r = z \sum_{r=1}^{\infty} a_{r-1} z^{r-1} = zA(z)$$

$$\sum_{r=1}^{\infty} z^r = \frac{z}{1-z}$$

We obtain

$$A(z) - a_0 = 3zA(z) + \frac{2z}{1-z}$$

That is,

$$(1 - 3z)A(z) = \frac{2z}{1-z} + 1$$

which simplifies to

$$(1 - 3z)A(z) = \frac{1+z}{1-z}$$

or

$$A(z) = \frac{1+z}{(1-3z)(1-z)}$$

$$= \frac{2}{1-3z} - \frac{1}{1-z}$$

Consequently, we have

$$a_r = 2 \cdot 3^r - 1 \qquad r \geq 0$$

We state now a general procedure for determining the generating function of the numeric function **a** from the difference equation

$$C_0 a_r + C_1 a_{r-1} + C_2 a_{r-2} + \dots + C_k a_{r-k} = f(r)$$

which is valid for $r \geq s$, where $s \geq k$. Multiplying both sides of this equation by z^r and summing from $r = s$ to $r = \infty$, we obtain

$$\sum_{r=s}^{\infty} (C_0 a_r + C_1 a_{r-1} + C_2 a_{r-2} + \dots + C_k a_{r-k}) z^r = \sum_{r=s}^{\infty} f(r) z^r$$

Since

$$\sum_{r=s}^{\infty} C_0 a_r z^r = C_0 [A(z) - a_0 - a_1 z - a_2 z^2 - \ldots - a_{s-1} z^{s-1}]$$

$$\sum_{r=s}^{\infty} C_1 a_{r-1} z^r = C_1 z [A(z) - a_0 - a_1 z - a_2 z^2 - \ldots - a_{s-2} z^{s-2}]$$

$$\cdots\cdots\cdots\cdots\cdots\cdots\cdots\cdots\cdots\cdots\cdots\cdots$$

$$\sum_{r=s}^{\infty} C_k a_{r-k} z^r = C_k z^k [A(z) - a_0 - a_1 z - a_2 z^2 - \ldots - a_{s-k-1} z^{s-k-1}]$$

we have

$$A(z) = \frac{1}{C_0 + C_1 z + \ldots + C_k z^k} \left[\sum_{r=s}^{\infty} f(r) z^r \right.$$

$$+ C_0 (a_0 + a_1 z + a_2 z^2 + \ldots + a_{s-1} z^{s-1})$$

$$+ C_1 z (a_0 + a_1 z + a_2 z^2 + \ldots + a_{s-2} z^{s-2})$$

$$\left. + \ldots + C_k z^k (a_0 + a_1 z + a_2 z^2 + \ldots + a_{s-k-1} z^{s-k-1}) \right]$$

We have more illustrative examples:

Example 9.12 Suppose we toss a coin r times. There are 2^r possible sequences of outcomes. We want to know the number of sequences of outcomes in which heads never appear on successive tosses. Let a_r denote the number of such sequences. To each sequence of $r - 1$ heads and tails in which there are no consecutive heads, we can append a tail to obtain a sequence of r heads and tails in which there are no consecutive heads. To each sequence of $r - 2$ heads and tails in which there are no consecutive heads, we can append a tail and then a head to obtain a sequence of r heads and tails in which there are no consecutive heads. Moreover, these exhaust all sequences of r heads and tails in which there are no consecutive heads. We thus have the recurrence relation

$$a_r = a_{r-1} + a_{r-2} \tag{9.28}$$

Note that $a_1 = 2$ and $a_2 = 3$. The value of a_0 has no physical significance, and a reasonable choice of its value is 0. In this case, the difference equation is *not* valid for $r = 2$, and is only valid for $r \geq 3$.

We now proceed to show how we can obtain $A(z)$ from eq. (9.28). Multiplying both sides of (9.28) by z^r and summing from $r = 3$ to $r = \infty$, we obtain

$$\sum_{r=3}^{\infty} a_r z^r = \sum_{r=3}^{\infty} a_{r-1} z^r + \sum_{r=3}^{\infty} a_{r-2} z^r$$

That is,

$$A(z) - a_2 z^2 - a_1 z - a_0 = z[A(z) - a_1 z - a_0] + z^2[A(z) - a_0]$$

which simplifies to

$$A(z) = \frac{z^2 + 2z}{1 - z - z^2} = -1 + \frac{1+z}{1 - z - z^2}$$

Writing $A(z)$ as

$$A(z) = -1 + \frac{(5+3\sqrt{5})/10}{1-[(1+\sqrt{5})/2]z} - \frac{(-5+3\sqrt{5})/10}{1-[(1-\sqrt{5})/2]z}$$

we see that

$$a_r = \begin{cases} 0 & r=0 \\ \dfrac{5+3\sqrt{5}}{10}\left(\dfrac{1+\sqrt{5}}{2}\right)^r - \dfrac{-5+3\sqrt{5}}{10}\left(\dfrac{1-\sqrt{5}}{2}\right)^r & r \geq 1 \end{cases}$$

Since the value of a_0 has no physical significance, we can choose to set a_0 to 1 instead of 0, so that the difference equation in eq. (9.28) is valid for $r \geq 2$. In that case, we can multiply both sides of eq. (9.28) by z^r and sum from $r = 2$ to $r = \infty$. We obtain

$$\sum_{r=2}^{\infty} a_r z^r = \sum_{r=2}^{\infty} a_{r-1} z^r + \sum_{r=2}^{\infty} a_{r-2} z^r$$

That is,

$$A(z) - a_1 z - a_0 = z[A(z) - a_0] + z^2 A(z)$$

or

$$A(z) = \frac{1+z}{1-z-z^2}$$

which yields

$$a_r = \frac{5+3\sqrt{5}}{10}\left(\frac{1+\sqrt{5}}{2}\right)^r - \frac{-5+3\sqrt{5}}{10}\left(\frac{1-\sqrt{5}}{2}\right)^r \qquad r \geq 0 \qquad \blacksquare$$

Example 9.13 We shall solve the difference equation in Example 9.11 by determining first the generation function $A(z)$. For the difference equation

$$a_r - 5a_{r-1} + 6a_{r-2} = 2^r + r \qquad r \geq 2$$

with the boundary conditions $a_0 = 1$ and $a_1 = 1$, since

$$\sum_{r=2}^{\infty} a_r z^r - 5\sum_{r=2}^{\infty} a_{r-1} z^r + 6\sum_{r=2}^{\infty} a_{r-2} z^r = \sum_{r=2}^{\infty} 2^r z^r + \sum_{r=2}^{\infty} r z^r$$

we obtain

$$A(z) - a_0 - a_1 z - 5z[A(z) - a_0] + 6z^2 A(z) = \frac{4z^2}{1-2z} + z\left[\frac{1}{(1-z)^2} - 1\right]$$

which simplifies to

$$A(z) = \frac{1 - 8z + 27z^2 - 35z^3 + 14z^4}{(1-z)^2(1-2z)^2(1-3z)}$$

$$= \frac{5/4}{1-z} + \frac{1/2}{(1-z)^2} - \frac{3}{1-2z} - \frac{2}{(1-2z)^2} + \frac{17/4}{1-3z}$$

Consequently, we have

$$a_r = \frac{5}{4} + \frac{1}{2}(r+1) - 3 \cdot 2^r - 2(r+1)2^r + \frac{17}{4}3^r$$

$$= \frac{7}{4} + \frac{r}{2} - r2^{r+1} - 5 \cdot 2^r + \frac{17}{4}3^r$$

We strongly suggest that the reader follow the derivation carefully as a review of the relationship between a numeric function and its generating function. ∎

Example 9.14 Consider a certain nuclear reaction inside of a reactor containing nuclei and high- and low-energy free particles. There are two kinds of events: (1) A high-energy particle strikes a nucleus and is absorbed, causing it to emit three high-energy particles and one low-energy particle; and (2) a low-energy particle strikes a nucleus and is absorbed, causing it to emit two high-energy particles and one low-energy particle. We assume that every free particle causes an event 1 μs after it is emitted. Suppose a single high-energy particle is injected at time 0 into a system containing only nuclei. This is represented in Fig. 9.2. We want to determine the numbers of high-energy and low-energy particles in the system at

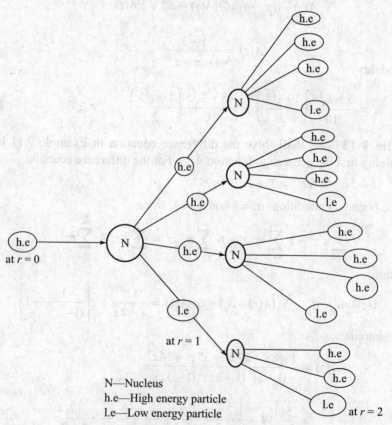

N—Nucleus
h.e—High energy particle
l.e—Low energy particle

Fig. 9.2 Nuclear reaction inside a reactor

time equal to $r\,\mu$s. Let a_r and b_r denote the number of high-energy and low-energy particles at time r, respectively. We have

$$a_r = 3a_{r-1} + 2b_{r-1}$$
$$b_r = a_{r-1} + b_{r-1} \tag{9.29}$$

Note that these are two simultaneous difference equations for the numeric functions **a** and **b**. The equations are valid for $r \geq 1$, and we have the boundary conditions

$$a_0 = 1 \qquad b_0 = 0$$

From eq. (9.29) we obtain

$$\sum_{r=1}^{\infty} a_r z^r = \sum_{r=1}^{\infty} 3a_{r-1} z^r + \sum_{r=1}^{\infty} 2b_{r-1} z^r$$

$$\sum_{r=1}^{\infty} b_r z^r = \sum_{r=1}^{\infty} a_{r-1} z^r + \sum_{r=1}^{\infty} b_{r-1} z^r$$

or

$$A(z) - 1 = 3zA(z) + 2zB(z) \tag{9.30}$$
$$B(z) = zA(z) + zB(z) \tag{9.31}$$

Simplifying eq. (9.30), we get

$$(1 - 3z)\,A(z) = 1 + 2zB(z) \tag{9.32}$$

Simplifying eq. (9.31), we get

$$zA(z) = (1 - z)\,B(z)$$

$$\Rightarrow \qquad A(z) = \frac{1-z}{z} B(z) \tag{9.33}$$

Substituting this value of $A(z)$ in eq. (9.32), we get

$$\frac{(1-3z)(1-z)}{z} B(z) = 1 + 2zB(z)$$

$$\Rightarrow \quad \left(\frac{(1-3z)(1-z)}{z} - 2z \right) B(z) = 1$$

$$\Rightarrow \qquad B(z) = \frac{z}{z^2 - 4z + 1}$$

Putting the value of $B(z)$ obtained above, in eq. (9.33), we get

$$\Rightarrow \qquad A(z) = \frac{1-z}{z^2 - 4z + 1}$$

Factorizing the denominator of $A(z)$ obtained above, we get

$$A(z) = \frac{1-z}{\{z - (2 + \sqrt{3})\}\{z - (2 - \sqrt{3})\}}$$

Multiplying the denominator by $1 = (2 - \sqrt{3})(2 + \sqrt{3})$, we get

$$A(z) = \frac{1-z}{\{1 - z(2 - \sqrt{3})\}\{1 - z(2 + \sqrt{3})\}}$$

Let,

$$A(z) = \frac{1-z}{\{1-(2-\sqrt{3})z\}\{1-(2+\sqrt{3})z\}}$$

$$= \frac{x}{1-(2-\sqrt{3})z} + \frac{y}{1-(2+\sqrt{3})z} \qquad (9.34)$$

$$\Rightarrow \qquad 1 - z = x\{1-(2+\sqrt{3})z\} + y\{1-(2-\sqrt{3})z\}$$

Solving the above equation, we get

$$y = \frac{1+\sqrt{3}}{2\sqrt{3}} = \frac{3+\sqrt{3}}{6}$$

$$x = \frac{1-\sqrt{3}}{2\sqrt{3}} = \frac{3-\sqrt{3}}{6}$$

Putting these values of x and y in eq. (9.34), we get

$$A(z) = \frac{(3+\sqrt{3})/6}{1-(2+\sqrt{3})z} + \frac{(3-\sqrt{3})/6}{1-(2-\sqrt{3})z} \qquad (9.35)$$

Similarly, we can solve for B(z). It may be shown that,

$$B(z) = \frac{z}{z^2 - 4z + 1}$$

$$= \frac{z}{\{1-z(2-\sqrt{3})\}\{1-z(2+\sqrt{3})\}}$$

Let

$$B(z) = \frac{z}{\{1-(2-\sqrt{3})z\}\{1-(2+\sqrt{3})z\}}$$

$$= \frac{x}{1-(2-\sqrt{3})z} + \frac{y}{1-(2+\sqrt{3})z} \qquad (9.36)$$

$$\Rightarrow \qquad z = x\{1-(2+\sqrt{3})\}z + y\{1-(2-\sqrt{3})z\}$$

Solving the above equation, we get

$$y = \frac{1}{2\sqrt{3}} = \frac{\sqrt{3}}{6}$$

$$x = \frac{-1}{2\sqrt{3}} = \frac{-\sqrt{3}}{6}$$

Putting these values of x and y in eq. (9.36), we get

$$B(z) = \frac{\sqrt{3}/6}{1-(2+\sqrt{3})z} - \frac{\sqrt{3}/6}{1-(2-\sqrt{3})z} \qquad (9.37)$$

It follows from eq. (9.35) and (9.37) that

$$a_r = \frac{3+\sqrt{3}}{6}(2+\sqrt{3})^r + \frac{3-\sqrt{3}}{6}(2-\sqrt{3})^r$$

$$b_r = \frac{\sqrt{3}}{6}(2+\sqrt{3})^r - \frac{\sqrt{3}}{6}(2-\sqrt{3})^r \qquad \blacksquare$$

We demonstrated in Example 9.14 how we can solve a set of *simultaneous difference equations* by the technique of generating functions. From a set of simultaneous difference equations relating several numeric functions we can obtain a set of simultaneous (algebraic) equations relating their generating functions. These equations can then be solved for closed-form expressions for the generating functions.

9.8 SORTING ALGORITHMS

Let us return to the simple example in Sec. 9.2 in which we showed that the numeric function $(3^0, 3^1, 3^2, ..., 3^r, ...)$ can be specified by the recurrence relation

$$a_r = 3a_{r-1} \qquad (9.38)$$

together with the boundary condition $a_0 = 1$. Equation (9.38) is a *recursive* specification of the value of **a** at r. It says that if a_{r-1} is known then a_r can be computed as three times a_{r-1}. However, if a_{r-2} is known then a_{r-1} can be computed as three times a_{r-2}; if a_{r-3} is known, then a_{r-2} can be computed as three times a_{r-3}; and so on. Consequently, knowing a_0 is sufficient to determine a_r for any r. Recalling our discussion in Sec. 9.1, we realize that such a point of view is not restricted to the description of numeric functions. It also suggests a concise and powerful way to describe computing algorithms. We present in this section some examples from the problem of sorting. As we discussed in Sec. 7.2, by sorting the n numbers that are stored in n registers $x_1, x_2, ..., x_n$, we mean to rearrange the contents of the registers so that the rearranged contents of registers $x_1, x_2, ..., x_n$ are in ascending order. A sorting procedure consists of a sequence of comparison steps, each of which compares the contents of registers x_i and x_j and places the smaller number in x_i and the larger in x_j. We shall denote a comparison step by $A(x_i, x_j)$.

We present first a sorting algorithm from Sec. 7.2; **BUBBLESORT**. However, our description of this algorithm will be different from that in Sec. 7.2 in that we shall show a recursive specification of the algorithm.* We introduce some notations that will enable us to give a "symbolic" specification of the algorithm. Let $S(x_1, x_2, ..., x_n)$ denote algorithm **BUBBLESORT** that sorts the numbers in registers $x_1, x_2, ..., x_n$ in ascending order, and let $M(x_1, x_2, ..., x_n)$ denote the algorithm **LARGEST2** presented in Sec. 7.2 that places in register x_n the largest number among the numbers in registers $x_1, x_2, ..., x_n$. We have

$$S(x_1, x_2, ..., x_n) \triangleq M(x_1, x_2, ..., x_n)S(x_1, x_2, ..., x_{n-1}) \qquad (9.39)$$

The symbol $\triangleq$ means "is defined to be" and the concatenation of the symbols of procedures means sequential execution of the corresponding procedures from left to right. Note that $M(x_1, x_2, ..., x_n)$ can be defined as

$$M(x_1, x_2, ..., x_n) \triangleq A(x_1, x_2)A(x_2, x_3) ... A(x_{n-2}, x_{n-1})A(x_{n-1}, x_n)$$

which is exactly the specification of algorithm **LARGEST2** in Sec. 7.2. The relation in eq. (9.39) can be written as

---

* We remind the reader that the bubble sort algorithm presented here is the same as that presented in Sec. 7.2 in that it consists of exactly the same sequence of comparison steps. The only difference is the way the comparison steps are specified. In general, an algorithm can be described in different ways, most notably, *nonrecursively* and *recursively*.

$$S(x_1, x_2, \ldots, x_n) \triangleq A(x_1, x_2)A(x_2, x_3) \ldots$$
$$A(x_{n-2}, x_{n-1})A(x_{n-1}, x_n)S(x_1, x_2, \ldots, x_{n-1})$$

which is a symbolic description of algorithm **BUBBLESORT**. With the boundary condition

$$S(x_1, x_2) \triangleq A(x_1, x_2)$$

our recursive specification of the algorithm is completed.

As an explicit example, we note that

$$S(x_1, x_2, x_3, x_4) \triangleq A(x_1, x_2)A(x_2, x_3)A(x_3, x_4)S(x_1, x_2, x_3)$$
$$\triangleq A(x_1, x_2)A(x_2, x_3)A(x_3, x_4)A(x_1, x_2)A(x_2, x_3)S(x_1, x_2)$$
$$\triangleq A(x_1, x_2)A(x_2, x_3)A(x_3, x_4)A(x_1, x_2)A(x_2, x_3)A(x_1, x_2)$$

Let a_n denote the number of comparison steps the bubble sort algorithm takes to sort n numbers. According to eq. (9.39), we have

$$a_n = (n-1) + a_{n-1} \tag{9.40}$$

Solving the recurrence relation in eq. (9.40) anti using the boundary condition $a_1 = 0$, we obtaint*

$$a_n = \frac{n(n-1)}{2}$$

We present now another sorting algorithm known as the *Bose-Nelson algorithm*, due to R. C. Bose and R. J. Nelson. which we shall denote $T(x_1, x_2, \ldots, x_n)$. To simplify our discussion, we assume that the number of numbers to be sorted is a power of 2. Let $P[(x_1, x_2 \ldots, x_n), (x_{n+1}, x_{n+2}, \ldots, x_{2n})]$ denote an algorithm that will arrange the numbers in registers $x_1, x_2, \ldots, x_{2n}$ in ascending order given that the numbers in registers $x_1, x_2, \ldots, x_n$ have already been arranged in ascending order, as have the numbers in registers $x_{n+1}, x_{n+2}, \ldots x_{2n}$. Clearly,

$$T(x_1, x_2, \ldots, x_{2n}) \triangleq T(x_1, x_2, \ldots, x_n)T(x_{n+1}, x_{n+2}, \ldots, x_{2n})$$
$$P[(x_1, x_2, \ldots, x_n), (x_{n+1}, x_{n+2}, \ldots, x_{2n})] \tag{9.41}$$

In other words, to sort the $2n$ numbers in registers $x_1, x_2, \ldots, x_{2n}$, we can first sort the n numbers in $x_1, x_2, \ldots, x_n$, and the n numbers in $x_{n+1}, x_{n+2}, \ldots, x_{2n}$, and then combine these two sorted sequences into one. The algorithm $P[(x_1, x_2, \ldots, x_n), (x_{n+1}, x_{n+2}, \ldots, x_{2n})]$ can be defined recursively as:

$$P[(x_1, x_2, \ldots, x_n), (x_{n+1}, x_{n+2}, \ldots, x_{2n})]$$
$$\triangleq P[(x_1, x_2, \ldots, x_{n/2}), (x_{n+1}, x_{n+2}, \ldots, x_{3n/2})]$$
$$P[(x_{n/2+1}, x_{n/2+2}, \ldots, x_n), (x_{3n/2+1}, x_{3n/2+2}, \ldots, x_{2n})]$$
$$P[(x_{n/2+1}, x_{n/2+2}, \ldots, x_n), (x_{n+1}, x_{n+2}, \ldots, x_{3n/2})] \tag{9.42}$$

Note that $P[(x_1, x_2, \ldots, x_{n/2}), (x_{n+1}, x_{n+2}, \ldots, x_{3n/2})]$ places the smallest $n/2$ numbers, among the $2n$ numbers in the registers, in registers $x_1, x_2, \ldots, x_{n/2}$ in ascending order. Similarly, $P[(x_{n/2+1}, x_{n/2+2}, \ldots, x_{2n}), (x_{3n/2+1}, x_{3n/2+2}, \ldots, x_{2n})]$ places the largest $n/2$ numbers, among the $2n$ numbers in the registers, in registers $x_{3n/2+1}, x_{3n/2+2}, \ldots, x_{2n}$ in ascending order. Finally, $P[(x_{n/2+1}, x_{n/2+2}, \ldots, x_n), (x_{n+1}, x_{n+2}, \ldots, x_{3n/2})]$ places

---

* See Prob. 9. 10.

the remaining n of the $2n$ numbers in registers $x_{n/2+1}, x_{n/2+2}, \ldots, x_{3n/2}$ in ascending order. Applying the relations in eq. (9.41) and eq. (9.42) repeatedly, we can express $T(x_1, x_2, \ldots, x_n), n = 2^r$, as a sequence of procedures of the forms $T(x_i, x_j)$ and $P[(x_i), (x_j)]$. However, both of $T(x_i, x_j)$ and $P[(x_i), (x_j)]$ are equal to $A(x_i, x_j)$.

For example, we note that

$$T(x_1, x_2, x_3, x_4) \triangleq T(x_1, x_2)T(x_3, x_4)P[(x_1, x_2), (x_3, x_4)]$$

Since

$$T(x_1, x_2) \triangleq A(x_1, x_2)$$
$$T(x_3, x_4) \triangleq A(x_3, x_4)$$

and

$$P[(x_1, x_2), (x_3, x_4)] \triangleq P[(x_1), (x_3)]P[(x_2), (x_4)]P[(x_2), (x_3)]$$
$$\triangleq A(x_1, x_3)A(x_2, x_4)A(x_2, x_3)$$

we have

$$T(x_1, x_2, x_3, x_4) \triangleq A(x_1, x_2)A(x_3, x_4)A(x_1, x_3)A(x_2, x_4)A(x_2, x_3)$$

as a complete specification of an algorithm that sorts four numbers stored in the registers x_1, x_2, x_3, x_4.

Let c_r denote the number of comparison steps that $P[(x_1, x_2, \ldots, x_{2r}), (x_{2r+1}, x_{2r+2}, \ldots, x_{2r+1})]$ takes. According to the relation in eq. (9.42), we have

$$c_r = 3c_{r-1} \tag{9.43}$$

Solving (9.43) with the boundary condition $c_0 = 1$, we obtain

$$c_r = 3^r$$

Let d_r denote the number of comparison steps the procedure $T(x_1, x_2, \ldots, x_{2r})$ takes. According to the relation in eq. (9.41), we have

$$d_r = 2d_{r-1} + c_{r-1}$$

or

$$d_r = 2d_{r-1} + 3^{r-1} \tag{9.44}$$

Solving eq. (9.44), we obtain

$$d_r = B2^r + 3^r$$

From the boundary condition $d_0 = 0$, we determine that $B = -1$. Thus,

$$d_r = 3^r - 2^r$$

Another algorithm is known as the *odd-even merge*, due to K. E. Batcher (see Batcher [1]), which we shall denote $U(x_1, x_2, \ldots, x_n)$. Again, we assume that n is a power of 2. Let

$$U(x_1, x_2, \ldots, x_{2n}) \triangleq U(x_1, x_2, \ldots, x_n)U(x_{n+1}, x_{n+2}, \ldots, x_{2n})$$
$$B[(x_1, x_2, \ldots, x_n), (x_{n+1}, x_{n+2}, \ldots, x_{2n})] \tag{9.45}$$

where the algorithm B is defined to be

$$B[(x_1, x_2, x_3, x_4, \ldots, x_{2n}), (y_1, y_2, y_3, y_4, \ldots, y_{2n})]$$
$$\triangleq B[(x_1, x_3, x_5, \ldots, x_{2n-1}), (y_1, y_3, y_5, \ldots, y_{2n-1})]$$
$$B[(x_2, x_4, x_6, \ldots, x_{2n}), (y_2, y_4, y_6, \ldots, y_{2n})]$$
$$A(x_2, x_3)A(x_4, x_5)A(x_6, x_7) \ldots A(x_{2n}, y_1)$$

$$A(y_2, y_3)A(y_4, y_5) \ldots A(y_{2n-2}, y_{2n-1}) \tag{9.46}$$

It is not immediately obvious that the algorithm defined in eq. (9.46) indeed merges two sorted sequences of numbers into one. We present first an illustrative example before we proceed to verify the validity of the algorithm. Suppose eight numbers, 2, 3, 6, 7, 1, 4, 5, 8, are stored in registers $x_1, x_2, x_3, x_4, y_1, y_2, y_3, y_4$, as shown in Fig. 9.3a, such that the numbers in registers x_1, x_2, x_3, x_4 are in ascending order, and the numbers in registers y_1, y_2, y_3, y_4 are in ascending order. According to eq. (9.46),

$$B[(x_1, x_2, x_3, x_4), (y_1, y_2, y_3, y_4)]$$
$$\triangleq B[(x_1, x_3), (y_1, y_3)]B[(x_2, x_4), (y_2, y_4)]A(x_2, x_3)A(x_4, y_1)A(y_2, y_3)$$

$B[(x_1, x_3), (y_1, y_3)]$ arranges the numbers in x_1, x_3, y_1, y_3 in ascending order, and $B[(x_2, x_4), (y_2, y_4)]$ arranges the numbers in x_2, x_4, y_2, y_4 in ascending order as shown in Fig. 9.3b. Finally, $A(x_2, x_3)$ arranges the numbers in x_2, x_3; $A(x_4, y_1)$ arranges the numbers in x_4, y_1; and $A(y_2, y_3)$ arranges the numbers in y_2, y_3 in ascending order as shown in Fig. 9.3c.

To verify the validity of eq. (9.46), we want first to show that after the execution of $B[(x_1, x_3, x_5, \ldots, x_{2n-1}), (y_1, y_3, y_5, \ldots, y_{2n-1})]$ and $B[(x_2, x_4, x_6, \ldots, x_{2n}), (y_2, y_4, y_6, \ldots, y_{2n})]$:

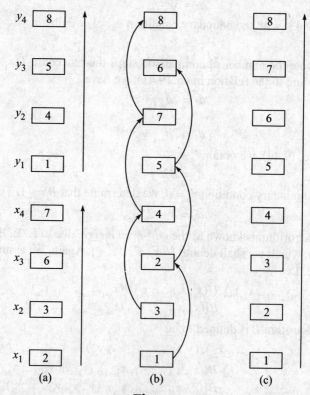

(a)   (b)   (c)

Fig. 9.3

1. The number in x_1 is the smallest of the $4n$ numbers.

2. The number in y_{2n} is the largest of the $4n$ numbers.

3. The two numbers in x_{2i} and x_{2i+1}, $1 \leq i \leq n - 1$, are the $2i$th and the $(2i + 1)$st smallest of the $4n$ numbers; the two numbers in x_{2n} and y_1 are the $2n$th and the $(2n + 1)$st smallest of the $4n$ numbers; and the two numbers in y_{2i} and y_{2i+1}, $1 \leq i \leq n - 1$, are the $(2n + 2i)$th and $(2n + 2i + 1)$st smallest of the $4n$ numbers.

If this is indeed the case, the comparisons $A(x_2, x_3)A(x_4, x_5) \ldots A(y_{2n-2}, y_{2n-1})$ will yield a sorted sequence of $4n$ numbers.

The reader can easily ascertain that (1) and (2) are obvious. To show that (3) is true, we shall only show that the two numbers in x_{2i} and x_{2i+1}, $1 \leq i \leq n - 1$, are the $2i$th and the $(2i + 1)$st smallest of the $4n$ numbers. The other two cases can be shown in a similar manner.* Consider the number that is in x_{2i} after the execution. This number is larger than exactly $i - 1$ of the numbers that were in $x_2, x_4, x_6, \ldots, x_{2n}, y_2, y_4, y_6, \ldots, y_{2n}$. Assume that this number is larger than k of the numbers that were in $x_2, x_4, x_6, \ldots, x_{2n}$, and is larger than $i - k - 1$ of the numbers that were in $y_2, y_4, y_6, \ldots, y_{2n}$. That is, this number is larger than the numbers that were in $x_2, x_4, x_6, \ldots, x_{2k}$ and those that were in $y_2, y_4, y_6, \ldots, y_{2(i-k-1)}$. In other words, this number is larger than the numbers that were in $x_1, x_2, x_3, x_4, \ldots, x_{2k}$ and those that were in $y_1, y_2, y_3, y_4, \ldots, y_{2(i-k-1)}$. Now, if this number was in $x_{2(k+1)}$, it is also larger than x_{2k+1}, and it might or might not be larger than the number that was in $y_{2(i-k-1)+1}$. On the other hand, if this number was in $y_{2(i-k)}$, it is also larger than $y_{2(i-k)-1}$, and it might or might not be larger than the number that was in x_{2k+1}. Consequently, we can conclude that this number is larger than $2i - 1$ or $2i$ of the $4n$ numbers in the registers.

In a similar way, let us consider the number that is in x_{2i+1} after the execution. Assume that this number is larger than k of the numbers that were in $x_1, x_3, \ldots, x_{2n-1}$, and is larger than $i - k$ of the numbers that were in $y_1, y_3, \ldots, y_{2n-1}$. That is, this number is larger than the numbers that were in $x_1, x_3, \ldots, x_{2k-1}$, and is larger than the numbers that were in $y_1, y_3, \ldots, y_{2(i-k)-1}$. Thus, this number is larger than the numbers that were in $x_1, x_2, x_3, \ldots, x_{2k-2}, x_{2k-1}$, and those that were in $y_1, y_2, y_3, \ldots, y_{2(i-k)-2}, y_{2(i-k)-1}$. Now, if this number was in x_{2k+1}, it is also larger than the number that was in x_{2k}, and it might or might not be larger than the number that was in $y_{2(i-k)}$. If this number was in $y_{2(i-k)+1}$, it is larger than the number that was in $y_{2(i-k)}$, and it might or might not be larger than the number that was in x_{2k}. Consequently, we can conclude that this number is larger than $2i - 1$ or $2i$ of the $4n$ numbers in the registers.

We now complete the proof of (3) by noting that if the number in x_{2i} is the $2i$th smallest number, then the number in x_{2i+1} must be the $(2i + 1)$st smallest number, and vice versa.

---

* We do not really have three cases in (3). It is only because of the notation we have chosen that we have to make three parallel statements.

Let c_r denote the number of comparison steps the algorithm $B[(x_1, x_2, \ldots, x_{2^r}),$ $(y_1, y_2, \ldots, y_{2^r})]$ takes. According to the relation in eq. (9.46), we have

$$c_r = 2c_{r-1} + (2^r - 1) \qquad (9.47)$$

Solving (9.47), with the boundary condition $c_0 = 1$, we obtain

$$c_r = r2^r + 1$$

Let d_r denote the number of comparison steps the algorithm $U(x_1, x_2, \ldots, x_{2^r})$ takes. According to the relation in eq. (9.45), we have

$$d_r = 2d_{r-1} + c_{r-1}$$

or

$$d_r = 2d_{r-1} + (r-1)2^{r-1} + 1 \qquad (9.48)$$

Solving the recurrence relation in eq. (9.48), with the boundary condition $d_0 = 0$, we obtain

$$d_r = (r^2 - r + 4)2^{r-2} - 1$$

9.9 DIVIDE-AND-CONQUER ALGORITHM

Divide-and-conquer is a top-down technique for designing algorithms that consist of dividing the problems into smaller sub-problems. If the problem is small, then it is solved directly. If the problem is large, then divide-and-conquer algorithm is used to solve the problem, and it consists of the following:

- Divide the problem into several sub-problems that are similar to the original problem but smaller in size,
- Solve (conquer) the sub-problem recursively (successively and independently), and then
- Combine these solutions to sub-problems to create a solution to the original problem.

Divide-and-conquer technique is often more efficient than "obvious" approaches, e.g. Mergesort and Quicksort. The divide-and-conquer technique is also used to solve the sub-problems, i.e. the sub-problems are further divided into sub sub-problems which are further divided into smaller problems, and so on. For example, in order to sort a list of integers using merge sort, we first split the list into two halves of equal sizes and sort each halve separately. Then, we merge the two sorted halves.

Another example of this recursive algorithm is a procedure for multiplying integers that reduces the problem of the multiplication of two integers to three multiplications of pair of integers with half as many bits. This reduction is successively carried out until integers with one bit are obtained.

In this section, we discuss some examples which use divide-and-conquer algorithms for solving specific problems. We start with the example of "Merge sort". After discussing merge sort, we illustrate some other examples such as "Fast multiplication of integers", "Binary search" and "Strassen's matrix multiplication algorithm".

Example 9.15 Merge Sort The merge sort algorithm divides the array to be sorted with n elements, into two arrays with $n/2$ elements each, where n is even. The arrays with $n/2$ elements are again divided into two arrays of $n/4$ elements each, and so on. Each part is then sorted. The two sorted arrays of $n/2$ elements are then merged into one sorted array. As a result, the number of comparisons used by the merge sort to sort an array of n elements is less than $f(n)$, where the function $f(n)$ satisfies the divide-and-conquer recurrence relation

$$f(n) = 2f(n/2) + n$$

Let us consider the following example:

Suppose the array A contains 16 elements as follows.

$$65, 43, 22, 54, 87, 11, 76, 48, 30, 60, 19, 75, 94, 27, 58, 80$$

Now divide the given array into two equal parts and repeat the process of dividing into two equal parts recursively until we get the least number of elements in the arrays.

65, 43, 22, 54, 87, 11, 76, 48		30, 60, 19, 75, 94, 27, 58, 80	
65, 43, 22, 54	87, 11, 76, 48	30, 60, 19, 75	94, 27, 58, 80
65, 43 22, 54	87, 11 76, 48	30, 60 19, 75	94, 27 58, 80

Now the array is divided into 8 number of arrays with 2 elements. Compare the two elements in each array and then merge each two arrays into a single array as follows.

43, 65 22, 54	11, 87 48, 76	30, 60 19, 75	27, 94 58, 80
22, 43, 54, 65	11, 48, 76, 87	19, 30, 60, 75	27, 58, 80, 94
11, 22, 43, 48, 54, 65, 76, 87		19, 27, 30, 58, 60, 75, 80, 94	

$$11, 19, 22, 27, 30, 43, 48, 54, 58, 60, 65, 75, 76, 80, 87, 94 \qquad ■$$

In this way we can sort a list of elements using merge sort by divide-and-conquer technique. Figure 9.4 shows the C code for merge sort using divide-and-conquer algorithm.

```
#include<stdio.h>
#include<conio.h>
#define MAX 100
int list[MAX];
void mergesort(int,int);
void merge(int,int,int,int);
void main()
{
int n,i,j=0;
clrscr();
printf("Enter the no of terms :");
scanf("%d",&n);
printf("Enter the terms to be sorted\n");
for(i=0;i<n;i++)
       scanf("%d",&list[i]);
mergesort(j,n-1);
printf("The sorted list is \n");
for(i=0;i<n;i++)
```

```
            printf("%d ",list[i]);
    getch();
    }
    void mergesort(int f,int l)
    {
            int m;
            if(l>f)
            {
            m=(f+1)/2;
            mergesort(f,m);
            mergesort(m+1,l);
            merge(f,m,m+1,l);
            }
    }
    void merge(int f1,int l1,int f2,int l2)
    {
            int i=f1,j=f2,temp[MAX],k=0;
            while(i<=l1 && j<=l2)
            {
                    if(list[i]<list[j])
                    {
                            temp[k]=list[i];
                            i++;
                            k++;
                    }
                    else
                    {
                            temp[k]=list[j];
                            j++;
                            k++;
                    }
            }
            while(i<=l1)
            {
                    temp[k]=list[i];
                    k++;
                    i++;
            }
            while(j<=l2)
            {
                    temp[k]=list[j];
                    k++;
                    j++;
            }
            for(i=f1,k=0;i<=l2;i++,k++)
                    list[i]=temp[k];
    }
    Output:
    Enter the no of terms : 16
    Enter the terms to be sorted:
    65 43 22 54 87 11 76 48 30 60 19 75 94 27 58 80
    The sorted list is :
    11 19 22 27 30 43 48 54 58 60 65 75 76 80 87 94
```

Fig. 9.4 C code for merge sort using divide-and-conquer algorithm

Example 9.16 Fast Multiplication of Integers

There are some more efficient algorithms than the conventional algorithm for multiplying integers. In this section, we will discuss one of these algorithms, which use a divide-and-conquer technique. In this fast multiplication algorithm, we proceed by splitting each of two $2n$-bit integers into two parts each containing n-bits. Then, the original multiplication is converted to three multiplications of n-bit integers along with shifts and additions, from the multiplication of two $2n$-bit integers. If the lengths of both the integers are not same, then initial bits of 0's are added in these binary equivalents.

Let us consider two integers x and y with binary expansions of length $2n$ each.

$$x = (x_{2n-1} x_{2n-2} \cdots x_1 x_0)_2$$
$$y = (y_{2n-1} y_{2n-2} \cdots y_1 y_0)_2$$

Let
$$x = 2^n P_1 + P_0, \quad y = 2^n Q_1 + Q_0$$

where

$$P_1 = (x_{2n-1} x_{2n-2} \cdots x_{n+1} x_n)_2$$
$$P_0 = (x_{n-1} x_{n-2} \cdots x_1 x_0)_2$$
$$Q_1 = (y_{2n-1} y_{2n-2} \cdots y_{n+1} y_n)_2$$
$$Q_0 = (y_{n-1} y_{n-2} \cdots y_1 y_0)_2$$

Now the multiplication of the two integers x and y can be written as

$$xy = (2^{2n} + 2^n) P_1 Q_1 + 2^n (P_1 - P_0)(Q_0 - Q_1) + (2^n + 1) P_0 Q_0$$

Here, this multiplication of two integers x and y can be carried out using three multiplications of n-bit integers, together with additions, subtractions and shifts. If $f(n)$ is the total number of bit operations needed and S_n is the total number of bit operations used by these operations to multiply two n-bit integers then

$$f(2n) = 3f(n) + S_n$$

Let us consider the following example.

Find out the product of two integers 14 and 10 by using fast multiplication algorithm.

Solution: The binary equivalent of 14 is $(1110)_2$

The binary equivalent of 10 is $(1010)_2$

Let $x = (1110)_2$ and $y = (1010)_2$.

Divide x and y into two parts each as

$$P_1 = (11)_2$$
$$P_0 = (10)_2$$
$$Q_1 = (10)_2$$
$$Q_0 = (10)_2$$

By using fast multiplication algorithm x and y can be written as

$$x = 2^2 (11)_2 + (10)_2$$
$$y = 2^2 (10)_2 + (10)_2$$

Now the product of x and y can be written as

$$xy = (2^{2n} + 2^n) P_1 Q_1 + 2^n (P_1 - P_0)(Q_0 - Q_1) + (2^n + 1) P_0 Q_0; \text{ where } n = 2$$
$$= (2^4 + 2^2)(11)_2 (10)_2 + 2^2 ((11)_2 - (10)_2)((10)_2 - (10)_2) + (2^2 + 1)(10)_2 (10)_2$$

By simplifying the above equation, we obtain the product as

$$xy = (140)_{10}$$

■

Let us consider another example.

Example 9.17 Find the product of two integers 128 and 123 using the fast multiplication algorithm.

Solution: The binary equivalent of 128 is $(10000000)_2$.
The binary equivalent of 123 is $(01111011)_2$.
Let

$x = (10000000)_2$ and

$y = (01111011)_2$.

Divide x and y into two parts each as

$P_1 = (1000)_2$

$P_0 = (0000)_2$

$Q_1 = (0111)_2$

$Q_0 = (1011)_2$

By using the fast multiplication algorithm, x and y can be expressed as

$x = 2^4(1000)_2 + (0000)_2$

$y = 2^4(0111) + (1011)_2$

Now, the product of x and y can be written as

$$xy = (2^{2n} + 2^n) P_1 Q_1 + 2^n(P_1 - P_0) \times (Q_0 - Q_1) + (2^n + 1) P_0 Q_0; \text{ where } n = 4$$

$$= (2^8 + 2^4)(1000)_2 \times (0111)_2 + 2^4((1000)_2 - (0000)_2) \times ((1011)_2 - (0111)_2)$$
$$+ (2^4 + 1)(0000)_2 \times (1011)_2$$

$$= (256 + 16) \times (00111000)_2 + 16 \times (1000)_2 \times (0100)_2 + 17 \times (0000)_2$$

$$= 272 \times 56 + 16 \times (00100000)_2 + 17 \times 0$$

$$= 15232 + 16 \times 32 + 0$$

$$= 15744$$

So, the product of the two integers, 128 and 123 using the fast multiplication algorithm is 15744. ■

Example 9.18 Binary Search *Binary search* is an extremely well-known instance of divide-and-conquer algorithm. This algorithm is a technique for finding a particular value in a sorted list in minimum possible comparisons. To carry out the binary search, we have to follow the following steps:

1. Take a sorted list.
2. Find out the middle element in the list.
3. Compare the item which is to be searched with the middle element of the list.

4. If the item is equal to the middle element then search is completed. If the item is less than the middle element, then search the item in the first half of the list, otherwise search in the second half of the list.

$A[1]$	$A[2]$	$A[3]$	$\cdots$	$A[m-1]$	$A[m]$	$A[m+1]$	$\cdots$	$A[n-2]$	$A[n-1]$	$A[n]$

Let $A[1 \ldots n]$ be a non-decreasing sorted array; i.e. $A[i] = A[j]$, where $1 \leq i \leq j \leq n$ and p be the item which is to be searched.

Let m be the middle position; then

$$m = (1 + n)/2 \quad \text{or} \quad (\text{low} + \text{high})/2.$$

Suppose, the middle element in the list A is $q = A[m]$.

According to this algorithm, compare p with q.

i. If $p = q$, then search is completed successfully.

ii. If $p < q$, then search for p in the first half of the list, i.e. $A[1]$ to $A[m-1]$

iii. If $p > q$, then search for p in the second half of the list, i.e. $A[m+1]$ to $A[n]$.

This binary search algorithm reduces the search for an element in an array of size n to the binary search of the element in an array of size $n/2$, when n is even. Two comparisons are required to implement this reduction; one is to determine in which half of the list the element is present and the second one is to determine whether any terms of the list are left. Thus, if $f(n)$ is the number of comparisons needed to search an element in the list of size n then it follows that

$$f(n) = f(n/2) + 2$$

when n is even.

Now, let us consider the following example:

Find out the position of the element 67 in the sorted array A, where $A = \{9, 16, 25, 49, 50, 67, 84\}$.

Solution: The number of elements in the array A is 7. The given number to be searched is 67. Let us find out the middle position m.

$$m = (1 + 7)/2$$
$$= 4$$

Now the middle element is $A[m] = 49$. Compare 67 with 49. Clearly $67 > 49$.

So, search for 67 in the second half, i.e. from $A[5]$ to $A[7]$.

Again recursively use the binary search algorithm for searching in the second half of the array.

Now, the middle element is 67 which is equal to the search element. So, the search is completed successfully and the position of 67 in the array is found to be 6. ■

The program to implement the binary search is given in Fig. 9.5.

```
#include<stdio.h>
#include<conio.h>
void main()
{
        int array[100],temp=0,first,last,mid,n,i,count=0,item;
        clrscr();
        printf("Enter the number of elements :");
        scanf("%d",&n);
        printf("Enter the elements in sorted order\n");
        for(i=0;i<n;i++)
                scanf("%d",&array[i]);
        printf("Enter the item to be searched :");
        scanf("%d",&item);
        first=0;
        last=n-1;
        while((first<=last)&&(item!=array[mid]))
        {
                mid=(first+last)/2;
                if(item==array[mid])
        {
                printf("search is successfully completed\n");
                temp=mid;
                printf("The item's position is : %d",temp+1);
                count=count+1;
        }
        if(item<array[mid])
                last=mid-1;
        else
                first=mid+1;
        }
        if(temp==0)
                printf("search is not successfully completed\n");
        getch();
}
Output:
Enter the no of elements: 7
Enter the elements in sorted order
10
15
33
45
67
71
88
Enter the item to be searched: 71
Search is successfully completed.

The item's position is 6.
```

Fig. 9.5 Program for Binary Search

Example 9.19 Strassen's Matrix Multiplication Algorithm As another illustration of divide-and-conquer algorithms, we consider a problem on matrix multiplication. Let **A** and **B** be two 2×2 matrices.

$$\mathbf{A} = \begin{bmatrix} a_{11} & a_{12} \\ a_{21} & a_{22} \end{bmatrix}$$

$$\mathbf{B} = \begin{bmatrix} b_{11} & b_{12} \\ b_{21} & b_{22} \end{bmatrix}$$

The product of **A** and **B**, denoted as **C**, can be computed as

$$\mathbf{C} = \mathbf{AB} = \begin{bmatrix} c_{11} & c_{12} \\ c_{21} & c_{22} \end{bmatrix}$$

where

$$c_{11} = a_{11}b_{11} + a_{12}b_{21}$$
$$c_{12} = a_{11}b_{12} + a_{12}b_{22}$$
$$c_{21} = a_{21}b_{11} + a_{22}b_{21}$$
$$c_{22} = a_{21}b_{12} + a_{22}b_{22}$$

We note immediately that such a computation requires four addition operations and eight multiplication operations. Let d_1 denote the cost of an addition operation, and d_2 denote the cost of a multiplication operation. The total cost of multiplying two 2×2 matrices is

$$4d_1 + 8d_2$$

Once again, one may ask if there is a "better" algorithm to multiply two 2×2 matrices? As it turns out, an alternative algorithm can do so. One such alternative algorithm is due to Strassen. (Later, we shall determine if this alternative algorithm is indeed a better algorithm.) This alternative algorithm computes the first seven intermediate results:

$$m_1 = (a_{11} + a_{22})(b_{11} + b_{22})$$
$$m_2 = (a_{12} - a_{22})(b_{21} + b_{22})$$
$$m_3 = (a_{11} - a_{21})(b_{11} + b_{12})$$
$$m_4 = (a_{11} + a_{12})b_{22} \tag{9.49}$$
$$m_5 = (a_{21} + a_{22})b_{11}$$
$$m_6 = a_{11}(b_{12} - b_{22})$$
$$m_7 = a_{22}(b_{21} - b_{11})$$

These intermediate results can then be used to compute the entries of the matrix **C**:

$$c_{11} = m_1 + m_2 - m_4 + m_7$$
$$c_{12} = m_4 + m_6$$
$$c_{21} = m_5 + m_7$$
$$c_{22} = m_1 - m_3 - m_5 + m_6$$

A quick count indicates that such an algorithm requires 18 addition operations and 7 multiplication operations. Thus, the total cost is

$$18d_1 + 7d_2$$

It is far from obvious that such an algorithm is superior to the first algorithm, which is the classical matrix multiplication algorithm. As a matter of fact, one would immediately point out that the first algorithm requires 12 arithmetic operations, while the second one requires 25 arithmetic operations. On the other hand, an advocate of the second algorithm might argue that the second algorithm will be less expensive than the first if a multiplication operation is significantly more expensive than an addition operation. One might point out that such an argument is unrealistic because, in practice, costs for multiplication and addition are about the same. However, before we conclude prematurely that this is an empty exercise in algorithm design, let us consider the more general problem of multiplying two $n \times n$ matrices $\mathbf{A}$ and $\mathbf{B}$. To simplify our discussion, we shall assume that n is a power of 2. One recalls that computing the product of two $n \times n$ matrices by the classical multiplication algorithm requires n^3 multiplication operations and $n^2(n-1)$ addition operations, that is, a total of $2n^3 - n^2$ arithmetic operations. (The ijth entry of the product is computed as $\sum_{k=1}^{n} a_{ik} b_{kj}$, which requires n multiplication operations and $(n-1)$ addition operations.) We recognize that the second algorithm presented above can be used to multiply two $n \times n$ matrices. Given two $n \times n$ matrices $\mathbf{A}$ and $\mathbf{B}$, we can partition them into $(n/2) \times (n/2)$ submatrices:

$$\mathbf{A} = \left[\begin{array}{c|c} \mathbf{a}_{11} & \mathbf{a}_{12} \\ \hline \mathbf{a}_{21} & \mathbf{a}_{22} \end{array} \right]$$

$$\mathbf{B} = \left[\begin{array}{c|c} \mathbf{b}_{11} & \mathbf{b}_{12} \\ \hline \mathbf{b}_{21} & \mathbf{b}_{22} \end{array} \right]$$

The product $\mathbf{AB}$ can then be expressed as

$$\mathbf{C} = \mathbf{AB} = \left[\begin{array}{c|c} \mathbf{c}_{11} & \mathbf{c}_{12} \\ \hline \mathbf{c}_{21} & \mathbf{c}_{22} \end{array} \right]$$

where $\mathbf{a}_{11}$, $\mathbf{a}_{12}$, $\mathbf{a}_{21}$, $\mathbf{a}_{22}$, $\mathbf{b}_{11}$, $\mathbf{b}_{12}$, $\mathbf{b}_{21}$, $\mathbf{b}_{22}$, $\mathbf{c}_{11}$, $\mathbf{c}_{12}$, $\mathbf{c}_{21}$, and $\mathbf{c}_{22}$* are all $(n/2) \times (n/2)$ submatrices. We can then compute

$$\mathbf{m}_1 = (\mathbf{a}_{11} + \mathbf{a}_{22})(\mathbf{b}_{11} + \mathbf{b}_{22})$$
$$\mathbf{m}_2 = (\mathbf{a}_{12} - \mathbf{a}_{22})(\mathbf{b}_{21} + \mathbf{b}_{22})$$
$$\mathbf{m}_3 = (\mathbf{a}_{11} - \mathbf{a}_{21})(\mathbf{b}_{11} + \mathbf{b}_{12})$$
$$\mathbf{m}_4 = (\mathbf{a}_{11} + \mathbf{a}_{12})\mathbf{b}_{22}$$
$$\mathbf{m}_5 = (\mathbf{a}_{21} + \mathbf{a}_{22})\mathbf{b}_{11}$$
$$\mathbf{m}_6 = \mathbf{a}_{11}(\mathbf{b}_{12} - \mathbf{b}_{22})$$
$$\mathbf{m}_7 = \mathbf{a}_{22}(\mathbf{b}_{21} - \mathbf{b}_{11})$$

Note that, these are repetitions of the relations in eq. (9.49). We merely replaced the roman letters by boldface ones to emphasize that $\mathbf{m}_1$, $\mathbf{m}_2$, ..., $\mathbf{m}_7$, $\mathbf{a}_{11}$, ..., $\mathbf{a}_{22}$, $\mathbf{b}_{11}$, ..., $\mathbf{b}_{22}$ are all matrices. Of course, in these equations all multiplications are multiplications of $(n/2) \times (n/2)$ matrices, and all additions are additions of $(n/2) \times (n/2)$ matrices. Finally, we can compute

---

* We use boldface type letters to indicate that these are matrices.

$$\mathbf{c}_{11} = \mathbf{m}_1 + \mathbf{m}_2 - \mathbf{m}_4 + \mathbf{m}_7$$
$$\mathbf{c}_{12} = \mathbf{m}_4 + \mathbf{m}_6$$
$$\mathbf{c}_{21} = \mathbf{m}_5 + \mathbf{m}_7$$
$$\mathbf{c}_{22} = \mathbf{m}_1 - \mathbf{m}_3 - \mathbf{m}_5 + \mathbf{m}_6$$

Let us consider an example.

Example 9.20 Find the multiplication of two matrices **A** and **B** using Strassen's multiplication algorithm, where

$$\mathbf{A} = \begin{bmatrix} 1 & 2 \\ 0 & -1 \end{bmatrix}, \qquad \mathbf{B} = \begin{bmatrix} 3 & -1 \\ 2 & 0 \end{bmatrix}.$$

Solution:

Given:
$$\mathbf{A} = \begin{bmatrix} a_{11} & a_{12} \\ a_{21} & a_{22} \end{bmatrix} = \begin{bmatrix} 1 & 2 \\ 0 & -1 \end{bmatrix}$$

$$\mathbf{B} = \begin{bmatrix} b_{11} & b_{12} \\ b_{21} & b_{22} \end{bmatrix} = \begin{bmatrix} 3 & -1 \\ 2 & 0 \end{bmatrix}$$

Let
$$\mathbf{C} = \mathbf{A} \times \mathbf{B} = \begin{bmatrix} c_{11} & c_{12} \\ c_{21} & c_{22} \end{bmatrix}$$

Now, we have to compute the intermediate results $m_1, m_2, m_3, m_4, m_5, m_6, m_7$. According to Strassen's matrix multiplication algorithm,

$$m_1 = (a_{11} + a_{22})(b_{11} + b_{22}) = (1 - 1)(3 + 0) = 0$$
$$m_2 = (a_{12} - a_{22})(b_{21} + b_{22}) = (2 - (-1))(2 + 0) = 6$$
$$m_3 = (a_{11} - a_{21})(b_{11} + b_{12}) = (1 - 0)(3 - 1) = 2$$
$$m_4 = (a_{11} + a_{12})(b_{22}) = (1 + 2)(0) = 0$$
$$m_5 = (a_{21} + a_{22})(b_{11}) = (0 - 1)(3) = -3$$
$$m_6 = (a_{11})(b_{21} - b_{22}) = (1)(-1 - 0) = -1$$
$$m_7 = (a_{22})(b_{21} - b_{11}) = (-1)(2 - 3) = 1$$

Now, we use these intermediate results to compute the entries of the matrix **C**, as follows:

$$c_{11} = m_1 + m_2 - m_4 + m_7 = 7$$
$$c_{12} = m_4 + m_6 = -1$$
$$c_{21} = m_5 + m_7 = -2$$
$$c_{22} = m_1 - m_3 - m_5 + m_6 = 0$$

Now, the final resultant matrix can be written as

$$\mathbf{C} = \begin{bmatrix} c_{11} & c_{12} \\ c_{21} & c_{22} \end{bmatrix} = \begin{bmatrix} 7 & -1 \\ -2 & 0 \end{bmatrix} \qquad \blacksquare$$

The program for finding the multiplication of two 2×2 matrices using Strassen's algorithm is given in Fig. 9.6.

```
/* Multiplication of two 2 × 2 matrices using Strassen's algorithm*/
#include<stdio.h>
#include<conio.h>
int main()
{
  float a[2][2],b[2][2],m1,m2,m3,m4,m5,m6,m7,c11,c12,c21,c22;
  int i,j;
  printf("\n------Multiplication of Two 2 × 2 Matrices--------");
  printf("\nPlease enter the first matrix A:");
  for(i=0;i<2;i++)
     for(j=0;j<2;j++) {
        printf("\nElement[%d][%d] :",i+1,j+1);
        scanf("%f",&a[i][j]);
     }
     printf("\nPlease enter the Second matrix B:");
     for(i=0;i<2;i++)
        for(j=0;j<2;j++) {
           printf("\nElement[%d][%d] :",i+1,j+1);
           scanf("%f",&b[i][j]);
        }
  m1=(a[0][0]+a[1][1])*(b[0][0]+b[1][1]);
  m2=(a[0][1]-a[1][1])*(b[1][0]+b[1][1]);
  m3=(a[0][0]-a[1][0])*(b[0][0]+b[0][1]);
  m4=(a[0][0]+a[0][1])*(b[1][1]);
  m5=(a[1][0]+a[1][1])*(b[0][0]);
  m6=(a[0][0])*(b[0][1]-b[1][1]);
  m7=(a[1][1])*(b[1][0]-b[0][0]);
  c11=m1+m2-m4+m7;
  c12=m4+m6;
  c21=m5+m7;
  c22=m1-m3-m5+m6;
  printf("\nThe resultant Matrix is:\n%0.1f\t%0.1f\n%0.1f\t%0.1f",c11,c12,c21,c22);
getch();
}

Output:
------Multiplication of Two 2 × 2 Matrices--------
Please enter the first matrix A:
Element[1][1]    :1
Element[1][2]    :2
Element[2][1]    :0
Element[2][2]    :-1

Please enter the Second matrix B:
Element[1][1]    :3
Element[1][2]    :-1
Element[2][1]    :2
Element[2][2]    :0
The resultant Matrix is:
7.0        -1.0
-2.0        0.0
```

Fig. 9.6 Program for multiplication of two 2 × 2 matrices using Strassen's algorithm

We note that the total cost of multiplying **A** and **B** is 7 matrix multiplications and 18 matrix additions (of $(n/2) \times (n/2)$ matrices). If we use the classical method to carry out multiplication of $(n/2) \times (n/2)$ matrices, the total number of arithmetic operations will be

$$7 \times \left[2\left(\frac{n}{2}\right)^3 - \left(\frac{n}{2}\right)^2 \right] + 18 \times \left(\frac{n}{2}\right)^2 = \frac{7}{4}n^3 + \frac{11}{4}n^2$$

which is superior to $2n^3 - n^2$ for large n. However, we can do better than that by employing our new multiplication algorithm recursively to compute the products of the submatrices. In other words, to compute the product of two $n \times n$ matrices, we need to perform 7 multiplications and 18 additions of $(n/2) \times (n/2)$ matrices, while each of the multiplication operations of $(n/2) \times (n/2)$ matrices, can be performed with seven multiplications and 18 additions of $(n/4) \times (n/4)$ matrices, and so on. Let f_r denote the total number of arithmetic operations required to multiply two $2^r \times 2^r$ matrices. We have

$$f_r = 7f_{r-1} + 18 \cdot 2^{2r-2} \qquad r \geq 1 \tag{9.50}$$

with the boundary condition $f_0 = 1$. Solving eq. (9.50), we obtain

$$f_r = 7 \cdot 7^r - \frac{18}{3} \cdot 4^r$$

Thus, for $n = 2^r$,

$$f_r = 7 \cdot 7^{\lg n} - \frac{18}{3} \cdot n^2 = 7n^{2.81} - \frac{18}{3} \cdot n^2$$

Since the time complexity of the algorithm presented above is $\Theta(n^{2.81})$, the time complexity of the matrix multiplication problem is $O(n^{2.81})$.

The above procedure can be extended to 4×4 matrices. Suppose A and B are two 4×4 matrices, such as

$$A = \begin{pmatrix} a_{11} & a_{12} & a_{13} & a_{14} \\ a_{21} & a_{22} & a_{23} & a_{24} \\ a_{31} & a_{32} & a_{33} & a_{34} \\ a_{41} & a_{42} & a_{43} & a_{44} \end{pmatrix}, \quad \text{and} \quad B = \begin{pmatrix} b_{11} & b_{12} & b_{13} & b_{14} \\ b_{21} & b_{22} & b_{23} & b_{24} \\ b_{31} & b_{32} & b_{33} & b_{34} \\ b_{41} & b_{42} & b_{43} & b_{44} \end{pmatrix}$$

The multiplication of two 4×4 matrices A and B is equivalent to the multiplications of a pair of 2×2 matrices whose elements are each 2×2 matrices. To compute the product, first divide A and B into two 2×2 matrices as,

$$A = \begin{bmatrix} A_{11} & A_{12} \\ A_{21} & A_{22} \end{bmatrix}, \quad B = \begin{bmatrix} B_{11} & B_{12} \\ B_{21} & B_{22} \end{bmatrix}$$

where

$$A_{11} = \begin{bmatrix} a_{11} & a_{12} \\ a_{21} & a_{22} \end{bmatrix} \quad A_{12} = \begin{bmatrix} a_{13} & a_{14} \\ a_{23} & a_{24} \end{bmatrix} \quad A_{21} = \begin{bmatrix} a_{31} & a_{32} \\ a_{41} & a_{42} \end{bmatrix} \quad A_{22} = \begin{bmatrix} a_{33} & a_{34} \\ a_{43} & a_{44} \end{bmatrix}$$

and

$$B_{11} = \begin{bmatrix} b_{11} & b_{12} \\ b_{21} & b_{22} \end{bmatrix} \quad B_{12} = \begin{bmatrix} b_{13} & b_{14} \\ b_{23} & b_{24} \end{bmatrix} \quad B_{21} = \begin{bmatrix} b_{31} & b_{32} \\ b_{41} & b_{42} \end{bmatrix} \quad B_{22} = \begin{bmatrix} b_{33} & b_{34} \\ b_{43} & b_{44} \end{bmatrix}$$

Then, we may proceed in the same way as described above to compute the product of the matrices A and B.

Let us understand this with an example.

Example 9.21 Find the multiplication of the matrices A and B using Strassen's matrix multiplication algorithm, where

$$A = \begin{pmatrix} 1 & 2 & 0 & 1 \\ 2 & -1 & 0 & -1 \\ 3 & 0 & 1 & 0 \\ 1 & -1 & 0 & 0 \end{pmatrix} \quad B = \begin{pmatrix} 0 & -1 & 1 & 2 \\ 1 & 1 & -1 & 0 \\ 0 & 1 & 0 & 1 \\ 1 & 2 & 2 & 1 \end{pmatrix}$$

Solution: The multiplication of the two 4×4 matrices A and B is equivalent to the multiplications of a pair of 2×2 matrices whose elements are each 2×2 matrices. To find the multiplication, we first divide A and B into two 2×2 matrices as

$$\begin{bmatrix} A_{11} & A_{12} \\ A_{21} & A_{22} \end{bmatrix} \times \begin{bmatrix} B_{11} & B_{12} \\ B_{21} & B_{22} \end{bmatrix}$$

where, $\quad A_{11} = \begin{bmatrix} 1 & 2 \\ 2 & -1 \end{bmatrix}, A_{12} = \begin{bmatrix} 0 & 1 \\ 0 & -1 \end{bmatrix}, A_{21} = \begin{bmatrix} 3 & 0 \\ 1 & -1 \end{bmatrix}, A_{22} = \begin{bmatrix} 1 & 0 \\ 0 & 0 \end{bmatrix},$

$$B_{11} = \begin{bmatrix} 0 & -1 \\ 1 & 1 \end{bmatrix}, B_{12} = \begin{bmatrix} 1 & 2 \\ -1 & 0 \end{bmatrix}, B_{21} = \begin{bmatrix} 0 & 1 \\ 1 & 2 \end{bmatrix}, B_{22} = \begin{bmatrix} 0 & 1 \\ 2 & 1 \end{bmatrix}$$

Let, the resultant matrix C is given by

$$C = A \times B.$$

According to Strassen's matrix multiplication algorithm,

$$C = \begin{bmatrix} C_{11} & C_{12} \\ C_{21} & C_{22} \end{bmatrix} = \begin{bmatrix} A_{11} & A_{12} \\ A_{21} & A_{22} \end{bmatrix} \times \begin{bmatrix} B_{11} & B_{12} \\ B_{21} & B_{22} \end{bmatrix}$$

where $C_{11}, C_{12}, C_{21}, C_{22}$ are 2×2 matrices.

Now, we have to compute the intermediate results $M_1, M_2, M_3, M_4, M_5, M_6, M_7$. According to Strassen's matrix multiplication algorithm, M_1 is given by

$$M_1 = (A_{11} + A_{22}) \times (B_{11} + B_{22})$$

$$= \left(\begin{bmatrix} 1 & 2 \\ 2 & -1 \end{bmatrix} + \begin{bmatrix} 1 & 0 \\ 0 & 0 \end{bmatrix} \right) \times \left(\begin{bmatrix} 0 & -1 \\ 1 & 1 \end{bmatrix} + \begin{bmatrix} 0 & 1 \\ 2 & 1 \end{bmatrix} \right)$$

$$= \begin{bmatrix} 2 & 2 \\ 2 & -1 \end{bmatrix} \times \begin{bmatrix} 0 & 0 \\ 3 & 2 \end{bmatrix}$$

We can again apply Strassen's matrix multiplication algorithm to the above result, as the result is a multiplication of two 2×2 matrices. First, we compute the intermediate results $m_1, m_2, m_3, m_4, m_5, m_6, m_7$ for the above multiplication of two 2×2 matrices. According to Strassen's matrix multiplication algorithm,

$$m_1 = (a_{11} + a_{22})(b_{11} + b_{22}) = (2 - 1)(0 + 2) = 2$$
$$m_2 = (a_{12} - a_{22})(b_{21} + b_{22}) = (2 - (-1))(3 + 2) = 15$$
$$m_3 = (a_{11} + a_{21})(b_{11} + b_{12}) = (2 - 2)(0 + 0) = 0$$
$$m_4 = (a_{11} + a_{12})(b_{22}) = (2 + 2)(2) = 8$$
$$m_5 = (a_{21} + a_{22})(b_{11}) = (2 - 1)(0) = 0$$
$$m_6 = (a_{11})(b_{12} - b_{22}) = (2)(0 - 2) = -4$$
$$m_7 = (a_{22})(b_{21} - b_{11}) = (-1)(3 - 0) = -3$$

Now, these intermediate results can be used to compute the entries of the matrix M_1, as follows:

$$c_{11} = m_1 + m_2 - m_4 + m_7 = 6$$
$$c_{12} = m_4 + m_6 = 4$$
$$c_{21} = m_5 + m_7 = -3$$
$$c_{22} = m_1 - m_3 - m_5 - m_6 = -2$$

Now, M_1 can be expressed as

$$M_1 = \begin{bmatrix} c_{11} & c_{12} \\ c_{21} & c_{22} \end{bmatrix} = \begin{bmatrix} 6 & 4 \\ -3 & -2 \end{bmatrix}$$

Similarly, we can compute the values of M_2, M_3, M_4, M_5, M_6 and M_7. It may be shown that,

$$M_2 = \begin{bmatrix} 3 & 1 \\ -3 & -3 \end{bmatrix}, M_3 = \begin{bmatrix} -2 & 0 \\ 1 & 1 \end{bmatrix}, M_4 = \begin{bmatrix} 6 & 4 \\ -4 & 0 \end{bmatrix},$$

$$M_5 = \begin{bmatrix} 0 & -4 \\ -1 & -2 \end{bmatrix}, M_6 = \begin{bmatrix} -5 & -1 \\ 5 & 3 \end{bmatrix}, M_7 = \begin{bmatrix} 0 & 2 \\ 0 & 0 \end{bmatrix},$$

Now, we use these intermediate results to compute the entries of the final resultant matrix **C**, as follows:

$$C_{11} = M_1 + M_2 - M_4 + M_7$$

$$= \begin{bmatrix} 6 & 4 \\ -3 & -2 \end{bmatrix} + \begin{bmatrix} 3 & 1 \\ -3 & -3 \end{bmatrix} - \begin{bmatrix} 6 & 4 \\ -4 & 0 \end{bmatrix} + \begin{bmatrix} 0 & 2 \\ 0 & 0 \end{bmatrix}$$

$$= \begin{bmatrix} 3 & 3 \\ -2 & -5 \end{bmatrix}$$

$$C_{12} = M_4 + M_6$$

$$= \begin{bmatrix} 6 & 4 \\ -4 & 0 \end{bmatrix} + \begin{bmatrix} -5 & -1 \\ 5 & 3 \end{bmatrix}$$

$$= \begin{bmatrix} 1 & 3 \\ 1 & 3 \end{bmatrix}$$

$$C_{21} = M_5 + M_7$$

$$= \begin{bmatrix} 0 & -4 \\ -1 & -2 \end{bmatrix} + \begin{bmatrix} 0 & 2 \\ 0 & 0 \end{bmatrix}$$

$$= \begin{bmatrix} 0 & -2 \\ -1 & -2 \end{bmatrix}$$

$$C_{22} = M_1 - M_3 - M_5 + M_6$$

$$= \begin{bmatrix} 6 & 4 \\ -3 & -2 \end{bmatrix} - \begin{bmatrix} -2 & 0 \\ 1 & 1 \end{bmatrix} - \begin{bmatrix} 0 & -4 \\ -1 & -2 \end{bmatrix} + \begin{bmatrix} -5 & -1 \\ 5 & 3 \end{bmatrix}$$

$$= \begin{bmatrix} 3 & 7 \\ 2 & 2 \end{bmatrix}$$

Now, the final resultant matrix can be written as

$$\mathbf{C} = \begin{bmatrix} C_{11} & C_{12} \\ C_{21} & C_{22} \end{bmatrix}, \text{ or}$$

$$\mathbf{C} = \begin{pmatrix} 3 & 3 & 1 & 3 \\ -2 & -5 & 1 & 3 \\ 0 & -2 & 3 & 7 \\ -1 & -2 & 2 & 2 \end{pmatrix}$$

∎

Estimation of the Size of the Functions From the above examples, it may be observed that the recurrence relation of the form

$$f(n) = p\, f(n/q) + g(n)$$

may arise in many different situations. Now, let us derive the estimates of the size of the functions that satisfy the above recurrence relation. Let f satisfy this recurrence relation, whenever n is divisible by q. Let $n = q^m$, where m is a positive integer. Then

$$\begin{aligned} f(n) &= p\, f(n/q) + g(n) \\ &= p^2 f(n/q^2) + p\, g(n/q) + g(n) \\ &= p^3 f(n/q^3) + p^2 g(n/q^2) + p\, g(n/q) + g(n) \\ &= p^m f(n/b^m) + \sum_{i=0}^{m-1} p^i g(n/q^i) \end{aligned}$$

But, we have $n/q^m = 1$, then

$$f(n) = p^m f(1) + \sum_{i=0}^{m-1} p^i g(n/q^i)$$

This equation for $f(n)$ can be used to estimate the size of a function that satisfies divide-and-conquer relation.

Problems

9.1 Solve the following recurrence relations:

    (a) $a_r - 7a_{r-1} + 10a_{r-2} = 0$, given that $a_0 = 0$ and $a_1 = 3$.

    (b) $a_r - 4a_{r-1} + 4a_{r-2} = 0$, given that $a_0 = 1$ and $a_1 = 6$.

9.2 Solve the following recurrence relations:

    (a) $a_r - 7a_{r-1} + 10a_{r-2} = 3^r$, given that $a_0 = 0$ and $a_1 = 1$.

    (b) $a_r + 6a_{r-1} + 9a_{r-2} = 3$, given that $a_0 = 0$ and $a_1 = 1$.

    (c) $a_r + a_{r-1} + a_{r-2} = 0$, given that $a_0 = 0$ and $a_1 = 2$.

9.3 Solve the following recurrence relations:

    (a) $a_r - a_{r-1} - a_{r-2} = 0$, given that $a_0 = 1$ and $a_1 = 1$.

    (b) $a_r - 2a_{r-1} + 2a_{r-2} - a_{r-3} = 0$, given that $a_0 = 2$. $a_1 = 1$, and $a_2 = 1$.

9.4 Given that $a_0 = 0$, $a_1 = 1$, $a_2 = 4$, and $a_3 = 12$ satisfy the recurrence relation

$$a_r + C_1 a_{r-1} + C_2 a_{r-2} = 0$$

determine a_r.

9.5 The solution of the recurrence relation is

$$C_0 a_r + C_1 a_{r-1} + C_2 a_{r-2} = f(r)$$

is

$$3^r + 4^r + 2$$

Given that $f(r) = 6$ for all r, determine C_0, C_1, and C_2.

9.6 The solution of the recurrence relation

$$a_r = A a_{r-1} + B 3^r \qquad r \geq 1$$

is

$$a_r = C 2^r + D 3^{r+1} \qquad r \geq 0$$

Given that $a_0 = 19$ and $a_1 = 50$, determine the constants $A, B, C,$ and D.

9.7 Let

$$4a_r + C_1 a_{r-1} + C_2 a_{r-2} = f(r) \qquad r \geq 2$$

be a second-order linear recurrence with constant coefficients. For some boundary conditions a_0 and a_1, the solution of the recurrence is

$$1 - 2r + 3 \cdot 2^r$$

Determine $a_0, a_1, C_1, C_2,$ and $f(r)$. (The solution is not unique.)

9.8 Consider the recurrence relation

$$a_r = a_{r-1} - a_{r-2}$$

    (a) Solve the recurrence relation, given that $a_r = 1$ and $a_2 = 0$.

(b) Can you solve the recurrence relation if it is given that $a_0 = 0$ and $a_3 = 0$?

(c) Repeat part (b) if it is given that $a_0 = 1$ and $a_3 = 2$.

9.9 (a) Determine the particular solution for the difference equation

$$a_r - 3a_{r-1} + 2a_{r-2} = 2^r$$

(b) Determine the particular solution for the difference equation

$$a_r - 4a_{r-1} + 4a_{r-2} = 2^r$$

9.10 (a) Determine the particular solution for the difference equation

$$a_r - 2a_{r-1} = f(r)$$

where $f(r) = 7r^2$

(b) Repeat part (a) for $f(r) = 7r^2$.

(c) Determine the particular solution for the difference equation

$$a_r - a_{r-1} = 7r$$

(d) Repeat part (c) if $f(r) = 7r^2$.

(e) Let

$$C_0 a_r + C_1 a_{r-1} + \ldots + C_k a_{r-k} = f(r)$$

be a difference equation with a characteristic root 1. Let $f(r) = r^t$. What can be said about the general form of the particular solution $a_r^{(p)}$?

9.11 (a) Solve the recurrence relation

$$a_r + 3a_{r-1} + 2a_{r-2} = f(r)$$

where

$$f(r) = \begin{cases} 1 & r = 2 \\ 0 & \text{otherwise} \end{cases}$$

with the boundary condition $a_0 = a_r = 0$.

(b) Repeat part (a) for

$$f(r) = \begin{cases} 1 & r = 5 \\ 0 & \text{otherwise} \end{cases}$$

(c) Consider the recurrence relation

$$C_0 a_r + C_1 a_{r-1} + C_2 a_{r-2} + \ldots + C_k a_{r-k} = f(r)$$

Let $\hat{a}_r$ denote the solution of the recurrence relation for $f(r) = \hat{f}(r)$ with the boundary conditions $\hat{a}_0 = \hat{a}_1 = \hat{a}_2 = \ldots = \hat{a}_{k-1} = 0$. Let $\tilde{a}_r$ denote the solution of the recurrence relation for $f(r) = \tilde{f}(r)$ with the boundary conditions $\tilde{a}_0 = \tilde{a}_1 = \tilde{a}_2 = \cdots = \tilde{a}_{k-1} = 0$. Given that $\hat{f}(r) = 0$ for $r < k$, and

$$\tilde{f}(r) = \begin{cases} 0 & 0 \le r \le l-1 \\ \hat{f}(r-l) & r \ge l \end{cases}$$

for some fixed l, what can we conclude about $\hat{a}_r$ and $\tilde{a}_r$?

9.12 (a) Consider the recurrence relation

$$C_0 a_r + C_1 a_{r-1} + C_2 a_{r-2} + \ldots + C_k a_{r-k} = f(r)$$

Let $\hat{a}_r$ denote the solution of the recurrence relation for $f(r) = \hat{f}(r)$ with the boundary conditions $\hat{a}_0 = \hat{a}_1 = \hat{a}_2 = \cdots = \hat{a}_{k-1} = 0$. Let $\tilde{a}_r$ denote the solution of the recurrence relation for $f(r) = \tilde{f}(r)$ with the boundary conditions $\tilde{a}_0 = \tilde{a}_1 = \tilde{a}_2 = \cdots = \tilde{a}_{k-1} = 0$.

Show that $\bar{a}_r = \hat{a}_r + \tilde{a}_r$ is the solution of the recurrence relation for $f(r) = \hat{f}(r) + \tilde{f}(r)$ with the boundary conditions $\bar{a}_0 = \bar{a}_1 = \bar{a}_2 = \cdots = \bar{a}_{k-1} = 0$, provided that $\hat{f}(r) = \tilde{f}(r) = 0$ for $r < k$.

(b) Solve the recurrence equation

$$a_r + 5a_{r-1} + 6a_{r-2} = f(r)$$

where

$$f(r) = \begin{cases} 0 & r = 0, 1, 5 \\ 6 & \text{otherwise} \end{cases}$$

given that $a_0 = a_1 = 0$.

9.13 Gossip is spread among r people via telephone. Specifically, in a telephone conversation between A and B, A tells B all the gossip he has heard, and B reciprocates. Let a_r denote the minimum number of telephone calls among r people so that all gossip will be known to everyone.

(a) Show that $a_2 = 1$, $a_3 = 3$, and $a_4 = 4$.

(b) Show that

$$a_r \leq a_{r-1} + 2$$

(c) Show that

$$a_r \leq 2r - 4 \qquad \text{for } r \geq 4$$

[Indeed, it can be shown that $a_r = 2r - 4$. See B. Baker and R. Shostak, Gossips and Telephones. *Discrete Mathematics*, **2**: 191–193, (1972).]

9.14 Let a_r denote the number of partitions of a set of r elements. Show that

$$a_{r+1} = \sum_{i=0}^{r} \binom{r}{i} a_i$$

where $a_0 = 1$.

9.15 Consider an air-traffic-control system in which the desired altitude of an aircraft, a_r, is computed by a computer every second and is compared with the actual altitude of the aircraft, b_{r-1}, determined by a tracking radar 1 second earlier. Depending on whether a_r is larger or smaller than b_{r-1}, the altitude of the aircraft will be changed accordingly. Specifically, the change in altitude at the rth second, $b_r - b_{r-1}$, is proportional to the difference $a_r - b_{r-1}$. That is,

$$b_r - b_{r-1} = K(a_r - b_{r-1})$$

where K is a proportional constant.

(a) Determine b_r, given that $a_r = 1000 \left(\dfrac{3}{2}\right)^2$, $K = 3$, and $b_0 = 0$.

(b) Determine b_r, given that

$$a_r = \begin{cases} 1000 \left(\dfrac{3}{2}\right)^r & 0 \leq r \leq 9 \\ 1000 \left(\dfrac{3}{2}\right)^{10} & r \geq 10 \end{cases}$$

$K = 3$, and $b_0 = 0$.

9.16 *The Tower of Hanoi problem. r* circular rings of tapering sizes are slipped onto a peg with the largest ring at the bottom, as shown in Fig. 9P.1. These rings are to be transferred one at a time onto another peg, and there is a third peg available on which rings can be left temporarily. If, during the course of transferring the rings, no ring may ever be placed on top of a smaller one, in how many moves can these rings be transferred with their relative positions unchanged?

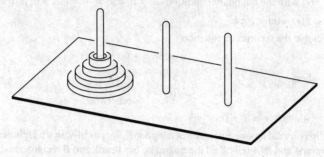

Fig. 9P.1

9.17 Consider the multiplication of bacteria in a controlled environment. Let a_r denote the number of bacteria there are on the rth day. We define the rate of growth on the rth day to be $a_r - 2a_{r-1}$. If it is known that the rate of growth doubles every day, determine a_r, given that $a_0 = 1$.

9.18 Consider the operation of a factory whose average profit in every two successive months is equal to the average new order in that period. Let a_r denote the new order received and b_r denote the monthly profit in the rth month.

   (a) Given that $a_r = 2^r$ for all $r \geq 0$ and $b_0 = 0$, determine b_r.

   (b) Repeat part (*a*) for

$$a_r = \begin{cases} 2^r & 0 \leq r \leq 9 \\ 2^{10} & r \geq 10 \end{cases}$$

9.19 A particle is moving in the horizontal direction. The distance it travels in each second is equal to two times the distance it traveled in the previous second. Let a_r denote the position of the particle in the rth second. Determine a_r, given that $a_0 = 3$ and $a_3 = 10$.

9.20 Consider the following algorithm for sorting r numbers for $r \geq 2$.

   (a) Use $2r - 3$ comparisons to determine the largest and second largest of the r numbers.

   (b) Recursively, sort the remaining $r - 2$ numbers.

   Let a_r denote the number of comparisons used for sorting r numbers. Determine a_r.

9.21 Let a_r denote the number of edges in a complete graph on r vertices.

   (a) Derive a recurrence relation for a_r in terms of a_{r-1}.

   (b) Solve the recurrence relation.

9.22 Let a_r be the number of subsets of the set $\{1, 2, ..., r\}$ that do not contain two consecutive numbers. Determine a_r.

Hint: Among the a_r subsets, how many of them do not contain the number r? How many of them contain the number r?

9.23 Consider the problem of covering a rectangular strip of length n with two types of domino. A blue domino has length 2, while an orange domino has length 1. Assuming you have sufficient dominoes of each type, how many different ways can the strip be covered?

9.24 How many r-digit binary sequences that have no adjacent 0s are there?

9.25 Let a_r denote the total assets of a bank at the end of the rth month which is equal to the sum of the total deposit in the rth month and 1.1 times the total assets at the end of the $(r-1)$st month. Given that the total deposit is a constant 100 (in thousands of dollars), determine a_r if $a_0 = 0$.

9.26 Let a_r denote the total dollar assets of a company in the rth year. Clearly, $a_r - a_{r-1}$ is the increase in assets during the rth year. If the increase in assets during each year is always five times the increase during the previous year, what are the total assets in the rth year? It is given that $a_0 = 3$ and $a_1 = 7$.

9.27 Let a_r denote the number of nonoverlapping regions into which the interior of a convex r-gon is divided by its diagonals. Suppose no three diagonals meet at one point.

(a) Show that

$$a_r - a_{r-1} = \frac{(r-1)(r-2)(r-3)}{6} + r - 2 \qquad r \geq 3$$

and $a_0 = a_1 = a_2 = 0$.

(b) Determine $A(z)$.

(c) Determine a_r from $A(z)$.

9.28 There are two kinds of particles inside a nuclear reactor. In every second, an α particle will split into three β particles, and a β particle will split into an α particle and two β particles. If there is a single α particle in the reactor at $t = 0$, how many particles are there altogether at $t = 100$?

9.29 How many spanning trees does the ladder graph in Fig. 9P.2 have?

Hint: Let a_r denote the number of spanning trees the ladder graph of r steps has. Let b_r denote the number of spanning trees that include the first step the ladder graph of r steps has. Express a_r in terms of a_{r-1} and b_r. Express b_r in terms of a_{r-1} and b_{r-1}.

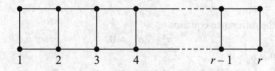

Fig. 9P.2

9.30 Let d_r denote the number of ways of permuting r integers $\{1, 2, ..., r\}$ so that the integer i will not be in the ith position for $1 \leq i \leq r$.

(a) Use a combinatorial argument to show that

$$d_r = (r-1)(d_{r-1} + d_{r-2})$$

(b) Show that

$$d_r = r!\left[1 - \frac{1}{1!} + \frac{1}{2!} - ... + (-1)^r \frac{1}{r!}\right]$$

satisfies the recurrence relation in part (a).

9.31 A sequence of binary digits is fed to a counter at the rate of 1 digit/s. The counter is designed to register 1 s in the input sequence. However, it is so slow that it is locked for exactly 7 s following each registration, during which time the input digits are ignored. Let a_r denote the number of binary sequences of length r at the end of which the counter is not locked. Find the difference equation which a_r satisfies, the boundary conditions, and the generating function $A(z)$.

9.32 For the graph in Fig. 9P.3, determine the number of directed paths of length n that start from vertex a and end at vertex d.

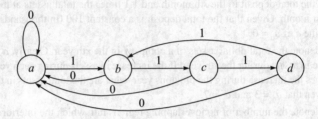

Fig. 9P.3

9.33 (a) Let $A(z)$ denote the generating function of a numeric function **a**. Show that

$$a_0 = \lim_{z \to 0} A(z)$$

(This result is known as the *initial-value theorem*.)

(b) Check the initial-value theorem for the numeric function **a**, where $a_r = 2^{r+1}$ for all r.

9.34 Solve the difference equation

$$a_r^2 - 2a_{r-1}^2 = 1$$

given that $a_0 = 2$.

Hint: Let $b_r = a_r^2$.

9.35 Solve the difference equation

$$ra_r + ra_{r-1} - a_{r-1} = 2^r$$

given that $a_0 = 273$.

Hint: Let $b_r = ra_r$.

9.36 (a) Solve the difference equation

$$a_r^2 - 2a_{r-1} = 0$$

given that $a_0 = 4$

Hint: Let $b_r = \lg a_r$, where lg denotes logarithm base 2

(b) Solve the difference equation

$$a_r = \sqrt{a_{r-1} + \sqrt{a_{r-2} + \sqrt{a_{r-3} + \sqrt{\cdots}}}}$$

given that $a_0 = 4$.

Hint: Compute a_r^2.

9.37 Solve the difference equation

$$a_r - ra_{r-1} = r! \qquad \text{for } r \geq 1$$

given that $a_0 = 2$.

Hint: Let $b_r = a_r/r!$.

9.38 The product of two 2×2 matrices **A** and **B** can be computed using 7 multiplications and 15 additions. We compute first the following intermediate results:

$$s_1 = a_{21} + a_{22} \qquad m_1 = s_2 s_6 \qquad t_1 = m_1 + m_2$$
$$s_2 = s_1 - a_{11} \qquad m_2 = a_{11} b_{11} \qquad t_2 = t_1 + m_4$$
$$s_3 = a_{11} - a_{21} \qquad m_3 = a_{12} b_{21}$$
$$s_4 = a_{12} - s_2 \qquad m_4 = s_3 s_7$$
$$s_5 = b_{12} - b_{11} \qquad m_5 = s_1 s_5$$
$$s_6 = b_{22} - s_5 \qquad m_6 = s_4 b_{22}$$
$$s_7 = b_{22} - b_{12} \qquad m_7 = a_{22} s_8$$
$$s_8 = s_6 - b_{21}$$

The elements of the product matrix **C** can then be computed as:

$$c_{11} = m_2 + m_3$$
$$c_{12} = t_1 + m_5 + m_6$$
$$c_{21} = t_2 - m_7$$
$$c_{22} = t_2 + m_5$$

Confirm that these equations yield the correct results.

9.39 How many comparisons are required for a binary search in a list of 32 elements?

9.40 Multiply $(1101)_2$ and $(1001)_2$ using the fast multiplication algorithm.

9.41 How many operations are required to multiply two 16×16 matrices using Strassen's algorithm.

9.42 Suppose that $f(n) = f(n/3) + 1$ when n is divisible by 3, and $f(1) = 1$. Compute (a) $f(6)$ (b) $f(9)$ (c) $f(18)$.

9.43 Suppose that $f(n) = 2f(n/2) + 3$ when n is even, and $f(1) = 5$. Compute (a) $f(4)$ (b) $f(32)$ (c) $f(256)$ (d) $f(512)$.

9.44 Suppose that the votes of n students for different candidates for the cultural society are the elements of a sequence. A candidate wins the election if he receives a majority of the votes. Devise a divide-and-conquer algorithm that determines whether a candidate received a majority and, if so, determine who this candidate is?

9.45 Establish a divide-and-conquer relation for the number of multiplications needed to compute x^m, where x is a real number and m is a positive integer.

9.46 Compute $f(n)$ when $n = 2^k$, where f satisfies the recurrence relation $f(n) = 8 f(n/2) + n^2$ with $f(1) = 1$.

9.47 Find the minimum and maximum of a sequence using divide-and-conquer algorithm. Write down the recurrence relation.

9.48 How many comparisons are required to locate the maximum and minimum elements in a sequence with 64 elements?

9.49 Using divide-and-conquer algorithm, develop a method to determine the closest pair of points in a set of n points $(x_1, y_1), \ldots, (x_n, y_n)$ in the plane, where the distance between two points (x_i, y_i) and (x_j, y_j) is the Euclidean distance $((x_i - x_j)^2 + (y_i - y_j)^2)^{1/2}$. Write down the recurrence relation.

Programming Exercises

1. Write a program for solving a kth order recurrence relation using recurrion.
2. Write the pseudocode for the fast multiplication of integers.
3. Write a program to implement Strassen's algorithm for multiplying two $n \times n$ matrices.
4. Write a program to find the minimum and maximum of a sequence using divide-and-conquer algorithm.
5. Write the pseudocode to determine the closest pair of points in a set of n points, using divide-and-conquer algorithm.

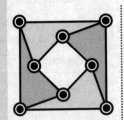

Objective

To present the concepts of groups and rings. Also, we aim at describing the application of groups to error detection and correction.

GROUPS AND RINGS

10.1 INTRODUCTION

Consider the operation of a vending machine* that delivers a pack of gum when two dimes are deposited, a candy bar when a dime and a quarter are deposited, and a pack of cigarettes when two quarters are deposited. Let $A = \{$dime, quarter$\}$ and $B = \{$gum, candy, cigarettes$\}$. The operation of the vending machine can be described formally as a function from $A \times A$ to B, which is shown in Fig. 10.1a. The table in Fig. 10.1a can be set up in an alternative way as that shown in Fig. 10.1b, where the rows indicate the first coin deposited and the columns indicate the second coin deposited.

As another example, suppose that the hair color of a child is determined by that of her parents, as shown in Fig. 10.2. Clearly, the relationship between the hair color of a child and that of her parents can be described by a function from $A \times A$ to A, where $A = \{$light, dark$\}$.

Let A and B be two sets. A function from $A \times A$ to B is called a *binary operation* on the set A. We shall encounter most frequently functions from $A \times A$ to A. A function from $A \times A$ to A is said to be a binary operation that is *closed*. In the example of the vending machine, a binary operation on the set $\{$dime, quarter$\}$ was defined. This binary operation is not a closed operation. In the example of the hair color of children, a binary operation on the set $\{$light, dark$\}$ was defined. Moreover, this binary operation is closed. Intuitively, a binary operation specifies a way in which two elements are "combined" to yield a third element.

---

* To be precise, we describe here only the operation of a vending machine when two coins, which are dimes and quarters, are deposited. The operation of real vending machines is less restrictive.

Coins deposited	Merchandise delivered
(dime, dime)	gum
(dime, quarter)	candy
(quarter, dime)	candy
(quarter, quarter)	cigarettes

(a)

1st coin deposited \ 2nd coin deposited	dime	quarter
dime	gum	candy
quarter	candy	cigarettes

Merchandise delivered

(b)

Fig. 10.1

A binary operation can be described using functional notation. That is, let the function from $A \times A$ to A be named f. Clearly, $f(a_1, a_2)*$ will denote the image of the ordered pair (a_1, a_2) in $A \times A$. An alternative way is to write $f(a_1, a_2)$ as $a_1 fa_2$.[†] In this case, instead of the customary letter names for functions, we use "operator symbols" such as $\star, *, +, \cdot, \square, \oplus, \ldots$ as the names of binary operations on a set. Thus, we can write

Father \ Mother	light	dark
light	light	dark
dark	dark	dark

Child

Fig. 10.2

$$\star(a_1, a_2) \qquad +(\text{dime, quarter}) \qquad \square(\text{light, dark})$$

or

$$a_1 \star a_2 \qquad \text{dime} + \text{quarter} \qquad \text{light} \ \square \ \text{dark}$$

The definition of a binary operation can be extended immediately. A ternary operation on a set A is a function from $(A \times A) \times A$ to B for some set B, and an m-ary operation on a set A is a function from A^m to B for some set B.[‡]

A set together with a number of operations on the set is called an *algebraic system* or, simply, an *algebra*. We shall use a notation such as $(A, \star, *, \square)$ for an algebraic system, where A is a set, and $\star, *,$ and $\square$ are operations on A. Some authors consider relation on A which are not necessarily operations, as a part of the system. Since the operations and relations on the set A define a structure on the elements of A, an algebraic system is also called an algebraic structure. It is possible to consider more than one set a part of the system and operations on these sets. Our examples of the vending machine and the hair color of children are both examples of algebraic systems with one operation. Consider a self-service snack bar with two vending machines. We can describe the items one can purchase by the algebraic system ({dime, quarter}, $\star, *$), where the binary operations $\star$ and $*$ are described in Fig. 10.3. Consider the set of natural numbers N together with

---

[*] To be precise, we should write $f[(a_1, a_2)]$. However, there is no confusion in our notation.

[†] $f(a_1, a_2)$ is referred to as the *prefix* notation, and $a_1 fa_2$, is referred to as the *infix* notation.

[‡] We write A^m to denote $\underbrace{((A \times A) \times A) \times \ldots \times A}_{m \text{ times}}$.

★	dime	quarter
dime	gum	candy
quarter	candy	cigarettes

*	dime	quarter
dime	potato chips	cookies
quarter	cookies	sandwich

Fig. 10.3

the usual addition and multiplication operation of integers, + and ·. Clearly, $(N, +, \cdot)$ is an algebraic system on an algebra with two operations. Also, let $\square$ be a binary operation on N such that $\square(a, b)$ is equal to 0 or 1 depending on whether the sum of a and b is even or odd, and Δ be a ternary operation on N such that $\Delta(a, b, c)$ is equal to the maximum of a, b, and c. $(N, \square, \Delta)$ is also an algebraic system with two operations.

Let $(A, *)$ be an algebraic system and $B \subseteq A$, which is closed under the operation $*$. Then, $(B, *)$ is called a subalgebra of $(A, *)$. For example, $(E, +)$ is a subalgebra of $(N, +)$, where E is the set of even positive numbers, N is the set of natural numbers and $+$ is the usual addition operation. The concept of subalgebra may be applied to any algebraic system, if the subalgebra is closed under all the operations of the original system. A subalgebra is of the same type as the original system. Since, the operations of the systems are same, most of their properties are preserved.

Now, let us understand *direct product of algebras*, an important concept associated with any algebraic system.

Let $(A, *)$ and (B, o) be two algebraic systems of the same type. The algebraic system $(A \times B, \square)$ is called the *direct product of the algebras* $(A, *)$ and (B, o), if the operation $\square$ is defined for any $a_1, a_2 \in A$ and $b_1, b_2 \in B$ as

$$(a_1, b_1) \square (a_2, b_2) = (a_1 * a_2, b_1 \text{ o } b_2).$$

The algebraic systems $(A, *)$ and (B, o) are called the *factor algebra's* of $(A \times B, \square)$. The definition of *direct product* can be applied to any two algebraic systems of the same type. The operations in the direct product are defined in terms of the corresponding operations of the factor algebra's.

10.2 GROUPS

Let $\star$ be a binary operation on a set A. The operation $\star$ is said to be *associative* if

$$(a \star b) \star c = a \star (b \star c)$$

for all a, b, c in A.* Let A be a set of people and Δ be a binary operation such that $a \Delta b$ is equal to the taller one of a and b. (Assume that no two people in A are of the same height.) We note that Δ is an associative operation. On the other hand, let N be the set of all natural numbers and $\square$ be an operation such that $a \square b$ is equal to the value of $a^2 + b$. We ask the reader to check that the operation $\square$ is not associative. Intuitively, when an associative operation is to be carried

---

* It follows that when $\star$ is an associative operation, we can write $(a \star b) \star c$ as $a \star b \star c$ without any possible confusion.

out a certain number of times, the order in which the operations are carried out is not important.

Let $(A, \star)$ be an algebraic system where $\star$ is a binary operation on A. $(A, \star)$ is called a *semigroup* if the following conditions are satisfied:

1. $\star$ is a closed operation.[†]
2. $\star$ is an associative operation.

Let A be the set of all positive even integers $\{2, 4, 6, \ldots\}$ and $+$ be the ordinary addition operation of integers. Since $+$ is a closed operation on A and is also an associative operation, $(A, +)$ is a semigroup. Let S be a finite alphabet.

Let A denote the set of all nonempty strings of letters from S. (For example, let $S = \{\alpha, \beta, \gamma\}$. We have $A = \{\alpha, \beta, \gamma, \alpha\alpha, \alpha\beta, \alpha\gamma, \ldots, \alpha\alpha\alpha, \alpha\alpha\beta, \ldots\}$.) Let $\cdot$ be a binary operation on A such that for any two strings a and b in A, $a \cdot b$ yields a string which is the concatenation of strings a and b. (For example, $\alpha\alpha \cdot \alpha\gamma\beta = \alpha\alpha\alpha\gamma\beta$.) We note that $(A, \cdot)$ is a semigroup.

Let $(A, \star)$ be a semigroup and B is a subset of A. Then, $(B, \star)$ is said to be a *subsemigroup* if the set B is closed under the operation $\star$.

If A and B are subsets of some semigroup then $A \star B$ denotes the set $\{a \star b \mid a \in A$ and $b \in B\}$. A subset B of a semigroup A is called a subsemigroup if it is closed under the same operation as the original semigroup, i.e. $B \star B$ is a subset of B. Let B be nonempty. B is called a *right ideal* if $B \star A$ is a subset of B, i.e. $B \star A \subseteq B$. B is called a *left ideal* if $A \star B$ is a subset of B, i.e. $A \star B \subseteq B$. If B is both a left ideal and a right ideal, then it is called an *ideal* (or a two-sided ideal). The intersection of two ideals is also an *ideal*. So, a semigroup can have at most one minimal ideal. An example of a semigroup with no minimal ideal is the set of positive integers under addition.

Example 10.1 Let $(A, +)$ be a semigroup where A is the set of all positive even integers and $+$ is the ordinary addition operation of integers. Let B be the set of all positive integers which are multiples of 4. Clearly, $B \subseteq A$ and B is closed under addition. So, $(B, +)$ is a subsemigroup. ∎

Example 10.2 Let $A = \{0, 1, 2, 3, 4, 5\}$ and $\star$ be the operation addition modulo 6. Clearly $(A, \star)$ is a semigroup. Let $B = \{0, 2, 4\}$. Clearly $B \subseteq A$ and B is closed under the operation $\star$. So, $(B, \star)$ is a subsemigroup. ∎

Example 10.3 Let A be a set of real numbers with the operation multiplication. Clearly $(A, \star)$ is a semigroup, Let B be the set of positive real numbers with the operation multiplication. Clearly, $B \subseteq A$ and B is closed under the operation multiplication. So, $(B, \star)$ is a subsemigroup. ∎

Example 10.4 Let A be the set of all 2×2 matrices with the operation addition $(+)$. So, $(A, +)$ is a semigroup. Let B be the set of all 2×2 matrices whose

---

[†] Note that it is possible to have an associative operation that is not closed. Consider the algebraic system $(\{1, 2, 3\}, +)$, where $+$ is the ordinary addition operation of integers.

elements are even. Clearly, $B \subseteq A$ and B is closed under the operation addition. So, $(B, +)$ is a subsemigroup. ∎

We can generate one semigroup called the direct product of the semigroups, from any two given semigroups.

Let $(A, *)$ and (B, o) be two semigroups. The *direct product of* $(A, *)$ and (B, o) is the algebraic system $(A \times B, \square)$, in which the operation $(\square)$ on $A \times B$ is defined by

$$(a_1, b_1) \; \square \; (a_2, b_2) = (a_1 * a_2, b_1 \text{ o } b_2), \text{ for any } (a_1, b_1) \text{ and } (a_2, b_2) \in A \times B.$$

From the definition, it can be shown that the algebraic system $(A \times B, \square)$ is a semigroup because the binary operation $\square$ on $A \times B$ is defined in terms of the operations $*$ and o which are both associative. Hence, the direct product of any two semigroups is a semigroup. If $(A, *)$ and (B, o) are both commutative semigroups, then their direct product is also commutative.

Let $(A, \star)$ be an algebraic system where $\star$ is a binary operation on A. An element e, in A, is said to be a *left identity* if for all x in A, $e \star x = x$. For example, for the algebraic system shown in Fig. 10.4a, both β and δ are left identities. An element e, in A, is said to be a *right identity* if for all x in A, $x \star e = x$. For example, for the algebraic system shown in Fig. 10.4b, α is a right identity. An element in A is said to be an *identity* if it is both a left identity and a right identity.

$\star$	α	β	γ	δ
α	δ	α	β	γ
β	α	β	γ	δ
γ	α	β	γ	γ
δ	α	β	γ	δ

(a)

$\star$	α	β	γ	δ
α	α	β	δ	γ
β	β	α	γ	δ
γ	γ	δ	α	β
δ	δ	δ	β	γ

(b)

Fig. 10.4

Suppose e_1 is a left identity and e_2 is a right identity of an algebraic system $(A, \star)$. Since e_1 is a left identity, $e_1 \star e_2 = e_2$. Since e_2 is a right identity, $e_1 \star e_2 = e_1$. Thus, we have $e_1 = e_2$. We conclude that if e is a left identity, then either e is also a right identity or there is no right identity at all. Similarly, if e is a right identity, then either e is also a left identity or there is no left identity at all. *It follows that, with respect to a binary operation, there is at most one identity.*

Intuitively, an identity is a "neutral" element in that, when it is "combined" with another element, its effect on the outcomes is nil. For example, let $(A, \star)$ be an algebraic system, where A is a set of colored lights and $\star$ is a binary operation such that $a \star b$ is the resultant colored light when light a is combined with light b. Clearly, white light is the identity of the algebraic system. As another example, let $(N, +)$ be an algebraic system, where N is the set of natural numbers and + is the ordinary addition operation of integers. Clearly, 0 is the identity of the algebraic system.

Let $(A, \star)$ be an algebraic system, where $\star$ is a binary operation on A. $(A, \star)$ is called a *monoid* if the following conditions are satisfied:

1. ★ is a closed operation.
2. ★ is an associative operation.
3. There is an identity.

For example, let A be a set of people of different heights. Let Δ be a binary operation such that $a \Delta b$ is equal to the taller one of a and b. We note that (A, Δ) is a monoid where the identity is the shortest person in A.

Let $(A, \star)$ be a monoid with the identity element e, and B is a subset of A. Then, $(B, \star)$ is said to be a *submonoid*, if the set B is closed under the operation $\star$ and $e \in B$. The definition of submonoid requires that the submonoid also to be a monoid itself under the same operation with the same identity element as the original monoid.

Let $(A, *)$ and (B, o) be two monoids with e_A and e_B as their identity elements respectively. Then, their direct product $(A \times B, \Box)$, is also a monoid with (e_A, e_B) as the identity element. This is because, for $\forall\, a \in A, b \in B$,

$$(e_A, e_B) \,\Box\, (a, b) = (e_A * a, e_B \circ b) = (a, b) \text{ and}$$
$$(a, b) \,\Box\, (e_A, e_B) = (a * e_A, b \circ e_B) = (a, b).$$

Example 10.5 Let A be the set of whole numbers (i.e. set of natural numbers including 0) with the operation addition (+). Clearly, $(A, +)$ is a monoid where the identity element is 0. Let B be the set of even whole numbers with the operation addition. Clearly, $B \subseteq A$ and B is closed under the operation addition and the identity element $0 \in B$. So, $(B, +)$ is a submonoid.

Let C be the set of odd whole numbers with the operation addition. Clearly, $C \subseteq A$, but C is not closed under the operation addition. Also, $0 \notin C$. So, $(C, +)$ is not a submonoid. ∎

Example 10.6 Let A be a nonempty set and $P(A)$ be its power set. Then, the algebraic systems $(P(A), \cup)$ and $(P(A), \cap)$ are monoids with the identities $\varnothing$ and A respectively. ∎

Let $(A, \star)$ be an algebraic system with an identity e. Let a be an element in A. An element b is said to be a *left inverse* of a if $b \star a = e$. An element b is said to be a *right inverse* of a if $a \star b = e$. For example, for the algebraic system in Fig. 10.5, α is an identity, so β is a left inverse of γ, and δ is a right inverse of γ. An element b is said to be an *inverse* of a if it is both a left and a right inverse of a. Clearly, if b is an inverse of a, a is also an inverse of b. Intuitively, an inverse of an element "cancels" the effect of the element when they are "combined." For example, let $(A, \star)$ be an algebraic system, where A is a set of chemicals containing acids, alkalis, and water, and ★ is a binary operation giving the product of the combination of two chemicals. In this case, water can be considered as a neutral chemical, and the inverse of an acid is an alkali, if their combination yields water.

★	α	β	γ	δ
α	α	β	γ	δ
β	β	δ	α	γ
γ	γ	β	β	α
δ	δ	α	γ	δ

Fig. 10.5

Let $(A, \star)$ be an algebraic system, where $\star$ is a binary operation. $(A, \star)$ is called a *group* if the following conditions are satisfied:

1. $\star$ is a closed operation.
2. $\star$ is an associative operation.
3. There is an identity.
4. Every element in A has a left inverse.

We observe that *because of associativity, a left inverse of an element* is *also a right inverse of the element in a group*. Let b be a left inverse of a and c be a left inverse of b. Let e denote the identity.* Since

$$(b \star a) \star b = e \star b = b$$

we have

$$c \star ((b \star a) \star b) = c \star b = e$$

From

$$\begin{aligned} c \star ((b \star a) \star b) &= ((c \star b) \star a) \star b \\ &= (e \star a) \star b \\ &= a \star b \end{aligned}$$

we have

$$a \star b = e$$

Thus, b is also a right inverse of a. Consequently, we can refer to the inverses of the elements without distinguishing left from right inverses.

Furthermore, we observe that *associativity also implies the uniqueness of the inverse of every element*. Suppose that both b and c are inverses of a. That is,

$$b \star a = e \quad \text{and} \quad c \star a = e$$

It follows that

$$(b \star a) \star b = (c \star a) \star b$$

or

$$b \star (a \star b) = c \star (a \star b)$$

or

$$b = c$$

From now on, we shall use a^{-1} to denote *the* inverse of a.

We have encountered many examples of groups before. Consider the algebraic system $(I, +)$, where I is the set of all integers and $+$ is the ordinary addition operation of integers. It is clear that $(I, +)$ is a group with 0 being the identity and the inverse of n being $-n$. Let $G = \{\text{EVEN}, \text{ODD}\}$ and a binary operation $\oplus$ be defined as in Fig. 10.6. We can check immediately that $(G, \oplus)$ is a group where EVEN is the identity and both EVEN and ODD are their own inverses. Consider the rotation of geometric figures in a plane. Let $R = \{0°, 60°, 120°, 180°, 240°, 300°\}$

---

* We remind the reader that the identity is unique.

denote six possible ways to rotate geometric figures drawn on a plane, namely, to rotate the figures by 0°, 60°, 120°, ..., 300°. Let $\star$ be a binary operation so that for a and b in R, $a \star b$ is the overall angular rotation corresponding to the successive rotations by a and then by b. $(R, \star)$

$\oplus$	EVEN	ODD
EVEN	EVEN	ODD
ODD	ODD	EVEN

Fig. 10.6

is a group with 0° being the identity, the inverse of 60° being 300°, the inverse of 180∘ being itself, and so on. Let $Z_n = \{0, 1, 2, ..., n - 1\}$. Let $\oplus$ be a binary operation on Z_n such that for a and b in Z_n

$$a \oplus b = \begin{cases} a + b & \text{if } a + b < n \\ a + b - n & \text{if } a + b \geq n \end{cases}$$

It can readily be checked that $(Z_n, \oplus)$ is a group for any n. $(Z_n, \oplus)$ is usually referred to as the *group of integers modulo n*.

As another example, let G be the set of all $n \times n$ real matrices with non-zero determinants and operation $\star$ be the matrix multiplication. Then, it can be verified that $(G, \star)$ is a group.

Let $\star$ be a binary operation on A. The operation $\star$ is said to be *commutative* if

$$a \star b = b \star a$$

for all a, b in A. Let A be a set of people and Δ be a binary operation such that $a \Delta b$ is equal to the taller one of a and b and is equal to a if a and b are of the same height. Clearly, Δ is not a commutative operation. (Is Δ still an associative operation?)

A group $(A, \star)$ is called a *commutative* group or an *abelian* group,∗ if $\star$ is a commutative operation. For example, $(Z_n, \oplus)$ is a commutative group. As another example, it may be verified that $(I, +)$ is a commutative group, where I is the set of integers. Similarly, it may be shown that $(R, *)$ is a commutative group, where R is the set of rational numbers and $*$ is the multiplication operation.

A group $(A, \star)$ is said to be *finite* if A is a finite set, and *infinite* if A is an infinite set. The size of A is often referred to as the *order* of the group.

10.3 SUBGROUPS

Let $(A, \star)$ be an algebraic system and B be a subset of A. The algebraic system $(B, \star)$ is said to be a *subsystem* of $(A, \star)$. The notion of a subsystem is a very natural one. Suppose $(A, \star)$ is an algebraic system describing the interaction of a set of atomic particles. If we are only interested in the interaction of some of the particles, we can consider only a subsystem of $(A, \star)$. Let $(N, +)$ be an algebraic system describing the addition of natural numbers. Clearly, $(E, +)$ is a subsystem of $(N, +)$ if E is the set of all even numbers. Also, consider the example of the

---

∗ In honor of the Norwegian mathematician N. H. Abel (1802–1829).

rotation of geometric figures in a plane. We note that ($\{0°, 120°, 240°\}$, ★) is a subsystem of the algebraic system ($\{0°, 60°, 120°, 180°, 240°, 300°\}$, ★). So is ($\{0°, 180°\}$, ★).

Let (A, ★) be a group, and B be a subset of A. (B, ★) is said to be a *subgroup* of A if (B, ★) is also a group by itself. Suppose we want to check whether (B, ★) is a subgroup for a given subset B of A. We note that:

1. We should test whether ★ is a closed operation on B.
2. ★ is known to be an associative operation.
3. Since there is only one element e in A such that $e ★ x = x ★ e = x$ for all x in A, we must check that e is in B. In other words, the identity of (A, ★) must be in B as the identity of (B, ★).
4. Since the inverse of every element in A is unique, for every element b in B, we must check that its inverse is also in B.

It may be noted that, for any group (A, ∗), the algebraic systems ($\{e\}$, ∗) and (A, ∗) are the trivial subgroups of (A, ∗). All other subgroups of (A, ∗) are called *proper subgroups*.

For example, let (I, +) be an algebraic system, where I is the set of all integers and + is the ordinary addition operation of integers. Clearly, (I, +) is a group. Moreover, (E, +) is a subgroup, where E is the set of all even integers. Also, in the example of the rotation of geometric figures in the plane, both ($\{0°, 120°, 240°\}$, ★) and ($\{0°, 180°\}$, ★) are subgroups of the group ($\{0°, 60°, 120°, 180°, 240°, 300°\}$, ★).

We want to show that:

Theorem 10.1 Let (A, ★) be a group and B a subset of A. If B is a finite set, then (B, ★) is a subgroup of (A, ★) if ★ is a closed operation on B.

Proof Let a be an element in B. If ★ is a closed operation on B, the elements $a, a^2, a^3, \ldots$ are all in B.∗ Because B is a finite set, according to the pigeonhole principle, we must have $a^i = a^j$ for some i and j, $i < j$. That is, $a^i = a^2 ★ a^{j-i}$. It follows that a^{j-i} is the identity of (A, ★), and it is included in the subset B. If $j - i > 1$, according to $a^{j-i} = a ★ a^{j-i-1}$, we can conclude that a^{j-i-1} is the inverse of a, and it is included in the subset B. If $j - i = 1$, we have $a^i = a^i ★ a$. Thus, a must be the identity element and is its own inverse. Consequently, that ★ is a closed operation on B guarantees that (B, ★) is a subgroup. ∎

10.4 GENERATORS AND EVALUATION OF POWERS

Let (A, ★) be an algebraic system in which A is a set of colors and the binary operation ★ gives the color that the combination of two colors yields, e.g. red ★ yellow = orange. Suppose we are given a subset of the colors in A; we might want to know all the colors we can obtain by trying all possible combinations of the

---

∗ We use a^m to denote $\underbrace{a ★ a ★ a \ldots ★ a}_{m \text{ times}}$.

given colors. Also, consider the group ($\{0°, 60°, 120°, 180°, 240°, 300°\}$, $\star$) that describes the rotation of geometric figures in the plane. Suppose we can rotate the figures only by $120°$ each time. Successive rotations by $120°$ will yield the rotations $\{0°, 120°, 240°\}$. On the other hand, suppose we can rotate the figures only by $60°$ each time. Successive rotations by $60°$ will yield all the rotations in $\{0°, 60°, 120°, 180°, 240°, 300°\}$.

Let (A, $\star$) be an algebraic system, where $\star$ is a closed operation, and $B = \{a_1, a_2, \ldots\}$ be a subset of A. Let B_1 denote the subset of A which contains B as well as all elements $a_i \star a_j$ for a_i and a_j in B. B_1 is called the set *generated directly* by B. Similarly, let B_2 denote the set generated directly by B_1, ..., and B_{i+1} denote the set generated directly by B_i. Let B^* denote the union of B, B_1, B_2, ... The algebraic system (B^*, $\star$) is called the *subsystem generated* by B, and an element is said to be generated by B if it is in B^*. Note that $\star$ is a closed operation on $B*$. Thus, for a group (A, $\star$), if B^* is finite then (B^*, $\star$) is a subgroup. If B^* = A, B is called a *generating set* or a *set of generators* of the algebraic system (A, $\star$). In the example on the combination of colors, a generating set is a subset of the set of colors whose combinations will yield all the colors in the original set. In the example on the rotation of geometric figures in the plane, $\{60°\}$ is a generating set, so is $\{120°, 180°\}$.

A group that has a generating set consisting of a single element is known as a *cyclic group*. Figure 10.7*a* shows a cyclic group for which $\{\beta\}$ is a generating set. Note that $\{\delta\}$ is also a generating set. For the example of the rotation of geometric figures in the plane, the group ($\{0°, 60°, 120°, 180°, 240°, 300°\}$, $\star$) is also a cyclic group. We ask the reader to verify that the group in Fig. 10.7*b* is not a cyclic group.

$\star$	α	β	γ	δ		$\star$	α	β	γ	δ
α	α	β	γ	δ		α	α	β	γ	δ
β	β	γ	δ	α		β	β	α	δ	γ
γ	γ	δ	α	β		γ	γ	δ	α	β
δ	δ	α	β	γ		δ	δ	γ	β	α

(a)   (b)

Fig. 10.7

Let (A, $\star$) be a cyclic group and $\{a\}$ be a generating set of (A, $\star$). Clearly, the elements in A can be expressed as a, a^2, a^3, ... Since, because of associativity, $a^i \star a^j = a^j \star a^i = a^{i+j}$, it follows immediately that *any cyclic group* is *commutative*.

We digress for a moment to present an interesting problem in connection with the concept of generating sets of algebraic systems. Let B be a generating set of an algebraic system (A, $\star$). For an element a in A, we would want to know the various ways of generating the element a. By generating the element a we mean to obtain a through successive combinations of the elements in the generating set. A way of generating a can be specified by a sequence of elements in a

$$a_1 \quad a_2 \quad a_3 \quad \cdots \quad a_r$$

such that $a_r = a$, and each a_i, $1 \leq i \leq r$, can be expressed as $a_j \star a_k$, where a_j and a_k are either elements from B or elements preceding a_i in the sequence. Since a sequence of r elements corresponds to generating the element a in r applications of the operation $\star$ to elements in the generating set and elements that have already been generated, it will be interesting to determine short sequences that generate a given element.

Our problem is motivated by that of finding efficient procedures to evaluate the power x^n for a given x and a positive integer n. Consider the algebraic system $(I, +)$, where I is the set of all positive integers and $+$ is the ordinary addition operation of integers. Clearly, $B = \{1\}$ is a generating set of the system. For a given integer n, we would like to know the various ways in which n can be generated. For example, the following sequences show some of the ways to generate the integer 9:

$$2 \quad 3 \quad 4 \quad 5 \quad 6 \quad 7 \quad 8 \quad 9$$
$$2 \quad 3 \quad 4 \quad 5 \quad 9$$
$$2 \quad 4 \quad 8 \quad 9$$

In the literature, a sequence of elements in I that leads to the generation of an integer n is called an *addition chain* for n. The connection between an addition chain for n and a procedure for evaluating x^n for a given value of x becomes obvious once we recall that $x^j \cdot x^k = x^{j+k}$.

The problem of determining a shortest addition chain for a given integer n is extremely interesting and has been studied rather extensively. However, a thorough discussion of the subject is beyond the scope of this book. As an illustration, we present here two simple procedures for determining addition chains for n.[*]

If n can be factored as pq, we can determine addition chains for p and q first and then combine them to obtain an addition chain for pq. Let

$$p_1 \quad p_2 \quad \cdots \quad p_{i-1} \quad p$$

and

$$q_1 \quad q_2 \quad \cdots \quad q_{j-1} \quad q$$

be addition chains for p and q. Clearly,

$$q_1 \quad q_2 \quad \cdots \quad q_{j-1} \quad q \quad p_1 q \quad \cdots \quad p_{i-1} q \quad pq$$

is an addition chain for n.

Consider the example $n = 45$, which can be written as 5×9. Since

$$2 \quad 3 \quad 5$$

is an addition chain for 5, and

$$2 \quad 4 \quad 8 \quad 9$$

is an addition chain for 9, we obtain

$$2 \quad 4 \quad 8 \quad 9 \quad 18 \quad 27 \quad 45$$

as an addition chain for 45.

---

[*] See also Prob. 7.19.

Alternatively, since

$$9 = 3 \times 3$$

and since

$$2 \quad 3$$

is an addition chain for 3, we obtain

$$2 \quad 3 \quad 6 \quad 9$$

as an addition chain for 9, and

$$2 \quad 3 \quad 6 \quad 9 \quad 18 \quad 27 \quad 45$$

as an addition chain for 45.

The second procedure is a recursive one. If n is an even number, we can determine an addition chain for $n/2$, and then add $n/2$ to $n/2$ to obtain n. Thus, if

$$a_1 \quad a_2 \quad \dots \quad n/2$$

is an addition chain for $n/2$ then

$$a_1 \quad a_2 \quad \dots \quad n/2 \quad n$$

is an addition chain for n. If n is an odd number, we can determine an addition chain for $(n-1)/2$, add $(n-1)/2$ to $(n-1)/2$ to obtain $n-1$, and then add 1 to $n-1$ to obtain n. Thus, if

$$a_1 \quad a_2 \quad \dots \quad (n-1)/2$$

is an addition chain for $(n-1)/2$ then

$$a_1 \quad a_2 \quad \dots \quad (n-1)/2 \quad n-1 \quad n$$

is an addition chain for n. Now, this procedure can be applied to determine an addition chain for $n/2$ or $(n-1)/2$. For example,

$$2 \quad 4 \quad 5 \quad 10 \quad 11 \quad 22 \quad 44 \quad 45$$

is an addition chain for the integer 45 determined by this procedure.

10.5 COSETS AND LAGRANGE'S THEOREMS

Let us extend the example of the vending machine in Sec. 10.1 such that two coins from the set {nickel, dime, quarter, half-dollar, dollar} are to be deposited in each purchase. If we have already deposited a quarter in the machine, we might want to know the items we will receive if the second coin to be deposited is either a dime, or a quarter, or a half-dollar. Also, consider the example on the rotation of geometric figures in the plane. Suppose an initial rotation of either 0, or 120, or 240° is followed by a subsequent rotation of 60°. We want to know all the possible total angular rotations. Let $(A, \star)$ be an algebraic system, where $\star$ is a binary operation. Let a be an element in A and H be a subset of A. The *left coset of H with respect to a*, which we shall denote $a \star H$, is the set of elements $\{a \star x \mid x \in H\}$. Similarly, the *right coset of H with respect to a*, which we shall denote $H \star a$, is the set of elements $\{x \star a \mid x \in H\}$. Clearly, in the example of the vending machine, we want to determine the left coset of the set {dime, quarter, half-dollar} with respect to a quarter, and in the example of rotation of geometric figures, we want to determine the right coset of the set $\{0°, 120°, 240°\}$ with respect to $60°$.

We can say a great deal more about cosets when we restrict ourselves to cosets in groups. Let $(A, \star)$ be a group and $(H, \star)$ be a subgroup of $(A, \star)$. We have:

Theorem 10.2 Let $a \star H$ and $b \star H$ be two cosets of H. Either $a \star H$ and $b \star H$ are disjoint or they are identical.

Proof Suppose $a \star H$ and $b \star H$ are not disjoint, and have f as a common element. That is, there exist h_1 and h_2 in H such that $f = a \star h_1 = b \star h_2$. We can write $a = b \star h_2 \star h_1^{-1}$. For any element x in $a \star H$, since $x = a \star h_3$ for some h_3 in H, we have $x = b \star h_2 \star h_1^{-1} \star h_3$ which is an element in $b \star H$ because $h_2 \star h_1^{-1} \star h_3$ is an element in H. In a similar way we can show that any element in $b \star H$ is also an element in $a \star H$. We thus conclude that the two sets $a \star H$ and $b \star H$ are equal.[*] ∎

Let $(A, \star)$ be a group, and $(H, \star)$ be a subgroup of $(A, \star)$. Because $(A, \star)$ is a group, for any a in A and any distinct h_1 and h_2 in H, $a \star h_1 \neq a \star h_2$. It follows that the size of any coset of H is the same as that of H. Furthermore, because H contains the identity of the group, if we compute all the left (right) cosets of H, we would have exhausted all the elements in A. Consequently, we can conclude that the left cosets of H form a partition of A, in which all blocks are of the same size. Thus, the size of A is equal to the number of distinct left cosets of H times the size of H. In other words we have:

Theorem 10.3 (Lagrange) The order of any subgroup of a finite group divides the order of the group.

There are some immediate consequences of Lagrange's theorem. First, we note that a group of prime order has no nontrivial subgroup.[†] It follows that a group of prime order must be cyclic, and any set containing a single element other than the identity is a generating set. ∎

*10.6 PERMUTATION GROUPS AND BURNSIDE'S THEOREM

We study in this section an important class of groups. A one-to-one function from a set S onto itself is called a *permutation* of the set S. We use the notation $\begin{pmatrix} abcd \\ bdca \end{pmatrix}$ for the permutation of the set $\{a, b, c, d\}$ that maps a into b, b into d, c into c, and d into a; that is, in the upper row the elements in the set are written down in an arbitrary order, and in the lower row the image of an element will be written below the element itself.

---

[*] We want to remind the reader that this does not mean $a \star h = b \star h$ for all h in H.
[†] A subgroup is said to be trivial if it contains either all elements in the group or the identity only.

For a set of n elements, S, let A denote the set of $n!$ permutations of S. We define a binary operation $\circ$ on A to be the composition of two functions. (See Prob. 4.32.) We note that *the binary operation $\circ$ is a closed operation on A.* Let π_1 and π_2 be two permutations of the set $S = \{a, b, c, ..., x, y, z\}$. To show that $\pi_1 \circ \pi_2$ is also a permutation of the set S, we have only to show that no two elements in S are mapped into the same element by $\pi_1 \circ \pi_2$. Suppose that π_2 maps the element a into b and π_1 maps the element b into $c \cdot \pi_1 \circ \pi_2$ will then map the element a into c. Let x be any element distinct from a. Since π_2 is a permutation of the set S, π_2 maps x into an element that is distinct from b, say y. Similarly, π_1 maps y into an element that is distinct from c, say z. Thus, $\pi_1 \circ \pi_2$ maps x into z. We conclude that $\pi_1 \circ \pi_2$ always maps two distinct elements (for example, a and x) into two distinct elements (for example, c and z) and is, therefore, a permutation of the set S. For example, let

$$\pi_1 = \begin{pmatrix} abcd \\ adbc \end{pmatrix} \qquad \pi_2 = \begin{pmatrix} abcd \\ bacd \end{pmatrix}$$

we have

$$\pi_1 \circ \pi_2 = \begin{pmatrix} abcd \\ dabc \end{pmatrix}$$

We also note that the *binary operation $\circ$ is associative.* That is, for any permutations π_1, π_2, and π_3 of a set, we have $(\pi_1 \circ \pi_2) \circ \pi_3 = \pi_1 \circ (\pi_2 \circ \pi_3)$. This fact can be seen as follows: Suppose π_3 maps a into b, π_2 maps b into c, and π_1 maps c into d. Since $\pi_1 \circ \pi_2$ maps b into d, $(\pi_1 \circ \pi_2) \circ \pi_3$ maps a into d. Similarly, since $\pi_2 \circ \pi_3$ maps a into c, $\pi_1 \circ (\pi_2 \circ \pi_3)$ maps a into d. For example, let

$$\pi_1 = \begin{pmatrix} abcd \\ adbc \end{pmatrix} \qquad \pi_2 = \begin{pmatrix} abcd \\ bacd \end{pmatrix} \qquad \pi_3 = \begin{pmatrix} abcd \\ dabc \end{pmatrix}$$

Then

$$(\pi_1 \circ \pi_2) \circ \pi_3 = \left[\begin{pmatrix} abcd \\ adbc \end{pmatrix} \begin{pmatrix} abcd \\ bacd \end{pmatrix} \right] \begin{pmatrix} abcd \\ bdac \end{pmatrix} = \begin{pmatrix} abcd \\ dabc \end{pmatrix} \begin{pmatrix} abcd \\ bdac \end{pmatrix} = \begin{pmatrix} abcd \\ acdb \end{pmatrix}$$

and

$$\pi_1 \circ (\pi_2 \circ \pi_3) = \begin{pmatrix} abcd \\ adbc \end{pmatrix} \left[\begin{pmatrix} abcd \\ bacd \end{pmatrix} \begin{pmatrix} abcd \\ bdac \end{pmatrix} \right] = \begin{pmatrix} abcd \\ adbc \end{pmatrix} \begin{pmatrix} abcd \\ adbc \end{pmatrix} = \begin{pmatrix} abcd \\ acdb \end{pmatrix}$$

It follows that $(A, \circ)$ is a group in which the permutation mapping every element in S into itself is the identity, and the inverse of a permutation π is one that maps $\pi(a)$ into a for all a in S. For example, for $S = \{a, b, c, d\}$, the identity of

$(A, \circ)$ is $\begin{pmatrix} abcd \\ abcd \end{pmatrix}$ the inverse of $\begin{pmatrix} abcd \\ bcad \end{pmatrix}$ is $\begin{pmatrix} abcd \\ cabd \end{pmatrix}$. A subgroup of $(A, \circ)$ is usually

referred to as a *permutation group* of the set S.

Let $(G, \circ)$ be a permutation group of a set $S = \{a, b, ...\}$. A binary relation on the set S, called the *binary relation induced by $(G, \circ)$*, is defined to be such that element a is related to element b if and only if there is a permutation in G that maps a into b. For example, let

$$G = \left\{ \begin{pmatrix} abcd \\ abcd \end{pmatrix}, \begin{pmatrix} abcd \\ bacd \end{pmatrix}, \begin{pmatrix} abcd \\ abdc \end{pmatrix}, \begin{pmatrix} abcd \\ badc \end{pmatrix} \right\}$$

The binary relation induced by $(G, \circ)$ is shown in Fig. 10.8. We note that *the binary relation on S induced by a permutation group* $(G, \circ)$ *is an equivalence relation.* Since the identity permutation is in G, every element in S is related to itself in the binary relation on S induced by $(G, \circ)$. Therefore, the reflexive law is satisfied. If there is a permutation π_1 in G that maps a into b, the inverse of π_1, which is also in G, will map b into a. Therefore, the binary relation on S induced by

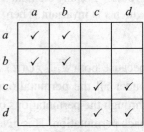

Fig. 10.8

$(G, \circ)$ satisfies the symmetric law. If there is a permutation π_1 mapping a into b and a permutation π_2 mapping b into c, the permutation $\pi_2 \circ \pi_1$, which is also in G, will map a into c. Therefore, the binary relation on S induced by $(G, \circ)$ satisfies the transitive law.

We are now ready to prove a result due to Burnside which is usually referred to as *Burnside's theorem*. Given a set S and a permutation group $(G, \circ)$ of S, we wish to find the number of equivalence classes into which S is divided by the equivalence relation on S induced by $(G, \circ)$. This problem can be solved most directly by finding the equivalence relation and then counting the number of equivalence classes. However, when the set S contains a large number of elements, such counting becomes prohibitively tedious. Burnside's theorem enables us to find the number of equivalence classes in an alternative way by counting the number of elements that are invariant under the permutations in the group. An element is said to be *invariant* under a permutation, or is called an *invariance*, if the permutation maps the element into itself.

Theorem 10.4 (Burnside) The number of equivalence classes into which a set S is divided by the equivalence relation induced by a permutation group $(G, \circ)$ of S is given by

$$\frac{1}{|G|} \sum_{\pi \in G} \psi(\pi)$$

where $\psi(\pi)$ is the number of elements that are invariant under the permutation π.

So that we can appreciate more the meaning of Burnside's theorem, let us illustrate its application before proceeding to the proof. Let $S = \{a, b, c, d\}$, and let G be the permutation group consisting of

$$\pi_1 = \begin{pmatrix} abcd \\ abcd \end{pmatrix} \qquad \pi_2 = \begin{pmatrix} abcd \\ bacd \end{pmatrix} \qquad \pi_3 = \begin{pmatrix} abcd \\ abdc \end{pmatrix} \qquad \pi_4 = \begin{pmatrix} abcd \\ badc \end{pmatrix}$$

The equivalence relation on S induced by G is shown in Fig. 10.8. Clearly, S is divided into two equivalence classes, $\{a, b\}$ and $\{c, d\}$. To compute the number of equivalence classes according to Burnside's theorem, we note that since $\psi(\pi_1)$ = 4, $\psi(\pi_2) = 2$, $\psi(\pi_3) = 2$, and $\psi(\pi_4) = 0$, the number of equivalence classes is

$$\frac{1}{4}(4 + 2 + 2 + 0) = 2$$

Proof: For any element s in S, let $\eta(s)$ denote the number of permutations under which s is invariant. Then

$$\sum_{\pi \in G} \psi(\pi) = \sum_{s \in S} \eta(s)$$

because both $\sum_{\pi \in G} \psi(\pi)$ and $\sum_{s \in S} \eta(S)$ count the total number of invariants under all the permutations in G. [One way to count the invariances is to go through the permutations one by one and count the number of invariances under each permutation. This gives $\sum_{\pi \in G} \psi(\pi)$ as the total count. Another way to count the invariances is to go through the elements one by one and count the number of permutations under which an element is invariant. That gives $\sum_{s \in S} \eta(S)$ as the total count.]

Let a and b be two elements in S that are in the same equivalence class. We want to show that there are exactly $\eta(a)$ permutations mapping a into b. Since a and b are in the same equivalence class, there is at least one such permutation which we shall denote by π_x. Let $\{\pi_1, \pi_2, \pi_3, \ldots\}$ be the set of the $\eta(a)$ permutations under which a is invariant. Then, the $\eta(a)$ permutations in the set $\{\pi_x \circ \pi_1, \pi_x \circ \pi_2, \pi_2, \pi_x \circ \pi_3, \ldots\}$ are permutations that map a into b. First, we see that these permutations are all distinct because, if $\pi_x \circ \pi_1 = \pi_x \circ \pi_2$, we have

$$\pi_x^{-1} \circ (\pi_x \circ \pi_1) = \pi_x^{-1} \circ (\pi_x \circ \pi_2).$$

This gives $\pi_1 = \pi_2$, which is impossible. Secondly, we see that no other permutation in G maps a into b. Suppose that there is a permutation π_y that maps a into b. Then, $\pi_x^{-1} \circ \pi_y$ is a permutation that maps a into a, because π_x^{-1} maps b into a. Since $\pi_x^{-1} \circ \pi_y$ is a permutation in the set $\{\pi_1, \pi_2, \pi_3, \ldots\}$, $\pi_x \circ (\pi_x^{-1} \circ \pi_y) = \pi_y$ is a permutation in the set $\{\pi_x \circ \pi_1, \pi_x \circ \pi_2, \pi_x \circ \pi_3, \ldots\}$. Therefore, we conclude that there are exactly $\eta(a)$ permutations in G that map a into b.

Let $a, b, c, \ldots, h$ be the elements in S that are in one equivalence class. All the permutations in G can be categorized as those that map a into a, those that map a into b, those that map a into c, $\ldots$, and those that map a into h. Since we have shown that there are exactly $\eta(a)$ permutations in each of these categories, we have

$$\eta(a) = \frac{|G|}{\text{number of elements in the equivalence class containing } a}$$

Using a similar argument, we obtain

$$\eta(b) = \eta(c) = \ldots = \eta(h)$$

$$= \frac{|G|}{\text{number of elements in the equivalence class containing } a}$$

and, therefore,

$$\eta(a) + \eta(b) + \eta(c) + \ldots + \eta(h) = |G|$$

It follows that, for any equivalence class of elements in S,

$$\sum_{\text{all } s \text{ in equivalence class}} \eta(s) = |G|$$

and

$$\sum_{s \in S} \eta(s) = \left(\begin{array}{c}\text{number of equivalence classes} \\ \text{into which } S \text{ is divided}\end{array}\right) \times |G|$$

Therefore, we have

Number of equivalence classes into which S is divided

$$= \frac{1}{|G|}\sum_{s \in S} \eta(s) = \frac{1}{|G|}\sum_{\pi \in G} \psi(\pi)$$ ∎

We now consider some illustrative examples.

Example 10.7 We want to find the number of distinct strings of length 2 that are made up of blue beads and yellow beads. The two ends of a string are not marked, and two strings are, therefore, indistinguishable if interchanging the ends of one will yield the other. Let b and y denote blue and yellow beads, respectively. Let bb, by, yb, and yy denote the four different strings of length 2 when equivalence between strings is not taken into consideration. The problem is to find the number of equivalence classes into which the set $S = \{bb, by, yb, yy\}$ is divided by the equivalence relation induced by the permutation group $(\{\pi_1, \pi_2\}, \circ)$, where

$$\pi_1 = \begin{pmatrix} bb & by & yb & yy \\ bb & by & yb & yy \end{pmatrix} \quad \pi_2 = \begin{pmatrix} bb & by & yb & yy \\ bb & yb & by & yy \end{pmatrix}$$

The permutation π_1 merely indicates that every string is equivalent to itself, and the permutation π_2 specifies the equivalence between strings when the two ends of a string are interchanged. According to Burnside's theorem, the number of distinct strings is

$$\frac{1}{2}(4 + 2) = 3$$

Similarly, for the case of distinct strings of length 3 made up of blue beads and yellow beads, we have the set $S = \{bbb, bby, byb, ybb, byy, yby, yyb, yyy\}$ and the permutation group $(G, \circ)$, $G = \{\pi_1, \pi_2\}$, where π_1 is the identity permutation and π_2 is the permutation that maps a string into one that is obtained from the former by interchanging its ends; for example, bbb is mapped into bbb, bby is mapped into ybb, byb is mapped into byb, and so on. The number of elements that are invariant under π_1 is eight. The number of elements that are invariant under π_2 is four, since a string will be mapped into itself under π_2 if the beads at the two ends of a string are of the same color, and there are four such strings. Therefore, the number of distinct strings is equal to

$$\frac{1}{2}(8 + 4) = 6$$ ∎

Example 10.8 Suppose we want to find the number of distinct bracelets of five beads made up of yellow, blue, and white beads. Two bracelets are said to be indistinguishable if the rotation of one will yield another. However, to simplify the problem, we assume that the bracelets cannot be flipped over. Let S be the set of the 3^5 ($= 243$) distinct bracelets when rotational equivalence is not considered. Let $(\{\pi_1, \pi_2, \pi_3, \pi_4, \pi_5\}, \circ)$ be a permutation group, where π_1 is the identity permutation and π_2 is the permutation that maps a bracelet into one which is the former rotated clockwise by one bead position. For example,

is mapped into

Similarly, π_3, π_4, and π_5 are permutations that map a bracelet into one which is the former rotated clockwise by two, three, and four bead positions, respectively.

The number of elements that are invariant under π_1 is 243. The number of elements that are invariant under π_2 is three because only when all five beads in a bracelet are of the same color will its rotation by one bead position yield the same bracelet. Similarly, the number of elements that are invariant under each of π_3, π_4, and π_5 is also three. Therefore, the number of distinct bracelets is

$$\frac{1}{5}(243 + 3 + 3 + 3 + 3) = 51$$

The result on the number of distinct bracelets leads immediately to a very interesting proof of what is known as *Fermat's little theorem* in number theory. For a prime number p, let us determine the number of distinct bracelets of p beads made up of beads of a distinct colors when rotational equivalence is considered. The number of distinct bracelets is

$$\frac{1}{p}(a^p + a + a + \ldots + a) = \frac{1}{p}[a^p + (p-1)a]$$

Since the number of distinct bracelets is a whole number, p divides $a^p + (p-1)$ a, or p divides $a^p - a$. If p does not divide a then p must divide $a^{p-1} - 1$, which is exactly Fermat's theorem. ■

Example 10.9 We can solve the problem in Example 2.8 using Burnside's theorem. Let S be the set of the 10^5 5-digit numbers and $(\{\pi_1, \pi_2\}, \circ)$ be a permutation group of S, where π_1 is the identity permutation, and π_2 is a permutation that maps a number into itself if it is not readable as a number when turned upside down (for example, 13765 is mapped into 13765) and maps a number into the number obtained by reading the former upside down whenever it is possible (for example, 89166 is mapped into 99168). The number of invariances under π_1 is 10^5. The number of invariances under π_2 is $(10^5 - 5^5) + 3 \times 5^2$ because there are $10^5 - 5^5$ numbers that contain one or more of the digits 2, 3, 4, 5, and 7 and cannot be read upside down, and because there are 3×5^2 numbers that will read the same either right side up or upside down, for example, 16891 (the center digit of these numbers must be 0 or 1 or 8, the last digit must be the first digit turned upside down, and the fourth digit must be the second digit turned upside down). Therefore, the number of distinct slips to be made up is

$$\frac{1}{2}(10^5 + 10^5 - 5^5 + 3 \times 5^2) = 10^5 - \frac{1}{2} \times 5^5 + \frac{3}{2} \times 5^2 \quad \blacksquare$$

10.7 DIHEDRAL GROUPS

Let $V = \{x, y, z\}$ be a set and let r denote a permutation of the elements of V, i.e., $r: V \to V$ is a one-to-one onto mapping. One of the convenient ways for describing the permutation r is as follows:

Let, $\quad r(x) = z$, $r(y) = x$ and $r(z) = y$.

Then r may be represented as

$$r = \begin{pmatrix} x & y & z \\ z & x & y \end{pmatrix}$$

where the image of any element of V is entered below the element. According to this notation

$$r_1 = \begin{pmatrix} x & y & z \\ z & x & y \end{pmatrix} = \begin{pmatrix} x & z & y \\ z & y & x \end{pmatrix} = \begin{pmatrix} y & x & z \\ x & z & y \end{pmatrix} = \dots.$$

Now, let us consider a set $V = \{x, y\}$ consisting of only two elements. Let the permutation on the elements of this set be denoted by r_1, r_2, where

$$r_1 = \begin{pmatrix} x & y \\ x & y \end{pmatrix} \text{ and } r_2 = \begin{pmatrix} x & y \\ y & x \end{pmatrix}$$

It may be observed that $V_2 = \{r_1, r_2\}$ is the set of all possible permutations of the elements of $\{x, y\}$.

Let $\oplus$ denote a binary operation on V_2 representing the (right) composition of permutation. For $i, j = 1, 2$ we mean by $r_i \oplus r_j$ the permutation obtained by permuting the elements of V by an application of r_i, followed by an application of the permutation r_j. Let, r_i and r_j be two functions and let $*$ denote the left composition of functions; then

$$r_i \oplus r_j = r_j * r_i \text{ for } i, j = 1, 2$$

So, $(r_i \oplus r_j)(x) = (r_j \oplus r_i)(x) = r_j(r_i(x))$. Similarly, the left compositions for y can be computed. The composition of permutations is associative because $*$ is associative. Also, r_1 is the identity element with respect to the operation $\oplus$ on V_2 as described in Table 10.1.

Table 10.1

$\oplus$	r_1	r_2
r_1	r_1	r_2
r_2	r_2	r_1

It may be noted that $(V_2, \oplus)$ is independent of the elements of the set $\{x, y\}$ but depends upon the number of elements in this set. Any other set of two elements will generate the same permutation group $(V_2, \oplus)$. So, we say that the degree of a permutation group is the cardinality of the set on which the permutations are defined. Accordingly, the degree of $(V_2, \oplus)$ is 2.

Now, let us consider 6 (i.e. 3!) permutations of the elements of the set $\{1, 2, 3\}$. Let us denote the set of all permutations by $V_2 = \{r_1, r_2, \ldots, r_6\}$. The elements $r_1, \ldots r_6$ are described below:

$$r_1 = \begin{pmatrix} 1 & 2 & 3 \\ 1 & 2 & 3 \end{pmatrix} \qquad r_2 = \begin{pmatrix} 1 & 2 & 3 \\ 2 & 1 & 3 \end{pmatrix} \qquad r_3 = \begin{pmatrix} 1 & 2 & 3 \\ 3 & 2 & 1 \end{pmatrix}$$

$$r_4 = \begin{pmatrix} 1 & 2 & 3 \\ 1 & 3 & 2 \end{pmatrix} \qquad r_5 = \begin{pmatrix} 1 & 2 & 3 \\ 2 & 3 & 1 \end{pmatrix} \qquad r_6 = \begin{pmatrix} 1 & 2 & 3 \\ 3 & 1 & 2 \end{pmatrix}$$

The composition of permutations on V_3 is given in Table 10.2 .

Table 10.2

$\oplus$	r_1	r_2	r_3	r_4	r_5	r_6
r_1	r_1	r_2	r_3	r_4	r_5	r_6
r_2	r_2	r_1	r_5	r_6	r_3	r_4
r_3	r_3	r_6	r_1	r_5	r_4	r_2
r_4	r_4	r_5	r_6	r_1	r_2	r_3
r_5	r_5	r_4	r_2	r_3	r_6	r_1
r_6	r_6	r_3	r_4	r_2	r_1	r_5

Any entry in the table can easily be determined; for example,

$$r_3 \oplus r_5 = \begin{pmatrix} 1 & 2 & 3 \\ 3 & 2 & 1 \end{pmatrix} \oplus \begin{pmatrix} 1 & 2 & 3 \\ 2 & 3 & 1 \end{pmatrix} = \begin{pmatrix} 1 & 2 & 3 \\ 3 & 2 & 1 \end{pmatrix} \oplus \begin{pmatrix} 3 & 2 & 1 \\ 1 & 3 & 2 \end{pmatrix} = \begin{pmatrix} 1 & 2 & 3 \\ 1 & 3 & 2 \end{pmatrix}$$
$$= r_4$$

In general, the set V_n of all permutations of n elements is a permutation group $(V_n, \oplus)$. This group is also called the *symmetric group*. The group $(V_n, \oplus)$ is of order $n!$ and degree n.

By observing the symmetries of regular polygons, we can obtain some other important permutation groups known as *dihedral groups*. For this purpose, let us first consider an equilateral triangle whose vertices are denoted by a, b and c, as shown in Fig. 10.9

Now, consider all possible rotations and reflections which leave the final position of the triangle unchanged from its original position except for the renaming of vertices. We shall denote such rotations by r_1, r_2 ..... A rotation is described as a transformation of the set of vertices. For example, let r_1 denote either no rotation or a rotation of the triangle about the center of gravity 0 through 360°. We may describe r_1 by writing, as before,

$$r_1 = \begin{pmatrix} a & b & c \\ a & b & c \end{pmatrix}$$

Fig. 10.9 An equilateral triangle

Similarly, let us denote the counterclockwise rotation of the triangle about 0 and through 120° and through 120° and 240° by r_5 and r_6 respectively. It may be observed that

$$r_5 = \begin{pmatrix} a & b & c \\ b & c & a \end{pmatrix} \text{ and } r_6 = \begin{pmatrix} a & b & c \\ c & a & b \end{pmatrix}$$

All other rotations of the triangle through any multiple of 120°, whether clockwise or counterclockwise, will result in one of the rotations r_1, r_5, or r_6. In fact, r_1 can be considered as a rotation r_5 followed by the rotation r_6. We may express this idea by writing $r_1 = r_5 \oplus r_6$ where $\oplus$ denotes the composition of rotation. Accordingly, $r_5 \oplus r_5 = r_6$, $r_6 \oplus r_6 = r_5$, $r_6 \oplus r_5 = r_5 \oplus r_6 = r_1$, and so on. The composition of the rotations on $\{r_1, r_5, r_6\}$ is given in Table 10.3. It may be easily verified that $(\{r_1, r_5, r_6\}, \oplus)$ is a group.

Table 10.3

$\oplus$	r_1	r_5	r_6
r_1	r_1	r_5	r_6
r_5	r_5	r_6	r_1
r_6	r_6	r_1	r_5

It may be noted that the rotations r_1, r_5 and r_6 do not exhaust all possible rigid rotations of the triangle which may result in the triangle's returning to its original position. For example, a rotation through 180° about any one of the lines aA, bB, or cC is not described by r_1, r_5, or r_6. Any such rotation can also be considered as a reflection of the triangle. Let us denote these rotations by r_4, r_3, and r_2, respectively, where all the rotations $r_1, r_2, ..., r_6$ are the same. Note that after the rotations or reflections r_2, r_3, or r_4, only two of the vertices are interchanged. There are no other rotations which return the triangle to the original position. The set of all such rotations, $\{r_1, r_2, ..., r_6\}$, can also be interpreted as the set of all the symmetries of the equilateral triangle. This set under the operation of composition is denoted by $(D_3, \oplus)$ and is called a *dihedral group*. $(D_3, \oplus)$ is of order 6 and degree 3 because it is a permutation

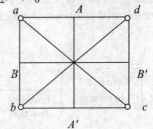

Fig. 10.10 A square

group obtained from the permutation of the vertices of the triangle. Actually, in this case the dihedral group is the same as the group $(V_3, \oplus)$.

As a final example, we ask the reader to obtain the dihedral group $(D_4, \oplus)$ by considering the symmetries of a square as shown in Fig 10.10.

10.8 CODES AND GROUP CODES

The coding problem is that of representing distinct messages by distinct sequences of letters from a given alphabet. For example, messages such as "emergency," "help is on the way," "all is clear," and so on, can be represented by sequences of dots and dashes. We assume in our discussion in this section that the alphabet is the binary alphabet $B = \{0, 1\}$. We define $B^m = B \times B \times B \ldots \times B$ (m factors). A sequence of letters from an alphabet is often referred to as a *word*. A *code* is a collection of words that are to be used to represent distinct messages. A word in a code is also called a *codeword*. A *block code* is a code consisting of words that are of the same length. One of the criteria for choosing a block code to represent a set of messages is its ability to correct errors. Suppose a codeword is transmitted from its origin to its destination. In the course of transmission, interferences such as noises might cause some of the 1s in the codeword to be received as 0s, and some of the 0s to be received as 1s. The data transmission process is shown in Fig. 10.11. Consequently, the received word might no longer be the transmitted one, and it is our desire to recover the transmitted word if at all possible. This is what we mean by error correction.

Let A denote the set of all binary sequences of length n. Let $\oplus$ be a binary operation on A such that for $\mathbf{x}$ and $\mathbf{y}$ in A, $\mathbf{x} \oplus \mathbf{y}$ is a sequence of length n that has 1s in those positions $\mathbf{x}$ and $\mathbf{y}$ differ and has 0s in those positions $\mathbf{x}$ and $\mathbf{y}$ are the same. For example, let $\mathbf{x} = 00101$ and $\mathbf{y} = 10110$, then $\mathbf{x} \oplus \mathbf{y} = 10011$. We ask the reader to show that $(A, \oplus)$ is a group. Note that the all zero word is the identity and every word is its own inverse in $(A, \oplus)$.

Let $\mathbf{x}$ be a word in A. We define the weight of $\mathbf{x}$, denoted $w(\mathbf{x})$, to be the number of 1s in $\mathbf{x}$. Thus, the weight of 1110000 is 3, and so is that of 1001100. For $\mathbf{x}$ and $\mathbf{y}$ in A, we define Hamming distance, or simply, the distance between $\mathbf{x}$ and $\mathbf{y}$, denoted $d(\mathbf{x}, \mathbf{y})$, to be the weight of $\mathbf{x} \oplus \mathbf{y}$, $w(\mathbf{x} \oplus \mathbf{y})$. For example, the distance between 1110000 and 1001100 is 4, and the distance between 1110000 and 0001111 is 7. Note that the distance between two words is exactly the number of positions at which they differ.

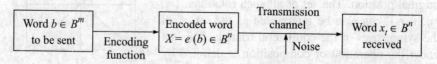

Fig. 10.11   Data transmission

It is obvious that for any **x** and **y**, $d(\mathbf{x}, \mathbf{y}) = d(\mathbf{y}, \mathbf{x})$. We now show that for any **x, y, z** in A

$$d(\mathbf{x}, \mathbf{y}) \leq d(\mathbf{x}, \mathbf{z}) + d(\mathbf{z}, \mathbf{y})$$

Clearly,

$$w(\mathbf{u} \oplus \mathbf{v}) \leq w(\mathbf{u}) + w(\mathbf{v})$$

Thus, we have

$$w(\mathbf{x} \oplus \mathbf{y}) = w(\mathbf{x} \oplus \mathbf{z} \oplus \mathbf{z} \oplus \mathbf{y})$$
$$\leq w(\mathbf{x} \oplus \mathbf{z}) + w(\mathbf{z} \oplus \mathbf{y})$$

or

$$d(\mathbf{x}, \mathbf{y}) \leq d(\mathbf{x}, \mathbf{z}) + d(\mathbf{z}, \mathbf{y})$$

Parity Check Code: The following encoding function $e : B^m \to B^{m+1}$ is called the parity $(m, m + 1)$ check code:

Suppose, $b = b_1 b_2 b_3 \ldots b_m \in B^m$. We define, the encoding function $e(b)$ as

$$e(b) = b_1 b_2 b_3 \ldots b_m \, b_{m+1}$$

where

$$b_{m+1} = \begin{cases} 0 & \text{if } |b| \text{ is even} \\ 1 & \text{if } |b| \text{ is odd} \end{cases}, \text{ (|b| represents weight of b)}.$$

It may be observed that b_{m+1} is zero iff the number of 1s in b is an even number. Thus, every code word $e(b)$ has even weight. A single error in the transmission of a code word will modify the received word to a word of odd weight and therefore can be detected. In the similar fashion, we can argue that any odd number of errors can be detected.

For the illustration of this encoding function, let us assume $m = 3$, then

$$\left. \begin{aligned} e(000) &= 0000 \\ e(001) &= 0011 \\ e(010) &= 0101 \\ e(011) &= 0110 \\ e(100) &= 1001 \\ e(101) &= 1010 \\ e(110) &= 1100 \\ e(111) &= 1111 \end{aligned} \right\} \text{ Code words}$$

Let $b = 111$. Then, $x = e(b) = 1111$. If transmission channel transmits x as $x_t = 1101$, then $|x_t| = 3$, and we can say that an odd number of errors (at least one) has occurred.

It may be noted that, if the received word has even weight, then we cannot guarantee that the code word was correctly transmitted, as this encoding function cannot detect an even number of errors.

Example 10.10   Consider (3, 4) parity check code. For each of the received words determine whether an error will be detected?
 (a) 0010
 (b) 1001

Solution:
 (a) 0010 – yes (since weight = 1, which is odd).
 (b) 1001 – no (since weight = 2, which is even) ■

Example 10.11   Consider (6, 7) parity check code. For each of the received words determine whether an error will be detected?
 (a) 1101010
 (b) 1010011
 (c) 0011111
 (d) 1001101

Solution:
 (a) 1101010 – No (since even weight, so no error will be detected)
 (b) 1010011 – No (since even weight, so no error will be detected)
 (c) 0011111 – Yes (since odd weight, so an error will be detected)
 (d) 1001101 – No (since even weight, so no error will be detected) ■

Example 10.12   Consider the (2, 6) encoding function e.

$$e(00) = 000000 \qquad e(10) = 101010$$
$$e(01) = 011110 \qquad e(11) = 111000$$

 (a) Find the minimum distance of e.
 (b) How many errors will e detect?

Solution:
 (a) $d(e(00), e(01))$
   $= |(000000) \oplus (011110)| = |(011110)| = 4$
   $d(e(01), e(10))$
   $= |(011110) \oplus (101010)| = |(110100)| = 3$
   $d(e(10), e(11))$
   $= |(101010) \oplus (111000)| = |(010010)| = 2$

  Similarly finding all, we found that the minimum distance is 2.

 (b) A code will detect k or fewer errors iff its minimum distance is at least $k+1$. Since here the minimum distance is 2, so we have

$$2 \geq k + 1$$
$$\Rightarrow \qquad k \leq 1.$$

  So, the code will detect one or fewer errors. ■

Example 10.13 Consider the (3, 9) encoding function e.

$$e(000) = 000000000 \qquad e(100) = 010011010$$
$$e(001) = 011100101 \qquad e(101) = 111101011$$
$$e(010) = 010101000 \qquad e(110) = 001011000$$
$$e(100) = 110010001 \qquad e(111) = 110000111$$

(a) Find the minimum distance of e.

(b) How many errors will e detect?

Solution:

(a) $d(e(000), e(010)) = 3$
$d(e(000), e(110)) = 3$
$d(e(000), e(001)) = 5$
$d(e(000), e(011)) = 4$
$d(e(000), e(100)) = 4$
$d(e(001), e(111)) = 5$
$d(e(001), e(110)) = 6$
$d(e(010), e(100)) = 3$

In this way from all the pair of combinations, we find the minimum distance is 3.

(b) It can detect at most 2 or fewer number of errors, as the minimum distance is 3. ∎

Example 10.14 Show that the (2, 5) encoding function $e : B^3 \rightarrow B^7$ defined by

$$e(00) = 00000 \qquad e(10) = 10101$$
$$e(01) = 01110 \qquad e(11) = 11011$$

is a group code.

Solution: To prove, it is a group code, we have to examine the following steps:

(a) Identity Element: Since 00000 belongs to the set, hence check for identity is satisfied.

(b) For Closer:

$(00000) \oplus (01110) = 01110$, which belongs to the set.
$(00000) \oplus (10101) = 10101$, which belongs to the set.
$(01110) \oplus (10101) = 11011$, which belongs to the set.
$(01110) \oplus (11011) = 10101$, which belongs to the set.
$(10101) \oplus (11011) = 01110$, which belongs to the set.

By checking this way, we found that if x, y belong to the set, then $x \oplus y$ also belong to the set. It can be easily verified that $\oplus$ is associative. Also, for each element inverse exists. Hence, it is a group code. ∎

Suppose, $e: B^m \rightarrow B^n$, is an (m, n) encoding function. We define an onto function $d: B^n \rightarrow B^m$ such that if $d(x_t) = b' \in B^m$ and the transmission channel has no noise, then $b' = b$. This onto function d is known as an (n, m) decoding function associated with the encoding function e. Here, $x = e(b)$ is the encoded word and x_t is the received word. The decoding function d should be an onto function because every received word can be decoded to give a transmitted word.

Example 10.15   Let us again consider the parity check code which was defined earlier. The corresponding decoding function $d: B^{m+1} \to B^m$ can be defined as follows:

If

$$z = z_1 z_2 \cdots z_m z_{m+1}$$

then

$$d(z) = z_1 z_2 \cdots z_m.$$

It may be observed that, if

$$b = b_1 b_2 b_3 \cdots b_m \in B^m$$

then

$$(d \circ e)(b) = d(e(b)) = b$$

For example, suppose $m = 4$. Then, $d(10100) = 1010$ and $d(11111) = 1111$. ∎

Let e be an (m, n) encoding function and d be an (n, m) decoding function. We say that the pair (e, d) corrects t or fewer errors if whenever $x = e(b)$ is transmitted correctly or with t or fewer errors and x_t is the received word, then $d(x_t) = b$. So, x_t is decoded as the original word b.

Let G be a block code. We define the *distance* of G to be the minimum distance between any pair of distinct codewords in G. The distance of a block code is closely related to its ability to correct errors, as we shall show. Suppose that corresponding to the transmission of a codeword in G, the word **y** was received. Our question is to determine from **y** the codeword that was transmitted. To motivate our discussion, let us assume the simple case that **y** turns out to be one of the codewords in G. In this case, one probably would jump to the obvious conclusion that the transmitted word was indeed **y**. We note that even such an obvious conclusion needs clarification. Since we assume that in the course of transmission, errors can occur in any of the positions, every one of the codewords in G could have been the transmitted word. When we decided that the transmitted word was **y**, we have tacitly assumed that when a word was transmitted, it was more likely that no error had occurred than that some errors had occurred. Let us not commit ourselves to such an assumption for the time being and state in a general way how we are to determine the transmitted word corresponding to a received word **y**. Let $x_1, x_2, \ldots, x_N$ denote the codewords in G. We shall compute the conditional probability $P(x_i|y)$ for $i = 1, 2, \ldots, N$, where $P(x_i|y)$ is the probability that x_i was the transmitted word given that **y** was the received word. If $P(x_k|y)$ is the largest of all conditional probabilities computed, we shall conclude that x_k was the transmitted word. Such a criterion for determining the transmitted word is known as the *maximum-likelihood decoding criterion*.

The computation of the conditional probability $P(x_i|y)$ can be quite involved since the probability depends on many factors in the communication system. There is, however, another criterion that can be used to determine the transmitted word. We compute $d(x_i, y)$ for $i = 1, 2, \ldots, N$, and conclude that x_k was the transmitted word if $d(\mathbf{x}_k, \mathbf{y})$ is the smallest among all distances computed. This is known as the *minimum-distance decoding criterion*. If we assume that the occurrence of errors in the positions are independent, and that the probability of the occurrence of an error is p then $P(\mathbf{x}_i|\mathbf{y}) = (1 - p)^{n-t}p^t$, where t is the distance between $\mathbf{x}_i$ and $\mathbf{y}$. For $p < \dfrac{1}{2}$, the smaller $d(\mathbf{x}_i,\mathbf{y})$ is, the larger $P(\mathbf{x}_i|\mathbf{y})$ will be.* Consequently, the minimum-distance decoding criterion is equivalent to the maximum-likelihood decoding criterion. (In this case, the conclusion that the transmitted word was $\mathbf{y}$ when the received word $\mathbf{y}$ is a codeword is justified.)

We note immediately that *a code of distance $2t + 1$ can correct t or fewer transmission errors when the minimum-distance decoding criterion is followed.* Suppose a codeword $\mathbf{x}$ was transmitted and the word $\mathbf{y}$ was received. If no more than t errors have occurred in the course of transmission, we have

$$d(\mathbf{x}, \mathbf{y}) \leqq t$$

Let $\mathbf{x}_1$ be another codeword. Since

$$d(\mathbf{x}, \mathbf{x}_1) \geqq 2t + 1$$

and

$$d(\mathbf{x}, \mathbf{x}_1) \leqq d(\mathbf{x}, \mathbf{y}) + d(\mathbf{y}, \mathbf{x}_1)$$

we have

$$d(\mathbf{y}, \mathbf{x}_1) \geqq t + 1$$

Therefore, the minimum-distance decoding criterion will indeed select $\mathbf{x}$ as the transmitted word.

Example 10.16 How many errors can be corrected by $(3, 4)$ parity check code?

Solution: Since the distance between any two code words in $(3, 4)$ parity check code is two, so according to the minimum-distance decoding criterion, it can correct zero errors, i.e., it cannot correct any errors. ∎

We study now a class of block codes known as *group codes*. A subset G of A is called a group code if $(G, \oplus)$ is a subgroup of $(A, \oplus)$, where A is the set of binary sequences of length n.

We show now that the distance of G is equal to the minimum weight of the nonzero words in G. This result makes it much easier to compute the distance of a group code since it is no longer necessary to compute the distance between every pair of distinct words in G exhaustively. Suppose $\mathbf{x}$ is a nonzero word in G. Since

$$w(\mathbf{x}) = d(\mathbf{x}, \mathbf{0})*$$

and since $\mathbf{0}$ is in G, we have

$$w(\mathbf{x}) \geqq \min_{\mathbf{y}, \mathbf{z} \in G} [d(\mathbf{y}, \mathbf{z})] \qquad (10.1)$$

---

* See Prob. 10.42 for the case $p > \dfrac{1}{2}$.

On the other hand, for any **y** and **z** in G, since

$$d(\mathbf{y}, \mathbf{z}) = w(\mathbf{y} \oplus \mathbf{z})$$

and since **y** $\oplus$ **z** is also in G, we have

$$d(\mathbf{y}, \mathbf{z}) \geq \min_{\substack{\mathbf{x} \in G \\ \mathbf{x} \neq \mathbf{0}}} [w(\mathbf{x})] \tag{10.2}$$

From (10.1) we obtain

$$\min_{\substack{\mathbf{x} \in G \\ \mathbf{x} \neq \mathbf{0}}} [w(\mathbf{x})] \geq \min_{\mathbf{y}, \mathbf{z} \in G} [d(\mathbf{y}, \mathbf{z})] \tag{10.3}$$

From (10.2) we obtain

$$\min_{\mathbf{y}, \mathbf{z} \in G} [d(\mathbf{y}, \mathbf{z})] \geq \min_{\substack{\mathbf{x} \in G \\ \mathbf{x} \neq \mathbf{0}}} [w(\mathbf{x})] \tag{10.4}$$

Combining (10.3) and (10.4) we obtain

$$\min_{\substack{\mathbf{x} \in G \\ \mathbf{x} \neq \mathbf{0}}} [w(\mathbf{x})] = \min_{\mathbf{y}, \mathbf{z} \in G} [d(\mathbf{y}, \mathbf{z})]$$

For group codes, there is an efficient way to determine the transmitted word corresponding to a received word according to the minimum-distance decoding criterion. Let $(G, \oplus)$ be a group code. Let **y** be a received word. Since $d(\mathbf{x}_i, \mathbf{y}) = w(\mathbf{x}_i \oplus \mathbf{y})$, the weights of the words in the coset $G \oplus \mathbf{y}$ are the distances between the codewords in G and **y**. Let **e** denote the word[†] of smallest weight in $G \oplus \mathbf{y}$. Let $\mathbf{e} = \mathbf{x}_j \oplus \mathbf{y}$ where $\mathbf{x}_j$ is in G. According to the minimum-distance decoding criterion, $\mathbf{e} \oplus \mathbf{y} = \mathbf{x}_j$ is the transmitted codeword. Since this argument is valid for all **y** in the coset $G \oplus \mathbf{y}$, our decoding procedure can be stated as:

1. Determine all cosets of G.
2. For each coset, pick the word of the smallest weight,[‡] which we shall refer to as the leader of the coset.
3. For a received word **y**, $\mathbf{e} \oplus \mathbf{y}$ is the transmitted word, where **e** is the leader of the coset containing **y**.

As an example, let $G = \{0000, 0011, 1101, 1110\}$. It can easily be checked that $(G, \oplus)$ is a group. The rows in Fig. 10.12 are the distinct cosets of G. We ask the reader to check that according to the minimum distance decoding criterion the received word 1011 will be decoded as 0011, the received word 1010 will be decoded as 1110, and the received word 1111 will be decoded either as 1101 or 1110 depending on whether 0010 or 0001 was chosen as the leader of the coset containing the word 1111.

0000	0011	1101	1110
1000	1011	0101	0110
0100	0111	1001	1010
0010	0001	1111	1100

Fig. 10.12

---

* **0** denotes the all-zero word.

† Or one of the words of smallest weight.

‡ Or one of the words of smallest weight.

The C code for computing the transmitted word from a received word is given in Fig. 10.13.

```c
/* Program to compute the transmitted word from a received word*/
#include<stdio.h>
#include<stdlib.h>
#include<math.h>
#include<conio.h>
void tobin(int x);
int todec(int);
int weight(int);
void main()
{
        int a[4],b[4],c[4],d[4],i,x,r,t,p,q,u,s,l,m;
        char ch='y';
        a[0]=0;
        clrscr();
        printf("\nEnter 4 binary numbers:");
        for(i=0;i<4;i++)
        {
                scanf("%d",&x);
                a[i]=todec(x);
        }
        printf("\n\nA=");
        for(i=0;i<4;i++)
        {
                tobin(a[i]);
                printf("\t");
        }
        printf("\nEnter another binary number which is not in A:");

        scanf("%d",&x);
        b[0]=todec(x);
        for(i=1;i<4;i++)
                b[i]=b[0]^a[i];
        l=4;
        printf("\n\nB=");
        for(i=0;i<4;i++)
        {
                tobin(b[i]);
                printf("\t");
                m=weight(b[i]);
                if(l>m)
                {
                        q=b[i];
                        l=m;
                }
        }
        printf("\nEnter another binary number which is not in A & B:");
        scanf("%d",&x);
        c[0]=todec(x);
        for(i=1;i<4;i++)
                c[i]=c[0]^a[i];

        printf("\n\nC=");
        l=4;
        for(i=0;i<4;i++)
        {
                tobin(c[i]);
                printf("\t");
                m=weight(c[i]);
                if(l>m)
                {
```

```
                                    u=c[i];
                                    l=m;
                            }
                }
        printf("\nEnter another binary number which is not in A,B & C:");
        scanf("%d",&x);
        d[0]=todec(x);
        for(i=1;i<4;i++)
                d[i]=d[0]^a[i];
        clrscr();
        printf("\n******CO-SET TABLE*****\n");
        l=4;
        for(i=0;i<4;i++)
        {
                tobin(a[i]);
                printf("\t");
                m=weight(a[i]);
                if(l>m)
                {
                        p=a[i];
                        l=m;
                }
        }
        printf("\n");
        for(i=0;i<4;i++)
        {
                tobin(b[i]);
                printf("\t");
        }
        printf("\n");
        for(i=0;i<4;i++)
        {
                tobin(c[i]);
                printf("\t");
        }
        printf("\n");
        l=4;
        for(i=0;i<4;i++)
        {
                tobin(d[i]);
                printf("\t");
                m=weight(d[i]);
                if(l>m)
                {
                        t=d[i];
                        l=m;
                }
        }
        while(ch=='y')
        {
        printf("\n\nEnter the recieved word:");
        scanf("%d",&x);
        r=todec(x);
        for(i=0;i<4;i++)
        {
                if(r==a[i])
                    {  t=r^p;break;}
                else if(r==b[i])
                        {t=r^q;break;}
                else if(r==c[i])
                        {t=r^u;break;}
                else if(r==d[i])
                        {t=r^s;break;}
```

```
                else
                     continue;
        }
        printf("\nTransmitted word:");
        tobin(t);
        fflush(stdin);
        printf("\n\nDo you want to continue(y/n):");
        scanf("%c",&ch);
        }
        getch();
}
void tobin(int x)
{
        int j,i=0,a[4]={0,0,0,0},r;
        while(x!=0)
        {
                r=x%2;
                x=x/2;
                a[i]=r;
                i++;
        }
        for( j=3;j>=0;j-)
                printf("%d",a[j]);

}

int todec(int a)
{
        int b=0,r,i=0;
        while(a!=0)
        {
                r=a%10;
                if(r==1)
                        b+=pow(2,i);
                i++;
                a=a/10;
        }
        return b;
}
/*To find the weight of binary number*/
int weight(int x)
{
        int j,i=0,a[4]={0,0,0,0},r,1=0;
        while(x!=0)
        {
                r=x%2;
                x=x/2;
                a[i]=r;
                i++;
        }
        for( j=3;j>=0;j--)
        {
                if(a[j]==1)
                        1++;
        }
        return 1;
}
```

Fig. 10.13 C code for computing the transmitted word from a received word

10.9 ISOMORPHISMS AND AUTOMORPHISMS

Let $(A, \star)$ be the algebraic system shown in Fig. 10.14a. Since the names of the elements of A, a, b, c, and d as well as the name of the operation on A, $\star$ are abstract names, there is no reason we cannot change them to other abstract names. For example, by changing a, b, c, d to α, β, γ, δ and $\star$ to $*$, we obtain the algebraic system $(B, *)$ in Fig. 10.14b. Clearly, one would agree that the two systems $(A, \star)$ and $(B, *)$ are "essentially the same." We say that an algebraic system $(B, *)$ is *isomorphic* to the algebraic system $(A, \star)$ if we can obtain $(B, *)$ from $(A, \star)$ by renaming the elements and/or the operation in $(A, \star)$. In a more formal but equivalent way, we say that $(B, *)$ is isomorphic to $(A, \star)$ if there exists a one-to-one onto function f from A to B such that for all a_1 and a_2 in A

$$f(a_1 \star a_2) = f(a_1) * f(a_2)$$

The function f is called an *isomorphism* from $(A, \star)$ to $(B, *)$, and $(B, *)$ is called an *isomorphic image* of A. For example, the function f such that

$$f(a) = \alpha$$
$$f(b) = \beta$$
$$f(c) = \gamma$$
$$f(d) = \delta$$

is an isomorphism from the algebraic system $(A, \star)$ in Fig. 10.14a to the algebraic system $(B, *)$ in Fig. 10.14b. Note that the function g such that

$$g(a) = \delta$$
$$g(b) = \gamma$$
$$g(c) = \beta$$
$$g(d) = \alpha$$

is also an isomorphism from $(A, \star)$ to $(B, *)$.

As another example, we note that in Fig. 10.15 the algebraic systems $(B, \oplus)$, $(C, *)$, and $(D, +)$ are all isomorphic to the algebraic system $(A, \star)$. As a matter of fact, the system $(B, \oplus)$ corresponds to the addition of even and odd numbers, the system $(C, *)$ corresponds to the rotation of geometric figures in the plane by 0 and 180°, and the system $(D, +)$ corresponds to the situation of purchasing two items in a five-and-ten store, where the element 0¢ in D stands for amounts that are multiples of 10¢, the element 5¢ stands for amounts that are multiples of 10¢ plus 5¢, and the binary operation + determines whether the total purchase

$\star$	a	b	c	d		$*$	α	β	γ	δ
a	a	b	c	d		α	α	β	γ	δ
b	b	a	a	c		β	β	α	α	γ
c	b	d	d	c		γ	β	δ	δ	γ
d	a	b	c	d		δ	α	β	γ	δ

(a)	(b)

Fig. 10.14

★	a	b
a	a	b
b	b	a

⊕	EVEN	ODD
EVEN	EVEN	ODD
ODD	ODD	EVEN

$(A, \star)$ $\qquad\qquad\qquad$ $(B, \oplus)$

*	0°	180°
0°	0°	180°
180°	180°	0°

+	0¢	5¢
0¢	0¢	5¢
5¢	5¢	0¢

$(C, *)$ $\qquad\qquad\qquad$ $(D, +)$

Fig. 10.15

price is a multiple of 10¢ or is a multiple of 10¢ plus 5¢. Indeed, the notion of isomorphism between two algebraic systems links abstract algebraic systems to physical situations we encounter in practice. Consequently, properties of abstract algebraic systems will have direct interpretation in terms of physical situations. From an applications viewpoint, this indeed is *the* reason to study abstract algebraic systems.

An isomorphism from an algebraic system $(A, \star)$ to $(A, \star)$ is called an *automorphism* on $(A, \star)$. For example, the function f such that

$$f(a) = d$$
$$f(b) = c$$
$$f(c) = b$$
$$f(d) = a$$

is an automorphism on the algebraic system $(A, \star)$ in Fig. 10.14a. A physical interpretation of an automorphism on an algebraic system is a way in which the elements in the system interchange their roles.

Example 10.17 As an illustrative example on the notion of isomorphism between groups, we shall show that there is a unique group, up to isomorphism, of order p for any prime p. We recall that for any integer n, $(Z_n, \oplus)$ is a group. Let $(G, \star)$ be a group of order p. Since any group of prime order is cyclic, the elements in G can be represented as $a^0, a, a^2, \ldots, a^{p-1}$ for any element a in G that is not the identity.* The function $f(a^i) = i$ is clearly an isomorphism from $(G, \star)$ to $(Z_p, \oplus)$. Consequently, we conclude that any group of order p is isomorphic to $(Z_p, \oplus)$. ∎

10.10 HOMOMORPHISMS AND NORMAL SUBGROUPS

The notion of isomorphic algebraic systems can be generalized immediately. Let $(A, \star)$ and $(B, *)$ be two algebraic systems. Let f be a function from A onto B such that for any a_1 and a_2 in A

$$f(a_1 \star a_2) = f(a_1) * f(a_2)$$

f is called a *homomorphism* from $(A, \star)$ to $(B, *)$, and $(B, *)$ is called a *homomorphic image* of $(A, \star)$.

For example, for the two algebraic systems in Fig. 10.14a and b, the function f such that

$$f(\alpha) = 1 \qquad\qquad f(\beta) = 1 \qquad\qquad f(\gamma) = 1$$
$$f(\delta) = 0 \qquad\qquad f(\in) = 0$$
$$f(\zeta) = -1$$

is a homomorphism from the algebraic system $(\{\alpha, \beta, \gamma, \delta, \in, \zeta\}, \star)$ to the algebraic system $(\{1, 0, -1\}, *)$.

There is an alternative way to look at the notion of a homomorphism from one algebraic system to another. Let $(A, \star)$ be an algebraic system and R be an equivalence relation on A. R is called a *congruence relation* on A (with respect to $\star$) if (a_1, a_2) and (b_1, b_2) in R implies that $(a_1 \star b_1, a_2 \star b_2)$ is also in R. For example, for the algebraic system in Fig. 10.17a, the equivalence relation R in Fig. 10.17b is a congruence relation. On the other hand, for the algebraic system in Fig. 10.18a, the equivalence relation R in Fig. 10.18b is not a congruence relation. [For instance, although (a, b) and (c, d) are in R, $(a \star c, b \star d)$, which is equal to (d, a), is not in R.] The equivalence classes into which A is divided are called *congruence classes*. We can define a new algebraic system $(B, *)$ as follows: Let $B = \{A_1, A_2, \ldots, A_r\}$ be the partition of A induced by R.[†] Let the binary operation $*$ be such that for any A_i and A_j in B, $A_i * A_j$ is equal to the congruence class A_k containing the element $a_1 \star a_2$, where a_1 is any element in A_i and a_2 is any element in A_j. Note that because R is a congruence relation, the operation $*$ is well defined. (That is, the congruence class $A_i * A_j$ is uniquely determined no matter what elements a_1 in A_i and a_2 in A_j we happen to pick.) We note immediately that $(B, *)$ is a homomorphic image of $(A, \star)$, since the function

$$f(a) = A_i, \quad \text{if} \quad a \in A_i$$

$\star$	α	β	γ	δ	ε	ζ
α	α	β	α	α	γ	δ
β	β	α	γ	β	γ	ε
γ	α	γ	α	β	γ	ε
δ	α	β	β	δ	ε	ζ
ε	γ	γ	γ	ε	ε	ζ
ζ	δ	ε	ε	ζ	ζ	ζ

$*$	1	0	-1
1	1	1	0
0	1	0	-1
-1	0	-1	-1

(a)   (b)

Fig. 10.16

---

[*] a^0 stands for the identity of $(G, \star)$.

[†] Let us remind the reader that a partition is a set of subsets and that it is perfectly all right that the elements of the set B in the algebraic system $(B, *)$ happen to be sets themselves.

★	a	b	c	d
a	a	a	d	c
b	b	a	c	d
c	c	d	a	b
d	d	d	b	a

	a	b	c	d
a	✓	✓		
b	✓	✓		
c			✓	✓
d			✓	✓

(a)   (b)

Fig. 10.17

is a homomorphism from $(A, \bigstar)$ to $(B, *)$.* Intuitively, a homomorphic image of an algebraic system can be viewed as a gross description of the behavior of the system when some of the characters distinguishing some of the elements in the system are ignored. Consequently, elements that become indistinguishable can be placed in one congruence class, and the system's behavior can be described by how these congruence classes interact.

★	a	b	c	d
a	a	a	d	c
b	b	a	d	a
c	c	b	a	b
d	c	d	b	a

	a	b	c	d
a	✓	✓		
b	✓	✓		
c			✓	✓
d			✓	✓

(a)   (b)

Fig. 10.18

As an example, consider the algebraic system in Fig. 10.16a as a description of the interaction of six different kinds of particles $\{\alpha, \beta, \gamma, \delta, \in, \zeta\}$. Suppose α, β, and γ are positively charged particles; δ and $\in$ are neutral particles; and ζ is a negatively charged particle. If we let $\{1, 0, -1\}$ denote the three kinds of particles, Fig. 10.16b shows how the three kinds of particles interact. Indeed, as was pointed out above, the function f such that

$$f(\alpha) = 1 \qquad f(\beta) = 1 \qquad f(\gamma) = 1$$
$$f(\delta) = 0 \qquad f(\in) = 0$$
$$f(\zeta) = -1$$

is a homomorphism from the algebraic system $(\{\alpha, \beta, \gamma, \delta, \in, \zeta\}, \bigstar)$ to the algebraic system $(\{1, 0, -1\}, *)$.

As another example, consider the algebraic system $(I, \cdot)$, where I is the set of all integers and $\cdot$ is the ordinary multiplication operation of integers. Suppose

---

* We ask the reader to show the converse, namely, a homomorphism from $(A, \bigstar)$ to $(B, *)$ induces a congruence relation on A.

we are not interested in distinguishing all the integers in *I* but rather in making a distinction among positive integers, negative integers, and zero. We note immediately that the algebraic system $(B, \odot)$ in Fig. 10.19 is a homomorphic image of $(I, \cdot)$ and that the function *f* such that

$$f(n) = \begin{cases} \text{POSITIVE} & \text{if } n \text{ is a positive integer} \\ \text{NEGATIVE} & \text{if } n \text{ is a negative integer} \\ \text{ZERO} & \text{if } n = 0 \end{cases}$$

is indeed a homomorphism from $(I, \cdot)$ to $(B, \odot)$.

$\odot$	POSITIVE	NEGATIVE	ZERO
POSITIVE	POSITIVE	NEGATIVE	ZERO
NEGATIVE	NEGATIVE	POSITIVE	ZERO
ZERO	ZERO	ZERO	ZERO

Fig. 10.19

Given a group $(G, \star)$, one would like to know how to determine a homomorphic image of $(G, \star)$, and furthermore, all homomorphic images of $(G, \star)$.* We recall our discussion in Sec. 10.5 that a subgroup of $(G, \star)$ induces a partition of *G* into cosets of the subgroup. It is therefore a reasonable guess to ask whether this partition divides *G* into congruence classes. The answer to this question is negative, although an additional condition on the subgroup will do the trick.

Let *H* be a subgroup of *G*. *H* is said to be a *normal subgroup* if, for any element *a* in *G*, the left coset $a \star H$ is equal to the right coset $H \star a$. (Note that, if *G* is a commutative group, any subgroup of *G* is normal.) For example, for the group $(A, \star)$ shown in Fig. 10.20a, $(H, \star)$ is a normal subgroup, where $H = \{\alpha, \beta, \gamma\}$. For instance,

$\star$	α	β	γ	δ	ε	ζ
α	α	β	γ	δ	ε	ζ
β	β	γ	α	ε	ζ	δ
γ	γ	α	β	ζ	δ	ε
δ	δ	ζ	ε	α	γ	β
ε	ε	δ	ζ	β	α	γ
ζ	ζ	ε	δ	γ	β	α

$(A, \star)$

(a)

$*$	$\{\alpha, \beta, \gamma\}$	$\{\delta, \varepsilon, \zeta\}$
$\{\alpha, \beta, \gamma\}$	$\{\alpha, \beta, \gamma\}$	$\{\delta, \varepsilon, \zeta\}$
$\{\delta, \varepsilon, \zeta\}$	$\{\delta, \varepsilon, \zeta\}$	$\{\alpha, \beta, \gamma\}$

$(B, *)$

(b)

Fig. 10.20

---

* It is not difficult to see that a homomorphic image of a group is always a group. See Prob. 10.36.

$$\delta \star H = \{\delta \star \alpha, \delta \star \beta, \delta \star \gamma\} = \{\delta, \zeta, \in \}$$
$$H \star \delta = \{\alpha \star \delta, \beta \star \delta, \gamma \star \delta\} = \{\delta, \in, \zeta\}$$

We want to show now that the distinct left (right) cosets of a normal subgroup H are congruence classes of G. Let $a \star H$ and $b \star H$ be two cosets. We want to show that for all elements a_1 in $a \star H$ and all elements b_1 in $b \star H$, the elements $a_1 \star b_1$ are all in one coset of H. Let

$$a_1 = a \star h_1$$
$$b_1 = b \star h_2$$

for some h_1 and h_2 in H. We have

$$
\begin{aligned}
a_1 \star b_1 &= (a \star h_1) \star (b \star h_2) \\
&= (a \star h_1) \star (h_3 \star b) &&\text{for some } h_3 \in H \\
&= a \star h_4 \star b &&\text{for some } h_4 \in H \\
&= a \star b \star h_5 &&\text{for some } h_5 \in H
\end{aligned}
$$

Thus, $a_1 \star b_1$ is in the coset $(a \star b) \star H$.

For example, for the group $(A, \star)$ shown in Fig. 10.18a and the normal subgroup $(H, \star)$, where $H = \{\alpha, \beta, \gamma\}$, the congruence classes are $\{\alpha, \beta, \gamma\}$ and $\{\delta, \in, \zeta\}$. Consequently, we have the homomorphic image $(B, *)$ shown in Fig. 10.20b, where $B = \{\{\alpha, \beta, \gamma\}, \{\delta, \in, \zeta\}\}$. As another example, for the group $(I, +)$, where I is the set of all integers and $+$ is the ordinary addition operation of integers, $(E, +)$ is a normal subgroup where E is the set of all even integers. Corresponding to the subgroup $(E, +)$, we have the homomorphic image shown in Fig. 10.21, where EVEN is the congruence class of all even integers and ODD is the congruence class of all odd integers.

$\oplus$	EVEN	ODD
EVEN	EVEN	ODD
ODD	ODD	EVEN

Fig. 10.21

Our next question is whether exhausting all normal subgroups of $(A, \star)$ will have exhausted all homomorphic images of $(A, \star)$. It turns out that this indeed is the case, as we shall show. Let f be a homomorphism from $(A, \star)$ to $(B, *)$. We want to show that f corresponds to a partition of A into congruence classes induced by a normal subgroup. Let H be all the elements in A whose images under f are the identity of B, which we shall denote $\in$.

We show first that $(H, \star)$ is a subgroup of $(A, \star)$:

1. We want to show that $\star$ is closed on H. For any a and b in H, since

    $$f(a \star b) = f(a) * f(b) = \in * \in = \in$$

    $a \star b$ is also in H.

2. We want to show that e, the identity of A, is in H. For an arbitrary element a in A, we have

    $$f(a \star e) = f(a) * f(e)$$

    or

    $$f(a) = f(a) * f(e)$$

Since $(B, *)$ is a group, $f(e)$ must be the identity of $(B, *)$. Consequently, e is in H.

3. We want to show that a^{-1} is in H for any element a in H. Since

$$f(a \star a^{-1}) = f(a) * f(a^{-1})$$

or

$$f(e) = f(a) * f(a^{-1})$$

or

$$\in = \in * f(a^{-1})$$

or

$$\in = f(a^{-1})$$

we conclude a^{-1} is in H.

We show now that $(H, \star)$ is a normal subgroup: For any a in A and any h in H

$$
\begin{aligned}
f(a \star h \star a^{-1}) &= f(a) * f(h) * f(a^{-1}) \\
&= f(a) * \in * f(a^{-1}) \\
&= f(a) * f(a^{-1}) \\
&= f(a \star a^{-1}) \\
&= f(e) \\
&= \in
\end{aligned}
$$

Thus, $a \star h \star a^{-1}$ is in H. That is, $a \star h \star a^{-1} = h_1$ or $a \star h = h_1 \star a$ for some h_1 in H. We conclude that H is normal.

Finally, we show that if a and b are in the same coset of H, then $f(a) = f(b)$. Since b can be written as

$$b = a \star h$$

for some h in H, we have

$$f(b) = f(a) * f(h) = f(a).$$

Conversely, we want to show that, if $f(a) = f(b)$, then a and b are in the same coset of H. Since

$$
\begin{aligned}
f(a^{-1} \star b) &= f(a^{-1}) * f(b) \\
&= f(a^{-1}) * f(a) \\
&= \in
\end{aligned}
$$

$a^{-1} \star b$ is in H, that is, $a^{-1} \star b = h$ or $b = a \star h$ for some h in H.

10.11 RINGS, INTEGRAL DOMAINS, AND FIELDS

We have so far studied algebraic systems with one binary operation. We turn now to study briefly several classes of algebraic systems with two binary operations. It is clear that given two algebraic systems $(A, \star)$ and $(A, *)$, we can always "combine" them to yield an algebraic system with two binary operations

---

* For example, $\beta \star (\alpha * \beta) = \beta$ and $(\beta \star \alpha) * (\beta \star \beta) = \alpha.$

$(A, \star, *)$. On the other hand, an algebraic system with two operations can be more than merely a "conglomerate" of two algebraic systems with one operation if the two operations are related in some way. For example, let $(A, \star, *)$ be an algebraic system such that for any a and b in A, $a \star b = b * a$. We observe that the two operations $\star$ and $*$ are related in that either both of them are commutative operations or both of them are not. (Why?)

A most natural and important way in which two binary operations can be related is the property of *distributivity*. Let $(A, \star, *)$ be an algebraic system with two binary operations. The operation $*$ is said to *distribute* over the operation $\star$ if for any a, b, and c in A,

$$a * (b \star c) = (a * b) \star (a * c)$$

and

$$(b \star c) * a = (b * a) \star (c * a)$$

For example, for the algebraic system $(\{\alpha, \beta\}, \star, *)$ where $\star$ and $*$ are as defined in Fig. 10.22, the operation $*$ is distributive over the operation $\star$, while the operation $\star$ is *not* distributive over the operation $*$.[*]

We are particularly interested in the classes of algebraic systems with two operations which are known as *rings*, *integral domains*, and *fields*.

10.11.1 Rings

An algebraic system $(A, +, \bullet)$ is called a *ring* if the following conditions are satisfied:

$\star$	α	β		$*$	α	β
α	α	β		α	α	α
β	β	α		β	α	β

Fig. 10.22

1. $(A, +)$ is an abelian group.
2. $(A, \bullet)$ is a semigroup.
3. The operation $\bullet$ is distributive over the operation $+$.

Let Z_n be the set of integers $\{0, 1, 2, ..., n-1\}$. Let $\oplus$ be a binary operation on Z_n such that

$$a \oplus b = \begin{cases} a+b & \text{if} \quad a+b < n \\ a+b-n & \text{if} \quad a+b \geq n \end{cases}$$

Let $\odot$ be a binary operation on Z_n such that

$$a \odot b = \text{the remainder of } ab \text{ divided by } n$$

It was pointed out in Sec. 10.2 that $(Z_n, \oplus)$ is an abelian group. Furthermore, it is not difficult to see that $\odot$ is a closed and an associative operation.[*] Consequently, $(Z_n, \odot)$ is a semigroup. We leave it to the reader to show that $\odot$ distributes over $\oplus$ and thus to conclude that $(Z_n, \oplus, \odot)$ is a ring.

We shall consistently refer to the two operations in a ring $(A, +, \cdot)$ as the addition and the multiplication operation. We shall also refer to $a + b$ as the *sum* of a and b, and $a \cdot b$ as the *product* of a and b. The identity of the abelian group $(A, +)$ is referred to as the *additive identity* and will be denoted 0. The inverse of

---

[*] See Problem 10.4.

an element a of the group $(A, +)$ is referred to as the *additive inverse* of a and will be denoted $-a$. We sometimes write $a - b$ to mean the sum of a and the additive inverse of b.

We now show that for any element a in a ring $(A, +, \cdot)$, $0 \cdot a = a \cdot 0 = 0$. Since

$$0 \cdot a = (0 + 0) \cdot a = 0 \cdot a + 0 \cdot a$$

we have

$$0 \cdot a = 0$$

That $a \cdot 0 = 0$ can be proved in a similar way.[†]

10.11.1.1 Subrings

A name can be given to the subsets of a ring which are themselves rings, just like in case of groups. Let $(A, +;)$ be a ring and $B \subseteq A$ $(B \neq \varnothing)$. $(B, +;)$ is called a subring of $(A, +;)$ if $(B, +;)$ itself is a ring.

So, a nonempty subset B of a ring A with respect to operation $+$ and is a subring of A if and only if B satisfies all the conditions needed for a ring. However, as in the case of groups, we can dispense with some of them. The subring criterion may be stated as the following theorem:

Theorem 10.5 Let $(A, +, .)$ be a ring and B be a nonempty subset of A. Then $(B, +, .)$ is a subring of $(A, +, .)$ if and only if

(a) $a + b \in B$, for $a, b \in B$,

(b) $-a \in B$, for $a \in B$,

(c) $a . b \in B$, for $a, b \in B$

Proof: Let $(A, +, .)$ be a ring and $B \subseteq A$ $(B \neq \varnothing)$. Suppose, B is a subring of A. Then, according to the definition of ring, $(B, +)$ is an abelian group. Since $B \subseteq A$, so $(B, +)$ is a subgroup of $(A, +)$. $(B, +)$ is a subgroup of $(A, +)$ if and only if

(a) $a + b \in B$, for $a, b \in B$,

(b) $-a \in B$, for $a \in B$.

Now, let us consider the multiplication operation. If $(B, +, .)$ is to be a ring then the operation . on B must be a binary operation and this holds if and only if

(c) $a . b \in B$, for $a, b \in B$.

So, if a nonempty subset B of a ring A is a subring of A then (a), (b) and (c) hold. On the other hand, if B is a nonempty subset of a ring A and (a), (b) and (c) hold then $(B, +)$ is a subgroup of $(A, +)$. In fact, $(B, +)$ is an abelian group. The operation is a binary operation on B and associativity of multiplication and distributivity of multiplication over addition hold in B since they hold in A. So, $(B, +, .)$ is a subring of $(A, +, .)$. ∎

[†] Note, indeed, how "useful" the property of distributivity is. See also Theorem 11.9.

Some Properties of Subrings

(a) Every ring has two trivial subrings: the ring itself and the set {0}.

(b) A subring of a commutative ring is a commutative ring.

(c) If A is a ring and B_i is an arbitrary collection of subrings of A, then B_i is a subring of A.

(d) If A is a ring and B is a subset of A then, the intersection of all subrings of A that contains B, is a subring of A. It is called the subring generated by B.

(e) A subring of a ring is a ring in its own right. Several irregular things might occur here.

Let B be a substring of A.

(i) It is possible for a ring A to have an identity, but B may not have.

(ii) It is possible for B to have an identity, but A may not have.

(iii) It is possible for both A and B to have identity elements, but they are two different elements.

Example 10.18   Let R be the set of all real numbers and Q be the set of all rational numbers. It may be observed that, $Q \subseteq R$ and R is a ring with respect to the operations addition (+) and multiplication (•). It is known that the set of all rational numbers Q is closed under addition operation. For every element $q \in Q$, its additive inverse is also in Q. It may also be checked that Q is closed under multiplication operation. Hence, Q is a subring of R. It may be noted that both R and Q have the same identity 1. ∎

Example 10.19   Let M be the ring of all 2×2 matrices with respect to matrix addition and multiplication operations and N be the set of all matrices of the form $\begin{pmatrix} x & 0 \\ 0 & 0 \end{pmatrix}$.

It can be seen that $(M, +;)$ is a ring.

It may be observed that N is closed under addition operation, i.e.

$$\begin{pmatrix} x & 0 \\ 0 & 0 \end{pmatrix} + \begin{pmatrix} y & 0 \\ 0 & 0 \end{pmatrix} = \begin{pmatrix} x+y & 0 \\ 0 & 0 \end{pmatrix} \in N.$$

For every element $x \in N$, its additive inverse is also in N, i.e.

$$\begin{pmatrix} x & 0 \\ 0 & 0 \end{pmatrix} = \begin{pmatrix} -x & 0 \\ 0 & 0 \end{pmatrix} \in N.$$

N is also closed under multiplication operation, i.e.

$$\begin{pmatrix} x & 0 \\ 0 & 0 \end{pmatrix} \cdot \begin{pmatrix} y & 0 \\ 0 & 0 \end{pmatrix} = \begin{pmatrix} xy & 0 \\ 0 & 0 \end{pmatrix} \in N.$$

So, N is a subring of M.

It may be noted that, $\begin{pmatrix} 1 & 0 \\ 0 & 1 \end{pmatrix}$ is the identity of M. However, $\begin{pmatrix} 1 & 0 \\ 0 & 1 \end{pmatrix} \notin N$.

The identity of N is $\begin{pmatrix} 1 & 0 \\ 0 & 1 \end{pmatrix}$. So, in this case, the identity of M is not the same as the identity of the subring N. ∎

10.11.2   Integral Domains

Let $(A, +, \cdot)$ be an algebraic system with two binary operations. $(A, +, \cdot)$ is called an *integral domain* if:

1. $(A, +)$ is an abelian group.
2. The operation $\cdot$ is commutative. Furthermore, if $c \neq 0$ and $c \cdot a = c \cdot b$, then $a = b$, where 0 denotes the additive identity.
3. The operation $\cdot$ is distributive over the operation $+$.

For example, let A be the set of all integers, and $+$ and $\cdot$ be the ordinary addition and multiplication operations of integers. We note that $(A, +)$ is an abelian group with 0 being the identity and $-n$ being the inverse of n for any integer n. We also note that the operation $\cdot$ is commutative. Furthermore, for any nonzero integer c, $c \cdot a = c \cdot b$ implies $a = b$. Since $\cdot$ is distributive over $+$, it follows that $(A, +, \cdot)$ is an integral domain.

10.11.3   Fields

Let $(A, +, \cdot)$ be an algebraic system with two binary operations. $(A, +, \cdot)$ is called a *field* if:

1. $(A, +)$ is an abelian group.
2. $(A - \{0\}, \cdot)$ is an abelian group.
3. The operation $\cdot$ is distributive over the operation $+$.

We ask the reader to check that $(F, +, \cdot)$ is a field, where F is the set of all rational numbers, and $+$ and $\cdot$ are the ordinary addition and multiplication operations of rational numbers. Other examples of fields are $(R, +, \cdot)$, where R is the set of all real numbers and $+$ and $\cdot$ are the ordinary addition and multiplication operations of real numbers, and $(C, +, \cdot)$, where C is the set of all complex numbers, and $+$ and $\cdot$ are the ordinary addition and multiplication operations of complex numbers. (One probably realizes now, if not earlier, that when we studied addition, subtraction, multiplication, and division of rational, real, and complex numbers in grade school, we studied the operations in the fields of rational, real, and complex numbers. Furthermore, subtraction is not really an "independent" operation in that it is equivalent to addition of the additive inverse of an element. Similarly, division is equivalent to multiplication by the multiplicative inverse of an element.)

As another example, we show that the algebraic system $(Z_n, \oplus, \odot)$ is a field if and only if n is a prime. It is clear that both $\oplus$ and $\odot$ are commutative operations. We recall that $(Z_n, \oplus)$ is a group for any n. Let us show that $(Z_n - \{0\}, \odot)$ is a group if and only if n is a prime. If n is not a prime, $n = ab$ for some a and b in $Z_n - \{0\}$. That is, $a \odot b = 0$. Since the operation $\odot$ is not closed on the set $Z_n - \{0\}$, $(Z_n, - \{0\}, \odot)$ cannot possibly be a group. Let us examine the case when n is a prime. First of all, for any a and b in $Z_n - \{0\}$, $a \odot b$ is not equal to 0. Therefore, the operation $\odot$ is closed on the set $Z_n - \{0\}$. Furthermore, it is clear that the operation $\odot$ is an associative operation and that 1 is the identity of $(Z_n, - \{0\}$,

⊙). Finally, let us show that for any a and any two distinct elements b and c in Z_n $- \{0\}$, $a \odot b$ is not equal to $a \odot c$. Assume that $a \odot b$ is equal to $a \odot c$. That is,

$$ab = kn + r$$
$$ac = ln + r$$

for some k, l and r. Without loss of generality, suppose that $b > c$ and $k > l$. We have

$$ab - ac = kn - ln$$

or

$$a(b - c) = (k - l)n \tag{10.5}$$

Since both a and $b - c$ are less than n, (10.5) is an impossibility when n is a prime. It now follows from the pigeonhole principle that, for every a in $Z_n - \{0\}$, there exists a b in $Z_n - \{0\}$ such that

$$a \odot b = 1.$$

That is, b is the inverse of a in $(Z_n, - \{0\}, \odot)$. We thus conclude that $(Z_n - \{0\}, \odot)$ is an abelian group. We leave it to the reader to show that the operation $\odot$ is distributive over the operation $\oplus$. For a prime n, $(Z_n, \oplus, \odot)$ is usually referred to as the *field of integers modulo n*.

The identity of the group $(A - \{0\}, \cdot)$ is referred to as the *multiplicative identity*, which is commonly denoted 1. The *inverse* of an element a in the group $(A - \{0\}, \cdot)$ is referred to as the *multiplicative inverse* of a and will be denoted $1/a$. We sometimes write a/b to mean the product of a and multiplicative inverse of b.

*10.12 RING HOMOMORPHISMS

We introduced the notion of homomorphisms on algebraic systems with one binary operation in Sec. 10.10. We study now homomorphisms on algebraic systems with two operations and, in particular, on rings, in further detail. Let $(A, +, \cdot)$ and $(B, \oplus, \odot)$ be two algebraic systems. An onto function f from A to B is said to be a *homomorphism from* $(A, +, \cdot)$ *to* $(B, \oplus, \odot)$ if for any a and b in A

$$f(a + b) = f(a) \oplus f(b)$$
$$f(a \cdot b) = f(a) \odot f(b)$$

Furthermore, $(B, \oplus, \odot)$ is called a *homomorphic image* of $(A, +, \cdot)$.

Alternatively, let R be a congruence relation on A with respect to both the operations $+$ and $\cdot$. That is, R is an equivalence relation on A and if (a_1, a_2) and (b_1, b_2) are in R, then $(a_1 + b_1, a_2 + b_2)$ and $(a_1 \cdot b_1, a_2 \cdot b_2)$ are also in R. Let $B = \{A_1, A_2, ..., A_r\}$ be the set of congruence classes into which A is divided. We define two binary operations $\oplus$ and $\odot$ on B such that $A_i \oplus A_j$ is equal to the congruence class $a_1 + a_2$ is in, and $A_i \odot A_j$ is equal to the congruence class $a_1 \cdot a_2$ is in, for any a_1 in A_i and a_2 in A_j. Following our discussion in Sec. 10.10, $(B, \oplus, \odot)$ is a homomorphic image of $(A, +, \cdot)$.

$\oplus$	EVEN	ODD		$\odot$	EVEN	ODD
EVEN	EVEN	ODD		EVEN	EVEN	EVEN
ODD	ODD	EVEN		ODD	EVEN	ODD

Fig. 10.23

For example, let N be the set of natural numbers and $+$ and $\cdot$ be the ordinary addition and multiplication operations of natural numbers. Consider the algebraic system $(\{\text{EVEN, ODD}\}, \oplus, \odot)$, where the operations $\oplus$ and $\odot$ are as defined in Fig. 10.23. We note that $(\{\text{EVEN, ODD}\}, \oplus, \odot)$ is a homomorphic image of $(N, +, \cdot)$. Furthermore, the function f such that

$$f(n) = \begin{cases} \text{EVEN} & \text{if } n \text{ is an even number} \\ \text{ODD} & \text{if } n \text{ is an odd number} \end{cases}$$

is the corresponding homomorphism from $(N, +, \cdot)$ to $(\{\text{EVEN, ODD}\}, \oplus, \odot)$.

Let us investigate now the problem of determining the homomorphic images of a ring.* Let $(A, +, \cdot)$ be a ring and $(H, +)$ be a subgroup of $(A, +)$. Let R denote the equivalence relation that H induces on A. Because $(A, +)$ is an abelian group, R is a congruence relation with respect to $+$. We want to know under what condition R is also a congruence relation with respect to $\cdot$. Suppose that (a, b) and (c, d) are in R. That is,

$$a = b + h_1$$
$$c = d + h_2$$

for some h_1 and h_2 in H. It follows that

$$\begin{aligned} a \cdot c &= (b + h_1) \cdot (d + h_2) \\ &= (b \cdot d) + (b \cdot h_2) + (h_1 \cdot d) + (h_1 \cdot h_2). \end{aligned}$$

We note that, *if* both $b \cdot h_2$ and $h_1 \cdot d$ are in H, then

$$(b \cdot h_2) + (h_1 \cdot d) + (h_1 \cdot h_2)$$

is also in H, and we shall have $(a \cdot c, b \cdot d)$ in R.

Such an observation motivates the definition of an ideal in a ring. Let $(A, +, \cdot)$ be a ring and H be a subset of A. H is said to be an *ideal* if the following conditions are satisfied:

1. $(H, +)$ is a subgroup of $(A, +)$.
2. For any a in A and h in H, $a \cdot h$ and $h \cdot a$ are both in H.†

It follows immediately from our discussion that an ideal of a ring $(A, +, \cdot)$ induces a congruence relation on A with respect to both the operations $+$ and $\cdot$, and consequently defines a homomorphic image of $(A, +, \cdot)$.

---

* It is not hard to show that a homomorphic image of a ring is always a ring. (See Prob. 10.36).
† Intuitively, any element in A is "swallowed" into the ideal when multiplied by an element in the ideal.

On the other hand, we shall show that every homomorphism of a ring corresponds to an ideal of the ring. Let f be a homomorphism from a ring $(A, +, \cdot)$ to $(B, \oplus, \odot)$. Let H be the set of elements of A that are mapped into the additive identity of $(B, \oplus, \odot)$ under f. [We remind the reader that, since it is a homomorphic image of $(A, +, \cdot)$, $(B, \oplus, \odot)$ is a ring.] It has been shown in Sec. 10.9 that H is a normal subgroup of $(A, +)$. To show that H is an ideal, we note that for any a in A and h in H,

$$f(a \cdot h) = f(a) \odot f(h) = f(a) \odot 0 = 0$$

where 0 denotes the additive identity of $(B, \oplus, \odot)$. Thus, $a \cdot h$ is in H. In a similar way, we can show that $h \cdot a$ is in H. Thus, we can conclude that H is an ideal.

For example, consider the ring $(Z_6, \oplus, \odot)$ shown in Fig. 10.24a. We can check immediately that $\{0, 2, 4\}$ is an ideal. The two congruence classes are $\{0, 2, 4\}$ and $\{1, 3, 5\}$, and the homomorphic image is shown in Fig. 10.24b.

$\oplus$	0	1	2	3	4	5
0	0	1	2	3	4	5
1	1	2	3	4	5	0
2	2	3	4	5	0	1
3	3	4	5	0	1	2
4	4	5	0	1	2	3
5	5	0	1	2	3	4

$\odot$	0	1	2	3	4	5
0	0	0	0	0	0	0
1	0	1	2	3	4	5
2	0	2	4	0	2	4
3	0	3	0	3	0	3
4	0	4	2	0	4	2
5	0	5	4	3	2	1

(a)

$+$	$\{0, 2, 4\}$	$\{1, 3, 5\}$
$\{0, 2, 4\}$	$\{0, 2, 4\}$	$\{1, 3, 5\}$
$\{1, 3, 5\}$	$\{1, 3, 5\}$	$\{0, 2, 4\}$

$\cdot$	$\{0, 2, 4\}$	$\{1, 3, 5\}$
$\{0, 2, 4\}$	$\{0, 2, 4\}$	$\{0, 2, 4\}$
$\{1, 3, 5\}$	$\{0, 2, 4\}$	$\{1, 3, 5\}$

(b)

Fig. 10.24

As another example, consider the ring $(I, +, \cdot)$, where I is the set of all integers, and $+$ and $\cdot$ are the ordinary addition and multiplication operations of integers. Let H be the set of all multiples of n $\{ \ldots, -2n, -n, 0, n, 2n, 3n, \ldots \}$ for any integer n. Clearly, H is an ideal. Moreover, a corresponding homomorphic image is $(Z_n, \oplus, \odot)$.

*10.13 POLYNOMIAL RINGS AND CYCLIC CODES

Let $(A, \star, *)$ be an algebraic system where $\star$ is an m-ary operation and $*$ is an n-ary operation. We sometimes refer to the elements in A as *constants*. A *variable* (or an *indeterminant*) is a symbolic name that is not the name of any element in A. We define *algebraic expressions* in $(A, \star, *)$ according to the following rules:

1. Any constant is an algebraic expression.
2. Any variable is an algebraic expression.
3. If $e_1, e_2, ..., e_m$ are algebraic expressions then $\star(e_1, e_2, ..., e_m)$ is an algebraic expression.
4. If $e_1, e_2, ..., e_n$ are algebraic expressions then $*(e_1, e_2, ..., e_n)$ is an algebraic expression.

For example, if x and y are variables, the following are algebraic expressions in $(Z_4, \oplus, \odot)$:

$$2$$
$$2 \oplus x$$
$$(3 \odot (x \oplus x)) \odot (x \odot y)$$

Let $(A, +, \cdot)$ be a ring. An algebraic expression in $(A, +, \cdot)$ of the form

$$a_0 + (a_1 \cdot x) + (a_2 \cdot x^2) + ... + (a_{n-1} \cdot x^{n-1}) + (a_n \cdot x^n)^* \qquad n \geq 0 \quad (10.6)$$

is called a *polynomial*, where $a_0, a_1, ..., a_{n-1}, a_n$ are constants and x is a variable. Note that because $+$ and $\cdot$ are associative operations, the expression in (10.6) is unambiguous. We shall use notation such as $A(x)$, $B(x)$, ... for polynomials. The *degree* of a polynomial is the largest n for which a_n is not equal to 0. Following the convention of omitting the multiplication operation symbol and the parentheses in (10.6), we rewrite (10.6) as

$$a_0 + a_1 x + a_2 x^2 + ... + a_{n-1} x^{n-1} + a_n x^n.$$

We discuss briefly the construction of polynomial rings. Let $(F, +, \cdot)$ be a field. Let $F[x]$ denote the set of all polynomials in $(F, +, \cdot)$ with the variable being x. We define an algebraic system $(F[x], \boxplus, \boxdot)$, where $\boxplus$ and $\boxdot$ are two binary operations defined as follows: For

$$A(x) = a_0 + a_1 x + a_2 x^2 + ... + a_n x^n$$
$$B(x) = b_0 + b_1 x + b_2 x^2 + ... + b_m x^m$$

we have

$$A(x) \boxplus B(x) = C(x) = c_0 + c_1 x + c_2 x^2 + ... + c_r x^r$$

where

$$c_i = a_i + b_i^{*\dagger}$$

and

$$A(x) \boxdot B(x) = D(x) = d_0 + d_1 x + d_2 x^2 + ... + d_r x^r$$

where

$$d_i = (a_0 \cdot b_i) + (a_1 \cdot b_{i-1}) + ... + (a_i \cdot b_0).$$

It is routine to check that $(F[x], \boxplus, \boxdot)$ is a ring, which is commonly called a *polynomial ring*.

---

* We use x^i to denote $\underbrace{x \cdot x \ldots x.}_{i \text{ times}}$

† We assume that $a_i = 0$ for $i > n$ and $b_i = 0$ for $i > m$.

Let $(F, +, \cdot)$ be a field. Let $F_n[x]$ denote the set of polynomials of degree less than n in $F[x]$. Let $G(x)$ be a polynomial of degree n in $F[x]$. Let $(F_n[x], \boxplus\!\!\!\triangle, \triangle\!\!\!\cdot)$ be an algebraic system, where $\boxplus\!\!\!\triangle$ and $\triangle\!\!\!\cdot$ are two binary operations defined as follows. For

$$A(x) = a_0 + a_1 x + a_2 x^2 + \ldots + a_{n-1} x^{n-1}$$
$$B(x) = b_0 + b_1 x + b_2 x^2 + \ldots + b_{n-1} x^{n-1}$$

we have

$$A(x) \,\boxplus\!\!\!\triangle\, B(x) = A(x) \boxplus B(x)$$

and

$$A(x) \,\triangle\!\!\!\cdot\, B(x) = \text{the remainder of } A(x) \boxdot B(x) \text{ divided by } G(x)^*.$$

Again, it is routine to check that $(F_n[x], \boxplus\!\!\!\triangle, \triangle\!\!\!\cdot)$ is a ring, which is commonly referred to as the *ring of polynomials modulo* $G(x)$.

For example, let $(F, +, \cdot)$ be the field of integers modulo 2. There are four polynomials in $F_2[x]$, namely, 0, 1, x, $1 + x$. Let $G(x)$ be $1 + x^2$. The operations $\boxplus\!\!\!\triangle$ and $\triangle\!\!\!\cdot$ are defined in Fig. 10.25.

$\boxplus\!\!\!\triangle$	0	1	x	$1+x$
0	0	1	x	$1+x$
1	1	0	$1+x$	x
x	x	$1+x$	0	1
$1+x$	$1+x$	x	1	0

$\triangle\!\!\!\cdot$	0	1	x	$1+x$
0	0	0	0	0
1	0	1	x	$1+x$
x	0	x	1	$1+x$
$1+x$	0	$1+x$	$1+x$	0

Fig. 10.25

Construction of polynomial rings leads immediately to the construction of Galois fields. A detailed discussion of the subject is beyond the scope of this book.

As an illustrative example, let us consider a class of codes, known as *cyclic codes*. We recall our discussion in Sec. 10.8 that a block code is a collection of words of the same length. A block code is called a *cyclic code* if for every codeword $a_0 a_1 a_2 \ldots a_{n-2} a_{n-1}$, the sequence $a_{n-1} a_0 a_1 a_2 \ldots a_{n-2}$ is also a codeword. In other words, for a cyclic code, a *cyclic shift* of a codeword is also a codeword. We show now a very compact way to describe cyclic codes.

Let $(F, +, \cdot)$ be the field of integers modulo 2. First of all, we note that a binary sequence $a_0 a_1 a_2 \ldots a_{n-1}$ can be conveniently represented as a polynomial

$$a_0 + a_1 x + a_2 x^2 + \ldots + a_{n-1} x^{n-1}$$

in the polynomial ring $(F[x], \boxplus, \boxdot)$. Let $(F_n[x], \boxplus\!\!\!\triangle, \triangle\!\!\!\cdot)$ be the ring of polynomials modulo $1 + x^n$. Let I be an ideal of $(F_n[x], \boxplus\!\!\!\triangle, \triangle\!\!\!\cdot)$. We want to show that the polynomials in I constitute a cyclic code. Because $(I, \boxplus\!\!\!\triangle)$ is a group, the

---

* Division of polynomials is carried out in the same way as was done in high school algebra with, of course, addition and multiplication being the field operations in $(F, +, \cdot)$.

polynomials in I indeed constitute a group code. Let $A(x)$ be a polynomial in I. According to the definition of an ideal, $x \triangle A(x)$ is also a polynomial in I. Let

$$A(x) = a_0 + a_1 x + a_2 x^2 + \ldots + a_{n-1} x^{n-1}.$$

$$x \triangle A(x) = \text{remainder of } \frac{a_0 x + a_1 x^2 + \ldots + a_{n-1} x^n}{1 + x^n}$$

$$= \text{remainder of } \frac{a_0 x + a_1 x^2 + \ldots + a_{n-1} + a_{n-1}(1 + x^n)}{1 + x^n}$$

$$= a_{n-1} + a_0 x + a_1 x^2 + \ldots + a_{n-2} x^{n-1}$$

Therefore, the polynomials in I constitute a cyclic code.

On the other hand, let I denote a set of polynomials corresponding to the codewords in a cyclic code. Clearly, $(I, \triangle)$ is an abelian group. If $A(x)$ is in I, $x \triangle A(x)$ is in I, $x^j \triangle A(x)$ is in I, and $b_j x^j \triangle A(x)$ is in I, because the polynomials in I form a cyclic code. It follows that $B(x) \triangle A(x)$ is in I for any $B(x)$ in $F_n[x]$.

Problems

10.1 Let N be the set of all natural numbers. For each of the following determine whether $*$ is an associative operation:

(a) $a * b = \max(a, b)$

(b) $a * b = \min(a, b + 2)$

(c) $a * b = a + b + 3$

(d) $a * b = a + 2b$

(e) $a * b = \begin{cases} \min(a, b) & \text{if } \min(a, b) < 10 \\ \max(a, b) & \text{if } \min(a, b) \leq 10 \end{cases}$

10.2 Let $(A, \bigstar)$ be an algebraic system where $\bigstar$ is a binary operation such that, for any a and b in A, $a \bigstar b = a$.

(a) Show that $\bigstar$ is an associative operation.

(b) Can $\bigstar$ ever be a commutative operation?

10.3 Let $(A, \bigstar)$ be an algebraic system such that for all a, b, c, d in A

$$a \bigstar a = a$$
$$(a \bigstar b) \bigstar (c \bigstar d) = (a \bigstar c) \bigstar (b \bigstar d)$$

Show that

$$a \bigstar (b \bigstar c) = (a \bigstar b) \bigstar (a \bigstar c)$$

10.4 Let Z_n denote the set of integers $\{0, 1, 2, \ldots, n-1\}$. Let $\odot$ be binary operation on Z_n such that

$a \odot b = $ the remainder of ab divided by n

(a) Construct the table for the operation $\odot$ for $n = 4$.

(b) Show that $(Z_n, \odot)$ is a semigroup for any n.

10.5 Let $(A, *)$ be a semigroup. Let a be an element in A. Consider a binary operation $\square$ on A such that, for every x and y in A,

$$x \square y = x * a * y$$

Show that $\square$ is an associative operation.

10.6 Let $(A, *)$ be a semigroup. Furthermore, for every a and b in A, if $a \neq b$, then $a * b \neq b * a$.

(a) Show that for every a, in A,

$$a * a = a$$

(b) Show that for every a, b in A,

$$a * b * a = a$$

(c) Show that for every a, b, c in A,

$$a * b * c = a * c$$

Hint: Note that a $* b = b * a$ implies $a = b$.

10.7 Let $(A, *)$ be a semigroup. Show that, for a, b, c in A, if $a * c = c * a$ and $b * c = c * b$, then $(a * b) * c = c * (a * b)$.

10.8 Let $(\{a, b\}, *)$ be a semigroup where $a * a = b$. Show that:

(a) $a * b = b * a$

(b) $b * b = b$

10.9 Let $(A, *)$ be a commutative semigroup. Show that if $a * a = a$ and $b * b = b$, then $(a * b) * (a * b) = a * b$.

10.10 Let $(A, *)$ be a semigroup. Show that, if A is a finite set, there exists a in A such that $a * a = a$.

10.11 Let $(A, *)$ be a semigroup. Furthermore, let there be an element a in A such that for every x in A there exist u and v in A satisfying the relation

$$a * u = v * a = x$$

Show that there is an identity element in A.

10.12 Let $(A, *)$ be a semigroup and e be a left identity. Furthermore, for every x in A there exists $\hat{x}$ in A such that $\hat{x} * x = e$.

(a) Show that for any a, b, c in A, if $a * b = a * c$, then $b = c$.

(b) Show that $(A, *)$ is a group by showing that e is an identity element.

Hint: Note that $\hat{x} * x * \hat{x} * x = e$.

10.13 Let $(A, \bigstar)$ be an algebraic system such that for all a, b in A

$$(a \bigstar b) \bigstar a = a$$
$$(a \bigstar b) \bigstar b = (b \bigstar a) \bigstar a$$

(a) Show that $a \bigstar (a \bigstar b) = a \bigstar b$ for all a and b.

(b) Show that $a \bigstar a = (a \bigstar b) \bigstar (a \bigstar b)$ for all a and b.

(c) Show that $a \bigstar a = b \bigstar b$ for all a and b.

(d) Let e denote the element $a \bigstar a$. Show that $e \bigstar a = a$ and $a \bigstar e = e$.

(e) Show that $a \bigstar b = b \bigstar a$ if and only if $a = b$.

(f) Let $(A, \star)$ satisfy the additional condition

$$a \star b = (a \star b) \star b$$

Show that $\star$ is idempotent and commutative.

10.14 A *central groupoid* is an algebraic system $(A, \star)$, where $\star$ is a binary operation such that

$$(a \star b) \star (b \star c) = b$$

for all a, b, c in A.

(a) Show that

$$a \star ((a \star b) \star c) = a \star b$$
$$(a \star (b \star c)) \star c = b \star c$$

in a central groupoid.

(b) Let $(A, \star)$ be an algebraic system where $\star$ is a binary operation such that

$$(a \star ((b \star c) \star d)) \star (c \star d) = c$$

for all a, b, c, d in A. Show that $(A, \star)$ is a central groupoid.

Hint: Use the result $(a \star ((d \star (b \star c)) \star d)) \star ((b \star c) \star d) = b \star c$ to show $(b \star c) \star (c \star d) = c$.

(c) Construct a directed graph with four vertices in which there is exactly one path of length 2 between any two vertices.

(d) Let $G = (V, E)$ be a directed graph in which there is exactly one path of length 2 between any two vertices. For any two vertices a and b in V, let (a, c) and (c, b) be the two edges in the path from a to b. We define an algebraic system $(V, \star)$ such that $a \star b = c$. Show that $(V, \star)$ is a central groupoid.

(e) Let $(A, \star)$ be a central groupoid. We construct a directed graph $G = (A, E)$ such that there is an edge (a, c) in E if and only if there is b in A such that $a \star b = c$. Show that there is exactly one path of length 2 between any two vertices in A.

(f) Let $(A, \star)$ be a central groupoid and $G = (A, E)$ be the corresponding directed graph as defined in part (e). For $a \in A$, let

$$R(a) = \{b \mid (a, b) \in E\}$$
$$L(a) = \{b \mid (b, a) \in E\}$$

Show that for any a and b in A, $R(a)$ and $L(b)$ have the same number of elements. Show that for any a and b in A, $R(a)$ and $R(b)$ have the same number of elements.

(g) Let $(A, \star)$ be a central groupoid. Show that A has m^2 elements for some integer m.
Hint: Suppose there are m elements in $R(a)$. What can be said about the sets $R(b_1)$, $R(b_2)$, ..., $R(b_m)$ for $b_1, b_2, ..., b_m$ in $R(a)$?

10.15 Let $(A, \star)$ be a group. Show that for any $a, b, c, d, a_1, b_1, c_1, d_1$ in A, if

$$a \star c = a_1 \star c_1$$
$$a \star d = a_1 \star d_1$$
$$b \star c = b_1 \star c_1$$
$$b \star d = b_1 \star d_1$$

then

$$b \bigstar d = b_1 \bigstar d_1$$

Hint: Note that $b \bigstar d = b \bigstar (c \bigstar c^{-1}) \bigstar (a^{-1} \bigstar a) \bigstar d$.

10.16 (a) Show that every group containing exactly two elements is isomorphic to $(Z_2, \oplus)$.

(b) Show that every group containing exactly three elements is isomorphic to $(Z_3, \oplus)$.

(c) How many nonisomorphic groups that contain exactly four elements are there?

10.17 Let $(A, \bigstar)$ and $(B, *)$ be two algebraic systems. The cartesian product of $(A, \bigstar)$ and $(B, *)$ is an algebraic system $(A \times B, \square)$, where $\square$ is a binary operation such that for any (a_1, b_1) and (a_2, b_2) in $A \times B$

$$(a_1, b_1) \square (a_2, b_2) = (a_1 \bigstar a_2, b_1 * b_2)$$

Show that the cartesian product of two groups is a group.

10.18 Let $(A, \cdot)$ be a group.

(a) Show that $(ab)^{-1} = b^{-1}a^{-1}$.

(b) Show that $(a_1 a_2 \ldots a_{r-1} a_r)^{-1} = a_r^{-1} a_{r-1}^{-1} \ldots a_2^{-1} a_1^{-1}$.

(c) Show that $(b^i b^j)^{-1} = b^{-j} a^{-1}$. [$b^{-j}$ denotes $(b^{-1})^j$ and a^{-i} denotes $(a^{-1})^i$.]

10.19 Let $(A, *)$ be a monoid such that for every x in A, $x * x = e$, where e is the identity element. Show that $(A, *)$ is an abelian group.

10.20 Let $(G, \bigstar)$ be a group and H be a nonempty subset of G. Show that $(H, \bigstar)$ is a subgroup if for any a and b in H, $a \bigstar b^{-1}$ is also in H.

10.21 Show that any subgroup of a cyclic group is cyclic.

10.22 The *order* of an element a in a group is defined to be the least positive integer m such that $a^m = e$. (If no positive power of a equals e, the order of a is defined to be infinite.) Show that, in a finite group, the order of an element divides the order of the group.

10.23 Let H_1 and H_2 be subgroups of a group G, neither of which contains the other. Show that there exists an element of G belonging neither to H_1 nor H_2.

10.24 Let $(H, \cdot)$ be a subgroup of a group $(G, \cdot)$. Let $N = \{x \mid x \in G, xHx^{-1} = H\}$. Show that $(N, \cdot)$ is a subgroup of $(G, \cdot)$.

10.25 Let $(A, \bigstar)$ be a group where A has an even number of elements. Show that there is an element a in A such that $a \bigstar a = e$, where e is the identity element and $a \neq e$.

10.26 Let $(A, \bigstar)$ be a group. Let B be a subset of A such that $2|B| > |A|$. Show that, for any a in A, $a = b_1 \bigstar b_2$ for some b_1 and b_2 in B.

Hint: Consider the set $C = \{a \bigstar b^{-1} \mid b \in B\}$.

10.27 Let $(H, \cdot)$ and $(K, \cdot)$ be subgroups of a group $(G, \cdot)$. Let
$$HK = \{h \cdot k \mid h \in H, k \in K\}$$

Show that $(HK, \cdot)$ is a subgroup of $(G, \cdot)$ if and only if $HK = KH$.

10.28 Let $(A, \bigstar)$ be a group. Show that $(A, \bigstar)$ is an abelian group if and only if $a^2 \bigstar b^2 = (a \bigstar b)^2$ for all a and b in A.

10.29 Let $(A, \bigstar)$ be a group. Show that $(A, \bigstar)$ is an abelian group if $a^3 \bigstar b^3 = (a \bigstar b)^3$, $a^4 \bigstar b^4 = (a \bigstar b)^4$, and $a^5 \bigstar b^5 = (a \bigstar b)^5$ for all a and b in A.

10.30 Let $(G, \bigstar)$ be a group of even order. Let $(H, \bigstar)$ be a subgroup of $(G, \bigstar)$ where $|H| = |G|/2$. Show that $(H, \bigstar)$ is a normal subgroup.

10.31 Let $(H, \bigstar)$ be a subgroup of a group $(G, \bigstar)$. Show that $(H, \bigstar)$ is a normal subgroup if and only if $a \bigstar H \bigstar a^{-1} \subseteq H$ for every $a \in G$.

10.32 Let $(G, \star)$ be a group. Let $H = \{a \mid a \in G$ and $a \star b = b \star a$ for all $b \in G\}$. Show that H is a normal subgroup.

10.33 (a) Let $(H, \star)$ and $(K, \star)$ be subgroups of a group $(G, \star)$. Show that $(H \cap K, \star)$ is also a subgroup.

(b) Show that, if $(H, \star)$ and $(K, \star)$ are normal subgroups, then $(H \cap K, \star)$ is also a normal subgroup.

10.34 Let $(H, \star)$ and $(K, \star)$ be subgroups of a group $(G, \star)$. Show that the function f from $H \times K$ to G such that $f[(h, k)] = h \star k$ for all h in H and k in K is an isomorphism from the cartesian product of $(H, \star)$ and $(K, \star)$ to $(G, \star)$ if and only if:

1. H and K are normal subgroups;
2. $\{h \star k \mid h \in H, k \in K\} = G$;
3. $H \cap K = \{e\}$, where e is the identity element.

10.35 Let $(H, \star)$ be a normal subgroup of a group $(G, \star)$. Show that the homomorphic image of $(G, \star)$ induced by the subgroup $(H, \star)$ is an abelian group if and only if $a \star b \star a^{-1} \star b^{-1}$ is in H for all a and b in G.

10.36 Let $(A, \star)$ and $(B, *)$ be two algebraic systems and f be a homomorphism from $(A, \star)$ to $(B, *)$.

(a) Show that, if $\star$ is an associative operation, so is $*$.

(b) Show that, if e is an identity element in $(A, \star)$, then $f(e)$ is an identity element in $(B, *)$.

(c) Show that, if b is an inverse of a in $(A, \star)$, then $f(b)$ is an inverse of $f(a)$ in $(B, *)$.

(d) Show that a homomorphic image of a ring is a ring.

10.37 Let f_1 and f_2 be homomorphisms from an algebraic system $(A, \star)$ to another algebraic system $(B, *)$. Let g be a function from A to B such that

$$g(a) = f_1(a) * f_2(a)$$

for all a in A. Show that g is a homomorphism from $(A, \star)$ to $(B, *)$ if $(B, *)$ is a commutative semigroup.

10.38 Let f and g be homomorphisms from a group $(G, \star)$ to a group $(H, *)$. Show that $(C, \star)$ is a subgroup of $(G, \star)$, where

$$C = \{x \in G \mid f(x) = g(x)\}$$

10.39 A rod divided into six segments is to be colored with one or more of four different colors. In how many ways can this be done?

10.40 In how many distinct ways can the sectors of the circle in Fig. 10P.1 be painted with three colors?

10.41 (a) Determine the number of distinct 2×2 chessboards whose cells are painted white and black. Two chessboards are considered distinct if one cannot be obtained from another through rotation.

(b) Repeat part (a) for 4×4 chessboards.

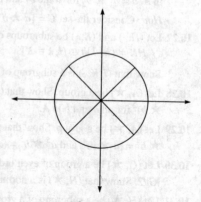

Fig. 10P.1

10.42 (a) Show that for $p < \dfrac{1}{2}$, $(1-p)^{n-1}p^{t1} > (1-p)^{n-t2}p^{t2}$ for $t_1 < t_2$.

(b) Show that for $p > \dfrac{1}{2}$, $(1-p)^{n-t1}p^{t1} < (1-p)^{n-t2}p^{t2}$ for $t_1 < t_2$.

10.43 (a) Consider the code $G = \{00000, 11111\}$. Set up the coset table to show that G can indeed correct all single- and double-transmission errors.

(b) A code G contains 16 codewords: 0000000, 1111111, 1101000 and all its cyclic shifts, 0010111 and all its cyclic shifts. Show that $(G, \oplus)$ is a group code. Set up the coset table to show that G can correct all single-transmission errors.

10.44 Let $(A, \bigstar, *)$ be an algebraic system with e_1 and e_2 being the identity elements with respect to the operations $\bigstar$ and $*$, respectively. Given that the operations $\bigstar$ and $*$ distribute over each other show that $x \bigstar x = x$ and $x * x = x$ for all x in A.

Hint: Show that $e_1 = e_1 * e_1$ and $e_2 = e_2 \bigstar e_2$.

10.45 Let $(A, \bigstar, *)$ be an algebraic system, where

$$a \bigstar b = a$$

for all a, b in A, and $*$ is an arbitrary binary operation. Show that $*$ distributes over $\bigstar$.

10.46 Let $(A, +, \cdot)$ be a ring such that $a \cdot a = a$ for all a in A.

(a) Show that $a + a = 0$ for all a, where 0 is the additive identity.

(b) Show that the operation $\cdot$ is commutative.

10.47 Show that an integral domain that has a finite number of elements is a field.

10.48 An $n \times n$ *Latin square* is an $n \times n$ arrangement of n distinct symbols so that no symbol appears more than once in any row or any column. For a Latin square A, we shall use a_{ij} to denote the symbol in the ith row and the jth column of A. Two $n \times n$ Latin squares A and B are said to be *orthogonal* if for no i, j, k, l such that $a_{ij} = a_{kl}$ and $b_{ij} = b_{kl}$. A set of Latin squares is said to be orthogonal if every two of them are orthogonal.

(a) Construct a 4×4 Latin square.

(b) Construct a pair of 3×3 orthogonal Latin squares.

(c) Let $(\{b_0, b_1, ..., b_{n-1}\}, +, \cdot)$ be a field where b_0 is the additive identity. Let us construct $(n-1)$ $n \times n$ squares $A_1, A_2, ..., A_{n-1}$, such that

$$a_{ij}^{(r)} = b_r \cdot b_i + b_j \qquad i, j = 0, 1, 2, ..., n-1$$
$$r = 1, 2, ..., n-1$$

where $a_{ij}^{(r)}$ is the ijth entry of the square A_r. Show that each square is a Latin square. Show that the set is an orthogonal set.

10.49 A ring $(A, +, \cdot)$ is said to be a *commutative ring with unity* if $(A, \cdot)$ is a commutative monoid.

(a) An ideal H of a ring is said to be a *prime ideal* if, for any two elements a and b that are not in H, $a \cdot b$ is not in H either. Show that the homomorphic image of a commutative ring with unity induced by an ideal is an integral domain if and only if the ideal is prime.

(b) An ideal H is said to be a *maximal ideal* if the only ideals of the ring that contain H are H and the ring itself. Show that the homomorphic image of a commutative ring with unity induced by an ideal is a field if and only if the ideal is maximal.

10.50 (a) Let $(F, +, \cdot)$ be the field of integers modulo 2 and $(F[x], \boxplus, \boxdot)$ the corresponding ring of polynomials. Construct the ring of polynomials modulo $1 + x + x^2$.

(b) Let $(F, +, \cdot)$ be the field of integers modulo 3 and $(F[x], \boxplus, \boxdot)$ the corresponding ring of polynomials. Construct the ring of polynomials modulo $2 + 2x + x^2$.

10.51 Let $(R, +, \cdot)$ be the field of real numbers. Let $(R[x], \boxplus, \boxdot)$ be the corresponding ring of polynomials, and $(R_2[x], \triangle\!\!\!\!\triangle, \triangle\!\!\!\!\blacktriangle)$ be the ring of polynomials modulo $1 + x^2$.

(a) For $a + bx$ and $c + dx$ in $R_2[x]$ determine $(a + bx) \triangle\!\!\!\!\triangle (c + dx)$ and $(a + bx) \triangle\!\!\!\!\blacktriangle (c + dx)$.

(b) Do you see any similarities between $(R_2, \triangle\!\!\!\!\triangle, \triangle\!\!\!\!\blacktriangle)$ and the field of complex numbers?

10.52 Find the weights of given words.

(a) 1011   (b) 0110

(c) 1110

10.53 Find the weight of given words.

(a) 011101   (b) 11111

(c) 010101

10.54 Consider $(m, 3m)$ encoding function, where $m = 4$. For each of the received words determine whether an error will occur or not?

(a) 011010011111   (b) 110110010110

10.55 Explain how $|x \oplus y|$ counts the number of position in which x and y differ.

10.56 Find the distance between x and y

(a) $x = 1100010$ (b) $x = 0100110$

     $y = 1010001$ $y = 0111010$

(c) $x = 00111001$ (d) $x = 11010010$

     $y = 10101001$ $y = 00100111$

10.57 Prove the theorems.

(a) $d(x, y) = d(y, x)$, where $(x, y) \in B^m$

(b) $d(x, y) \geq 0$, where $(x, y) \in B^m$

10.58 Prove the theorem.

     $d(x, y) = 0$ iff $x = y$.

10.59 Find the minimum distance of the (2, 4) encoding function e.

          $e(00) = 0000$ $e(10) = 0110$

          $e(01) = 1011$ $e(11) = 1100$

10.60 Find the minimum distance of the (3, 8) encoding function e.

          $e(000) = 00000000$ $e(100) = 01100101$

          $e(001) = 01110010$ $e(101) = 10110000$

          $e(010) = 10011100$ $e(110) = 11110000$

          $e(011) = 01110001$ $e(111) = 00001111$

10.61 Show that the (3,7) encoding function $e: B^3 \to B^7$ defined by

          $e(000) = 0000000$ $e(100) = 1000101$

          $e(001) = 0010110$ $e(101) = 1010011$

$$e(010) = 0101000 \qquad e(110) = 1101101$$
$$e(011) = 0111110 \qquad e(111) = 1111011$$

is a group code.

10.62 Find the minimum distance of the group code defined below:

$$e(00) = 00000 \qquad\qquad e(10) = 10101$$
$$e(01) = 01110 \qquad\qquad e(11) = 11011$$

10.63 Find the minimum distance of the group code defined below:

$$e(000) = 0000000 \qquad e(100) = 1000101$$
$$e(001) = 0010110 \qquad e(101) = 1010011$$
$$e(010) = 0101000 \qquad e(110) = 1101101$$
$$e(011) = 0111110 \qquad e(111) = 1111011$$

Programming Exercises

1. Write a program to compute the weight of a code word.
2. Write a program to compute the Hamming distance between two code words.
3. Let $H = \{[0], [2], [4], [6]\}$. Write a program to compute the right cosets of H.
4. Given a finite operation table, write a program to determine whether the operation satisfies the associativity property.
5. Let G be a finite group and H be a subgroup of G. Write a program to determine whether H is a normal subgroup of G.

Objective

To present the principles and properties of boolean algebra and the application of boolean algebra to switching circuits.

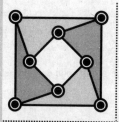

CHAPTER

ELEVEN

BOOLEAN ALGEBRAS

11.1 LATTICES AND ALGEBRAIC SYSTEMS

We recall that a lattice is a partially ordered set in which every two elements have a unique least upper bound and a unique greatest lower bound. For example, Fig. 11.1 shows a lattice. There is a natural way to define an algebraic system with two operations corresponding to a given lattice. Let $(A, \leq)$ be a lattice. We define an algebraic system $(A, \vee, \wedge)$, where $\vee$ and $\wedge$ are two binary operations on A such that for a and b in A, $a \vee b$ is equal to the least upper bound of a and b, and $a \wedge b$ is equal to the greatest lower bound of a and b. We shall refer to $(A, \vee, \wedge)$ as the algebraic system defined by the lattice $(A, \leq)$. For example, the algebraic system defined by the lattice in Fig. 11.1 is shown in Fig. 11.2. The binary operation $\vee$ is often referred to as the *join* operation and the binary operation $\wedge$ is

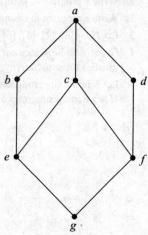

Fig. 11.1

$\vee$	a	b	c	d	e	f	g
a	a	a	a	a	a	a	a
b	a	b	a	a	b	a	b
c	a	a	c	a	c	c	c
d	a	a	a	d	a	d	d
e	a	b	c	a	e	c	e
f	a	a	c	d	c	f	f
g	a	b	c	d	e	f	g

$\wedge$	a	b	c	d	e	f	g
a	a	b	c	d	e	f	g
b	b	b	e	g	e	g	g
c	c	e	c	f	e	f	g
d	d	g	f	d	g	f	g
e	e	e	e	g	e	g	g
f	f	g	f	f	g	f	g
g	g	g	g	g	g	g	g

Fig. 11.2

often referred to as the *meet* operation. The symbols + (plus) and .(dot) can also be used for the join and meet operations respectively. Consequently, the least upper bound of a and b is also referred to as the *join* of a and b, and the greatest lower bound of a and b is also referred to as the *meet* of a and b.

For example, let $\mathcal{P}(S)$ be the power set of a given set S. We recall that ($\mathcal{P}(S)$, $\subseteq$) is a lattice. Consequently, it defines a corresponding algebraic system ($\mathcal{P}(S)$, $\vee$, $\wedge$). For $S = \{a, b, c\}$, the lattice ($\mathcal{P}(S)$, $\subseteq$) is shown in Fig. 11.3a and the tables for the operations $\vee$ and $\wedge$ are shown in Fig. 11.3b. We recognize that the join of two subsets of S is the union of the two subsets and the meet of two subsets of S

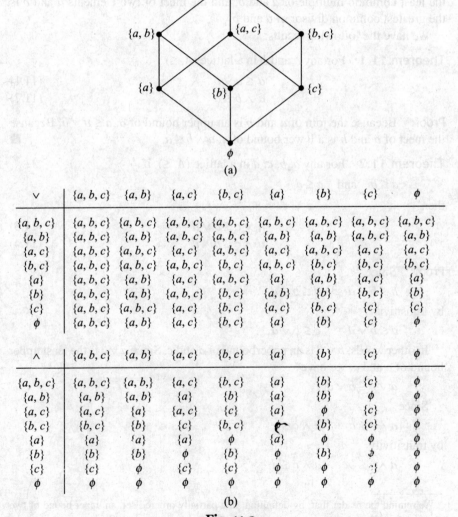

$\vee$	$\{a, b, c\}$	$\{a, b\}$	$\{a, c\}$	$\{b, c\}$	$\{a\}$	$\{b\}$	$\{c\}$	ϕ
$\{a, b, c\}$	$\{a, b, c\}$	$\{a, b, c\}$	$\{a, b, c\}$	$\{a, b, c\}$	$\{a, b, c\}$	$\{a, b, c\}$	$\{a, b, c\}$	$\{a, b, c\}$
$\{a, b\}$	$\{a, b, c\}$	$\{a, b\}$	$\{a, b, c\}$	$\{a, b, c\}$	$\{a, b\}$	$\{a, b\}$	$\{a, b, c\}$	$\{a, b\}$
$\{a, c\}$	$\{a, b, c\}$	$\{a, b, c\}$	$\{a, c\}$	$\{a, b, c\}$	$\{a, c\}$	$\{a, b, c\}$	$\{a, c\}$	$\{a, c\}$
$\{b, c\}$	$\{a, b, c\}$	$\{a, b, c\}$	$\{a, b, c\}$	$\{b, c\}$	$\{a, b, c\}$	$\{b, c\}$	$\{b, c\}$	$\{b, c\}$
$\{a\}$	$\{a, b, c\}$	$\{a, b\}$	$\{a, c\}$	$\{a, b, c\}$	$\{a\}$	$\{a, b\}$	$\{a, c\}$	$\{a\}$
$\{b\}$	$\{a, b, c\}$	$\{a, b\}$	$\{a, b, c\}$	$\{b, c\}$	$\{a, b\}$	$\{b\}$	$\{b, c\}$	$\{b\}$
$\{c\}$	$\{a, b, c\}$	$\{a, b, c\}$	$\{a, c\}$	$\{b, c\}$	$\{a, c\}$	$\{b, c\}$	$\{c\}$	$\{c\}$
ϕ	$\{a, b, c\}$	$\{a, b\}$	$\{a, c\}$	$\{b, c\}$	$\{a\}$	$\{b\}$	$\{c\}$	ϕ

$\wedge$	$\{a, b, c\}$	$\{a, b\}$	$\{a, c\}$	$\{b, c\}$	$\{a\}$	$\{b\}$	$\{c\}$	ϕ
$\{a, b, c\}$	$\{a, b, c\}$	$\{a, b,\}$	$\{a, c\}$	$\{b, c\}$	$\{a\}$	$\{b\}$	$\{c\}$	ϕ
$\{a, b\}$	$\{a, b\}$	$\{a, b\}$	$\{a\}$	$\{b\}$	$\{a\}$	$\{b\}$	ϕ	ϕ
$\{a, c\}$	$\{a, c\}$	$\{a\}$	$\{a, c\}$	$\{c\}$	$\{a\}$	ϕ	$\{c\}$	ϕ
$\{b, c\}$	$\{b, c\}$	$\{b\}$	$\{c\}$	$\{b, c\}$	ϕ	$\{b\}$	$\{c\}$	ϕ
$\{a\}$	$\{a\}$	$\{a\}$	$\{a\}$	ϕ	$\{a\}$	ϕ	ϕ	ϕ
$\{b\}$	$\{b\}$	$\{b\}$	ϕ	$\{b\}$	ϕ	$\{b\}$	ϕ	ϕ
$\{c\}$	$\{c\}$	ϕ	$\{c\}$	$\{c\}$	ϕ	ϕ	ϕ	ϕ
ϕ	ϕ	ϕ	ϕ	ϕ	ϕ	ϕ	ϕ	ϕ

(b)

Fig. 11.3

is the intersection of the two subsets. [When we introduced the notions of union and intersection of sets in Chapter 1, we intentionally did not bring up the notion of binary operations. Indeed, all the results in Sec. 1.2 on the combination of sets to yield new sets can be phrased conveniently in terms of binary operations on $\mathcal{P}(S)$.]

As another example, let $(N, \leq)$ be a partially ordered set, where N is the set of natural numbers and $\leq$ is the "less than or equal to" relationship among natural numbers. One can readily check that $(N, \leq)$ is a lattice, and it defines an algebraic system $(N, \vee, \wedge)$ such that $a \vee b = \max (a, b)$ and $a \wedge b = \min (a, b)$.

Also, as another example, let N^+ be the set of all positive integers, let $|$ be a binary relation on N^+ such that $a \,|\, b$ if and only if a divides b. We ask the reader to check that $(N^+, |)$ is a lattice. Furthermore, the join of two elements a and b is the least common multiple of a and b, and the meet of two elements a and b is the greatest common divisor of a and b.

We have the following results:

Theorem 11.1 For any a and b in a lattice $(A, \leq)$

$$a \leq a \vee b \tag{11.1}$$
$$a \wedge b \leq a \tag{11.2}$$

Proof: Because the join of a and b is an upper bound of a, $a \leq a \vee b$. Because the meet of a and b is a lower bound of a, $a \wedge b \leq a$. ∎

Theorem 11.2 For any a, b, c, d in a lattice $(A, \leq)$, if

$$a \leq b \quad \text{and} \quad c \leq d$$

then

$$a \vee c \leq b \vee d \tag{11.3}$$
$$a \wedge c \leq b \wedge d \tag{11.4}$$

Proof: Since

$$b \leq b \vee d \qquad d \leq b \vee d$$

by transitivity

$$a \leq b \vee d \qquad c \leq b \vee d$$

In other words, $b \vee d$ is an upperbound of a and c. Since $a \vee c$ is the least upper bound of a and c, we have*

$$a \vee c \leq b \vee d$$

Since

$$a \wedge c \leq a \qquad a \wedge c \leq c$$

by transitivity

$$a \wedge c \leq b \qquad a \wedge c \leq d$$

---

* We remind the reader that, by definition, in a partially ordered set, an upper bound of two elements is either a least upper bound or larger than a least upper bound.

In other words, $a \wedge c$ is a lower bound of b and d. Since $b \wedge d$ is the greatest lower bound of b and d, we have

$$a \wedge c \leq b \wedge d \qquad \blacksquare$$

11.2 PRINCIPLE OF DUALITY

The principle of duality is an important concept that appears in many different places and contexts. We begin with some simple illustrative examples. In the United States, all passenger cars have the driver's seat at the left front. Consequently, we observe traffic regulations such as the following:

Cars always travel on the right side of a street.
On a multilane divided highway, left lanes are passing lanes.
Cars may make right turns at a red light.

However, since all passenger cars in England have the driver's seat at the right front, they observe traffic regulations such as these:

Cars always travel on the left side of a street.
On a multilane divided highway, right lanes are passing lanes.
Cars may make left turns at a red light.

We note how the concepts of left and right can be interchanged in these two situations so that meaningful traffic rules in the United States become meaningful traffic rules in England, and conversely. We say that the concepts of left and right are dual concepts.

As another example, let us tell a story which we freely adapt from the Chinese fiction *Flowers in the Mirror*.* There was a country called The Land of Gentlemen. The following conversation is a typical example of the behavior of its people:

Customer:	I want to buy this vase. It is very beautiful.
Storekeeper:	The vase does not really look that good. Please note that there are some defects in the paint job.
Customer:	You would not call these defects, would you? The vase is a perfect piece of art work. How much do you want for it?
Storekeeper:	Usually, I will sell a vase like this for $10. Since you have been a good customer of ours for many years, I will sell it for $15.
Customer:	$15 is too low. I cannot allow myself to take advantage of you. How about $20?
Storekeeper:	I would be making a good profit at $15. Since you insist, let us agree on $16.
Customer:	My wife will complain that I do not pay enough for things I buy. However, I am willing to buy the vase at $18.

* The original title is *Ching Hua Yuan*. It was written by Li Ju-Chen (1763–1830). An English translation by Lin Tai-Yi was published by the University of California Press, 1965.

It is interesting that the many concepts in business bargaining in The Land of Gentlemen are opposite to those we are more accustomed to. As a matter of fact, it is quite obvious how we can rephrase a conversation between a customer and a storekeeper in The Land of Gentlemen to make it sound more familiar to us, and, conversely, how we can rephrase a conversation between a customer and a storekeeper that we frequently overhear to make it sound more familiar to the people in The Land of Gentlemen by suitable substitution of the concepts of high and low prices, profitable and nonprofitable business transactions, good and bad quality of work, and so on. Again, these pairs of concepts are pairs of dual concepts.

We hope the reader is now ready for a more serious discussion. Let $(A, \leq)$ be a partially ordered set. Let $\leq_R$ be a binary relation on A such that for a and b in A, $a \leq_R b$ if and only if $b \leq a$. It is not hard to see that $(A, \geq_R)$ is also a partially ordered set. Furthermore, if $(A, \leq)$ is a lattice so is $(A, \leq_R)^*$. We note that the lattices $(A, \leq)$ and $(A, \leq_R)$ are closely related, and so are the algebraic systems defined by them. To be specific, the join operation of the algebraic system defined by $(A, \leq)$ is the meet operation of the algebraic system defined by $(A, \leq_R)$, and the meet operation of the algebraic system defined by $(A, \leq)$ is the join operation of the algebraic system defined by $(A, \leq_R)$. Consequently, given any valid statement concerning the general properties of lattices we can obtain another valid statement by replacing the relation $\leq$ with $\geq$,[†] the term *join operation* with the term *meet operation*, and the term *meet operation* with the term *join operation*. This is known as the *principle of duality for lattices*.

As an example, we note that the relation in eq. (11.1) can be stated as, "The join of any two elements in a lattice is larger than or equal to each of the two elements." Correspondingly, we have, "The meet of any two elements in a lattice is less than or equal to each of the two elements," which is the relation in eq. (11.2). Similarly, the relation in eq. (11.4) can be obtained from the relation in eq. (11.3), and, conversely, according to the principle of duality. We shall see more examples on the application of the principle of duality as we proceed to show some of the general properties of algebraic systems defined by lattices.[‡]

11.3 BASIC PROPERTIES OF ALGEBRAIC SYSTEMS DEFINED BY LATTICES

We show now some of the basic properties possessed by algebraic systems defined by lattices. Let $(A, \vee, \wedge)$ be an algebraic system defined by a lattice $(A, \leq)$. We have:

---

[*] See Prob. 3.27.

[†] Clearly, $a \leq_R b$ if and only if $a \geq b$.

[‡] There are other important examples illustrating the principle of duality. In electrical engineering, the concepts of voltage and current, resistance and conductance, inductance and capacitance are dual concepts. In graph theory, the concepts of circuit and cut-set, tree and cotree are dual concepts.

Theorem 11.3 Both the join and meet operations are commutative.

Proof: It follows directly from the definition of the least upper bound and the greatest lower bound of two elements in a lattice. ∎

Theorem 11.4 Both the join and meet operations are associative.

Proof: We first show that the join operation $\vee$ is associative. That is, for a, b, c in A,

$$a \vee (b \vee c) = (a \vee b) \vee c$$

Let

$$a \vee (b \vee c) = g$$

and

$$(a \vee b) \vee c = h$$

Since g is the join of a and $(b \vee c)$,

$$a \leq g \qquad b \vee c \leq g$$

Furthermore, $b \vee c \leq g$ means that

$$b \leq g \qquad c \leq g$$

Since the join of a and b is the least upper bound of a and b, from $a \leq g$ and $b \leq g$ we obtain

$$a \vee b \leq g$$

which, together with $c \leq g$, leads to

$$(a \vee b) \vee c \leq g$$

We have thus shown that

$$h \leq g$$

In a similar manner, we can show that

$$g \leq h$$

Consequently, because of the antisymmetry property of a partial ordering relation, we conclude that

$$g = h$$

According to the principle of duality, the meet operation $\wedge$ is also associative. ∎

Theorem 11.5 For every a in A, $a \vee a = a$ and $a \wedge a = a$.

Proof: According to eq. (11.1),

$$a \leq a \vee a$$

Since $a \leq a$, we obtain*

$$a \vee a \leq a$$

It follows that

---

* If $g \leq f$ and $h \leq f$, then $g \vee h \leq f$ because $g \vee h$ is the least upper bound of g and h.

$$a \vee a = a$$

According to the principle of duality, we also have

$$a \wedge a = a$$ ∎

The results in Theorem 11.5 are known as the *idempotent property* of the join and meet operations.

Theorem 11.6 For any a and b in A,

$$a \vee (a \wedge b) = a$$
$$a \wedge (a \vee b) = a$$

Proof: Since $a \vee (a \wedge b)$ is the join of a and $a \wedge b$, we have

$$a \leq a \vee (a \wedge b) \tag{11.5}$$

Since

$$a \leq a \qquad a \wedge b \leq a$$

according to (11.3), we have

$$a \vee (a \wedge b) \leq a \vee a \tag{11.6}$$

Since

$$a \vee a = a$$

eq. (11.6) becomes

$$a \vee (a \wedge b) \leq a \tag{11.7}$$

Combining eqs. (11.5) and (11.7), we obtain

$$a \vee (a \wedge b) = a$$

That $a \wedge (a \vee b) = a$ follows from the principle of duality. ∎

The results in Theorem 11.6 are known as the *absorption property* of the join and meet operations.

For example, consider the lattice of natural numbers ordered by the "less than or equal to" relationship, $(N, \leq)$. Because the maximum of two numbers a and b is the same as the maximum of the two numbers b and a, the join operation in $(N, \vee, \wedge)$ is commutative. Similarly, the meet operation is also commutative. Because both max (max $(a, b), c$) and max $(a, \max (b, c))$ are equal to the maximum of the three numbers a, b, and c, the join operation in $(N, \vee, \wedge)$ is associative. Similarly, the meet operation is associative. The idempotent property for the join and meet operations follows from the facts that the maximum of a and a is a, and that the minimum of a and a is a. The equations

$$\max [a, \min (a, b)] = a$$
$$\min [a, \max (a, b)] = a$$

yield the absorption property.

As another example, consider the lattice of positive integers ordered by the "divides by" relationship, $(N^+, |)$. Because the least common multiple of a and b is the same as the least common multiple of b and a, the join operation in $(N^+, \vee, \wedge)$ is commutative. Similarly, the meet operation is commutative. Because both $(a \vee b) \vee c$ and $a \vee (b \vee c)$ are the least common multiple of the three numbers

a, b, and c, the join operation is associative. Similarly, the meet operation is associative. The least common divisor of a and a is a, as is the greatest common divisor of a and a. Therefore, the idempotent property of the join and meet operations follows. The equations

$$\text{lcm} [a, \gcd (a, b)] = a$$
$$\gcd [a, \text{lcm} (a, b)] = a$$

yield the absorption property.

11.4 DISTRIBUTIVE AND COMPLEMENTED LATTICES

We study now classes of lattices that possess additional properties. Naturally, one can anticipate that these lattices will define algebraic systems that are even more "structured." A lattice is said to be a *distributive* lattice if the meet operation distributes over the join operation and the join operation distributes over the meet operation. That is, for any a, b, and c,

$$a \wedge (b \vee c) = (a \wedge b) \vee (a \wedge c)$$
$$a \vee (b \wedge c) = (a \vee b) \wedge (a \vee c)^*$$

The lattice in Fig. 11.3a is a distributive lattice. However, the lattice in Fig. 11.4 is not a distributive lattice. Note that in the lattice in Fig. 11.4,

$$b \wedge (c \vee d) = b \wedge a = b$$
$$(b \wedge c) \vee (b \wedge d) = e \vee e = e$$

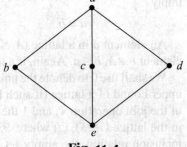

Fig. 11.4

Our definition of a distributive lattice is slightly redundant as shown in Theorem 11.7.

Theorem 11.7 If the meet operation is distributive over the join operation in a lattice, then the join operation is also distributive over the meet operation. If the join operation is distributive over the meet operation, then the meet operation is also distributive over the join operation.

Proof: Given that

$$a \wedge (b \vee c) = (a \wedge b) \vee (a \wedge c)$$

we obtain

---

* Because of commutativity, the equations

$$(a \vee b) \wedge c = (a \wedge c) \vee (b \wedge c)$$
$$(a \wedge b) \vee c = (a \vee c) \wedge (b \vee c)$$

are implied.

$$(a \vee b) \wedge (a \vee c) = [(a \vee b) \wedge a] \vee [(a \vee b) \wedge c]$$
$$= a \vee [(a \vee b) \wedge c]$$
$$= a \vee [(a \wedge c) \vee (b \wedge c)]$$
$$= [a \vee (a \wedge c)] \vee (b \wedge c)$$
$$= a \vee (b \wedge c)$$

By duality, we obtain the result that if the join operation $\vee$ is distributive over the meet operation $\wedge$ then the meet operation $\wedge$ is also distributive over the join operation $\vee$. ■

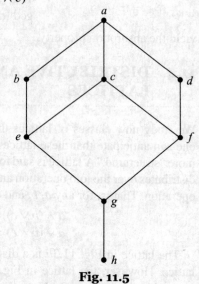

Fig. 11.5

An element a in a lattice $(A, \leq)$ is called a *universal lower bound* if for every element $b \ \varepsilon \ A$, $a \leq b$. For example, for the lattice shown in Fig. 11.5, h is a universal lower bound. It follows from the definition that if a lattice has a universal lower bound, it is unique. For if we assume that there are two universal lower bounds a and b then

$$a \leq b \quad \text{and} \quad b \leq a$$

imply

$$a = b$$

An element a in a lattice $(A, \leq)$ is called a *universal upper bound* if for every element $b \ \varepsilon \ A$, $b \leq a$. Again, if a lattice has a universal upper bound, it is unique.

We shall use 0 to denote the universal lower bound and 1 to denote the universal upper bound of a lattice (if such bounds exist). Note the 0 is indeed the identity of the join operation $\vee$, and 1 the identity of the meet operation $\wedge$. For example, in the lattice $(\mathscr{P}(S), \subseteq)$ where $\mathscr{P}(S)$ is the power set of a set S and $\subseteq$ is the set inclusion relation, the empty set ϕ is the universal lower bound and the set S is the universal upper bound. We have

Theorem 11.8 Let $(A, \leq)$ be a lattice with universal upper and lower bounds 0 and 1. For any element a in A,

$$a \vee 1 = 1 \quad a \wedge 1 = a$$
$$a \vee 0 = a \quad a \wedge 0 = 0$$

Proof: According to (11.1), $1 \leq a \vee 1$. Since 1 is the universal upper bound, $a \vee 1 \leq 1$. Thus, $a \vee 1 = 1$.

According to eq. (11.2), $a \wedge 1 \leq a$. Since $a \leq a$ and $a \leq 1$, according to eq. (11.4), $a \wedge a \leq a \wedge 1$, or $a \leq a \wedge 1$. Thus, $a \wedge 1 = a$.

The other two relations can be proved similarly. ■

Let $(A, \leq)$ be a lattice with universal lower and upper bounds 0 and 1. For an element a in A, an element b is said to be a *complement* of a if

$$a \vee b = 1 \quad \text{and} \quad a \wedge b = 0$$

Note that because of commutativity, if a is a complement of b, then b is also a complement of a. For example, for the lattice in Fig. 11.1, d is a complement of e and e is a complement of d. Note that an element might have more than one complement. For example, in the lattice in Fig. 11.1, both b and e are complements of d. Yet, on the other hand, in the lattice in Fig. 11.1, c has no complement. We note, however, that 0 is the unique complement of 1 and 1 is the unique complement of 0.*

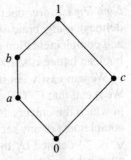

Fig. 11.6

A lattice is said to be a *complemented lattice* if every element in the lattice has a complement. (Clearly, a complemented lattice must have universal lower and upper bounds.) For example, the lattice in Fig. 11.6 is a complemented lattice, where the complement of a is c, the complement of b is also c, and it follows that the complements of c are a and b.

Theorem 11.9 shows again that distributivity is a very "useful" property.

Theorem 11.9 In a distributive lattice, if an element has a complement then this complement is unique.

Proof: Suppose that an element a has two complements b and c. That is,

$$a \vee b = 1 \qquad a \wedge b = 0$$
$$a \vee c = 1 \qquad a \wedge c = 0$$

We have

$$
\begin{aligned}
b &= b \wedge 1 \\
&= b \wedge (a \vee c) \\
&= (b \wedge a) \vee (b \wedge c) \\
&= 0 \vee (b \wedge c) \\
&= (a \wedge c) \vee (b \wedge c) \\
&= (a \vee b) \wedge c \\
&= 1 \wedge c \\
&= c
\end{aligned}
$$

$\blacksquare$

11.5 BOOLEAN LATTICES AND BOOLEAN ALGEBRAS

A complemented and distributive lattice is also called a *boolean lattice*. Let $(A, \leq)$ be a boolean lattice. Since every element in a boolean lattice has a unique complement, we can define a unary operation on A, denoted $^-$, so that for every a in A, $\bar{a}$ is the complement of a.[†] The unary operation $^-$ is referred to as the

---

* It is clear that 0 is a complement of 1 and 1 is a complement of 0. We ask the reader to show uniqueness. (See Prob. 11.14.)

† Instead of writing $-a$, the notation $\bar{a}$ is more convenient. Thus, for example, the complement of the join of a and b will be written as $\overline{a \vee b}$.

complementation operation. Consequently, we say that a boolean lattice $(A, \leq)$ defines an algebraic system $(A, \vee, \wedge, ^-)$, where $\vee$, $\wedge$, and $^-$ are the join, meet, and complementation operations, respectively. An algebraic system defined by a boolean lattice is known as a *boolean algebra*.

We can easily construct examples of boolean algebras. Let S be a finite set. We recall that $(\mathscr{P}(S), \subseteq)$ is a lattice. Furthermore, $(\mathscr{P}(S), \subseteq)$ is a boolean lattice in which the universal upper bound is S, the universal lower bound is ϕ, and the complement of any set T in $\mathscr{P}(S)$ is the set $S - T$. So, the algebraic system $(\mathscr{P}(S), \vee, \wedge, ^-)$ defined by the above boolean lattice $(\mathscr{P}(S), \subseteq)$ is a boolean algebra, where the $\vee$ (the join operation) represents the union of two subsets, $\wedge$ (the meet operation) represents the intersection of two subsets and $^-$ represents the complement of any set in $\mathscr{P}(S)$.

Boolean algebra can also be defined in several other ways, one of the most common ways to define boolean algebra is through specifying the properties that the operations must satisfy, as is done in the following definition:

Definition 11.1   A boolean algebra is a set A with elements 0 and 1, two binary operations $\vee$ and $\wedge$, and a unary operation $^-$ such that the following properties hold for all $a, b, c \in A$:

1. $a \vee 0 = a$ ⎫
2. $a \wedge 1 = a$ ⎬ Identity laws

3. $a \vee \bar{a} = 1$ ⎫
4. $a \wedge \bar{a} = 0$ ⎬ Complement laws

5. $(a \vee b) \vee c = a \vee (b \vee c)$ ⎫
6. $(a \wedge b) \wedge c = a \wedge (b) \wedge c)$ ⎬ Associative laws

7. $a \vee b = b \vee a$ ⎫
8. $a \wedge b = b \wedge a)$ ⎬ Commutative laws

9. $a \vee (b \wedge c) = (a \vee b) \wedge (a \vee c)$ ⎫
10. $a \wedge (b \vee c) = (a \wedge b) \vee (a \wedge c)$ ⎬ Distributive laws

It is possible to prove many other properties that hold for every boolean algebra, by using the properties given in Definition 11.1. For example, the idempotent laws and domination laws can be proved by using the laws mentioned in Definition 11.1.

Now, let us discuss some more examples of boolean algebra. The set $A = \{0,1\}$ with the operators OR, AND, and Complement satisfy all the above properties given in Definition 11.1, and hence is a boolean algebra. Similarly, the set of propositions in n variables, with the values F and T, with the operators $\vee$, $\wedge$ and $^-$ also satisfy the properties of boolean algebra. We now show:

Theorem 11.10   For any a and b in a boolean algebra

$$\overline{a \vee b} = \bar{a} \wedge \bar{b}$$

$$\overline{a \wedge b} = \bar{a} \vee \bar{b}$$

Proof: We have

$$(a \vee b) \vee (\overline{a} \wedge \overline{b}) = [(a \vee b) \vee \overline{a}] \wedge [(a \vee b) \vee \overline{b}]$$
$$= [(a \vee \overline{a}) \vee b] \wedge [a \vee (b \vee \overline{b})]$$
$$= 1 \wedge 1$$
$$= 1$$

and

$$(a \vee b) \wedge (\overline{a} \wedge \overline{b}) = [a \wedge (\overline{a} \wedge \overline{b})] \vee [b \wedge (\overline{a} \wedge \overline{b})]$$
$$= [(a \wedge \overline{a}) \wedge \overline{b}] \vee [(b \wedge \overline{b}) \wedge \overline{a}]$$
$$= 0 \vee 0$$
$$= 0$$

Thus, $\overline{a} \wedge \overline{b}$ is the complement of $a \vee b$. That is,

$$\overline{a \vee b} = \overline{a} \wedge \overline{b}$$

■

That $\overline{a \wedge b} = \overline{a} \vee \overline{b}$ follows from the principle of duality.

The results in Theorem 11.10 are known as *DeMorgan's laws*.

11.6 IDENTITY OF BOOLEAN ALGEBRA

In Boolean algebra, there are several identities. Some important identities are listed in Table 11.1. These identities can be used for simplifying the design of circuits. Each of the identities listed in Table 11.1 can be proved by constructing a truth table. Below, we will prove one of the absorption laws, by constructing the truth table. We leave the proofs of the other identities to the reader as exercises.

Table 11.1 Some important Boolean identities

BI_1	$\overline{\overline{a}} = a$ (double complement law)
BI_2	$a + a = a$ (idempotent law)
BI_3	$a \cdot a = a$ (idempotent law)
BI_4	$a + 0 = a$ (identity law)
BI_5	$a \cdot 1 = a$ (identity law)
BI_6	$a + 1 = 1$ (domination law)
BI_7	$a \cdot 0 = 0$ (domination law)
BI_8	$a + b = b + a$ (commutative law)
BI_9	$a \cdot b = b \cdot a$ (commutative law)
BI_{10}	$a + (b + c) = (a + b) + c$ (associative law)
BI_{11}	$a(bc) = (ab)c$ (associative law)
BI_{12}	$a + bc = (a + b)(a + c)$ (distributive law)
BI_{13}	$a + (b + c) = ab + ac$ (distributive law)
BI_{14}	$\overline{(ab)} = \overline{a} + \overline{b}$ (De Morgan's law)
BI_{15}	$\overline{(a + b)} = \overline{a}\,\overline{b}$ (De Morgan's law)
BI_{16}	$a + ab = a$ (absorption law)
BI_{17}	$a(a + b) = a$ (absorption law)
BI_{18}	$a + \overline{a} = 1$ (unity property)
BI_{19}	$a \cdot \overline{a} = 0$ (zero property)

It may be noted that when there is no confusion, we have omitted the symbol . and written the expressions simply as the algebraic products.

Example 11.1 Prove that the absorption law $a + ab = a$ is valid .

Solution: The validity of this identitity is shown in Table 11.2. It may be observed that the identity holds as the first and last columns of the table match.

Table 11.2 Verifying one of the absorption laws

a	b	ab	$a + ab$
0	0	0	0
0	1	0	0
1	0	0	1
1	1	1	1

We advise the reader to compare the boolean identities in Table 11.2 with the logical equivalences in Table 1.2 of Section 1.14. It may be observed that, each set of identities can be obtained by performing appropriate translations. For example, each of the identities in Table 11.2 can be transformed into a logical equivalence by replacing each boolean variable with a propositional variable, each 0 with a F, each 1 with a T, each Boolean sum with disjunction, each boolean product with a conjunction, each complementation with a negation and each = with a $\equiv$. ∎

Example 11.2 Translate the absorption law, $a + ab = a$ in Table 11.2 into a logical equivalence.

Solution: In order to translate a boolean identity into a logical equivalence, we first replace each boolean variable with a propositional variable. Let us replace the boolean variables a and b with the propositional variables p and q. Then, we replace each boolean sum with disjunction, each boolean product with a conjunction and the = symbol with a $\equiv$ symbol.

So, the above boolean identity is transformed into the following logical equivalence:

$$p \lor (p \land q) \equiv p$$

It may be observed that this logical equivalence is one of the absorption laws for propositional logic in Table 1.2 of Section 1.14. ∎

Example 11.3 Prove the absorption law, $a + ab = a$, using the other identities of boolean algebra.

Solution: Below, we present the steps which are used to prove the absorption law along with the laws used in each step:

$a + a.b = a. 1 + a . b$ (identity law)

$\quad = a . (1 + b)$ (distributive law)

$$= a \cdot (b + 1) \text{ (commutative law)}$$
$$= a \cdot 1 \text{ (domination law)}$$
$$= a \text{ (identity law)} \qquad \blacksquare$$

11.7 UNIQUENESS OF FINITE BOOLEAN ALGEBRAS

One might imagine that there is a great deal of freedom for constructing many different boolean algebras. As it turns out, this is not quite the case. We shall show that a finite boolean algebra* has exactly 2^n elements for some $n > 0$. Moreover, there is a unique boolean algebra of 2^n elements for every $n > 0$.

Let a and b be two elements in a lattice. We recall that a is said to *cover* b if $b < a$[†] and there is no element c such that $b < c$ and $c < a$. Let $(A, \leq)$ be a lattice with a universal lower bound 0. An element is called an *atom* if it covers 0. For example, for the lattice in Fig. 11.1, e and f are atoms.

Let $(A, \leq)$ be a finite lattice with a universal lower bound. We claim that, for any nonzero element* b there exists at least one atom a such that $a \leq b$. Clearly, if b is an atom, this is immediate. If b is not an atom, because $(A, \leq)$ is a finite lattice, there must be a chain in $(A, \leq)$ such that $0 < b_i < \dots < b_2 < b_1 < b$, where b_i is an atom. It follows that $b_i \leq b$.

We prove now a sequence of lemmas:

Lemma 11.1 In a distributive lattice, if $b \wedge \bar{c} = 0$ then $b \leq c$.

Proof: Since $b \wedge \bar{c} = 0$, we have

$$(b \wedge \bar{c}) \vee c = c$$

According to the distributive law, we have

$$(b \vee c) \wedge (\bar{c} \vee c) = c$$

or

$$b \vee c = c \qquad (11.8)$$

Since eq. (11.8) means that c is the least upper bound of b and c, $b \leq c$. $\blacksquare$

Lemma 11.2 Let $(A, \vee, \wedge, ^-)$ be a finite boolean algebra. Let b be any nonzero element in A, and $a_1, a_2, \dots, a_k$ be all the atoms of A such that $a_i \leq b$. Then $b = a_1 \vee a_2 \vee \dots \vee a_k$.

Proof: Since

$$a_1 \leq b \quad a_2 \leq b \quad \dots \quad a_k \leq b$$

it follows immediately

$$a_1 \vee a_2 \vee \dots \vee a_k \leq b$$

---

* A finite boolean algebra is one with a finite number of elements.

[†] We use the notation $b < a$ to mean $b \leq a$ and $b \neq a$.

* By a nonzero element we mean an element that is not equal to the universal lower bound 0.

For notational convenience, let c denote $a_1 \vee a_2 \vee \ldots \vee a_k$.

Let us suppose that $b \wedge \bar{c} \neq 0$. In that case, there exists an atom a such that $a \leq (b \wedge \bar{c})$. Since

$$b \wedge \bar{c} \leq b$$

and

$$b \wedge \bar{c} \leq \bar{c}$$

according to the transitive law, we have

$$a \leq b \tag{11.9}$$

and

$$a \leq \bar{c}$$

According to eq. (11.9) a is equal to one of the atoms $a_1, a_2, \ldots, a_k$. It follows that

$$a \leq c$$

Combining $a \leq \bar{c}$ and $a \leq c$, we obtain

$$a \leq c \wedge \bar{c}$$

or

$$a \leq 0$$

which is impossible.

It follows that we must have $b \wedge \bar{c} = 0$. In that case, according to Lemma 11.1, $b \leq c$. By the antisymmetry law, we have

$$b = a_1 \vee a_2 \vee \ldots \vee a_k \qquad ■$$

Lemma 11.3 Let $(A, \vee, \wedge, ^-)$ be a finite boolean algebra. Let b be any nonzero element in A, and $a_1, a_2, \ldots, a_k$ be all the atoms of A such that $a_i \leq b$. Then $b = a_1 \vee a_2 \vee \ldots \vee a_k$ is the *unique* way to represent b as a join of atoms.

Proof: Suppose that we have an alternative representation

$$b = a_{j1} \vee a_{j2} \vee \ldots \vee a_{jt}$$

Clearly, since b is the least upper bound of $a_{j1}, a_{j2}, \ldots, a_{jt}$

$$a_{j1} \leq b \quad a_{j2} \leq b \quad \ldots \quad a_{jt} \leq b$$

In other words, if b is expressed as a join of atoms, they must be atoms that are less than or equal to b.

Now consider an atom a_{ju}, $1 \leq u \leq t$. Since $a_{ju} \leq b$, we have

$$a_{ju} \wedge b = a_{ju}$$

That is,

$$a_{ju} \wedge (a_1 \vee a_2 \vee \ldots \vee a_k) = a_{ju}$$

or

$$(a_{ju} \wedge a_1) \vee (a_{ju} \wedge a_2) \vee \ldots \vee (a_{ju} \wedge a_k) = a_{ju}$$

Then, for some a_i, $1 \leq i \leq k$,

$$a_{ju} \wedge a_i \neq 0$$

Since both a_{ju} and a_i are atoms, we must have $a_{ju} = a_i$.

Thus, each atom in the alternative representation is an atom in the original one, and the lemma follows. ■

It follows from Lemmas 11.1, 11.2, and 11.3 that there is a one-to-one correspondence between the elements of a boolean lattice and the subsets of the atoms. As a matter of fact, this one-to-one correspondence is an isomorphism from $(A, \leq)$ to $(\mathscr{P}(S), \subseteq)$, where S is the set of atoms. We thus have:

Theorem 11.11 Let $(A, \vee, \wedge, ^-)$ be a finite boolean algebra. Let S be the set of atoms. Then $(A, \vee, \wedge, ^-)$ is isomorphic to the algebraic system defined by the lattice $(\mathscr{P}(S), \subseteq)$.

It follows immediately from Theorem 11.11 that there exists a unique finite boolean algebra of 2^n elements for any $n > 0$. Furthermore, there are no other finite boolean algebras.

11.8 BOOLEAN FUNCTIONS AND BOOLEAN EXPRESSIONS

Let $(A, \vee, \wedge, ^-)$ be a boolean algebra. Let us consider the functions from A^n to A. For example, the table in Fig. 11.7 shows a function f from $\{0, 1\}^3$ to $\{0, 1\}$, and the table in Fig. 11.8 shows a function f from $\{0, 1, 2, 3\}^2$ to $\{0, 1, 2, 3\}$. Although a function can always be described exhaustively in tabular form, we are interested in alternative ways of describing functions. We recall that there is the possibility of specifying a function by a "closed-form expression." Let us indeed pursue such an approach.

Let $(A, \vee, \wedge, ^-)$ be a boolean algebra. A *boolean expression* over $(A, \vee, \wedge, ^-)$ is defined as follows:*

1. Any element of A is a boolean expression.
2. Any variable name is a boolean expression.
3. If e_1 and e_2 are boolean expressions then $\bar{e}_1$, $e_1 \vee e_2$, $e_1 \wedge e_2$ are boolean expressions.

For example,

$$0 \vee x$$
$$((\overline{2 \wedge 3})) \vee (x_1 \vee \bar{x}_2) \wedge (\overline{x_1 \wedge x_3})$$

are boolean expressions over the boolean algebra $(\{0, 1, 2, 3\}, \vee, \wedge, ^-)$. A boolean expression that contains n *distinct* variables is usually referred to as a boolean expression of n variables.

Let $E(x_1, x_2, ..., x_n)$ be a boolean expression of n variables over a boolean algebra $(A, \vee, \wedge, ^-)$. By an assignment of values to the variables $x_1, x_2, ..., x_n$, we mean an assignment of elements of A to be the values of the variables. For an assignment of values to the variables we can evaluate the expression $E(x_1, x_2, ..., x_n)$ by substituting the variables in the expression by their values. For example, for the boolean expression

---

* See Sec. 10.12 for the definition of an algebraic expression over an algebraic system.

$$E(x_1, x_2, x_3) = (x_1 \vee x_2) \wedge (\bar{x}_1 \vee \bar{x}_2) \wedge (\overline{x_2 \vee x_3})$$

over the boolean algebra ($\{0, 1\}, \vee, \wedge, {}^-$) the assignment of values $x_1 = 0$, $x_2 = 1$, $x_3 = 0$ yields

$$E(0, 1, 0) = (0 \vee 1) \wedge (\bar{0} \vee \bar{1}) \wedge (\overline{1 \vee 0})$$
$$= 1 \wedge 1 \wedge 0$$
$$= 0$$

Two boolean expressions of n variables are said to be *equivalent* if they assume the same value for every assignment of values to the n variables. For example, the reader can readily check that the two boolean expressions

$$(x_1 \wedge x_2) \vee (x_1 \wedge \bar{x}_3)$$
$$x_1 \wedge (x_2 \vee \bar{x}_3)$$

are equivalent. We write

$$E_1(x_1, x_2, \ldots, x_n) = E_2(x_1, x_2, \ldots, x_n)$$

to mean the two expressions $E_1(x_1, x_2, \ldots, x_n)$ and $E_2(x_1, x_2, \ldots, x_n)$ are equivalent. Thus, when we say to manipulate or to simplify a boolean expression we always mean to manipulate or to simplify it into an equivalent form. Because elements of A will be assigned as values of the variables in a boolean expression, all equalities we derived in previous sections involving elements of a boolean algebra can be applied to manipulate and simplify boolean expressions. For example, we note that

$$(x_1 \wedge x_2) \vee (x_1 \wedge \bar{x}_3) = x_1 \wedge (x_2 \vee \bar{x}_3)$$
$$(x_1 \wedge x_2) \vee (x_1 \wedge \bar{x}_2) = x_1$$
$$x_1 \wedge x_2 = (x_1 \wedge x_2) \wedge 1$$
$$= (x_1 \wedge x_2) \wedge (x_3 \vee \bar{x}_3)$$
$$= (x_1 \wedge x_2 \wedge x_3) \vee (x_1 \wedge x_2 \wedge \bar{x}_3)$$

It is not difficult to see how we can specify a function from A^n to A by a boolean expression $E(x_1, x_2, \ldots, x_n)$. Namely, let each assignment of values to the variables $x_1, x_2, \ldots, x_n$ be an ordered n-tuple in the domain A^n, and let the corresponding value of $E(x_1, x_2, \ldots, x_n)$ be the corresponding image in the range A. For example, the reader can check immediately that the boolean expression

$$(\bar{x}_1 \wedge x_2 \wedge \bar{x}_3) \vee (x_1 \wedge \bar{x}_2) \vee (x_1 \wedge x_3)$$

over the boolean algebra ($\{0, 1\}, \vee, \wedge, {}^-$) defines the function f in Fig. 11.7.

On the other hand, we ask whether every function from A^n to A can be specified by a boolean expression over ($A, \vee, \wedge, {}^-$). The answer is negative. For example, there is no boolean expression over the boolean algebra of four elements that defines the function in Fig. 11.8. (See Prob. 11.24.) A function from A^n to A is called a *boolean function* if it can be specified by a boolean expression (of n variables).

	f
(0, 0)	1
(0, 1)	0
(0, 2)	0
(0, 3)	3
(1, 0)	1
(1, 1)	1
(1, 2)	0
(1, 3)	3
(2, 0)	2
(2, 1)	0
(2, 2)	1
(2, 3)	1
(3, 0)	3
(3, 1)	0
(3, 2)	0
(3, 3)	2

	f
(0, 0, 0)	0
(0, 0, 1)	0
(0, 1, 0)	1
(0, 1, 1)	0
(1, 0, 0)	1
(1, 0, 1)	1
(1, 1, 0)	0
(1, 1, 1)	1

Fig. 11.7   **Fig. 11.8**

11.9 NORMAL FORMS

We note, however, that for the case of the two-valued boolean algebra any function from $\{0, 1\}^n$ to $\{0, 1\}$ is a boolean function. As a matter of fact, we shall show two ways to obtain a boolean expression that specifies a given function from $\{0, 1\}^n$ to $\{0, 1\}$. A boolean expression of n variables $x_1, x_2, \ldots, x_n$ is said to be a *minterm* if it is of the form

$$\tilde{x}_1 \wedge \tilde{x}_2 \wedge \ldots \wedge \tilde{x}_n \qquad (11.10)$$

where we use $\tilde{x}_i$ to denote either x_i or $\bar{x}_i$. A boolean expression over $(\{0, 1\}, \vee, \wedge, ^-)$ is said to be in *disjunctive normal form* or the *sum of products* expression if it is a join of minterms. For example,

$$(\bar{x}_1 \wedge \bar{x}_2 \wedge \bar{x}_3) \vee (\bar{x}_1 \wedge x_2 \wedge \bar{x}_3) \vee (x_1 \wedge x_2 \wedge x_3) \qquad (11.11)$$

is a boolean expression in disjunctive normal form. Equation 11.11 can also be written as

$$\bar{x}_1 \bar{x}_2 \bar{x}_3 + \bar{x}_1 x_2 \bar{x}_3 + x_1 x_2 x_3$$

Furthermore, there are three minterms in the expression, namely, $\bar{x}_1 \wedge \bar{x}_2 \wedge \bar{x}_3$, $\bar{x}_1 \wedge x_2 \wedge \bar{x}_3$, and $x_1 \wedge x_2 \wedge x_3$.

A boolean expression of n variables $x_1, x_2, \ldots, x_n$ is said to be a *maxterm* if it is of the form

$$\tilde{x}_1 \vee \tilde{x}_2 \vee \ldots \vee \tilde{x}_n \qquad (11.12)$$

where, again we use $\tilde{x}_i$ to denote either x_i or $\bar{x}_i$. A boolean expression over $(\{0, 1\}, \vee, \wedge, ^-)$ is said to be in *conjunctive normal form* or the *product of sums expression* if it is a meet of maxterms. For example,

$$(x_1 \vee x_2 \vee \bar{x}_3) \wedge (x_1 \vee \bar{x}_2 \vee \bar{x}_3) \wedge (\bar{x}_1 \vee x_2 \vee x_3)$$
$$\wedge (\bar{x}_1 \vee x_2 \vee \bar{x}_3) \wedge (\bar{x}_1 \vee \bar{x}_2 \vee x_3) \qquad (11.13)$$

is a boolean expression in conjunctive normal form consisting of five maxterms.

Equation (11.13) can also be expressed as

$$(x_1 + x_2 + \bar{x}_3)(x_1 + \bar{x}_2 + \bar{x}_3)(\bar{x}_1 + x_2 + x_3)(\bar{x}_1 + x_2 + \bar{x}_3)(\bar{x}_1 + \bar{x}_2 + x_3).$$

Given a function from $\{0, 1\}^n$ to $\{0, 1\}$, we can obtain a boolean expression in disjunctive normal form corresponding to this function by having a minterm corresponding to each ordered n-tuple of 0s and 1s for which the value of the function is 1. Specifically, for each such n-tuple, we have a minterm

$$\tilde{x}_1 \wedge \tilde{x}_2 \wedge \ldots \wedge \tilde{x}_n$$

in which $\tilde{x}_i$ is x_i if the ith component of the n-tuple is 1 and is $\bar{x}_i$ if the ith component of the n-tuple is 0.[*] For example, the boolean expression in eq. (11.11) corresponds to the function f in Fig. 11.9.

Similarly, given a function from $\{0, 1\}^n$ to $\{0, 1\}$, we can obtain a boolean expression in conjunctive normal form corresponding to this function by having a maxterm corresponding to each ordered n-tuple of 0s and 1s at which the value of the function is 0. Specifically, for such n-tuple we have a maxterm

			f
0	0	0	1
0	0	1	0
0	1	0	1
0	1	1	0
1	0	0	0
1	0	1	0
1	1	0	0
1	1	1	1

Fig. 11.9

$$\tilde{x}_1 \vee \tilde{x}_2 \vee \ldots \vee \tilde{x}_n$$

in which $\tilde{x}_i$ is x_i if the ith component of the n-tuple is 0 and is $\bar{x}_i$ if the ith component of the n-tuple is 1. For example, the boolean expression in eq. (11.13) corresponds to the function f in Fig. 11.9.

11.10 SIMPLIFICATION OF LOGIC EXPRESSIONS USING KARNAUGH MAP

The *Karnaugh* (pronounced as "car-no") *map* was proposed by Maurice Karnaugh, a telecommunications engineer, at Bell Laboratories in 1953. A Karnaugh map (K-map) is a pictorial method used to simplify (minimize) Boolean expressions. It is a two-dimensional representation of a truth table.

Unlike a truth-table, in which the input values typically follow a standard binary sequence (00, 01, 10, 11), the K-map's input values must be ordered such that the values for adjacent columns vary only by a single bit, for example, the values for adjacent columns could be 00, 01, 11 and 10. This ordering is known as a *gray code* and it is a key factor in the way in which a Karnaugh map works.

---

[*] We ask the reader to convince herself that the boolean expression obtained indeed specifies the given function.

Using a K-map, expressions with two to four variables can be easily minimized. Expressions with five to six variables are difficult but achievable, and expressions with seven or more variables are extremely difficult (but, not impossible) to minimize using a K-map.

Figure 11.10 illustrates the correspondence between the Karnaugh map and the truth table for the general case of a two variable problem.

x_1	x_2	f
0	0	x
0	1	y
1	0	z
1	1	w

x_2 \ x_1	0	1
0	x	z
1	y	w

f

Fig. 11.10 The correspondence between the Karnaugh map and the truth table

The values inside the squares are copied from the output column of the truth table, therefore there is one square in the map for every row in the truth table. Around the edge of the K-map are the values of the two input variables: x_1 is along the top and x_2 is towards down the left hand side. Note that the value in the f column represents a particular function to which the K-map corresponds.

A Karnaugh map is a diagram consisting of squares. Each square of the map represents a product term of a Boolean expression. Any logic expression can be expressed as a sum of products (SOP) form, i.e. sum of *minterms* or as a product of sums (POS) form, i.e. product of *maxterms*. Therefore, a logic expression can easily be represented in a Karnaugh map.

A Karnaugh map for n variables is made up of 2^n squares. Since there are 2^n combinations of n-variables, so, each square corresponds to one of the combinations of n-variables. For the terms (combinations) which are present in the expression, 1s are written in the corresponding squares. For the terms which are not present in the expression, 0s are written in the corresponding squares. For clear understanding of the map, we omit explicit writing of 0s. So, blank squares represent the fact that they contain 0s.

11.10.1 Simplification of Logical Functions Using K-map

Simplification of logical functions with K-map is based on the principle of combining terms in adjacent cells. Two cells are said to be adjacent if the *minterms* that they have, differ in exactly one literal.

Karnaugh Map for Two Variables Two-Variable K-maps are trivial but can be used to introduce the methods we need to learn. Figure 11.11a shows a 2-input *OR gate*.

Consider the map of two variables as shown in Fig. 11.11b to understand the principle. In Fig. 11.11b, x_1 is the most significant bit and x_2 is the least significant

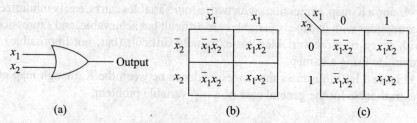

Fig. 11.11   2-input *OR gate* and two variable Karnaugh map

bit. The first row represents $\bar{x}_2$ and the second row represents x_2. Similarly the first and second columns represent $\bar{x}_1$ and x_1 respectively. For any cell, observe the variables in both the row and column. For example, the first cell of the first row denotes the variables $\bar{x}_2$ and $\bar{x}_1$. Hence, it represents the *minterm* $\bar{x}_1 \bar{x}_2$. Similarly the second, third and fourth cells represent $x_1\bar{x}_2$, $\bar{x}_1 x_2$ and $x_1 x_2$ respectively.

The map of Fig. 11.11*b* can also be shown as a map given in Fig. 11.11*c*. In Fig. 11.11*c*, the top, 0 and 1 indicate *0 and 1* logic for variable x_1. In other words, 0 represents $\bar{x}_1$ and 1 represents x_1. Similarly, at the left, 0 and 1 indicate *0 and 1* logic for variable x_2 (i.e. 0 represents $\bar{x}_2$ and 1 represents x_2).

The K-map for two variables can also be represented as in Fig. 11.12.

x_2\\x_1	0	1
0	0	2
1	1	3

Fig. 11.12   Alternative representation for two variable Karnaugh map

Let us consider an example:

$$y = \bar{x}_1 \bar{x}_2 + x_1 \bar{x}_2$$

This can also be represented as $y = \sum m(0, 2)$, where m stands for *minterm*. In this function, only two product terms are present. So two 1s are written in the corresponding squares as shown in Fig. 11.13.

x_2\\x_1	0	1
0	1 0	1 2
1	1	3

Fig. 11.13   A two variable Karnaugh map

Before simplifying the K-map for two-variables, we present some rules which are as follows:

1. Groups may not include any cell containing a *zero*.

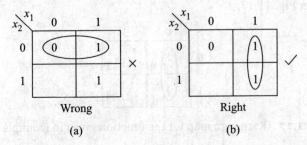

Wrong   Right

(a)   (b)

Fig. 11.14 Appropriate pairing methods

2. Groups may be formed horizontally or vertically but not diagonally.

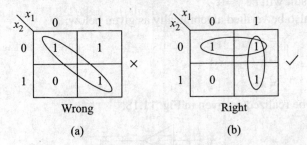

Wrong   Right

(a)   (b)

Fig. 11.15 Appropriate pairing methods

3. Groups must form 2^n-squares, i.e. two-squares, four-squares, eight squares, etc.

4. Each group should be as large as possible.

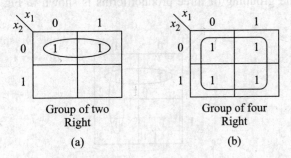

Group of two   Group of four
Right   Right

(a)   (b)

Fig. 11.16 Number of squares in a group

The following examples will illustrate the above rules.

Example 11.4 Simplify $y = \bar{x}_1 \bar{x}_2 + \bar{x}_1 x_2$ or $y = \sum m(0, 1)$

Solution: First, construct the Karnaugh map for the given function as shown in Fig. 11.17. Then group or encircle the adjacent squares containing 1s, which is also shown in Fig. 11.17.

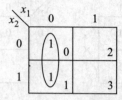

Fig. 11.17 Karnaugh map for the function given in Example 11.4

For simplification, consider the variable which is common to both the squares. In this case, $\bar{x}_1$ is common to both the squares as the first column denotes $\bar{x}_1$. The variable which is not common is rejected. In this case x_2 varies, so x_2 is discarded. Hence the result will be $y = \bar{x}_1$.

This can also be verified algebraically as given below:

$$y = \bar{x}_1 \bar{x}_2 + \bar{x}_1 x_2$$
$$= \bar{x}_1 (\bar{x}_2 + x_2)$$
$$= \bar{x}_1$$

This may be realized as given in Fig. 11.18.

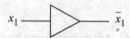

Fig. 11.18 Realization of the boolean function of Example 11.4

Example 11.5 Reduce $y = \bar{x}_1 \bar{x}_2 + x_1 \bar{x}_2 + x_1 x_2$ or $y = \sum m(0, 2, 3)$ using mapping.

Solution: The grouping of three product terms is shown in Fig. 11.19 using K-map.

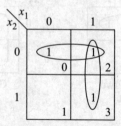

Fig. 11.19 Karnaugh map for the function given in Example 11.5

In this case, the 1 in first row and second column is common to all groups. Here, the 1s in first row are grouped or encircled which gives the result $\bar{x}_2$ and the 1s in the second column are grouped or encircled which gives the result x_1. Hence, the result is $y = x_1 + \bar{x}_2$.

This can also be verified algebraically as given below:

$$y = \bar{x}_1 \bar{x}_2 + x_1 \bar{x}_2 + x_1 x_2$$
$$= \bar{x}_1 \bar{x}_2 + x_1 \bar{x}_2 + x_1 \bar{x}_2 + x_1 x_2$$
$$= \bar{x}_2 (\bar{x}_1 + x_1) + x_1(\bar{x}_2 + x_2)$$
$$= \bar{x}_2 + x_1$$

This may be realized as given in Fig. 11.20.

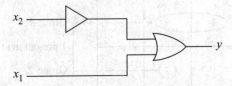

Fig. 11.20 Realization of the boolean function of Example 11.5

Karnaugh Map for Three Variables Figure 11.21*a* shows the Karnaugh map for 3 variables and Fig. 11.21*b* shows the alternative way of representing the variables.

In Fig. 11.21*a*, we have taken x as the most significant bit and x_3 as the least significant bit. In Fig. 11.21*b*, note the sequence of numbers across the map. It is not in binary sequence which would be 00, 01, 10, and 11. The straight binary codes are used in Veitch diagram. Karnaugh modified the Veitch diagram and used 00, 01, 11, 10 which is in gray (reflected binary) code sequence. Gray code sequence only changes one binary bit as we go from one number to the next in the sequence, unlike binary. That means, the adjacent squares will vary only by one bit, or boolean variable. This is what we need to organize the outputs of a logic function so that we may view commonality. Moreover, the column and

$x_3 \diagdown^{x_1 x_2}$	$\bar{x}_1 \bar{x}_2$	$\bar{x}_1 x_2$	$x_1 x_2$	$x_1 \bar{x}_2$
$\bar{x}_3$	$\bar{x}_1 \bar{x}_2 \bar{x}_3$	$\bar{x}_1 x_2 \bar{x}_3$	$x_1 x_2 \bar{x}_3$	$x_1 \bar{x}_2 \bar{x}_3$
x_3	$\bar{x}_1 \bar{x}_2 x_3$	$\bar{x}_1 x_2 x_3$	$x_1 x_2 x_3$	$x_1 \bar{x}_2 x_3$

(a)

$x_3 \diagdown^{x_1 x_2}$	00	01	11	10
0	$\bar{x}_1 \bar{x}_2 \bar{x}_3$	$\bar{x}_1 x_2 \bar{x}_3$	$x_1 x_2 \bar{x}_3$	$x_1 \bar{x}_2 \bar{x}_3$
1	$\bar{x}_1 \bar{x}_2 x_3$	$\bar{x}_1 x_2 x_3$	$x_1 x_2 x_3$	$x_1 \bar{x}_2 x_3$

(b)

Fig. 11.21 (a) Karnaugh map for three variable, (b) Alternative way of representing Karnaugh map for three variables

row headings must be in gray code order, otherwise the map will not work as a Karnaugh map. Squares sharing common boolean variables would no longer be adjacent, nor show visual patterns. Adjacent squares vary by only one bit because a gray code sequence varies by only one bit.

Now, let us consider some rules in addition to the rules given in the K-map for two variables.

1. Each square containing a one must be in at least one group.

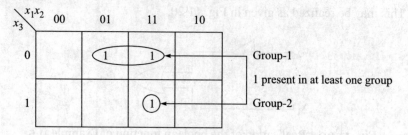

Fig. 11.22   K-map showing groups

2. A square containing 1 can be included in as many groups as desired.

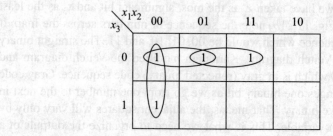

Fig. 11.23   K-map showing different groups containing 1s

3. A Group must be as large as possible even if groups may overlap.

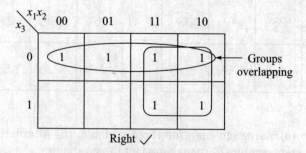

Fig. 11.24(a)   K-map with overlapping groups

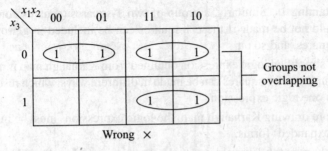

Fig. 11.24(b) K-map with non-overlapping groups

4. The map is considered to be folded or cylindrical. Therefore, squares at the ends of a row or column are treated as adjacent squares, i.e. the leftmost square can be grouped with the rightmost square and the top square in a column may be grouped with the bottom square. This is shown in Fig. 11.25.

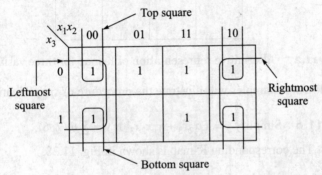

Fig. 11.25 Cylindrical or folded K-map

5. There should be as few groups as possible, as long as this does not contradict any of the previous rules. This is shown in Fig. 11.26.

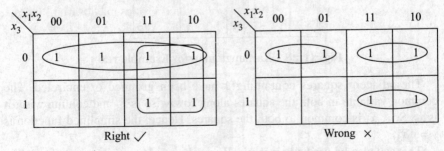

Fig. 11.26 K-map showing minimum number of possible groups

6. A square containing 1 should not be left alone to be included in the final expression, if there is a possibility of its inclusion in a group of two squares

containing 1s. Similarly, a group of two 1-squares (squares containing 1) should not be made if these 1-squares can be included in a group of four 1-squares, and so on.

7. The simplified logic expression obtained from Karnaugh map is not unique. Groupings of 1-squares can be made in different ways; which result in more than one logic expression.

8. Before drawing Karnaugh map, the logic expressions must be in canonical (or expanded) forms.

The K-map for 3-variables can also be represented as the following figure. In Fig. 11.27, x_1 is the most significant bit and x_3 is the least significant bit.

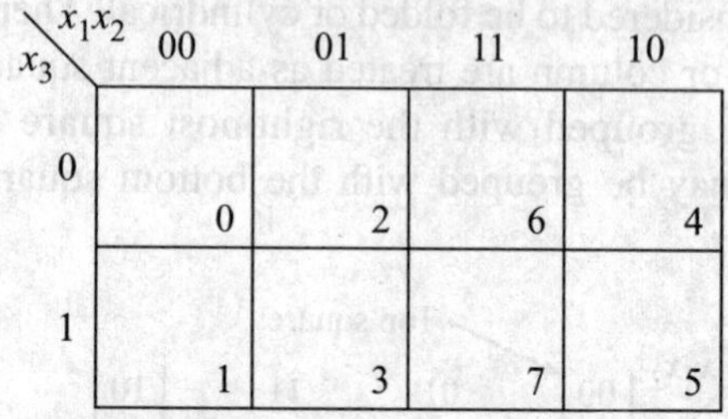

Fig. 11.27 Alternative representation of K-map for three variables

The following examples will illustrate the procedure of simplification.

Example 11.6 Simplify $y = \bar{x}_1 x_2 \bar{x}_3 + x_1 x_2 \bar{x}_3$ or $y = \sum m(2, 6)$.

Solution: The corresponding K-map is shown in Fig. 11.28.

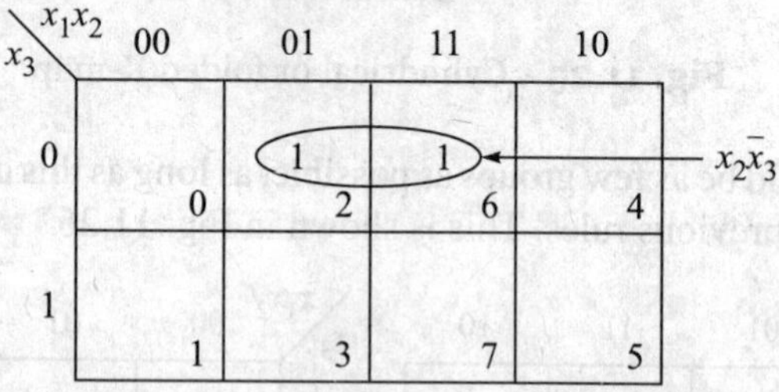

Fig. 11.28 Karnaugh map for Example 11.6

The adjacent squares containing 1 have been grouped or encircled. The common variable in both the squares along row wise is $\bar{x}_3$ and column wise, it is x_2. So $x_2\bar{x}_3$ is common to both the squares. Hence, the simplified function is $y = x_2\bar{x}_3$.

This can also be verified algebraically as given below:

$$y = \bar{x}_1 x_2 \bar{x}_3 + x_1 x_2 \bar{x}_3$$
$$= x_2 \bar{x}_3 (\bar{x}_1 + x_1)$$
$$= x_2 \bar{x}_3$$

This may be realized as given in Fig. 11.29.

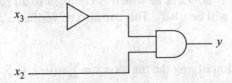

Fig. 11.29 Realization of the boolean function of Example 11.6

Example 11.7 Reduce $y = \bar{x}_1 x_2 \bar{x}_3 + x_1 x_2 \bar{x}_3 + x_1 x_2 x_3$ or $y = \sum m(2, 6, 7)$ using K-map.

Solution: The corresponding K-map is shown in Fig. 11.30.

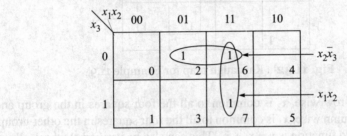

Fig. 11.30 Karnaugh map for Example 11.7

In this case the square containing $x_1 x_2 \bar{x}_3$ is common to both the groups. Observing row wise, the common variables are $x_2 \bar{x}_3$ and observing column-wise, the common variables are $x_1 x_2$. So, the simplified function is $y = x_1 x_2 + x_2 \bar{x}_3$.

This can also be verified algebraically as given below:

$$y = \bar{x}_1 x_2 \bar{x}_3 + x_1 x_2 \bar{x}_3 + x_1 x_2 x_3$$
$$= \bar{x}_1 x_2 \bar{x}_3 + x_1 x_2 \bar{x}_3 + x_1 x_2 \bar{x}_3 + x_1 x_2 x_3$$
$$= x_2 \bar{x}_3 (\bar{x}_1 + x_1) + x_1 x_2 (\bar{x}_3 + x_3)$$
$$= x_2 \bar{x}_3 + x_1 x_2$$

$\blacksquare$

Example 11.8 Simplify $y = \bar{x}_1 x_2 \bar{x}_3 + x_1 x_2 \bar{x}_3 + \bar{x}_1 x_2 x_3 + x_1 x_2 x_3$

Solution: The corresponding K-map is shown in Fig. 11.31.

x_3 \\ $x_1 x_2$	00	01	11	10
0		1	1	
	0	2	6	4
1		1	1	
	1	3	7	5

x_2

Fig. 11.31 Karnaugh map for Example 11.8

Observing row wise, the common variable to all four squares is x_2, but column wise, there is no variable which is common to all four squares. So the simplified function will be $y = x_2$. This can also be verified algebraically as done previously. ∎

Example 11.9 Simplifying the function $y = \sum m(0, 2, 4, 5, 6, 7)$

Solution: The corresponding K-map is shown in Fig. 11.32.

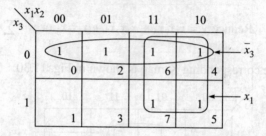

Fig. 11.32 Karnaugh map for Example 11.9

Considering row wise, $\bar{x}_3$ is common to all the four squares in the group and considering column wise, x_1 is common to all the four squares in the other group. So the simplified function is $y = x_1 + \bar{x}_3$. This can also be verified algebraically as done previously. ∎

Example 11.10 Reduce the function $\sum m(0, 1, 4, 5)$ using K-map.

Solution: The corresponding K-map is shown in Fig. 11.33.

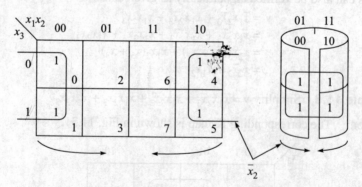

Fig. 11.33 Karnaugh map for Example 11.10

As the Karnaugh map is considered to be cylindrical, so four 1-squares of Fig. 11.33 are adjacent squares. The variable $\bar{x}_2$ is common to all four-squares. So the simplified function is $y = \bar{x}_2$. This can also be verified algebraically as done previously. ∎

Karnaugh Map for Four Variables Figure 11.34*a* shows Karnaugh map for four variables and Fig. 11.34*b* shows the alternative way of representing the variables.

x_3x_4 \\ x_1x_2	00	01	11	10
00	$\bar{x}_1\bar{x}_2\bar{x}_3\bar{x}_4$	$\bar{x}_1x_2\bar{x}_3\bar{x}_4$	$x_1x_2\bar{x}_3\bar{x}_4$	$x_1\bar{x}_2\bar{x}_3\bar{x}_4$
01	$\bar{x}_1\bar{x}_2\bar{x}_3x_4$	$\bar{x}_1x_2\bar{x}_3x_4$	$x_1x_2\bar{x}_3x_4$	$x_1\bar{x}_2\bar{x}_3x_4$
11	$\bar{x}_1\bar{x}_2x_3x_4$	$\bar{x}_1x_2x_3x_4$	$x_1x_2x_3x_4$	$x_1\bar{x}_2x_3x_4$
10	$\bar{x}_1\bar{x}_2x_3\bar{x}_4$	$\bar{x}_1x_2x_3\bar{x}_4$	$x_1x_2x_3\bar{x}_4$	$x_1\bar{x}_2x_3\bar{x}_4$

Fig. 11.34(a) Karnaugh map for four variables

x_3x_4 \\ x_1x_2	00	01	11	10
00	0	4	12	8
01	1	5	13	9
11	3	7	15	11
10	2	6	14	10

Fig. 11.34(b) Alternative representation for the Karnaugh map for four variables

The following examples illustrate the method of simplification of four variable Boolean functions.

Example 11.11 Simplify $y = \bar{x}_1\bar{x}_2\bar{x}_3x_4 + \bar{x}_1x_2\bar{x}_3x_4 + x_1x_2\bar{x}_3x_4 + x_1\bar{x}_2\bar{x}_3x_4 + x_1x_2\bar{x}_3\bar{x}_4 + x_1x_2x_3x_4 + x_1x_2x_3\bar{x}_4$ using K-map.

Solution: The corresponding K-map is shown in Fig. 11.35.

Considering row wise, $\bar{x}_3x_4$ is common to all four squares in one group and considering column wise, x_1x_2 is common to all four squares in another group. So,

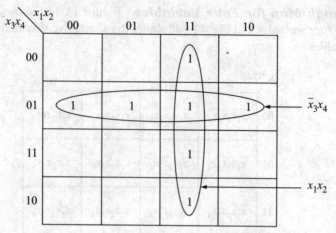

Fig. 11.35 Karnaugh map for Example 11.11

the simplified function is $y = x_1 x_2 + \bar{x}_3 x_4$. This can also be verified algebraically as done previously. ∎

Example 11.12 Figure 11.36 represents a boolean function on a four variable K-map. Find the corresponding boolean function.

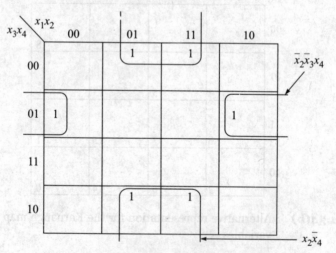

Fig. 11.36 Karnaugh map for Example 11.12

Solution: As the Karnaugh map is considered to be cylindrical, so four 1-squares (two on the upper edge and two on the lower edge) of the figure are considered as a group in which the common term is $x_2 \bar{x}_4$. Similarly, considering the left edge and right edge of the figure, the two 1s form a group in which the common term is $\bar{x}_2 \bar{x}_3 x_4$. So the simplified expression is $y = x_2 \bar{x}_4 + \bar{x}_2 \bar{x}_3 x_4$. This can also be verified algebraically as done previously. ∎

Example 11.13 Reduce $y = \sum m(4, 5, 10, 12, 13)$ using K-map

Solution: The corresponding K-map is shown in Fig. 11.37.

$x_3x_4 \backslash x_1x_2$	00	01	11	10
00	0	1 ⟵ 4	1 ⟵ 12	8 — $x_2\bar{x}_3$
01	1	1 5	1 13	9
11	3	7	15	11
10	2	6	14	①⟵ 10 — $x_1\bar{x}_2x_3\bar{x}_4$

Fig. 11.37 Karnaugh map for Example 11.13

Here, four 1-squares are grouped together since they are adjacent squares. Observing row wise, the variable $\bar{x}_3$ is common to all four 1-squares and observing column wise, the variable x_2 is common to all four 1-squares. So after simplification, $x_2\bar{x}_3$ will be common to all these four 1-squares. But the term $x_1\bar{x}_2x_3\bar{x}_4$ is left alone, so it is to be considered as a group of single 1-square. Hence the simplified function is $y = x_2\bar{x}_3 + x_1\bar{x}_2x_3\bar{x}_4$. This can also be verified algebraically as done previously. ∎

Example 11.14 Simplify the function $y = \bar{x}_1\bar{x}_2\bar{x}_3\bar{x}_4 + x_1\bar{x}_2\bar{x}_3\bar{x}_4 + \bar{x}_1\bar{x}_2x_3\bar{x}_4 + x_1\bar{x}_2x_3\bar{x}_4$ using K-map.

Solution: The corresponding K-map is shown in Fig. 11.38.

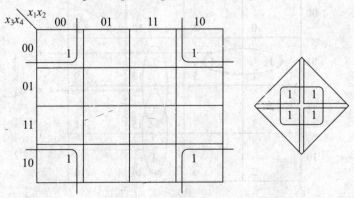

Fig. 11.38 Karnaugh map for Example 11.14

We know that the K-map is considered to be cylindrical. So, in this case, the four 1-squares can be grouped together as they can be viewed as adjacent squares. Observing the map rowwise, $\bar{x}_2$ is common to all the four 1-squares and observing the map columnwise, $\bar{x}_4$ is common to all the four 1-squares. So the term $\bar{x}_2\bar{x}_4$ is common to all four 1-squares. Hence, the simplified Boolean function is given by $y = \bar{x}_2\bar{x}_4$. This can also be verified algebraically as done previously. ∎

Example 11.15 Reduce $y = \sum m(1, 5, 13, 14, 15)$.

Solution: The corresponding K-map with grouping is shown in Fig. 11.39a and Fig. 11.39b.

In Fig. 11.39a there are three groups formed in which the common terms are $x_2\bar{x}_3x_4$, $\bar{x}_1\bar{x}_3x_4$ and $x_1x_2x_3$.

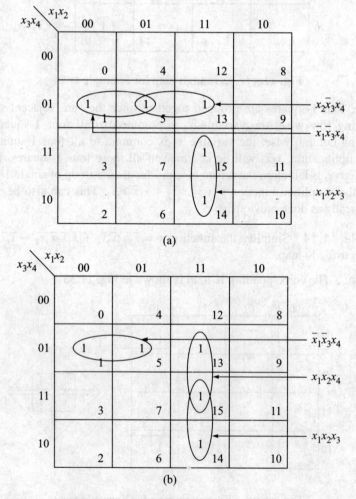

(a)

(b)

Fig. 11.39 Karnaugh map for Example 11.15

So the simplified boolean function is $y = x_2\bar{x}_3x_4 + \bar{x}_1\bar{x}_3x_4 + x_1x_2x_3$.

In Fig. 11.39b there are three groups formed in which the common terms are $\bar{x}_1\bar{x}_3x_4$, $x_1x_2x_4$ and $x_1x_2x_3$.

So the simplified boolean function is $y = \bar{x}_1\bar{x}_3x_4 + x_1x_2x_4 + x_1x_2x_3$. This can also be verified algebraically as done previously. ∎

From the above example, we observe that the boolean function obtained from a K-map may not be unique.

Example 11.16 Simplify $y = \sum m(0, 1, 2, 3, 4, 6, 8, 9, 10, 11, 12, 14)$ using K-map.

Solution: The corresponding K-map is shown in Fig. 11.40.

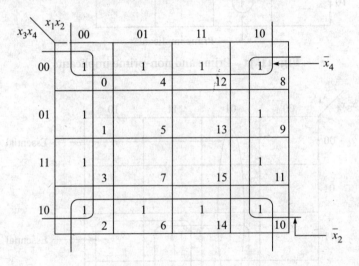

Fig. 11.40 Karnaugh map for Example 11.16

In the above K-map, there are two groups. Observing row wise, $\bar{x}_4$ is common to all eight 1-squares in a group. Again observing columnwise, $\bar{x}_2$ is common to all eight 1-squares in another group. So, the simplified function is given by $y = \bar{x}_2 + \bar{x}_4$. This can also be verified algebraically as done previously. ∎

Prime Implicant Each product term in a sum of product expression is known as an *implicant* of the function to be minimized. In a Karnaugh map, each implicant relates to a single 1-square or a group of adjacent 1-squares. A prime implicant is an implicant which cannot be entirely included within another larger implicant on a Karnaugh map. A non-essential prime implicant can be omitted without leaving any 1-square on enclosed. Figure 11.41 shows prime and non-prime implicants and Fig. 11.42 shows essential and non-essential implicants.

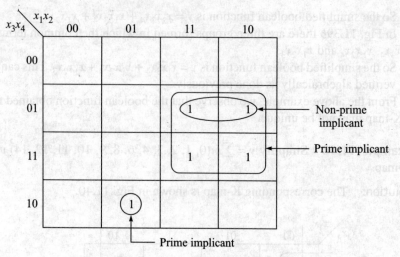

Fig. 11.41 Prime and non-prime implicants

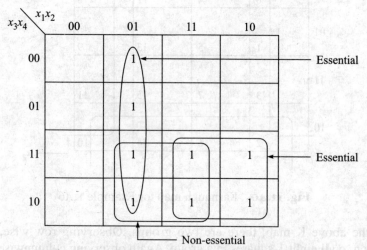

Fig. 11.42 Essential and non-essential implicants

11.10.2 Realization of Product of Sums Expression by Karnaugh Map

So far we have been finding *sum of product* (SOP) solutions to logic reduction problems. For each of the logic reduction problems, there is also a *product of sums* (POS) *solution*, which could be more useful depending on the application.

To find a product of sums expression from a Karnaugh map, groups of 0-squares are made. First a sum of products of complementary function (SOP) is obtained. Then product of sums expression is obtained by applying De Morgan's law.

Example 11.17 Find the minimum POS expression from the Karnaugh map as shown in Fig. 11.43.

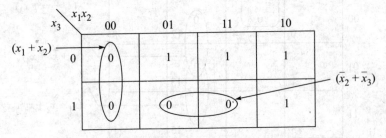

Fig. 11.43 Karnaugh map for Example 11.17

Solution: In the given K-map, groups of 0-squares are made. The complementary function is given by $E(x_1, x_2, x_3) = \bar{x}_1\bar{x}_2 + x_2x_3$.

Applying De Morgan's law, we have

$$F(x_1, x_2, x_3) = (\overline{\bar{x}_1\bar{x}_2 + x_2x_3})$$
$$= (x_1 + x_2)(\bar{x}_2 + \bar{x}_3)$$

The squares containing 0s in the given figure can also be represented as

$$F(x_1, x_2, x_3) = \prod M(0, 1, 3, 7)$$

For minimizing a given expression in POS form or for a given truth table, we write zeros in the cells corresponding to *maxterms* for 0 outputs, and then the K-map is simplified by following the same procedure as used for SOP form with ones replaced by zeros. In this case, groups of zeros are formed rather than groups of ones. ■

Example 11.18 Simplify $y = \prod M(4, 6, 10, 12, 13, 15)$.

Solution: The K-map corresponding to $y = \prod M(4, 6, 10, 12, 13, 15)$ is shown in Fig. 11.44.

Using the steps similar to simplification for SOP form, and applying DeMorgan's law, we obtain the minimized expression,

$$y = (x_1 + \bar{x}_2 + x_4)(\bar{x}_1 + \bar{x}_2 + x_3)(\bar{x}_1 + \bar{x}_2 + \bar{x}_4)(\bar{x}_1 + x_2 + \bar{x}_3 + x_4)$$ ■

Don't Care Conditions In all the previous maps, each *minterm* has been specified as a 1 or 0. The squares which do not contain 1 are assumed to contain 0 and vice versa. This is not always true since there are cases in which certain combinations of input variables do not occur. An example of this is a binary coded decimal system where the binary states 1010, 1011, 1100, 1101, 1110, and 1111 never occur. Also, for some functions the outputs corresponding to certain combinations of input variable do not matter. In such situations, the designer has got freedom to assume a 0 or 1 as output for each of these combinations. These situations are known as *don't care conditions*. A don't care condition is

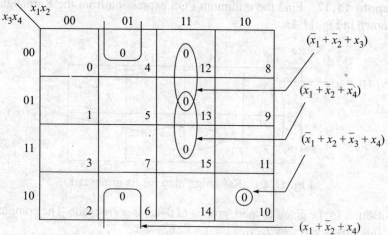

Fig. 11.44   Karnaugh map for Example 11.18

represented by an × (cross) mark in the corresponding square on a Karnaugh map. The corresponding squares are known as *don't care squares*. The × mark in the square may be assumed to be 1 or 0 depending upon which one leads to a simpler expression. Any one of such squares or some of them may be included or may not be included while forming groups. We use only those don't cares in a group if they simplify the logic. The Karnaugh map in terms of *minterms* and don't care conditions shown in Fig. 11.45a can also be represented as

$Y = \sum m(1, 3, 7, 11, 15) + \sum d(0, 2, 5)$, where d denotes *don't care conditions*. The simplified function is $y = \bar{x}_1 x_4 + x_3 x_4$.

The Karnaugh map in terms of *maxterms* and don't care conditions shown in Fig. 11.45b can also be represented as $Y = \prod M(3, 12, 13, 15) + d(0, 7, 10, 14)$.

The simplified function is $y = (\bar{x}_1 + \bar{x}_2)(x_1 + \bar{x}_3 + \bar{x}_4)$.

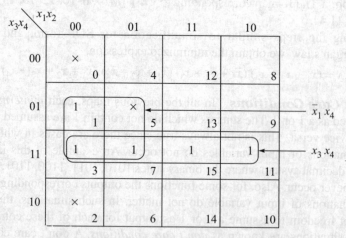

Fig. 11.45(a)   Karnaugh map in terms of minterms and don't care conditions

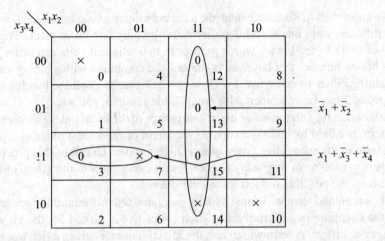

Fig. 11.45(b) Karnaugh map in terms of maxterms and don't care conditions

11.11 SIMPLIFICATION OF LOGIC EXPRESSIONS USING QUINE–McCLUSKEY METHOD

Boolean functions containing less than five variables can be easily simplified by using Karnaugh map (K-map). When the number of variables exceed five, the visualization of adjacent cells and drawing of Karnaugh map becomes much more difficult. So, boolean functions containing more than five variables may not be easily simplified by using K-map. Secondly, Karnaugh map reduction method requires intelligence for combining *minterms* to produce more simplified expressions, which cannot be easily computerized. To overcome these difficulties, a tabular method known as Quine–McCluskey method can be used. This method can be used for Boolean functions containing any number of variables. It was developed by W. V. Quine and E. J. McCluskey, Jr. in the 1950s. In the following, we discuss the detailed procedure to simplify an expression using Quine–McCluskey method. In the following, we use *term* and *word* interchangeably.

11.11.1 Combining Minterms

First collect all the terms or words in the Boolean expression which have no 1s in any bit. All these terms form group 1. Now, collect all the terms which have only one 1. The terms should be written in the ascending order of their values. For example, the terms 0001, 1000, 0100, and 0010 should be written as 0001, 0010, 0100, and 1000. This forms group 2. Now form group 3 which combines the terms having two 1s. Here, also all the terms are written in ascending order. Then, group the terms having three 1s and four 1s, and so on. In this way, the binary words are arranged in the order of the number of 1s contained in each word. Then, horizontal lines are drawn between each number of 1s category.

We know that, in Karnaugh map, the adjacent minterms can be reduced because they differ by only one literal, i.e. they differ by only one bit or place. The total number of 1s in the binary words present in two adjacent cells can differ by 1. So, a binary number that has four 1s can only be combined with a binary number containing either three or five 1s. Thus, group 1 can be combined with group 2 and group 2 can be combined with group 1 and group 3, and so on.

After arranging all the terms in various groups of different index (number of 1s in a term is called its index), compare every term of the lowest index group with each term in the successive group of next higher index. Continue this process by comparing each term in group of index r with every term in the group of index $r+1$ till all the possible reductions are considered.

The combined term will consist of the original fixed bits remaining unchanged and the changing or differing bit. A dash (–) or (X) is placed for the bit which changes or differs. A term which has already combined is given a tick mark (✓).

11.11.2 Selection of Prime Implicants

The terms which have been generated in the above steps are again compared in the same way. In the above steps, we combined 2 squares. Now, we look for 4 square combinations. So,

　i. the terms should differ by only a single 1 and

　ii. the dashes (–) or (X) should be at the same column or in the same position.

This process is continued till all possible combinations are formed. A term which has already combined is given a tick mark (✓). All those terms which remain unticked are called *prime implicants*, as they cannot be reduced further.

11.11.3 Final Terms

All the reduced terms or prime implicants (i.e., all the unticked terms) are not used in the final terms of the reduced expression. But, it contains the sum of one or more prime implicants.

Now, we construct a table in which all the prime implicants are listed in the left column and all the minterms are listed along the top row. To select the essential prime implicants, we scan the minterms columnwise and put a tick mark (✓) in the cells which are in front of the prime implicant and in the columns of the corresponding minterms. Whenever there is only one tick mark (✓) in a column in the table, the term corresponding to the row of this tick mark (✓), must be included in the final expression. All the minterms which have been ticked once contributed one essential prime implicant each. We explain this method with the following example.

Example 11.19 Reduce the following Boolean function

$$F = \sum m(0, 1, 2, 3, 8, 9, 13, 15)$$

Solution: The minterms of the above Boolean function are given in Fig. 11.46.

Then, we make groups based on the number of 1s present in the minterms as shown in Fig. 11.47.

No. of 1s	x_1 x_2 x_3 x_4	Minterms
0	0 0 0 0	0 ✓
1	0 0 0 1	1 ✓
	0 0 1 0	2 ✓
	1 0 0 0	8 ✓
2	0 0 1 1	3 ✓
	1 0 0 1	9 ✓
3	1 1 0 1	13 ✓
4	1 1 1 1	15 ✓

Minterm	Binary Designator $x_1 x_2 x_3 x_4$
0	0 0 0 0
1	0 0 0 1
2	0 0 1 0
3	0 0 1 1
8	1 0 0 0
9	1 0 0 1
13	1 1 0 1
15	1 1 1 1

Fig. 11.46   **Fig. 11.47**

Next, we search for two square Combinations from the table given in Fig. 11.47. The result of the combinations is shown in Fig. 11.48.

	x_1 x_2 x_3 x_4	
(0, 1)	0 0 0 X	✓
(0, 2)	0 0 X 0	✓
(0, 8)	X 0 0 0	✓
(1, 3)	0 0 X 1	✓
(1, 9)	X 0 0 1	✓
(2, 3)	0 0 1 X	✓
(8, 9)	1 0 0 X	✓
(9, 13)	1 X 0 1	
(13, 15)	1 1 X 1	

Fig. 11.48

Then we try for four square combinations from the table given in Fig. 11.48. The result in shown in Fig. 11.49.

	x_1 x_2 x_3 x_4
(0, 1, 2, 3)	0 0 X X
(0, 1, 8, 9)	X 0 0 X

Fig. 11.49

11.11.4 Constructing Prime Implicant Chart

Then, we construct a table by listing all the prime implicants in the left column and all the minterms along the top row. We put a tick mark ($\checkmark$) in the cells which are in front of the prime implicant and in the columns of the corresponding minterms, as shown in Fig. 11.50.

		0	1	2	3	8	9	13	15
	1 X 0 1						$\checkmark$	$\checkmark$	
$\checkmark$	1 1 X 1							$\checkmark$	$\checkmark$
$\checkmark$	0 0 X X	$\checkmark$	$\checkmark$	$\checkmark$	$\checkmark$				
$\checkmark$	X 0 0 X	$\checkmark$	$\checkmark$			$\checkmark$	$\checkmark$		
		$\checkmark$	$\checkmark$	$\checkmark$	$\checkmark$	$\checkmark$	$\checkmark$	$\checkmark$	$\checkmark$

Fig. 11.50

Whenever there is only one tick mark ($\checkmark$) in a column in the table, the term corresponding to the row of this tick mark ($\checkmark$) is included in the final expression. Since the column corresponding to minterm 2 has a single ($\checkmark$), so its corresponding term 00XX has to be included in the final expression. The column corresponding to minterm 3 has also a single ($\checkmark$). But, its corresponding term 00XX has already been included in the final expression. So, we ignore this possibility. The column corresponding to minterm 8 has a single ($\checkmark$), so its corresponding term X00X has to be included in the final expression. Similarly the term 11X1 is included in the final expression. So the reduced expression can be written as:

$$F = 00XX + X00X + 11X1.$$

This may be represented as

$$F = \bar{x}_1\,\bar{x}_2 + \bar{x}_2\,\bar{x}_3 + x_1 x_2 x_4,$$

which is the simplified expression. ∎

11.12 PROPOSITIONAL CALCULUS

We recall our discussion in Sec. 1.8 on propositions: A proposition is a statement that may either be true (T) or be false (F). Furthermore, propositions can be combined to yield new propositions. In particular, we introduced the notion of disjunction, conjunction, and negation of propositions. We show now that our discussion can be formulated in the framework of an algebraic system.

Consider an algebraic system ($\{F, T\}, \vee, \wedge, \bar{\ }$) where the definitions of the operations $\vee$, $\wedge$, and $\bar{\ }$ are shown in Fig. 11.51. The reader can check immediately that $(\{F, T\}, \vee, \wedge, {}^-)$ is a boolean algebra of two elements. Within such an algebraic framework, an atomic proposition is a variable that can assume either the value F (false) or the value T (true). A tautology corresponds to the constant T and a contradiction corresponds to the constant F. The disjunction of two propositions p and q can be represented by the algebraic expression $p \vee q$. Note that the definition of the binary operation $\vee$ in Fig. 11.51 is indeed consistent with the definition of the disjunction of two propositions as shown in the truth table of Fig. 1.9. Similarly, the conjunction of two propositions p and q can be represented by the algebraic expression $p \wedge q$, and the negation of a proposition p can be represented by the algebraic expression $\bar{p}$. Again, the definitions of the operation $\wedge$ and ${}^-$ are consistent with that of the conjunction and negation of propositions as shown in Fig. 1.9. It follows that a compound proposition can be represented by a boolean expression. Furthermore, the truth table of a compound proposition is exactly a tabular description of the value of the corresponding boolean expression for all possible combinations of the values of the atomic propositions. We conclude that all our results on manipulation and simplification of boolean expressions can be applied to manipulate and simplify compound propositions as the following examples illustrate.

$\vee$	F	T		$\wedge$	F	T		$-$	
F	F	T		F	F	F		F	T
T	T	T		T	F	T		T	F

Fig. 11.51

Example 11.20 Consider the statement, "I will go to the ball game either if there is no examination tomorrow or if there is an examination tomorrow and the game is a championship match." Let p denote the proposition, "There is an examination tomorrow" and q denote the proposition, "The game is a championship match." Clearly, I will go to the ball game if the proposition

$$\bar{p} \vee (p \wedge q)$$

is true. However, the equality

$$\bar{p} \vee (p \wedge q) = \bar{p} \vee q$$

enables us to simplify our statement to, "I will go to the ball game either if there is no examination tomorrow or if the game is a championship match." ■

Example 11.21 Consider the following instructions given to a maintenance technician:

1. The electric power should be turned on if it is not the case that nobody is in the office and the automatic monitoring system is not in operation.
2. The automatic monitoring system will be in operation if and only if nobody is in the office or a large payroll is left in the office.

Let p denote the proposition, "nobody is in the office," q denote the proposition "the automatic monitoring system is in operation," and r denote the proposition "a large payroll is left in the office." Clearly, the electric power should be turned on if the proposition

$$\overline{p \wedge q}$$

is true. However, since

$$q = p \vee r$$

we have

$$\overline{(p \wedge q)} = \overline{p \wedge (p \vee r)}$$
$$= \overline{p} \wedge \overline{(p \vee r)}$$
$$= T$$

Consequently, we can conclude that the instructions are completely superfluous and can be replaced by the simple instruction of always leaving the electric power on. ∎

Example 11.22 Consider the directed graph in Fig. 11.52. We want to determine a minimal subset of the edges which, if removed, would destroy all the directed circuits in the graph. (By a *minimal* set of edges, we mean a set such that the removal of any proper subset of it will not destroy all the directed circuits.) We note that in the graph in Fig. 11.52 there are five directed circuits, namely, (a, d, g, f, b), (a, e, f, b), (c, d, g, f), (c, e, f), and (g, i, h). In order to destroy the directed circuit (a, d, g, f, b), we should remove at least one of the edges a, d, g, f, b. In order to destroy the directed circuit (a, e, f, b),

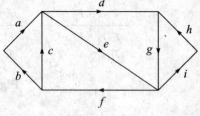

Fig. 11.52

we should remove at least one of the edges a, e, f, b. Consequently, in order to destroy all five directed circuits, we should remove at least one edge from each of them. From the algebraic expression,

$$(a \vee d \vee g \vee f \vee b) \wedge (a \vee e \vee f \vee b) \wedge (c \vee d \vee g \vee f)$$
$$\wedge (c \vee e \vee f) \wedge (g \vee i \vee h) = (a \wedge d \wedge e \wedge h) \vee (e \wedge g) \vee \dots$$

we note that the removal of the subset $\{a, d, e, h\}$, or $\{e, g\}$, ... will destroy all directed circuits in the graph. ∎

Finally, we recall that we defined in Sec. 1.8 two additional ways of combining propositions, namely, $p \rightarrow q$ and $p \leftrightarrow q$ for given propositions p and q. It is clear that we can augment our algebraic system by defining two operations $\rightarrow$ and $\leftrightarrow$ as shown in Fig. 11.53. However, such an augmentation is unnecessary in that we can always replace algebraic expressions involving the operations $\rightarrow$ and $\leftrightarrow$ by equivalent algebraic expressions involving only the operations $\wedge$, $\vee$, and $^-$. Specifically, from the truth tables for $p \rightarrow q$ and $p \leftrightarrow q$, we obtain

$\rightarrow$	F	T
F	T	T
T	F	T

$\leftrightarrow$	F	T
F	T	F
T	F	T

Fig. 11.53

$$p \to q = \overline{p} \vee q$$
$$p \leftrightarrow q = (p \wedge q) \vee (\overline{p} \wedge \overline{q})$$

for the boolean expressions corresponding to the compound propositions $p \to q$ and $p \leftrightarrow q$.*

As an example, we note that

$$p \to q = \overline{p} \vee q$$
$$= \overline{q} \vee \overline{p}$$
$$= \overline{q} \to \overline{p}$$

Therefore, the propositions, "If the temperature is above 30°C, we shall go to the beach," "Either the temperature is not above 30°C, or we shall go to the beach," and, "If we do not go to the beach, the temperature is not above 30°C" are equivalent. Similarly, the propositions, "If a group is cyclic, it is abelian," "Either a group is not cyclic or it is abelian," and, "If a group is not abelian, it is not cyclic" are equivalent.

As another example, we note that

$$p \leftrightarrow q = (\overline{p} \vee q) \wedge (p \vee \overline{p})^\dagger$$
$$= (p \to q) \wedge (q \to p)$$

Therefore, the statement, "There will be a $2 service charge if and only if the monthly balance of the checking account is less than $100" is equivalent to the statement, "If there is a $2 service charge then it must be the case that the monthly balance of the checking account is less than $100, and if the monthly balance of the checking account is less than $100 then there will be a $2 service charge."

At this point, we recall an observation in Sec. 1.8 that there is a strong similarity between composition of propositions to yield new propositions and composition of sets to yield new sets. Indeed, since many of the properties and results on sets and set operations and on propositions and proposition operations are that of boolean algebras, such a similarity is not a coincidence.

11.13 DESIGN AND IMPLEMENTATION OF DIGITAL NETWORKS

Suppose we want to design an electronic circuit that will sound a buzzer in an automobile if the temperature of the engine exceeds 200°F or if the automobile is in gear and the driver did not have the seat-belt buckled. Clearly, we have the relationship

$$b = p \vee (q \wedge \overline{r})$$

---

* Conceptually, the situation is similar to that of not defining subtraction as another operation in a ring since subtraction of an element is equivalent to the addition of the additive inverse of the element.

† This is the conjunctive normal form for the boolean expression corresponding to the compound statement $p \leftrightarrow q$.

where b is the proposition "sound the buzzer," p is the proposition "the temperature of the engine exceeds 200°F," q is the proposition "the automobile is in gear," and r is the proposition "the driver's seat-belt is buckled." To build an electronic circuit that will behave as described, we must first decide upon a convention for representing propositions by electric signals. For example, we might represent a proposition by an electric voltage. If the proposition is true, it will be represented by a high voltage (say 6 V), and if the proposition is false, it will be represented by a low voltage (say 0 V). Thus, in the foregoing example, corresponding to the proposition p, a high-voltage signal will appear if the temperature of the engine exceeds 200°F, and a low-voltage signal will appear if the temperature of the engine does not exceed 200°F. Similarly, corresponding to the proposition b, a high-voltage signal, which can be used to trigger the buzzer, will appear if the conditions to sound the buzzer are met, and a low-voltage signal, which will not be sufficient to trigger the buzzer, will appear if the conditions to sound the buzzer are not met. Once we have decided upon a convention for representing propositions by electric signals, we can design electronic circuits corresponding to the operations $\vee$, $\wedge$, and ‾. Throughout our discussion in the remainder of this section, we shall assume the convention of representing propositions by voltages as described in the foregoing.

An *OR-gate* is a circuit that has two inputs and one output as shown schematically in Fig. 11.54a. The output voltage of an OR-gate is high if either one or both of the input voltages is high, and the output voltage is low if both of the input voltages are low. Clearly, the output signal of an OR-gate corresponds to a proposition which is the disjunction of the proposition corresponding to the input signals.

An *AND-gate* is a circuit that has two inputs and one output as shown schematically in Fig. 11.54b. The output voltage of an AND-gate is high if both of the input voltages are high, and the output voltage is low if either one or both of the input voltages is low. Clearly, the output signal of an AND-gate corresponds to a proposition which is the conjunction of the propositions corresponding to the input signals.

A *NOT-gate*, or an *inverter*, is a circuit that has one input and one output, as shown schematically in Fig. 11.54c. Its output voltage is high if the input voltage is low, and its output voltage is low if the input voltage is high. The output signal of a NOT-gate corresponds to a proposition which is the negation of the proposition corresponding to the input signal.

It is quite obvious that we can interconnect these devices to form an electronic circuit that realizes any given boolean expression. For example, the circuit in Fig. 11.55 realizes the boolean expression

$$p \vee (q \wedge \bar{r})$$

corresponding to the problem of the buzzer in an automobile presented earlier. As another example, the circuit in Fig. 11.56 realizes the boolean expression

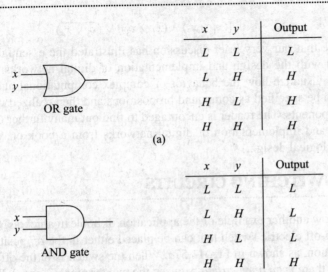

x	y	Output
L	L	L
L	H	H
H	L	H
H	H	H

OR gate

(a)

x	y	Output
L	L	L
L	H	L
H	L	L
H	H	H

AND gate

(b)

x	Output
L	H
H	L

NOT gate

(c)

Fig. 11.54

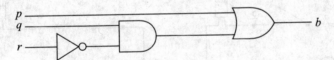

Fig. 11.55

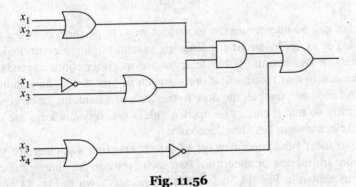

Fig. 11.56

$$[(x_1 \vee x_2) \wedge (\overline{x}_1 \vee x_3)] \vee (\overline{x_3 \vee x_4})$$

We hope that our very brief discussion has illustrated the essential ideas in connection with the design and implementation of digital networks. It is not difficult to visualize how the behavior of complex computational and control devices can be specified as compound propositions and then realized with electronic components. The reader is encouraged to find out many further details on the design and implementation of digital networks from a book on switching theory and logical design.

11.14 SWITCHING CIRCUITS

We show now another example of the application of boolean algebras. Consider a simple on-off electric switch that can be placed either in the *off* position or in the *on* position, as shown in Fig. 11.57a. When the switch is in the off position we say that there is an *open circuit* between the two terminals 1 and 2. When the switch is in the on position we say that there is a *closed circuit* between the two terminals 1 and 2. As is well known to the reader, we can use an on-off switch to turn on or off any electric appliance, as illustrated in Fig. 11.57b.

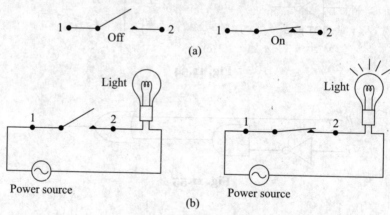

Fig. 11.57

Switches can be interconnected in various ways to perform complex control functions. For example, an air-conditioning system might be controlled by the thermostats in two rooms. If the temperature in either room exceeds 25°C, the thermostat in that room will close a switch to turn on the air-conditioning system. As another example, the door to the vault of a bank might be controlled electronically so that it cannot be opened unless two separate keys are used to close two electric switches simultaneously.

The two most fundamental ways of interconnecting switches are parallel connection and series connection. Two switches can be interconnected in *parallel*, as shown in Fig. 11.58a, and in *series*, as shown in Fig. 11.58b. It is immediately clear that in a parallel connection of two switches, there is an open circuit between terminals 1 and 2 if both switches are in the off position, and there is a closed circuit between terminals 1 and 2 if either one or both of the switches are in the on position. Similarly, in a series connection of two switches, there is an open circuit between terminals 1 and 2 if either one or both of the

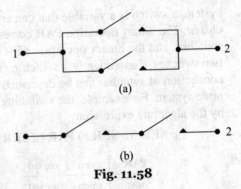

(a)

(b)

Fig. 11.58

switches are in the off position, and there is a closed circuit between terminals 1 and 2 if both switches are in the on position. Thus, in the example of the air-conditioning system, we will connect the two switches controlled by the thermostats in parallel. On the other hand, in the example of the door to the vault of a bank, we will connect the two switches controlled by the two keys in series.

Since we can view a parallel connection or a series connection of two switches as a "super" switch that is either open or closed, we can interconnect them with other switches to form complex switching networks, such as the one shown in Fig. 11.59, where symbolic names are used to denote different switches.

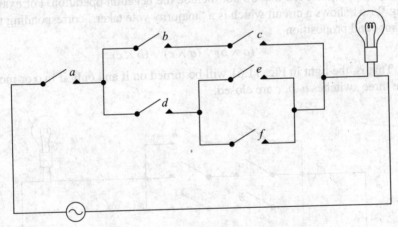

Fig. 11.59

One immediately realizes that the light in the network in Fig. 11.59 can be turned on by various settings of the switches in the network. For example, the light will be turned on if switches a, b, c are closed, or if switches a, d, f are closed, and so on. On the other hand, the light will be turned off if switch a is open or if switches b, e, f, are open, and so on. To study the behavior of complex switching networks, we define now an algebraic system. Let ({open, closed}, **PAR, SER**) be an algebraic system where **PAR** and **SER** are two binary operations whose definitions are shown in Fig. 11.60. Clearly, in this algebraic system, a switch is a variable that can either assume the value *open* or the value *closed*. The binary operation **PAR** corresponds to the parallel connection of two switches, and the binary operation **SER** corresponds to the series connection of two switches. Consequently, a switching network consisting of parallel and series connection of switches can be described by an algebraic expression in our algebraic system. For example, the switching network in Fig. 11.60 can be described by the algebraic expression:

$$a \text{ SER } ((b \text{ SER } c) \text{ PAR } (d \text{ SER } (e \text{ PAR } f)))$$

PAR	open	closed		SER	open	closed
open	open	closed		open	open	open
closed	closed	closed		closed	open	closed

Fig. 11.60

We recognize immediately that our algebraic system is isomorphic to the algebraic system $(\{0, 1\}, \vee, \wedge)$ which is obtained from the two-valued boolean algebra by dropping the negation operation. First of all, the results in boolean algebras can be applied directly to the study of the behavior of switching networks. Furthermore, we see the possibility of using switches to make up circuits to realize propositions that do not include the negation operation. For example, Fig. 11.61 shows a circuit which is a "majority vote taker," corresponding to the compound proposition

$$(a \wedge b) \vee (a \wedge c) \vee (b \wedge c)$$

That is, the light in Fig. 11.61 will be turned on if and only if two or more of the three switches a, b, c are closed.

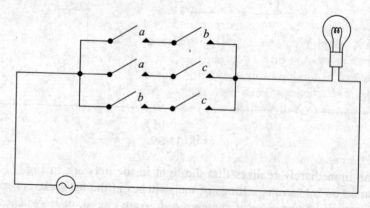

Fig. 11.61

In practice, an on-off switch is usually replaced by a *relay*. A relay is an electromechanical device shown schematically in Fig. 11.62a. When the on-off switch is closed, the electromagnetic coil is energized which, in turn, closes the

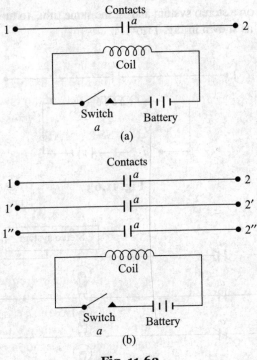

1   2

Contacts

Coil

Switch
a

Battery

(a)

1   2

1'   2'

1"   2"

Contacts

Coil

Switch
a

Battery

(b)

Fig. 11.62

contacts. Consequently, there will be a closed circuit between terminals 1 and 2. When the on-off switch is open, the electromagnetic coil is not energized and the contacts will be left open. Consequently, there is an open circuit between terminals 1 and 2. We shall use the same symbolic name to refer to both the on-off switch controlling the electromagnetic coil and the contacts which the coil controls. At this point, one might say that a relay functions in exactly the same way as does a single on-off switch, and might wonder why we go through an "indirect" step of using an on-off switch to control the contacts. One reason is that the electromagnetic coil can control more than one pair of contacts. Consequently, closing the on-off switch will close more than one pair of contacts, as Fig. 11.62*b* shows. A simple application is to use a switch to turn on several electric devices simultaneously such as a stereo system and several lamps. Secondly, a relay can control two kinds of contacts. What we have just described are known as *normally open* contacts, meaning that they are open when the controlling on-off switch is open and closed when the on-off switch is closed. Alternatively, we could have what are known as *normally closed* contacts. They are closed when the controlling on-off switch is open and open when the controlling on-off switch is closed. A pair of normally closed contacts is shown schematically in Fig. 11.63, where we use *a* to denote the on-off switch and $\bar{a}$ to denote the pair of normally closed contacts controlled by *a*. For example, one can use a single switch to turn on a stereo system and, at the same time, to turn off several lamps, or conversely, as shown in Fig. 11.64.

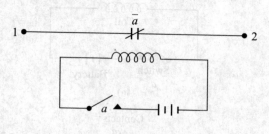

Fig. 11.63

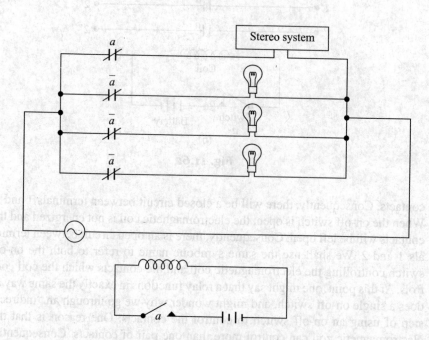

Fig. 11.64

We can connect relay contacts in parallel and in series in exactly the same manner as on-off switches are interconnected. For example, Fig. 11.65 shows a circuit which is a two-out-of-three vote taker. Note that the light will be turned on if and only if exactly two out of three of the on-off switches *a*, *b*, and *c* are closed.

One notes immediately that circuits made up of relay contacts connected in parallel and in series can be described by algebraic expressions in the algebraic system ({open, closed}, **SER, PAR**, ⁻), where ⁻ is a unary operation corresponding to the usage of a pair of normally closed contacts. The algebraic system ({open, closed}, **SER, PAR**, ⁻) is usually referred to as the *switching algebra*. Needless to say, the switching algebra is a two-valued boolean algebra, as the

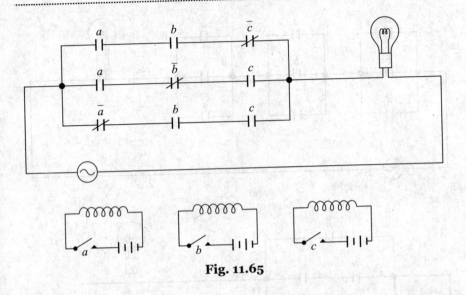

Fig. 11.65

reader has anticipated. Consequently, all results of boolean algebras can be applied to the analysis and synthesis of relay networks. We conclude our discussion with an illustrative example:

Example 11.23 A light is controlled by the switching circuit shown in Fig. 11.66*a*. The circuit can be described by the algebraic expression:

$$(a \textbf{ PAR } \bar{b} \textbf{ PAR } d) \textbf{ SER } (a \textbf{ PAR } b \textbf{ PAR } \bar{c}) \textbf{ SER } (a \textbf{ PAR } c \textbf{ PAR } d)$$

in the switching algebra. This expression corresponds to the expression

$$(a \vee \bar{b} \vee d) \wedge (a \vee b \vee \bar{c}) \wedge (a \vee c \vee d)$$

in the two-valued boolean algebra $(\{0, 1\}, \vee, \wedge, \bar{\ })$. Furthermore, we note that

$$(a \vee \bar{b} \vee d) \wedge (a \vee b \vee \bar{c}) \wedge (a \vee c \vee d)$$

$$= [a \vee ((\bar{b} \vee d) \wedge (b \vee \bar{c}))] \wedge (a \vee c \vee d)$$

$$= a \vee [(\bar{b} \vee d) \wedge (b \vee \bar{c}) \wedge (c \vee d)]$$

$$= a \vee [[(\bar{b} \wedge \bar{c}) \vee (b \wedge d) \vee (\bar{c} \wedge d)] \wedge (c \vee d)]$$

$$= a \vee (\bar{b} \wedge \bar{c} \wedge d) \vee (b \wedge c \wedge d) \vee (b \wedge d) \vee (\bar{c} \wedge d)$$

$$= a \vee (b \wedge d) \vee (\bar{c} \wedge d)$$

Since the expression

$$a \vee (b \wedge d) \vee (\bar{c} \wedge d)$$

corresponds to the expression

$$a \textbf{ PAR } (b \textbf{ SER } d) \textbf{ PAR } (\bar{c} \textbf{ SER } d)$$

in the switching algebra, the circuit in Fig. 11.66*b* will perform the same control function as that in Fig. 11.66*a*. ∎

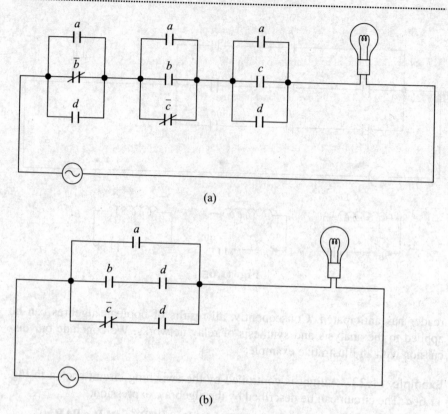

(a)

(b)

Fig. 11.66

Problems

11.1 Let a and b be two elements in a lattice $(A, \leq)$. Show that $a \wedge b = b$ if and only if $a \vee b = a$.

11.2 Let a, b, c be elements in a lattice $(A, \leq)$. Show that, if $a \leq b$, then $a \vee (b \wedge c) \leq b \wedge (a \vee c)$.

11.3 Let a, b, c be elements in a lattice $(A, \leq)$. Show that

$$a \vee (b \wedge c) \leq (a \vee b) \wedge (a \vee c)$$
$$(a \wedge b) \vee (a \wedge c) \leq a \wedge (b \vee c)$$

11.4 Let a and b be two elements in a lattice $(A, \leq)$. Show that $a \wedge b < a$ and $a \wedge b < b$ if and only if a and b are incomparable.

11.5 Let $(A, \vee, \wedge)$ be an algebraic system, where $\vee$ and $\wedge$ are binary operations satisfying the absorption law. Show that $\vee$ and $\wedge$ also satisfy the idempotent law.

11.6 We study in this problem the possibility of defining a lattice by an algebraic system with two binary operations. Let $(A, \vee, \wedge)$ be an algebraic system, where $\vee$ and $\wedge$ are binary operations satisfying the commutative, associative, and absorption laws.

(a) Define a binary relation $\leq$ on A such that for any a and b in A, $a \leq b$ if and only if $a \wedge b = a$. Show that $\leq$ is a partial ordering relation.

(b) Show that $a \vee b$ is the least upper bound of a and b in $(A, \leq)$. Show that $a \wedge b$ is the greatest lower bound of a and b in $(A, \leq)$.

11.7 Show that a lattice is distributive if and only if for any elements a, b, c in the lattice

$$(a \vee b) \wedge c \leq a \vee (b \wedge c)$$

11.8 Let $(A, \leq)$ be a distributive lattice. Show that, if

$$a \wedge x = a \wedge y \quad \text{and} \quad a \vee x = a \vee y$$

for some a, then $x = y$.

11.9 Show that a lattice $(A, \leq)$ is distributive if and only if for any elements a, b, c in A,

$$(a \wedge b) \vee (b \wedge c) \vee (c \wedge a) = (a \vee b) \wedge (b \vee c) \wedge (c \vee a)$$

Hint: To show that $(A, \leq)$ is distributive, consider the elements $a, b \vee c$, and $(a \vee b) \wedge (a \vee c)$.

11.10 A lattice $(A, \leq)$ is called a *modular lattice* if for any a, b, c in A, where $a \leq c$,

$$a \vee (b \wedge c) = (a \vee b) \wedge c$$

Show that a lattice is modular if and only if the following condition holds:

$$a \vee (b \wedge (a \vee c)) = (a \vee b) \wedge (a \vee c)$$

11.11 Show that for any elements a, b, c in a modular lattice

$$(a \vee b) \wedge c = b \wedge c$$

implies

$$(c \vee b) \wedge a = b \vee a$$

11.12 Let $(A, \leq)$ be a lattice. A subset I of A is called an *ideal* if the following conditions are satisfied:

1. For any a and b in I, $a \vee b$ is in I.
2. For any a in I and any x in A, $a \wedge x$ is in I.

(a) Show that condition 2 can be replaced by:

2'. If a is in I and $x \leq a$, then x is in I.

(b) Let I be a subset of A. Show that I is an ideal if and only if for any a and b in A:

1''. If a and b are in I, then $a \vee b$ is in I.

2''. If $a \vee b$ is in I, then both a and b are in I.

11.13 Let $(A, \leq)$ be a distributive lattice. Let a and b be two arbitrary elements in A. Let $I(a, b)$ denote the set

$$\{x \mid x \, \varepsilon \, A, \, a \wedge x = b \wedge x\}$$

Show that $I(a, b)$ is an ideal. (See Prob. 11.12 for the definition of an ideal.)

11.14 Show that in a lattice with universal lower bound 0 and universal upper bound 1, 0 is the *unique* complement of 1, and 1 is the *unique* complement of 0.

11.15 Show that

$$a \vee (\bar{a} \wedge b) = a \vee b$$
$$a \wedge (\bar{a} \vee b) = a \wedge b$$

in a boolean algebra.

11.16 Let $(A, \vee, \wedge, ^-)$ be a boolean algebra. Show that $(A, \oplus)$ is a commutative group, where $\oplus$ is defined as

$$a \oplus b = (a \wedge \bar{b}) \vee (\bar{a} \wedge b)$$

11.17 Let $(A, \star)$ be the algebraic system defined in Prob. 11.13 [including the condition in part (f)] with the additional property that for a, b, c in A,

$$a \star (b \star c) = b \star (a \star c)$$

$(A, \star)$ is called an *implication algebra*. We define a binary relation $\leq$ on A such that $a \leq b$ if and only if $a \star b = e$.

(a) Show that $\leq$ is a partial ordering relation.
(b) Show that $a \leq b$ if and only if $b = x \star a$ for some x in A.
(c) Show that for a and b in A, $(a \star b) \star b$ is a least upper bound of a and b.

11.18 Let $(A, \vee, \wedge, ^-)$ be a boolean algebra. Let $\star$ be a binary operation defined on A such that

$$a \star b = \overline{a} \vee b$$

Show that $(A, \star)$ is an implication algebra as defined in Prob. 11.17.

11.19 Let

$$E(x_1, x_2, x_3) = (x_1 \wedge x_2) \vee (x_1 \wedge x_3) \vee (\overline{x}_2 \wedge x_3)$$

be a boolean expression over the two-valued boolean algebra. Write $E(x_1, x_2, x_3)$ in both disjunctive and conjunctive normal forms.

11.20 Let

$$E(x_1, x_2, x_3) = \overline{(x_1 \vee x_2) \vee (\overline{x}_1 \wedge x_3)}$$

be a boolean expression over the two-valued boolean algebra. Write $E(x_1, x_2, x_3)$ in both disjunctive and conjunctive normal forms.

11.21 Let

$$E(x_1, x_2, x_3, x_4) = (x_1 \wedge x_2 \wedge \overline{x}_3) \vee (x_1 \wedge \overline{x}_2, \wedge x_4) \wedge (x_2 \wedge \overline{x}_3 \wedge \overline{x}_4)$$

be a boolean expression over the two-valued boolean algebra. Write $E(x_1, x_2, x_3, x_4)$ in both disjunctive and conjunctive normal forms.

11.22 (a) Express the function in Fig. 11P.1 in disjunctive normal form.
(b) Express the function in Fig. 11P.1 in conjunctive normal form.

11.23 Simplify the following boolean expressions:

(a) $(a \wedge b) \vee (a \wedge b \wedge c) \vee (b \wedge c)$
(b) $(a \wedge b) \vee (a \wedge \overline{b} \wedge c) \vee (b \wedge c)$
(c) $(a \wedge b) \vee (\overline{a} \wedge b \wedge \overline{c}) \vee (b \wedge c)$
(d) $((a \wedge \overline{b}) \vee c) \wedge (a \vee \overline{b}) \wedge c$

	f
$(0, 0, 0)$	1
$(0, 0, 1)$	0
$(0, 1, 0)$	1
$(0, 1, 1)$	0
$(1, 0, 0)$	0
$(1, 0, 1)$	1
$(1, 1, 0)$	0
$(1, 1, 1)$	1

Fig. 11P.1

11.24 We defined in Sec. 11.8 the notions of disjunctive normal form and conjunctive normal form for boolean expressions over the two-valued boolean algebra. We shall see in this problem how these notions can be extended to boolean algebras in general. Let $E(x_1, x_2, ..., x_n)$ be a boolean expression over a boolean algebra $(A, \vee, \wedge, ^-)$. We shall use the notation $E(x_i = a)$ to denote the boolean expression obtained from $E(x_1, x_2, ..., x_n)$ by substituting x_i by a, where a is an element of A.

(a) For any x_i, show that

$$E(x_1, x_2, ..., x_n) = (\overline{x}_i \wedge E(x_i = 0)) \vee (x_i, \wedge E(x_i = 1))$$

Hint: The equality can be proved by induction on the length of the expression $E(x_1, x_2, \ldots x_n)$, where the length of an expression is defined to be the total number of appearances of elements of A, variable names, the operations $\vee$, $\wedge$, $^-$ in the expression with replications counted. Thus, expressions of length one are elements of A and the variables $x_1, x_2, \ldots, x_n$.

(b) Use the result in part (a) to show that any boolean expression can be written as a join of expressions of the form

$$c_{\delta_1 \delta_2 \cdots \delta_n} \wedge \tilde{x}_1 \wedge \tilde{x}_2 \wedge \ldots \wedge \tilde{x}_n$$

where $c_{\delta_1 \delta_2 \cdots \delta_n}$ is an element of A, and $\bar{x}_i$ denotes either x_i or $\bar{x}_i$. Such a way of writing a boolean expression is called a *disjunctive normal form.*

(c) Let

$$E(x_1, x_2) = (2 \wedge x_1) \wedge (x_1 \vee \bar{x}_2)$$

be a boolean expression over the boolean algebra $(\{0, 1, 2, 3\}, \vee, \wedge, {}^-)$. Rewrite $E(x_1, x_2)$ in disjunctive normal form.

(d) Let f be a function from A^n to A for some boolean algebra $(A, \vee, \wedge, {}^-)$. If f is a boolean function, how can we determine a boolean expression that specifies the function f?

Hint: Consider the disjunctive normal form of the expression.

(e) Show that the function in Fig.11.8 is not a boolean function.

(f) For any x_i, show that

$$E(x_1, x_2, \ldots, x_n) = (x_i \vee E(x_i = 0)) \wedge (\bar{x}_i \vee E(x_i = 1))$$

(g) Use the result in part (f) to show that any boolean expression can be written as a meet of expressions of the form

$$d_{\delta_1 \delta_2 \cdots \delta_n} \vee \tilde{x}_1 \vee \tilde{x}_2 \vee \ldots \vee \tilde{x}_n.$$

where $d_{\delta_1 \delta_2 \cdots \delta_n}$ is an element of A and $\tilde{x}_i$ denotes either x_i or $\tilde{x}_i$. Such a way of writing a boolean expression is called a conjunctive normal form.

11.25 A student will receive a passing grade in a course if he meets one or more of the following conditions:

1. He got a B or better in the mid-term examination and an A in the final examination.
2. He got a B or better in both the mid-term and final examinations and did not miss any homework assignment.
3. He got a B or better in at least one of the mid-term and final examinations and he has an athletic scholarship.
4. His father is the instructor of the course.

Use the following propositions as variables to write a boolean expression describing the set of conditions stated above.

a : Getting a B in mid-term examination
b : Getting an A in mid-term examination
c : Getting a B in final examination
d : Getting an A in final examination
e : Missing some homework assignment
f : Having an athletic scholarship
g : Being the son of the instructor

Simplify the expression and thus obtain a simpler set of conditions.

11.26 The following table shows the contents of five tool boxes labeled a, b, c, d, and e:

	Screw driver	Wrench	Pliers	Hammer	saw
a	×	×			
b		×	×	×	
c	×		×		
d		×			×
e			×	×	

Write a boolean expression to show how selections of the tool boxes can be made so that each selection contains at least one tool of each kind.

11.27 A committee is to be selected from five candidates a, b, c, d, e. The selection must satisfy all the following conditions:

1. Either a or b must be included, but not both.
2. Either c or e or both must be included.
3. If d is included, then b must be included.
4. Either both a and c are included or neither is included.
5. If e is included, then c and d must be included.

How should the selection be made?

11.28 Show how the method of boolean algebras can be applied to determine the minimal dominating sets of a graph. Illustrate the procedure by determining the minimal dominating sets of the graph in Fig. 4P.2. (See Prob. 4.11 for the definition of a dominating set of a graph.)

Hint: For each vertex, either the vertex itself or one of the vertices adjacent to it must be included in a dominating set.

11.29 Simplify the circuit in Fig. 11P.2. (There is one circuit that uses only three OR-gates and AND-gates.)

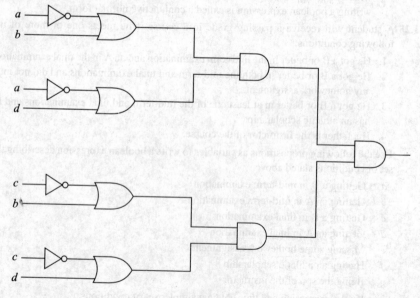

Fig. 11P.2

11.30 (a) Show how an OR-gate can be replaced by a suitable interconnection of AND-gates and NOT-gates.

(b) Show how an AND-gate can be replaced by a suitable interconnection of OR-gates and NOT-gates.

(c) A NOR-gate is a circuit that has two inputs and one output such that the output is equal to $\overline{x \vee y}$ for the inputs x and y. Show that we can realize any boolean expression using NOR-gates alone by showing how OR-gates, AND-gates, and NOT-gates can be replaced by suitable interconnections of NOR-gates.

(d) A NAND-gate is a circuit that has two inputs and one output such that the output is $\overline{x \wedge y}$ for the inputs x and y. Show that we can realize any boolean expression using NAND-gates alone by showing how OR-gates, AND-gates, and NOT-gates can be replaced by suitable interconnections of NAND-gates.

11.31 (a) Simplify the relay networks in Fig. 11P.3.

(b) Construct digital networks using OR-gates, AND-gates, and NOT-gates to realize the boolean expressions realized by the relay networks in Fig. 11P.3.

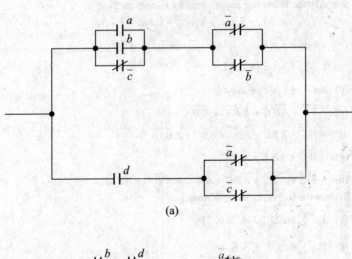

(a)

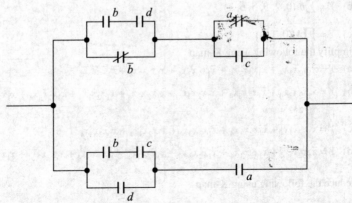

(b)

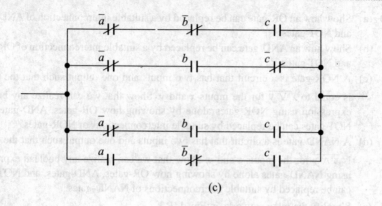

(c)

Fig. 11P.3

11.32 Simplify the following expressions by K-map method.

(a) $\bar{x}_1 x_2 \bar{x}_3 + x_1 x_2 \bar{x}_3 + \bar{x}_1 x_2 x_3 + x_1 x_2 x_3 + x_1 \bar{x}_2 x_3 + \bar{x}_1 \bar{x}_2 x_3$

(b) $x_1 x_2 \bar{x}_3 + x_1 x_2 x_3 + x_1 \bar{x}_2 \bar{x}_3 + x_1 \bar{x}_2 x_3 + \bar{x}_1 \bar{x}_2 x_3 + \bar{x}_1 x_2 x_3$

(c) $\bar{x}_1 x_2 \bar{x}_3 + \bar{x}_1 x_2 x_3 + \bar{x}_1 \bar{x}_2 \bar{x}_3$

(d) $\bar{x}_1 x_2 \bar{x}_3 + x_1 x_2 \bar{x}_3 + x_1 \bar{x}_2 \bar{x}_3$

(e) $\bar{x}_1 \bar{B} \bar{C} + \bar{A} \bar{B} C + A \bar{B} \bar{C} + A \bar{B} C$

(f) $\bar{A} B \bar{C} + ABC + AB\bar{C} + A\bar{B}C + A\bar{B}\bar{C}$

(g) $\bar{A} \bar{B} \bar{C} + AB \bar{C} + \bar{A} B \bar{C}$

(h) $\bar{A} \bar{B} \bar{C} + \bar{A} \bar{B}C + \bar{A} \bar{B}C + \bar{A} B \bar{C} + A \bar{B} \bar{C} + AB \bar{C}$

11.33 Reduce the following using K-map

(a) $Y = \sum m(0, 1, 2, 4, 5, 6, 7)$

(b) $Y = \sum m(0, 2, 3, 5, 6, 7)$

(c) $Y = \prod M(0, 1, 3)$

11.34 Simplify the following using K-map

(a) $Y = \bar{x}_1 x_2 \bar{x}_3 x_4 + x_1 x_2 \bar{x}_3 x_4 + \bar{x}_1 x_2 x_3 x_4 + x_1 x_2 x_3 x_4 + \bar{x}_1 \bar{x}_2 \bar{x}_3 \bar{x}_4$

(b) $Y = \bar{x}_1 \bar{x}_2 x_3 x_4 + \bar{x}_1 \bar{x}_2 x_3 \bar{x}_4 + \bar{x}_1 x_2 x_3 x_4 + \bar{x}_1 x_2 x_3 \bar{x}_4 + x_1 x_2 \bar{x}_3 \bar{x}_4 + x_1 x_2 \bar{x}_3 x_4 + x_1 x_2 x_3 x_4 + x_1 x_2 x_3 \bar{x}_4$

(c) $Y = \bar{x}_1 x_2 \bar{x}_3 \bar{x}_4 + \bar{x}_1 x_2 \bar{x}_3 x_4 + \bar{x}_1 x_2 x_3 x_4 + x_1 x_2 x_3 x_4 + x_1 \bar{x}_2 x_3 x_4$

(d) $Y = \bar{x}_1 x_2 \bar{x}_3 \bar{x}_4 + x_1 x_2 \bar{x}_3 x_4 + \bar{x}_1 \bar{x}_2 x_3 x_4 + \bar{x}_1 \bar{x}_2 x_3 \bar{x}_4 + x_1 x_2 x_3 x_4 + x_1 x_2 x_3 \bar{x}_4 + x_1 \bar{x}_2 \bar{x}_3 \bar{x}_4 + x_1 \bar{x}_2 x_3 x_4$

11.35 Reduce the following using K-map

(a) $Y = \sum m(1, 3, 4, 6, 9, 11)$

(b) $Y = \sum m(4, 5, 7, 11, 15)$

(c) $Y = \sum m(1, 2, 3, 6, 8, 12, 14, 15)$

(d) $Y = \sum m(1, 2, 3, 5, 6, 7, 8, 12, 13)$

(e) $Y = \sum m(2, 4, 10, 12, 14)$

(f) $Y = \sum m(0, 1, 2, 4, 6, 7, 10)$

(g) $Y = \prod M(4, 6, 10, 12, 13, 15)$

(h) $Y = \prod M(5, 6, 7, 14, 15)$

(i) $Y = \prod M(0, 1, 2, 3, 4, 6, 10, 11, 13)$

(j) $Y = \prod M(0, 1, 4, 5, 8, 12, 13, 14, 15)$

11.36 Define the following:

(a) Karnaugh map

(b) Prime implicant

(c) Non-prime implicant

(d) Essential prime implicant

(e) Non-essential prime implicant

11.37 Reduce to simplest POS form and implement in NOR logic:

$$Y = \sum m(0, 2, 4, 10, 11, 12, 14, 15)$$

11.38 Reduce to simplest form (POS or SOP) and implement in NAND logic:

$$Y = \sum m(1, 2, 3, 6, 10, 13, 14, 15)$$

11.39 Reduce to simplest form (POS or SOP) and implement in NOR logic:

$$Y = \sum m(0, 1, 3, 4, 6, 7, 10, 14)$$

11.40 Minimize the logic functions using K-map and implement in NAND/NOR gates:

(a) $Y = \sum m(1, 3, 5, 8, 9, 11, 15) + d(2, 13)$

(b) $Y = \prod M(1, 2, 3, 8, 9, 10, 11, 14) \cdot d(7, 15)$

11.41 Minimize the following expressions using K-map and implement in NOR gates only:

(a) $Y = \prod M(2, 7, 8, 9, 10, 12)$

(b) $Y = \prod M(1, 4, 6, 9, 10, 11, 14, 15)$

(c) $Y = \prod M(1, 2, 3, 5, 6, 7, 9, 10, 11, 13, 14, 15)$

11.42 Minimize the following functions and realize using minimum number of gates.

(a) $Y = \sum m(0, 3, 5, 6, 9, 10, 12, 15)$

(b) $Y = \sum m(0, 1, 2, 3, 11, 12, 14, 15)$

Simplify the following Boolean functions using Quine–McCluskey method.

11.43 $F(x_1, x_2, x_3) = x_1 x_2 x_3 + \bar{x}_1 \bar{x}_2 \bar{x}_3 + x_1 \bar{x}_2 x_3 + \bar{x}_1 x_2 x_3 + \bar{x}_1 \bar{x}_2 x_3$

11.44 $F(x_1, x_2, x_3, x_4) = x_1 \bar{x}_2 x_3 x_4 + x_1 \bar{x}_2 x_3 \bar{x}_4 + \bar{x}_1 x_2 x_3 x_4 + \bar{x}_1 x_2 x_3 \bar{x}_4 + \bar{x}_1 \bar{x}_2 x_3 x_4 + \bar{x}_1 \bar{x}_2 \bar{x}_3 x_4$

11.45 $F(x, y, z) = xy\bar{z} + \bar{x}\bar{y}\bar{z} + \bar{x}yz + \bar{x}\,\bar{y}\,\bar{z}$

11.46 $F(x, y, z) = xyz + xy\bar{z} + x\bar{y}z + x\bar{y}\bar{z} + \bar{x}yz + \bar{x}\bar{y}z + \bar{x}\bar{y}\bar{z}$

11.47 $F(w, x, y, z) = wxyz + w\bar{x}yz + w\bar{x}y\bar{z} + w\bar{x}\bar{y}z + \bar{w}xy\bar{z} + \bar{w}\bar{x}y\bar{z} + \bar{w}\bar{x}\bar{y}\bar{z}$

11.48 $F(a, b, c) = abc + ab\bar{c} + \bar{a}bc + \bar{a}b\bar{c}$

11.49 $F(a, b, c, d) = abcd + ab\bar{c}d + ab\bar{c}\bar{d} + a\bar{b}c\bar{d} + a\bar{b}\bar{c}d.$

INDEX